INTRODUCTION TO ORE-FORMING PROCESSES

Introduction to Ore-Forming Processes

LAURENCE ROBB

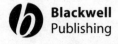
Blackwell
Publishing

Introduction to ORE-FORMING PROCESSES

Authorized reprint by Wiley India Pvt. Ltd., 4435-36/7, Ansari Road, Daryaganj, New Delhi – 110002.

This edition is authorized for sale in the Indian Sub-continent only.

Reprint: 2015

Printed at: *Delhi Press, Delhi*

ISBN: 978-81-265-5453-9

Contents

Preface

There are many excellent texts, available at both introductory and advanced levels, that describe the Earth's mineral deposits. Several describe the deposits themselves and others do so in combination with explanations that provide an understanding of how such mineral occurrences form. Few are dedicated entirely to the multitude of processes that give rise to the ore deposits of the world. The main purpose of this book is to provide a better understanding of the processes, as well as the nature and origin, of mineral occurrences and how they fit into the Earth system. It is intended for use at a senior undergraduate level (third and fourth year levels), or graduate level (North America), and assumes a basic knowledge in a wide range of core earth science disciplines, as well as in chemistry and physics. Although meant to be introductory, it is reasonably comprehensive in its treatment of topics, and it is hoped that practicing geologists in the minerals and related industries will also find the book useful as a summary and update of ore-forming processes. To this end the text is punctuated by a number of boxed case studies in which actual ore deposits, selected as classic examples from around the world, are briefly described to give context and relevance to processes being discussed in the main text.

Metallogeny, or the study of the genesis of ore deposits in relation to the global tectonic paradigm, is a topic that traditionally has been, and should remain, a core component of the university earth science curriculum. It is also the discipline that underpins the training of professional earth scientists working in the minerals and related industries of the world. A tendency in the past has been to treat economic geology as a vocational topic and to provide instruction only to those individuals who wished to specialize in the discipline or to follow a career in the minerals industries. In more recent years, changes in earth science curricula have resulted in a trend, at least in a good many parts of the world, in which economic geology has been sidelined. A more holistic, process-orientated approach (earth systems science) has led to a wider appreciation of the Earth as a complex interrelated system. Another aim of this book, therefore, is to emphasize the range of processes responsible for the formation of the enormously diverse ore deposit types found on Earth and to integrate these into a description of Earth evolution and global tectonics. In so doing it is hoped that metallogenic studies will increasingly be reintegrated into the university earth science curricula. Teaching the processes involved in the formation of the world's diminishing resource inventory is necessary, not only because of its practical relevance to the real world, but also because such processes form an integral and informative part of the Earth system.

This book was written mainly while on a protracted sabbatical in the Department of Earth Sciences at the University of Oxford. I am very grateful to John Woodhouse and the departmental staff who accommodated me and helped to provide the combination of academic rigor and quietitude that made writing this book such a pleasure. In particular Jenny Colls, Earth Science Librarian, was a tower of support in locating reference material. The "tea club" at the Banbury Road annexe provided both stimulation and the requisite libations to break the monotony. The staff at Blackwell managed to combine being really nice people with a truly professional attitude, and Ian Francis, Delia Sandford, Rosie Hayden, and Cee Pike were all a pleasure to work with. Dave Coles drafted all the diagrams and I am extremely grateful for his forebearance in dealing amiably with a list of figures that seemingly did not end. Several people took time to read through the manuscript for me and in so doing greatly improved both the style and content. They include John Taylor (copy-editing), Judith Kinnaird and Dave Waters (Introduction), Grant Cawthorn (Chapter 1), Philip Candela (Chapter 2), Franco Pirajno (Chapter 3), Michael Meyer (Chapter 4), John Parnell and Harold Reading (Chapter 5), and Mark Barley, Kevin Burke, and John Dewey (Chapter 6). The deficiencies that remain, though, are entirely my own. A particularly debt of gratitude is owed to David Rickard, who undertook the onerous task of reviewing the entire manuscript; his lucid comments helped to eliminate a number of flaws and omissions. Financial support for this project came from BHP Billiton in London and the Geological Society of South Africa Trust. My colleagues at Wits were extremely supportive during my long absences, and I am very grateful to Spike McCarthy, Paul Dirks, Carl Anhauesser, Johan Kruger, and Judith Kinnaird for their input in so many ways. Finally, my family, Vicki, Nicole, and Brendan, were subjected to a life-style that involved making personal sacrifices for the fruition of this project – there is no way of saying thank you and it is to them that I dedicate this book.

Laurence Robb
Johannesburg

Introduction: mineral resources

INTRODUCTION AND AIMS

Given the unprecedented growth of human population over the past century, as well as the related increase in demand for and production of natural resources, it is evident that understanding the nature, origin and distribution of the world's mineral deposits remains a strategic topic. The discipline of "economic geology," which covers all aspects pertaining to the description and understanding of mineral resources, is, therefore, one which traditionally has been, and should remain, a core component of the university earth science curriculum. It is also the discipline that underpins the training of professional earth scientists working in the minerals and related industries of the world. A tendency in the past has been to treat economic geology as a vocational topic and to provide instruction only to those individuals who wished to specialize in the discipline or to follow a career in the minerals industry. In more recent years, changes in earth science curricula have resulted in a trend, at least in a good many parts of the world, in which economic geology has been sidelined.

The conceptual development of earth systems science, also a feature of the latter years of the twentieth century, has led to dramatic shifts in the way in which the earth sciences are taught. A more holistic, process-orientated approach has led to a much wider appreciation of the Earth as a complex interrelated system. The understanding of feedback mechanisms has brought an appreciation that the solid Earth, its oceans and atmosphere, and the organic life forms that occupy niches above, at and below its surface, are intimately connected and can only be understood properly in terms of an interplay of processes. Examples include the links between global tectonics and climate patterns, and also between the evolution of unicellular organisms and the formation of certain types of ore deposits. In this context the teaching of many of the traditional geological disciplines assumes new relevance and the challenge to successfully teaching earth system science is how best to integrate the wide range of topics into a curriculum that provides understanding of the entity. Teaching the processes involved in the formation of the enormously diverse ore deposit types found on Earth is necessary, not only because of its practical relevance to the real world, but also because such processes form an integral and informative part of the Earth's evolution.

The purpose of this process-orientated book is to provide a better understanding of the nature and origin of mineral occurrences and how they fit into the Earth system. It is intended for use at a senior undergraduate level (third and fourth year levels), or a graduate level, and assumes a basic knowledge in a wide range of core earth science disciplines, as well as in chemistry and physics. It is also hoped that practicing geologists in the minerals and related industries will find the book useful as a summary and update of ore-forming processes. To this end the text is punctuated by a number of boxed case studies in which actual ore deposits, selected as classic examples from around the world, are briefly described to give context and relevance to processes being discussed in the main text.

A CLASSIFICATION SCHEME FOR ORE DEPOSITS

There are many different ways of categorizing ore deposits. Most people who have written about and described ore deposits have either unwittingly or deliberately been involved in their classification. This is especially true of textbooks where the task of providing order and structure to a set of descriptions invariably involves some form of classification. The best classification schemes are probably those that remain as independent of genetic linkages as possible, thereby minimizing the scope for mistakes and controversy. Nevertheless, genetic classification schemes are ultimately desirable, as there is considerable advantage to having processes of ore formation reflected in a set of descriptive categories. Guilbert and Park (1986) discuss the problem of ore deposit classification at some length in Chapters 1 and 9 of their seminal book on the geology of ore deposits. They show how classification schemes reflect the development of theory and techniques, as well as the level of understanding, in the discipline. Given the dramatic improvements in the level of understanding in economic geology over the past

few years, the Guilbert and Park (1986) classification scheme, modified after Lindgren's (1933) scheme, is both detailed and complex, and befits the comprehensive coverage of the subject matter provided by their book. In a more recent, but equally comprehensive, coverage of ore deposits, Misra (2000) has opted for a categorization based essentially on genetic type and rock association, similar to a scheme by Meyer (1981). It is the association between ore deposits and host rock that is particularly appealing for its simplicity, and that has been selected as the framework within which the processes described in this book are placed.

Rocks are classified universally in terms of a threefold subdivision, namely igneous, sedimentary and metamorphic, that reflects the fundamental processes active in the Earth's crust (Figure 1a). The scheme is universal because rocks are (generally!) recognizably either igneous or sedimentary, or, in the case of both precursors, have been substantially modified to form a metamorphic rock. Likewise, ores are rocks and can often be relatively easily attributed to an igneous or sedimentary/surficial origin, a feature that represents a good basis for classification. Such a classification also reflects the genetic process involved in ore formation, since igneous and sedimentary deposits are often syngenetic and formed at the same time as the host rock itself. Although many ores are metamorphosed, and whereas pressure and temperature increases can substantially modify the original nature of ore deposits, it is evident that metamorphism does not itself represent a fundamental process whereby ore deposits are created. Hydrothermalism, however, is a viable analogue in ore-forming processes for metamorphism and also involves modification of either igneous or sedimentary rocks, as well as heat (and mass) transfer and pressure fluctuation. A very simple classification of ores is, therefore, achieved on the basis of igneous, sedimentary/ surficial and hydrothermal categories (Figure 1b), and this forms the basis for the structure and layout of this book. This subdivision is very similar to one used by Einaudi (2000), who stated that all mineral deposits can be classified into three types based on process, namely magmatic deposits, hydrothermal deposits and surficial deposits formed by

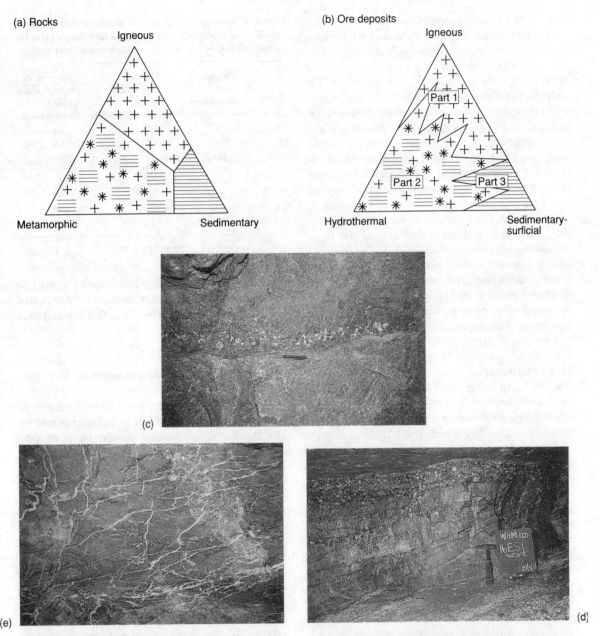

Figure 1 Classification of the principal rock types (a) and an analogous, but much simplified, classification of ore deposit types (b). Photographs show the interplay between ore forming processes. (c) Igneous ore type: the PGE-bearing Merensky Reef, Bushveld Complex, South Africa. This unit and the ores within it can be altered and redistributed by hydrothermal solutions. (d) Sedimentary ore type: Au- and U-bearing conglomerate from the Witwatersrand Basin, South Africa. Quartz veins cutting this unit attest to the action of later hydrothermal fluids in the sequence. (e) Hydrothermal ore type: quartz-carbonate vein network in an Archean orogenic or lode-gold deposit from the Abitibi greenstone belt in Canada. The deposit is associated with igneous (lamprophyre) intrusions that may be implicated in the mineralization process.

surface and groundwaters. One drawback of this type of classification, however, is that ore-forming processes are complex and episodic. Ore formation also involves processes that evolve, sometimes over significant periods of geologic time. For example, igneous processes become magmatic-hydrothermal as the intrusion cools and crystallizes, and sediments undergo diagenesis and metamorphism as they are progressively buried, with accompanying fluid flow and alteration. In addition, deformation of the Earth's crust introduces new conduits that also facilitate fluid flow and promote the potential for mineralization in virtually any rock type. Ore-forming processes can, therefore, span more than one of the three categories, and there is considerable overlap between igneous and hydrothermal and between sedimentary and hydrothermal, as illustrated diagrammatically in Figure 1b, and also in the accompanying photographs of the three major categories of ore types.

The main part of this book is subdivided into three sections termed Igneous (Part 1), Hydrothermal (Part 2), and Sedimentary/surficial (Part 3). Part 1 comprises Chapters 1 and 2, which deal with igneous and magmatic-hydrothermal ore-forming processes respectively. Part 2 contains Chapter 3 and covers the large and diverse range of hydrothermal processes not covered in Part 1. Part 3 comprises Chapter 4 on surficial and supergene processes, as well as Chapter 5, which covers sedimentary ore deposits, including a short section on the fossil fuels. The final chapter of the book, Chapter 6, is effectively an addendum to this threefold subdivision and is an attempt to describe the distribution of ore deposits, both spatially in the context of global tectonics and temporally in terms of crustal evolution through Earth history. This chapter is considered relevant in this day and age because the plate tectonic paradigm, which has so pervasively influenced geological thought since the early 1970s, provides another conceptual basis within which to classify ore deposits. In fact, modern economic geology, and the scientific exploration of mineral deposits, is now firmly conceptualized in terms of global tectonics and crustal evolution. Although there is still a great deal to be learnt, the links between

Table 1 Average crustal abundances for selected metals and typical concentration factors that need to be achieved in order to produce a viable ore deposit

	Average crustal abundance	Typical exploitable grade	Approximate concentration factor
Al	8.2%	30%	×4
Fe	5.6%	50%	×9
Cu	55 ppm	1%	×180
Ni	75 ppm	1%	×130
Zn	70 ppm	5%	×700
Sn	2 ppm	0.5%	×2500
Au	4 ppb	$5\,g\,t^{-1}$	×1250
Pt	5 ppb	$5\,g\,t^{-1}$	×1000

Note: 1 ppm is the same as $1\,g\,t^{-1}$.

plate tectonics and ore genesis are now sufficiently well established that studies of ore deposits are starting to contribute to a better understanding of the Earth system.

WHAT MAKES A VIABLE MINERAL DEPOSIT?

Ore deposits form when a useful commodity is sufficiently concentrated in an accessible part of the Earth's crust so that it can be profitably extracted. The processes by which this concentration occurs are the topic of this book. As an introduction it is pertinent to consider the range of concentration factors that characterize the formation of different ore deposit types. Some of the strategically important metals, such as Fe, Al, Mg, Ti, and Mn, are abundantly distributed in the Earth's crust (i.e. between about 0.5 and 10%) and only require a relatively small degree of enrichment in order to make a viable deposit. Table 1 shows that Fe and Al, for example, need to be concentrated by factors of 9 and 4 respectively, relative to average crustal abundances, in order to form potentially viable deposits.

By contrast, base metals such as Cu, Zn, and Ni are much more sparsely distributed and average crustal abundances are only in the range 55–75 parts per million (ppm). The economics of mining dictate that these metals need to be concentrated by factors in the hundreds in order to form poten-

Figure 2 Plot of crustal abundances against global production for an number of metal commodities (after Einaudi, 2000). The line through Fe can be regarded as a datum against which the rates of production of the other metals can be compared in the context of crustal abundances.

tially viable deposits, degrees of enrichment that are an order of magnitude higher than those applicable to the more abundant metals. The degree of concentration required for the precious metals is even more demanding, where the required enrichment factors are in the thousands. Table 1 shows that average crustal abundances for Au and Pt are in the range 4–5 parts per billion (ppb) and even though ore deposits routinely extract these metals at grades of around $5 \, g \, t^{-1}$, the enrichment factors involved are between 1000 and 1250 times.

Another useful way to distinguish between the geochemically abundant and scarce metals is to plot average crustal abundances against production estimates. This type of analysis was first carried out by Skinner (1976), who used a plot like that in Figure 2 to confirm that crustal abundance is a reasonable measure of the availability of a given resource. It is by design and of necessity that we use more of the geochemically abundant metals than we do the scarce ones. The nature of our technologies and the materials we use to manufacture mechanical items depend in large measure on the availability of raw materials. As an example, the technologies (geological and metallurgical) that resulted in the dramatic increase in global aluminum production over the latter part of the twentieth century allowed iron to be

replaced by aluminum in many products such as motor vehicles. More importantly, though, Figure 2 allows estimates to be made of the relative rates of depletion of certain metals relative to others. These trends are discussed again below.

Mineral resources and ore reserves

In the course of this book reference is made to the term "ore deposit" with little or no consideration of whether such occurrences might be economically viable. Although such considerations might seem irrelevant in the present context it is necessary to emphasize that professional institutions now insist on the correct definition and usage of terminology pertaining to exploration results, mineral resources, and ore reserves. Such terminology should be widely used and applied, as it would help in reducing the irresponsible, and sometimes even fraudulent, usage of terminology, especially with respect to the investor public. Correct terminology can also assist in the description and identification of genuine ore deposits from zones of marginal economic interest or simply anomalous concentrations of a given commodity.

Although the legislation that governs the public reporting of mineral occurrences obviously varies from one country to the next, there is

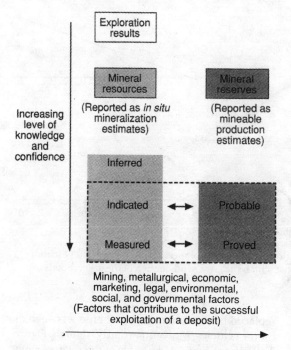

Figure 3 Simplified scheme illustrating the conceptual difference between mineral resources and ore reserves as applied to mineral occurrences. The scheme forms the basis for the professional description of ore deposits as defined by the Australian and South African Institutes of Mining and Metallurgy.

now reasonable agreement as to the definition of terms. In general it is agreed that different terms should apply to mineral occurrences depending on the level of knowledge and degree of confidence that is associated with the measurement of its quantity. Figure 3 is a matrix that reflects the terminology associated with an increased level of geological knowledge and confidence, and modifying factors such as those related to mining techniques, metallurgical extraction, marketing, and environmental reclamation. Exploration results can be translated into a *mineral resource* once it is clear that an occurrence of intrinsic economic interest exists in such form and quantity that there are reasonable prospects for its eventual exploitation. Such a resource can only be referred to as an *ore reserve* if it is a part of an economically extractable measured or indicated mineral resource. One problem with this

terminology is that what is economically extractable in a Third World artisinal operation may not of course be viable in a technically developed First World economy, and vice versa. The term "ore deposit" has no significance in the professional description of a mineral occurrence and is best used as a simply descriptive or generic term.

SOME USEFUL DEFINITIONS AND COMPILATIONS

Some general definitions

This section is not intended to provide a comprehensive glossary of terms used in this book. There are, however, several terms that are used throughout the text where a definition is either useful or necessary in order to avoid ambiguity. The following definitions are consistent with those provided in the *Glossary of Geology* (Bates and Jackson, 1987) and *The Encyclopedia of the Solid Earth Sciences* (Kearey, 1993).

- *Ore*: any naturally occurring material from which a mineral or aggregate of value can be extracted at a profit. In this book the concept extends to coal (a combustible rock comprising more than 50% by weight carbonaceous material) and petroleum (naturally occurring hydrocarbon in gaseous, liquid, or solid state).
- *Syngenetic*: refers to ore deposits that form at the same time as their host rocks. In this book this includes deposits that form during the early stages of sediment diagenesis.
- *Epigenetic*: refers to ore deposits that form after their host rocks.
- *Hypogene*: refers to mineralization caused by ascending hydrothermal solutions.
- *Supergene*: refers to mineralization caused by descending solutions. Generally refers to the enrichment processes accompanying the weathering and oxidation of sulfide and oxide ores at or near the surface.
- *Metallogeny*: the study of the genesis of mineral deposits, with emphasis on their relationships in space and time to geological features of the Earth's crust.
- *Metallotect*: any geological, tectonic, lithological, or geochemical feature that has played a role

Figure 4 Periodic table showing the 92 geologically relevant elements classified on the basis of their rock and mineral associations.

in the concentration of one or more elements in the Earth's crust.

• *Metallogenic Epoch*: a unit of geologic time favorable for the deposition of ores or characterized by a particular assemblage of deposit types.

• *Metallogenic Province*: a region characterized by a particular assemblage of mineral deposit types.

• *Epithermal*: hydrothermal ore deposits formed at shallow depths (less than 1500 meters) and fairly low temperatures (50–200 °C).

• *Mesothermal*: hydrothermal ore deposits formed at intermediate depths (1500–4500 meters) and temperatures (200–400 °C).

• *Hypothermal*: hydrothermal ore deposits formed at substantial depths (greater than 4500 meters) and elevated temperatures (400–600 °C).

Periodic table of the elements

The question of the number of elements present on Earth is a difficult one to answer. Most of the

element compilations relevant to the earth sciences show that there are 92 elements, the majority of which occur in readily detectable amounts in the Earth's crust. Figure 4 shows a periodic table in which these elements are presented in ascending atomic number and also categorized into groupings that are relevant to metallogenesis. There are in fact as many as 118 elements known to man, but those with atomic numbers greater than 92 (U: uranium) either occur in vanishingly small amounts as unstable isotopes that are the products of various natural radioactive decay reactions or are synthetically created in nuclear reactors. The heaviest known element, ununoctium (Uuo, atomic number 118), has been only transiently detected in a nuclear reactor and its actual existence is still conjectural. Some of the heavy, unstable elements are, however, manufactured synthetically and serve a variety of uses. Plutonium (Pu, atomic number 94), for example, is manufactured in fast breeder reactors and is used as a nuclear fuel and in weapons manufacture. Americium (Am, atomic number 95) is also manufactured in reactors and is widely used as the active agent in smoke detectors.

Of the 92 elements shown in Figure 4, almost all have some use in our modern technologically driven societies. Some of the elements (iron and aluminum) are required in copious quantities as raw materials for the manufacture of vehicles and in construction, whereas others (the rare earths, for example) are needed in very much smaller amounts for use in the alloys and electronics industries. Only three elements appear at this stage to have little or no use at all (Figure 4). These are astatine (At, atomic number 85), francium (Fr, atomic number 87), and protactinium (Pa, atomic number 91). Francium is radioactive and so short-lived that only some 20–30 g exists in the entire Earth's crust at any one time! Astatine, likewise, is very unstable and exists in vanishingly small amounts in the crust, or is manufactured synthetically. Radon (Rn, atomic number 86) is an inert or noble gas that is formed as a radioactive decay product of radium. It has limited use in medical applications, but, conversely, if allowed to accumulate can represent a serious health hazard in certain environments.

The useful elements can be broadly subdivided in a number of different ways. Most of the elements can be classified as metals (Figure 4), with a smaller fraction being non-metals. The elements B, Si, As, Se, Te, and At have intermediate properties and are referred to as metalloids. Another classification of elements, attributed to the pioneering geochemist Goldschmidt, is based on their rock associations and forms the basis for distinguishing between lithophile (associated with silicates and concentrated in the crust), chalcophile (associated with sulfides), siderophile (occur as the native metal and concentrated in the core), and atmophile (occur as gases in the atmosphere) elements. It is also useful to consider elements in terms of their ore mineral associations, with some preferentially occurring as sulfides and others as oxides (see Figure 4). Some elements have properties that enable them to be classified in more than one way and iron is a good example, in that it occurs readily as both an oxide and sulfide.

Common ore and gangue minerals

It is estimated that there are about 3800 known minerals that have been identified and classified (Battey and Pring, 1997). Only a very small proportion of these make up the bulk of the rocks of the Earth's crust, as the common rock forming minerals. Likewise, a relatively small number of minerals make up most of the economically viable ore deposits of the world. The following compilation is a breakdown of the more common ore minerals in terms of chemical classes based essentially on the anionic part of the mineral formula. Also included are some of the more common "gangue," which are those minerals that form part of the ore body, but do not contribute to the economically extractable part of the deposit. Most of these are alteration assemblages formed during hydrothermal processes. The compilation, including ideal chemical formulae, is subdivided into six sections, namely native elements, halides, sulfides and sulfo-salts, oxides and hydroxides, oxy-salts (such as carbonates, phosphates, tungstates, sulfates), and silicates. More detailed descriptions of both ore and gangue minerals can be found in a variety of mineralogical texts, such as Deer *et al.* (1982), Berry *et al.* (1983), and Battey and Pring (1997). More information on ore mineral textures and occurrences can be found in Craig and Vaughan (1994) and Ixer (1990).

1 Native elements

Both metals and non-metals exist in nature in the native form, where essentially only one element exists in the structure. Copper, silver, gold, and platinum are all characterized by cubic close packing of atoms, have high densities, and are malleable and soft. The carbon atoms in diamond are linked in tetrahedral groups forming well cleaved, very hard, translucent crystals. Sulfur occurs as rings of eight atoms and forms bipyramids or is amorphous.

Metals
Gold – Au
Silver – Ag
Platinum – Pt

Palladium – Pd
Copper – Cu

Non-metals
Sulfur – S
Diamond – C
Graphite – C

2 Halides

The halide mineral group comprises compounds made up by ionic bonding. Minerals such as halite and sylvite are cubic, have simple chemical formulae, and are highly soluble in water. Halides sometimes form as ore minerals, such as chlorargyrite and atacamite.

Halite – $NaCl$
Sylvite – KCl
Chlorargyrite – $AgCl$
Fluorite – CaF_2
Atacamite – $Cu_2Cl(OH)_3$

3 Sulfides and sulfo-salts

This is a large and complex group of minerals in which bonding is both ionic and covalent in character. The sulfide group has the general formula $A_M X_P$, where X, the larger atom, is typically S but can be As, Sb, Te, Bi, or Se, and A is one or more metals. The sulfo-salts, which are much rarer than sulfides, have the general formula $A_M B_N X_P$, where A is commonly Ag, Cu, or Pb, B is commonly As, Sb, or Bi, and X is S. The sulfide and sulfo-salt minerals are generally opaque, heavy and have a metallic to sub-metallic lustre.

Sulfides
Chalcocite – Cu_2S
Bornite – Cu_5FeS_4
Galena – PbS
Sphalerite – ZnS
Chalcopyrite – $CuFeS_2$
Pyrrhotite – $Fe_{1-x}S$
Pentlandite – $(Fe,Ni)_9S_8$
Millerite – NiS
Covellite – CuS
Cinnabar – HgS
Skutterudite – $(Co,Ni)As_3$

Sperrylite – $PtAs_2$
Braggite/cooperite – $(Pt,Pd,Ni)S$
Moncheite – $(Pt,Pd)(Te,Bi)_2$
Cobaltite – $CoAsS$
Gersdorffite – $NiAsS$
Loellingite – $FeAs_2$
Molybdenite – MoS_2
Realgar – AsS
Orpiment – As_2S_3
Stibnite – Sb_2S_3
Bismuthinite – Bi_2S_3
Argentite – Ag_2S
Calaverite – $AuTe_2$
Pyrite – FeS_2
Laurite – RuS_2

Sulfo-salts
Tetrahedrite – $(Cu,Ag)_{12}Sb_4S_{13}$
Tennantite – $(Cu,Ag)_{12}As_4S_{13}$
Enargite – Cu_3AsS_4

4 Oxides and hydroxides

This group of minerals is variable in its properties, but is characterized by one or more metal in combination with oxygen or a hydroxyl group. The oxides and hydroxides typically exhibit ionic bonding. The oxide minerals can be hard, dense, and refractory in nature (magnetite, cassiterite) but can also be softer and less dense, forming as products of hydrothermal alteration and weathering (hematite, anatase, pyrolucite). Hydroxides, such as goethite and gibbsite, are typically the products of extreme weathering and alteration.

Oxides
Cuprite – Cu_2O
Hematite – Fe_2O_3
Ilmenite – $FeTiO_3$
Hercynite – $FeAl_2O_4$
Gahnite – $ZnAl_2O_4$
Magnetite – Fe_3O_4
Chromite – $FeCr_2O_4$
Rutile – TiO_2
Anatase – TiO_2
Pyrolucite – MnO_2
Cassiterite – SnO_2
Uraninite – UO_2

Thorianite – ThO_2
Columbite-tantalite – $(Fe,Mn)(Nb,Ta)_2O_6$

Hydroxides (or oxyhydroxides)
Goethite – $FeO(OH)$
Gibbsite – $Al(OH)_3$
Boehmite – $AlO(OH)$
Manganite – $MnO(OH)$

5 Oxy-salts

The carbonate group of minerals form when anionic carbonate groups (CO_3^{2-}) are linked by intermediate cations such as Ca, Mg, and Fe. Hydroxyl bearing and hydrated carbonates can also form, usually as a result of weathering and alteration. The other oxy-salts, such as the tungstates, sulfates, phosphates, and vanadates, are analogous to the carbonates, but are built around an anionic group of the form XO_4^{n-}.

Carbonates
Calcite – $CaCO_3$
Dolomite – $CaMg(CO_3)_2$
Ankerite – $CaFe(CO_3)_2$
Siderite – $FeCO_3$
Rhodochrosite – $MnCO_3$
Smithsonite – $ZnCO_3$
Cerussite – $PbCO_3$
Azurite – $Cu_3(OH)_2(CO_3)_2$
Malachite – $Cu_2(OH)_2CO_3$

Tungstates
Scheelite – $CaWO_4$
Wolframite – $(Fe,Mn)WO_4$

Sulfates
Baryte(s) – $BaSO_4$
Anhydrite – $CaSO_4$
Alunite – $KAl_3(OH)_6(SO_4)_2$
Gypsum – $CaSO_4.2H_2O$
Epsomite – $MgSO_4.7H_2O$

Phosphates
Xenotime – YPO_4
Monazite – $(Ce,La,Th)PO_4$
Apatite – $Ca_5(PO_4)_3(F,Cl,OH)$

Vanadates
Carnotite – $K_2(UO_2)(VO_4)_2.3H_2O$

6 Silicates

The bulk of the Earth's crust and mantle is made up of silicate minerals that can be subdivided into several mineral series based on the structure and coordination of the tetrahedral SiO_4^{4-} anionic group. Silicate minerals are generally hard, refractory and translucent. Most of them cannot be regarded as ore minerals in that they do not represent the extractable part of an ore body, and the list provided below shows only some of the silicates more commonly associated with mineral occurrences as gangue or alteration products. Some silicate minerals, such as zircon and spodumene, are ore minerals and represent important sources of metals such as zirconium and lithium, respectively. Others, such as kaolinite, are mined for their intrinsic properties (i.e. as a clay for the ceramics industry).

Tekto (framework)
Quartz – SiO_2
Orthoclase – $(K,Na)AlSi_3O_8$
Albite – $(Na,Ca)AlSi_3O_8$
Scapolite – $(Na,Ca)_4[(Al,Si)_4O_8]_3 (Cl, CO_3)$
Zeolite (analcime) – $NaAlSi_2O_6.H_2O$

Neso (ortho)
Zircon – $Zr(SiO_4)$
Garnet (almandine) – $Fe_3Al_2(SiO_4)_3$
Garnet (grossular) – $Ca_3Al_2(SiO_4)_3$
Sillimanite – Al_2SiO_5
Topaz – $Al_2SiO_4(F,OH)_2$
Chloritoid – $(Fe,Mg,Mn)_2(Al,Fe)Al_3O_2(SiO_4)_2(OH)_4$

Cyclo (ring)
Beryl – $Be_3Al_2Si_6O_{18}$
Tourmaline –
$(Na,Ca)(Mg,Fe,Mn,Al)_3(Al,Mg,Fe)_6Si_6O_{18}$
$(BO_3)_3(OH,F)_4$

Soro (di)
Lawsonite – $CaAl_2Si_2O_7(OH)_2.H_2O$
Epidote – $Ca_2(Al,Fe)_3Si_3O_{12}(OH)$

Phyllo (sheet)
Kaolinite – $Al_4Si_4O_{10}(OH)_8$
Montmorillonite – $(Na,Ca)_{0.3}(Al,Mg)_2$
$Si_4O_{10}(OH)_2.nH_2O$
Illite – $KAl_2(Si,Al)_4O_{10}(H_2O)(OH)_2$
Pyrophyllite – $Al_2Si_4O_{10}(OH)_2$
Talc – $Mg_3Si_4O_{10}(OH)_2$
Muscovite – $KAl_2(AlSi_3O_{10})(OH)_2$
Biotite – $K(Fe,Mg)_3(Al,Fe)Si_3O_{10}(OH,F)_2$
Lepidolite – $K(Li,Al)_3(Si,Al)_4O_{10}(OH,F)_2$
Chlorite – $(Fe,Mg,Al)_{5-6}(Si,Al)_4O_{10}(OH)_8$

Ino (chain)
Tremolite-actinolite – $Ca_2(Fe,Mg)_5Si_8O_{22}(OH)_2$
Spodumene – $LiAlSi_2O_6$
Wollastonite – $CaSiO_3$

Unknown structure
Chrysocolla – $(Cu,Al)_2H_2Si_2O_5(OH)_4.nH_2O$

Geological time scale

The development of a geological time scale has been the subject of a considerable amount of thought and research over the past few decades and continues to occupy the minds and activities of a large number of earth scientists around the world. The definition of a framework within which to describe the secular evolution of rocks, and hence the Earth, has been, and continues to be, a contentious exercise. The International Commission on Stratigraphy (ICS is a working group of the International Union of Geological Sciences: IUGS) has been given the task of formalizing the geological time scale and this work is ongoing (www.micropress.org/stratigraphy/). In this book reference is often made to the timing of various events and processes and the provision of a time scale to which the reader can refer is, therefore, useful. Figure 5 is a time scale based on the 2000 edition of the International Stratigraphic Chart published and sanctioned by the ICS and IUGS. In this diagram global chronostratigraphic terms are presented in terms of eons, eras, periods, and epochs, and defined by absolute ages in millions of years before present (Ma). Also shown are the positions on the time scale of many of the ore deposits or metallogenic provinces referred to in the text.

NATURAL RESOURCES, SUSTAINABILITY, AND ENVIRONMENTAL RESPONSIBILITY

One of the major issues that characterized social and economic development toward the end of the twentieth century revolved around the widespread acceptance that the Earth's natural resources are finite, and that their exploitation should be carried out in a manner that will not detrimentally affect future generations. The concept of "sustainable development" in terms of the exploitation of mineral occurrences implies that future social and economic practice should endeavor not to deplete natural resources to the point where the needs of the future cannot be met. This would seem to be an impossible goal given the unprecedented population growth over the past century and the fact that many commodities will become depleted within the next 100 years. The challenge for commodity supply over the next century is a multifaceted one and will require a better understanding of the earth system, improved incentives to promote more efficient recycling of existing resources, and the means to find alternative sources for commodities that are in danger of serious depletion.

There has been a dramatic rise in global population over the past 150 years. The number of humans on Earth has risen from 1 billion in 1830 to 6 billion at the end of the twentieth century. Most predictions suggest that the populations of most countries will start to level off over the next 30 years and that global numbers will stabilize at around 11 billion people by the end of the twenty-first century. Societies in the next 100 years are, nevertheless, facing a scenario in which the demand for, and utilization of, natural resources continues to increase and certain commodities might well become depleted in this interval. Production trends for commodities such as oil, bauxite, copper, and gold (Figure 6) confirm that demand for resources mirrors population growth and is likely to continue to do so over the next few

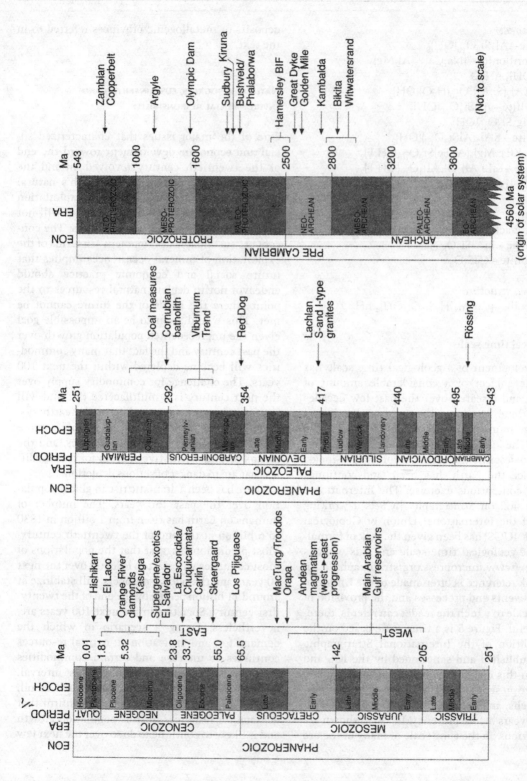

Figure 5 Geological time scale after the ICS (2000). Also shown are the ages of the various deposits and metallogenic provinces mentioned in the book.

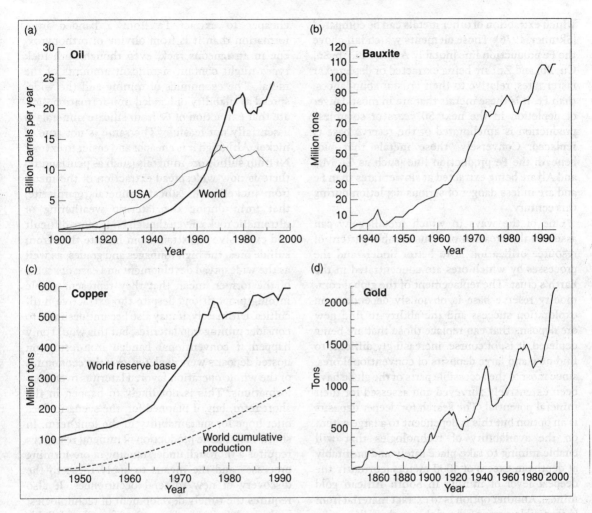

Figure 6 Global production trends for oil (a), bauxite (b), copper (c), and gold (d) over the twentieth century (after compilations in Craig *et al.*, 1996).

decades. World oil production increased precipitously until the late 1970s, but since then a variety of political and economic factors have contributed to tempering production (Figure 6a), thereby ensuring a longer-term reserve base. A similar levelling of production is evident for bauxite (Figure 6b) but such a trend is not yet evident for the precious metals such as gold or platinum. For some commodities, such as copper (Figure 6c), the world reserve base is also levelling off, a feature that in part also reflects fewer new and large discoveries. Critical shortages of most natural

commodities are not likely to present a problem during the early part of the twenty-first century (Einaudi, 2000), but this situation will deteriorate unless strategies for sustainability are put into place immediately.

The depletion of commodities in the Earth's crust is particularly serious for those metals that are already scarce in terms of crustal abundances and for which high degrees of enrichment are required in order to make viable ore deposits. Figure 2 illustrates the point by referring to the production of iron as a baseline measure against which extraction of other metals can be compared (Skinner, 1976). Those elements which fall above the Fe production line (notably Au, Ag, Bi, Sb, Sn, Cu, Pb, and Zn) are being extracted or depleted at faster rates, relative to their crustal abundances, than Fe. It is these metals that are in most danger of depletion in the next 50 years or so unless production is ameliorated or the reserve base is replaced. Conversely, those metals that plot beneath the Fe production line (such as Ti, Mg, and Al) are being extracted at slower rates than Fe and are in less danger of serious depletion during this century.

One of the ways in which metallogeny can assist in the creation of a sustainable pattern of resource utilization is to better understand the processes by which ores are concentrated in the Earth's crust. The replacement of the global commodity reserve base is obviously dependent on exploration success and the ability to find new ore deposits that can replace those that are being depleted. It is, of course, increasingly difficult to find new and large deposits of conventional ores, since most of the accessible parts of the globe have been extensively surveyed and assessed for their mineral potential. The search for deeper deposits is an option but this is dependent to a large extent on the availability of technologies that will enable mining to take place safely and profitably at depths in excess of 4000 meters (currently the deepest level of mining in South African gold mines). Another option is to extract material from inaccessible parts of the globe, such as the ocean floor, a proposal that has received serious consideration with respect to metals such as Mn and Cu. Again, there are technological barriers to such processes at present, but these can be overcome, as demonstrated by the now widespread exploration for, and extraction of, oil and gas from the sea floor. A third option to improve the sustainability of resource exploitation is to extract useful commodities from rocks that traditionally have not been thought of as viable ores. Such a development can only be achieved if the so-called "mineralogical barrier" (Skinner, 1976) is overcome. This concept can be described in terms of the amount of energy (or cost) required to extract a commodity from its ore. It is, for example, considerably

cheaper to extract Fe from a banded iron-formation than it is from olivine or orthopyroxene in an igneous rock, even though both rock types might contain significant amounts of the metal. The economics of mining and the widespread availability of banded iron-formation dictate that extraction of Fe from silicate minerals is essentially not feasible. The same is not true of nickel. Although it is cheaper and easier to extract Ni from sulfide ore minerals (such as pentlandite) there is now widespread extraction of the metal from nickeliferous silicate minerals (garnierite) that form during the lateritic weathering of ultramafic rocks. Even though Ni is more difficult and expensive to extract from laterite than from sulfide ores, the high tonnages and grades, as well as the widespread development and ease of access of the former, mean that they represent viable mining propositions despite the extractive difficulties. Ultimately, it may also become desirable to consider mining iron laterites, but this would only happen if conventional banded iron-formation hosted deposits were depleted, or if the economics of the whole operation favored laterites over iron-formations. This is not likely to happen in the short term, but, if planned for, the scenario does offer hope for sustainability in the long term. In short, sustainable production of mineral resources requires a thorough understanding of ore-forming processes and the means to apply these to the discovery of new mineral occurrences. It also requires the timely development of technologies, both in the earth sciences and in related fields of mining and extractive metallurgy, that will enable alternative supplies of mineral resources to be economically exploited in the future.

Mining and environmental responsibility

A global population of 11 billion by the end of the century presents a major problem in terms of the supply of most of the world's mineral resources. What is even more serious, though, is the enormous strain it will place on the Earth's fragile environment arising from the justifiable expectation that future technologically advanced societies will provide an adequate standard of living, in terms of food, water, housing, recreation, and material benefits, to all their peoples. In addition to commodity supply problems, the twenty-first century will be also be characterized by unprecedented depletion of even more critical resources in the form of soil, water, and clean air (Fyfe, 2000). Legislation that is aimed at dealing with issues such as atmospheric pollution and greenhouse gas emissions, factory waste and acid drainage, the burning and destruction of forests, the protection of endangered species, overgrazing, and erosion is highly desirable but far from globally applicable because it is perceived as a luxury that only the developed world can afford.

The study of ore-forming processes is occasionally viewed as an undesirable topic that ultimately contributes to the exploitation of the world's precious natural resources. Nothing could be further from the truth. An understanding of the processes by which metals are concentrated in the Earth's crust is essential knowledge for anyone

concerned with the preservation and remediation of the environment. The principles that underpin the natural concentration of ores in the crust are the same as those that can be utilized in issues such as the control of acid mine drainage, and soil and erosion management. Mining operations around the world are increasingly having to assume responsibility for reclamation of the landscape once the resource has been depleted. The industry now encompasses a range of activities extending from geological exploration and evaluation, through mining and beneficiation, and eventually to environmental reclamation. This is the mining cycle and its effective management in the future will be a multidisciplinary exercise carried out by highly skilled scientists and engineers. Earth systems science, and in particular the geological processes that gave rise to the natural concentration of the ore in the first place, will be central to this entire operation.

SUMMARY

The discipline of "economic geology" and in particular the field of metallogeny (the study of the genesis of ore deposits) remains critical to the teaching of earth systems science. A holistic approach involving the integration of knowledge relevant to the atmosphere, biosphere, and lithosphere is now regarded as essential to understanding the complexities of the earth system. The development of environmentally responsible and sustainable policies with respect to the future supply of all natural resources will demand a thorough

knowledge of the nature and workings of the earth system. Central to this is an understanding of metallogeny and the nature and origin of the entire spectrum of mineral resources, including the fossil fuels. The classification of mineral deposits in terms of process can be simply and effectively achieved in terms of rock associations, namely igneous, hydrothermal, and sedimentary. This breakdown forms the basis for the layout of this book.

FURTHER READING

Blunden, J. (1983) *Mineral Resources and Their Management*. Harlow: Longman, 302 pp.

Craig, J.R., Vaughan, D.J. and Skinner, B.J. (1996) *Resources of the Earth – Origin, Use and Environmental Impact*. Englewood Cliffs, NJ: Prentice Hall, 472 pp.

Ernst, W.G. (2000) *Earth Systems – Processes and Issues*. Cambridge: Cambridge University Press, 559 pp.

Kesler, S.E. (1994) *Mineral Resources, Economics and the Environment*. London: Macmillan, 400 pp.

PART ONE

Igneous Processes

CHAPTER ONE

Igneous ore-forming processes

TOPICS

METALLOGENY OF OCEANIC AND CONTINENTAL CRUST
FUNDAMENTAL MAGMA TYPES AND THEIR METAL ENDOWMENT
THE RELATIVE FERTILITY OF MAGMAS AND THE "INHERITANCE
  FACTOR"
  "late-veneer" hypothesis
  diamonds and kimberlite/lamproite
  metal concentrations in metasomatized mantle
  S- and I-type granites
PARTIAL MELTING AND CRYSTAL FRACTIONATION AS ORE-
  FORMING PROCESSES
TRACE ELEMENT DISTRIBUTION DURING PARTIAL MELTING
TRACE ELEMENT DISTRIBUTION DURING FRACTIONAL
  CRYSTALLIZATION
MONOMINERALIC CHROMITITE LAYERS
LIQUID IMMISCIBILITY AS AN ORE-FORMING PROCESS
SPECIAL EMPHASIS ON MINERALIZATION PROCESSES IN LAYERED
  MAFIC INTRUSIONS
  sulfide solubility
  sulfide–silicate partition coefficients
  the R factor
  PGE clusters and hiatus models

CASE STUDIES

Box 1.1 Diamondiferous kimberlites and lamproites:
the Orapa (Botswana) and the Argyle (Western Australia)
diamond mines
Box 1.2 Partial melting and concentration of
incompatible elements: the Rössing uranium deposit
Box 1.3 Boundary layer differentiation in granites and
incompatible element concentration: the Zaaiplaats tin
deposit, Bushveld Complex
Box 1.4 Crystal fractionation and formation of
monomineralic chromitite layers: the UG1 chromitite
seam, Bushveld Complex
Box 1.5 Silicate–sulfide immiscibility: the komatiite
hosted Ni–Cu deposits at Kambalda, Western Australia
Box 1.6 New magma injection and magma mixing:
the Merensky Reef, Bushveld Complex
Box 1.7 Magma contamination and sulfide
immiscibility: the Sudbury Ni–Cu deposits

1.1 INTRODUCTION

Igneous rocks host a large number of different
ore deposit types. Both mafic and felsic rocks
are linked to mineral deposits, examples of which
range from the chromite ores resulting from
crystal fractionation of mafic magmas to tin
deposits associated with certain types of granites.
The processes described in this chapter relate
to properties that are intrinsic to the magma

itself and can be linked genetically to its cooling
and solidification. Discussion of related processes, whereby an aqueous fluid phase forms or
"exsolves" from the magma as it crystallizes,
is placed in Chapter 2. The topics discussed
under the banners of igneous and magmatic–
hydrothermal ore-forming processes are intimately
linked and form Part 1 of this book.

A measure of the economic importance of ore
deposits hosted in igneous rocks can be obtained
from a compilation of mineral production data as
a function of host rock type. A country like South
Africa, for example, is underlain dominantly by
sedimentary rocks and these undoubtedly host
many of the valuable mineral resources (especially

Table 1.1 A comparison of the value of mineral production from igneous and sedimentary rocks in South Africa

Mineralization hosted in	Area (km²)	Value of sales, 1971 (10⁶ US$)	% of total area	% of total value	Unit value (US$/km²)
Granites	163 100	1973	13.3	3.4	12 000
Mafic layered complexes	36 400	7288	3.0	12.5	200 200
Total (igneous)	199 500	9261	16.3	15.9	46 400
Sedimentary rocks	1 023 900	49 137	83.7	84.1	47 900

Source: after Pretorius (1976).

if the fossil fuels are taken into consideration). Nevertheless, the value of ores hosted in igneous rocks *per unit area of outcrop* can be comparable with that for sedimentary rocks, as indicated in Table 1.1. Although South Africa is characterized by a rather special endowment of mineral wealth related to the huge Bushveld Complex, the importance of igneous-hosted ore deposits is nevertheless apparent.

1.2 MAGMAS AND METALLOGENY

It is well known that different igneous rocks host ore deposits with different metal associations, and that this must be related somehow to the environments in which magmas are generated and the resulting compositional characteristics they inherit from their various settings. It is widely recognized, for example, that many of the chalcophile and siderophile elements (such as Ni, Co, Pt, Pd, and Au) are more likely to be associated with mafic rock types, whereas concentrations of many lithophile elements (such as Li, Sn, Zr, U, and W) are typically found in association with felsic or alkaline rock types. This has implications for understanding ore genesis and, consequently, some of the factors related to these differences are discussed below.

1.2.1 Crustal architecture and mineral wealth

Although the greatest concentrations of siderophile and chalcophile elements almost certainly reside in the mantle and core of the Earth, these are generally inaccessible due to their very great depths. In fact, most of the world's economically exploitable mineral wealth effectively lies on the surface or just below the surface of the Earth. The world's deepest mine, the Western Deep Levels gold mine near Johannesburg, South Africa, extends to just over 4000 m depth and this places an effective limit on ore body exploitation, at least in terms of present technologies. Nevertheless, many mineral commodities are formed much deeper in the crust than 4 km, with some even being derived from the mantle. Diamonds, for example, are hosted in kimberlite magmas that have been brought to exploitable depths by a variety of igneous or tectonic mechanisms. Understanding ore genesis processes, therefore, requires a knowledge of lithospheric (i.e. crust and upper mantle) architecture, and also of the origin and nature of the igneous rocks in this section of the Earth.

The oceanic crust, which covers some two-thirds of the Earth surface, is thin (less than 10 km) and, compared to the continents, has a composition and structure that is relatively simple and consistent over its entire extent. The upper layer, on average only 0.4 km thick (Kearey and Vine, 1996), comprises a combination of terrigenous and pelagic sediments that are distributed mainly by turbidity currents. They are often highly reduced and metal charged. This is underlain by a layer, typically 1–2.5 km thick, that is both extrusive and intrusive in character and dominantly basaltic in composition. The basalts are, in turn, underlain by the main body of oceanic crust that is plutonic in character and formed by crystallization and fractionation of basaltic magma. This cumulate assemblage comprises mainly gabbro, pyroxenite, and peridotite. Sections of tectonized and meta-

Figure 1.1 Oceanic crustal architecture showing the main types of ore deposits characteristic of this environment. Only chromite and related deposits (Cr–Ni–Pt) are related to igneous ore-forming processes; VMS (Cu, Co, Zn) and sediment-hosted deposits (Mn, Co, Ni) are discussed in Chapters 3 and 5 respectively.

morphosed oceanic lithosphere can be observed in ophiolite complexes which represent segments of the ocean crust (usually back-arc basins) that have been thrust or obducted onto continental margins during continent–ocean collision.

The types of ore deposits that one might expect to find associated with ophiolitic rocks are shown in Figure 1.1. They include the category of podiform chromite deposits that are related to crystal fractionation of mid-ocean ridge basalt (MORB), and also have potential for Ni and Pt group element (PGE) mineralization. Accumulations of manganese in nodules on the sea floor, metal-rich concentrations in pelagic muds, and exhalative volcanogenic massive sulfide (VMS) Cu–Zn deposits also occur in this tectonic setting, but are not directly related to igneous processes and are discussed elsewhere (Chapters 3 and 5).

The continental crust differs markedly from its oceanic counterpart. It is typically 35–40 km thick, but thins to around 20 km under rift zones and thickens to 80 km or more beneath young mountain belts. Historically, the continental crust was thought to comprise an upper zone made up largely of granite (and its sedimentary derivatives) and a lower, more mafic zone, with the two layers separated by the Conrad discontinuity (which marks a change in seismic velocities, and, therefore crustal density). More recent geophysical and geological studies clearly indicate that crustal architecture is more complex and reflects a long-lived tectonic and magmatic history, extending back in some cases over 3800 million years (Figure 1.2).

The continents have been progressively constructed throughout geological time by a variety of magmatic, sedimentary, and orogenic processes taking place along active plate margins and, to a lesser extent, within the continents themselves. In addition, continental land masses have repeatedly broken apart and reamalgamated throughout geological history. These episodes, known as *Wilson cycles*, have rearranged the configuration of continental fragments several times in the geological past. In the early Proterozoic, for example, it is conceivable that segments of southern Africa and western Australia might have been part of the same continent. The significance of these cycles, and the pattern of crustal evolution with time, to global metallogeny is discussed in more detail in Chapter 6.

Figure 1.2 Continental crustal architecture showing the main types of igneous-related ore deposits characteristic of this environment.

The upper crust, which in some continental sections is defined as extending to the Conrad discontinuity at some 6 km depth, is made up of felsic to intermediate compositions (granite to diorite) together with the sedimentary detritus derived from the weathering and erosion of this material. Archean continental fragments (greater than 2500 Myr old) also contain a significant component of greenstone belt material, representing preserved fragments of ancient oceanic crust. The lower crust, between the Conrad and Mohorovicic discontinuities, is variable in composition but is typically made up of hotter, and usually more dense, material. This is because temperatures and pressures in the crust increase with depth at average rates of some 25 °C km^{-1} and 30 MPa km^{-1} respectively (Kearey and Vine, 1996). The lower crust is not necessarily compositionally different from the upper crust, but exists at higher metamorphic grades. It is also likely to be more anhydrous and residual, in the sense that magma now present at higher levels was extracted from the lower crust, leaving a residue of modified material. Some of the lower crust may be more mafic in composition, comprising material such as amphibolite, gabbro, and anorthosite.

Most of the world's known ore deposits are, of course, hosted in rocks of the continental crust, and the full range is not shown in Figure 1.2. Some of the more important igneous rock-related deposit types are shown and these include diamondiferous kimberlites, anorthosite-hosted Ti deposits, the Cr–V–Pt–Cu–Ni assemblage of ores in continental layered mafic suites, and the Sn–W–F–Nb–REE–P–U family of lithophile ores related to granites and alkaline intrusions.

1.2.2 Magma types and metal contents

Although their rheological properties are different, the outer two layers of the Earth, the more rigid lithosphere and the ductile asthenosphere, are largely solid. Zones within these layers that are anomalous in terms of pressure or temperature do, however, form and can cause localized melting of the rocks present. The nature of the rock undergoing melting and the extent to which it is melted are the main factors that control the composition of the magma that is formed. The magma composition, in turn, dictates the nature of metal concentrations that are likely to form in the rocks that solidify from that magma.

Although it is theoretically possible to form an almost infinite range of magma compositions (from ultramafic to highly alkaline), for ease of discussion this section is subdivided into four parts, each representing what is considered to be a fundamental magma type – these are basalt, andesite, rhyolite, and alkaline magmas, the latter including kimberlite.

Basalt

Basalts form in almost every tectonic environment, but the majority of basaltic magma production takes place along the mid-ocean ridges, and in response to hot-spot related plumes, to form oceanic crust. In addition, basalts are formed together with a variety of more felsic magmas, along island arcs and orogenic continental margins. Basaltic magma may also intrude or extrude continental crust, either along well defined fractures or rifts (such as continental flood basalt provinces, or the Great Dyke of Zimbabwe) or in response to intra-plate hot-spot activity (which might have been responsible for the formation of the Bushveld Complex of South Africa).

Basalt forms by partial melting of mantle material, much of which can generally be described as peridotitic in composition. Certain mantle rocks, such as lherzolite (a peridotite which contains clinopyroxene and either garnet or spinel), have been shown experimentally to produce basaltic liquids on melting, whereas others, like alpine-type peridotite (comprising mainly olivine and orthopyroxene), are too refractory to yield basaltic liquids and may indeed represent the residues left behind after basaltic magma has already been extracted from the mantle. Likewise, oceanic crust made up of hydrated (serpentinized) basalt and drawn down into a subduction zone is also a potential source rock for island arc and continental margin type magmatism. Komatiites, which are ultramafic basalt magmas (with >18% MgO) mainly restricted to Archean greenstone belts, have a controversial origin but are generally believed to represent high degrees of partial melting of mantle during the high heat-flow conditions that prevailed in the early stages of crust formation prior to 2500 Ma.

Ore deposits associated with mafic igneous rocks typically comprise a distinctive (mainly siderophile and chalcophile) metal assemblage of, among others, Ni, Co, Cr, V, Cu, Pt, and Au. Examination of Table 1.2 shows that this list corresponds to those elements that are intrinsically enriched in basaltic magmas. Figure 1.3 illustrates the relative abundances of these metals in three fundamental magma types and the significantly higher concentrations in basalt by comparison with andesite and rhyolite. The enhanced concentration of these metals in each case is related to the fact that the source materials from which the basalt formed must likewise have been enriched in those constituents. In addition, enhanced abundances also reflect the chemical affinity that these metals have for the major elements that characterize a basaltic magma (Mg and Fe) and dictate its mineral composition (olivine and the pyroxenes).

The chemical affinity that one element has for another is related to their atomic properties as reflected by their relative positions in the periodic table (see Figure 4, Introduction). The alkali earth elements (i.e. K, Na, Rb, Cs, etc.), for example, are all very similar to one another, but have properties that are quite different to the transition metals (such as Fe, Co, Ni, Pt, Pd). In addition, minor or trace elements, which occur in such low abundances in magmas that they cannot form a discrete mineral phase, are present by virtue of their ability either to substitute for another chemically similar element in a mineral lattice or to occupy a defect site in a crystal lattice. This behavior is referred to as diadochy or substitution and explains much, but not all, of the trace element behavior in rocks. Substitution of a trace element for a major element in a crystal takes place if their ionic radii and charges are similar. Typically radii should be within 15% of one another and charges should differ by no more than one unit provided the charge difference can be compensated by another substitution. Bond strength and type also effects diadochy and it preferentially occurs in crystals where ionic bonding dominates.

A good example of diadochic behavior is the substitution of Ni^{2+} for Mg^{2+} in olivine, or V^{3+} for Fe^{3+} in magnetite. Analytical data for the Ni content of basalts shows an excellent correlation between Ni and MgO contents (Figure 1.4), confirming the notion that the minor metal substitutes readily for Mg. The higher intrinsic Ni content of ultramafic basalts and komatiites would suggest that the latter rocks are perhaps better suited to hosting viable magmatic nickel deposits, an observation borne out by the presence of world class nickel deposits hosted in the Archean

Table 1.2 Average abundances of selected elements in the major magma types

	Basalt	Andesite	Rhyolite	Alkaline magma	Kimberlite	Clarke*
Li	10	12	50	–		20
Be	0.7	1.5	4.1	4–24		2.8
F	380	210	480	640		625
P	3200	2800	1200	1800	0.6–0.9%	1050
V	266	148	72	235	–	135
Cr	307	55	4	–		10
Co	48	24	4.4	–		25
Ni	134	18	6	–	1050	75
Cu	65	60	6	–	103	55
Zn	94	87	38	108		70
Zr	87	205	136	1800	2200	165
Mo	0.9–2.7	0.8–1.2	1	15		1.5
Sn	0.9	1.5	3.6	–		2
Nb	5	4–11	28	140	240	20
Sb	0.1–1.4	0.2	0.1–0.6	–	–	0.2
Ta	0.9	–	2.3	10		2
W	1.2	1.1	2.4	16		1.5
Pb	6.4	5	21	15		13
Bi	0.02	0.12	0.12	–		0.17
U	0.1–0.6	0.8	5	10		2.7
Th	0.2	1.9	26	35		7.2
Ag[†]	100	80	37	–		70
Au[†]	3.6	–	1.5	–		4
Pt[†]	17–30	–	3–12	–	19	10
S	782	423	284	598	2100	260
Ge	1.1	1.2	1.0–1.3	1.3–2.1	0.5	1.5
As	0.8	1.8	3.5	–	–	1.8
Cd	0.02	0.02	0.2–0.5	0.04	–	0.2

If no average is available, a range of values is provided. *Clarke is a term that refers to the average crustal abundance.
[†]Values as ppb, all other values as ppm.
Source: data from Taylor (1964), Wedepohl (1969), Krauskopf and Bird (1995).

Figure 1.3 Relative abundances of selected metals in basalt, andesite, and rhyolite (data from Table 1.2).

Figure 1.4 The relationship between Ni and MgO contents of basalts within which base metal mineralization does not occur (data from Naldrett, 1989a).

komatiites of the Kambalda mining district in Western Australia (see Box 1.5) and elsewhere in the world.

Andesite

Andesites are rocks that crystallize from magmas of composition intermediate between basalt and rhyolite (typically with SiO_2 contents between 53 and 63 wt%). Their petrogenesis remains contentious, although it is well known that they tend to occur dominantly in orogenic zones, either along island arcs or on continental margins beneath which subduction of oceanic crust is taking place (Hall, 1996). Discussion about the origin of andesite revolves around whether it represents a primary magma composition derived directly by an appropriate degree of melting of a suitable source rock, or an evolved melt formed by differentiation of a more mafic magma such as basalt.

Geological observations support the notion that andesite can be formed both as a primary magma composition and by *in situ* fractionation. The observation that andesitic volcanoes occur directly above aseismic sections of a Benioff zone (i.e. the subducted slab that produces earthquakes due to movement and fracturing of rock) suggests that melt production (and damping of seismic waves) has occurred in these areas. This would support the notion that andesitic magma

is produced by direct melting of hydrous oceanic crust or, more likely, the mantle wedge overlying the subduction zone as it is permeated by fluids expelled from the subjacent oceanic crust. Alternatively, andesitic magma can be produced by fractionation of phases such as hornblende and magnetite from relatively water-rich parent magmas (Osborn, 1979), or by contamination of an originally more mafic melt by felsic material or melt.

Irrespective of the mode of formation of andesite it is apparent that as a magma type it does not exhibit a primary association with any particular suite of metals or ore deposits. It appears instead that ore deposits tend to be associated with magmas representing the ends of the compositional spectrum, and that intermediate melt compositions are simply characterized by intermediate trace element abundances. Examination of Table 1.2 shows that andesites appear to have little or no metal specificity and are characterized by trace element abundances that are intermediate between those of basalt on the one hand and either granite or alkaline rocks on the other.

Rhyolite

Felsic magmas can also form in a variety of geological environments. They crystallize at depth to form a spectrum of rock compositions ranging from Na-rich tonalite to K-rich alkali granite, or extrude on surface to form dacitic to rhyolitic volcanic rocks. Very little granite magma forms in oceanic crust or along island arcs that have formed between two oceanic plates. Where oceanic granite does occur it is typically the result of differentiation of a more mafic magma type originally formed by mantle melting. Along the mid-Atlantic ridge in Iceland, for example, eruptions of the volcano Hekla are initiated by a pulse of felsic ash production which is rapidly followed by eruption of more typical basaltic andesite. This suggests that the intervening period between eruptions was characterized by differentiation of the magma and that the accompanying build-up of volatiles may have been responsible for the subsequent eruption (Baldridge *et al.*, 1973). These observations, among many others, clearly indicate that granitic melts

Figure 1.5 Relative abundances of selected "granitophile" elements in basalt, andesite, and rhyolite (data from Table 1.2).

can be the products of differentiation of more mafic magmas in oceanic settings.

Most felsic magmas, however, are derived from the partial melting of predominantly crustal material along ocean–continent island arcs and orogenic continental margins. Although Andean-type subduction zones might facilitate partial melting of the downgoing slab itself, the much higher proportion of felsic magma formed in this environment compared to oceanic settings points to a significant role for continental crust as a source. There is now general agreement that Andean-type subduction-related magmatism receives melt contributions from both the mantle lithosphere and the continental crust, with the wide-ranging compositions of so-called "calc–alkaline" igneous suites being attributed to a combination of both magma mingling and fractional crystallization (Best, 2003).

Significant quantities of felsic magma are produced in the latter stages of continent–continent collision and also in anorogenic continental settings where rifting and crustal thinning has taken place. Himalayan-type continent collision, for example, is usually accompanied by crustal thickening associated with intense thrusting, tectonic duplication and reverse metamorphic gradients. These processes cause dewatering of crustal material, which, in turn, promotes partial melting to form high-level leucogranite magmas derived from source rocks that often contain significant proportions of sedimentary material (Le Fort,

1975). Anorogenic continental magmatism, on the other hand, is usually related to crustal thinning (accompanying plume or hot-spot activity?) and is typified by the production of magmas with bimodal compositions (i.e. basalt plus rhyolite). A good example is the 2060 Myr old Bushveld Complex in South Africa, where early mafic magmas intruded to form the world's largest layered igneous complex, followed by emplacement of a voluminous suite of granites.

Ore deposits associated with felsic igneous rocks often comprise concentrations of the lithophile elements such as Li, Be, F, Sn, W, U, and Th. Table 1.2 shows that this list corresponds to those elements that are intrinsically enriched in rhyolitic magmas and Figure 1.5 illustrates, in bar graph form, the relative abundances of these elements and, in particular, the higher abundances in rhyolite by comparison with andesite and basalt.

The relative enrichment of certain lithophile elements in rhyolitic magmas is partially related to their geochemically incompatible nature. An incompatible element is one whose ionic charge and radius make it difficult to substitute for any of the stoichiometric elements in rock-forming minerals. Thus, incompatible elements tend to be excluded from the products of crystallization and concentrated into residual or differentiated magmas (such as the granitic magmas that might form by crystal fractionation of mafic magmas in oceanic settings). Alternatively, incompatible elements also tend to be concentrated in crustal melts derived from low degrees of partial melting of source rocks that may themselves have been endowed in the lithophile elements. These concepts are discussed in more detail in section 1.4 below.

A well known and interesting feature of ore deposits that are genetically associated with granite intrusions is that the origin and composition of the magma generally controls the nature of the metal assemblage in the deposit (Chappell and White, 1974; Ishihara, 1978, 1981). This control is almost certainly related in part to the metal endowment inherited by the magma from the rocks that were melted to produce it. Where a felsic magma is derived from melting of a sedimentary or supracrustal protolith (termed *S-type granites*), associated ore deposits are characterized by concentrations of metals such as Sn, W, U, and Th. Where it is derived from melting of older igneous protoliths in the crust (*I-type granite*) the ore association is typified by metals such as Cu, Mo, Pb, Zn, and Au. This association is metallogenically very significant and is discussed in more detail in section 1.3.4 below and again in Chapter 2.

Alkaline magmas and kimberlite

Although most magma compositions can be represented by the basalt–andesite–rhyolite spectrum, some deviate from this trend and are compositionally unusual. For example, magmas that are depleted in SiO_2 but highly enriched in the alkali elements (Na, K, and Ca) are relatively rare, but may be economically important as they frequently contain impressive concentrations of a wide range of ore-forming metals (such as Cu, Fe, P, Zr, Nb, REE, F, U, and Th). In addition, kimberlitic and related magma types (such as lamproites) are the main primary source of diamonds.

The most common alkaline mafic magma is nephelinite, which crystallizes to give a range of rock types (the ijolite suite; Hall, 1996) comprising rather unusual minerals, such as felspathoid, calcic-pyroxene, and carbonate assemblages. Nephelinite lavas are observed in oceanic settings such as the Cape Verde and Hawaiian islands, but are best seen in young (Paleocene to recent) continental volcanic settings such as the East African

rift valley, central Europe and southeast Australia. Old alkaline igneous complexes are rare, one of the best preserved being the 2050 Myr old Phalaborwa Complex in South Africa, which is mined for copper and phosphate as well as a host of minor by-products.

Nephelinite, as well as the associated, but rare, carbonatite melts (i.e. magmas comprising essentially $CaCO_3$ and lesser Na_2CO_3), are undoubtedly primary magma types derived from the mantle by very low degrees of partial melting under conditions of high P_{total} and P_{CO_2} (Hall, 1996). The relationship between nephelinitic and carbonatitic magmas is generally attributed to liquid immiscibility, whereby an original alkali-rich silicate magma rich in a carbonate component exsolves into two liquid fractions, one a silicate and the other a carbonate (Ferguson and Currie, 1971; Le Bas, 1987). Low degrees (2%) of partial melting of a garnet lherzolitic source in the mantle will typically yield olivine nephelinite compositions and these magmas may be spatially and temporally associated with basaltic volcanism (Le Bas, 1987). Nephelinite magma associated with carbonatite, on the other hand, is only considered possible if the source material also contained a carbonate phase (such as dolomite) and a soda-amphibole. This type of mantle source rock is likely to be the result of extensive metasomatism, a process that involves fluid ingress and enrichment of volatile and other incompatible elements. Melting of a fertile mantle source rock is probably the main reason why alkaline magmas are so enriched in the variety of ore constituents mentioned above. The extent of metal enrichment relative to average basalt is illustrated in Figure 1.6.

Kimberlitic and related ultramafic magmas crystallize to form very rare and unusual rocks, containing among other minerals both mica and olivine. Kimberlites are rich in potassium (K_2O typically 1–3 wt%) and, although derived from deep in the mantle, are also hydrated and carbonated. They usually occur in small (<1 km diameter) pipe-like bodies, or dykes and sills, and commonly extrude in highly explosive, gas-charged eruptions. The deep-seated origin of kimberlite is evident from the fact that it commonly transports garnet lherzolitic and eclogitic xenoliths to the

Figure 1.6 Relative abundances of selected metals in alkaline magmas (and kimberlite in the case of Cu and P) relative to average basalt (data from Table 1.2).

surface, rock types made up of very high pressure mineral assemblages that could only have come from the mantle. In addition, a small proportion of kimberlites also contain diamond xenocrysts. Diamond is the stable carbon polymorph under very reducing conditions, and at depths in excess of about 100 km and temperatures greater than 900 °C (Haggerty, 1999).

The origin of kimberlitic magmas is not too different from that of the alkaline rocks described above, and high pressure partial melting of a garnet peridotite source rock containing additional phlogopite or K-amphibole (richterite), as well as a carbonate phase, is viewed as a likely scenario (Hall, 1996). The enrichment of incompatible constituents (such as K, Rb, H_2O, and CO_2) in kimberlite, as with alkaline magmas in general, again indicates that metasomatism of the mantle has played an important role in the provision of a deep-seated environment capable of producing highly enriched, or fertile, magmas. These aspects are discussed in more detail in section 1.3 below.

1.3 WHY ARE SOME MAGMAS MORE FERTILE THAN OTHERS? THE "INHERITANCE FACTOR"

Geochemical inheritance is clearly an important factor in understanding the nature of ore-forming processes in igneous rocks. Magma may inherit a surplus of potential ore-forming trace elements because the source material from which it was derived was itself enriched in these components.

Further concentration of incompatible trace elements into residual magma, or of compatible trace elements into crystallizing phases, will take place during cooling and solidification of the magma, and these processes are discussed in more detail in section 1.4 below.

A pertinent question that relates to the issue of geochemical inheritance is why certain portions of the Earth's crust appear to be so much better endowed in mineral deposits than others. The spectacular concentrations of, for example, gold and platinum deposits in South Africa, related to the Witwatersrand Basin and Bushveld Complex respectively, perhaps point to some form of (mantle-related?) enrichment of these metals that is specific to this region and not to other parts of the globe. Why is it that Sudbury is so rich in Ni and the Andes are so well endowed with large Cu deposits, and is there an explanation for the tendency that diamondiferous kimberlites only occur in ancient, cratonic areas? These questions are addressed below in relation to some rather novel ideas suggesting that metals may have been preferentially concentrated in certain parts of the mantle and then subsequently transferred into the crust through a variety of mineralizing agencies.

1.3.1 The "late veneer" hypothesis of siderophile metal concentration – an extraterrestrial origin for Au and Pt?

In the very early stages of Earth evolution, prevailing theory suggests that the originally

Figure 1.7 Schematic representation of the "late veneer" hypothesis for the siderophile (precious) metal enrichment of the Earth's lithosphere. During initial segregation of the Earth (t_o) siderophile metals were comprehensively partitioned into the Fe–Ni core. Approximately 500 million years later $(t_o + 500\,Myr)$ intense meteorite bombardment of the Earth added to the siderophile metal budget of the Earth's lithosphere.

homogeneous, molten planet differentiated into a metallic core, comprising essentially Fe and FeO with lesser Ni, and a mantle which had a silicate composition. As this differentiation took place the siderophile metals (i.e. those with a strong affinity for Fe such as Au and the platinum group elements or PGE) were comprehensively partitioned into the core. Experiments by Holzheid *et al.* (2000) indicate that the average concentrations of elements such as Au, Pt and Pd in the Earth's mantle should be at least 10^{-4} times lower than average chondritic abundances. Such concentrations are, in fact, so low that they virtually preclude the possibility of forming ore deposits in rocks extracted from the mantle (i.e. the crust). Yet the actual concentration of these precious metals in the mantle, although depleted, is only about 150 times lower than average chondritic abundances. This depletion might be accommodated by the fact that there have been numerous ore deposits formed over geological time that have extracted these metals from the mantle. Another explanation is that the efficiency with which siderophile metals are partitioned between metal core and silicate mantle decreases with increasing pressure (depth) and that this could explain why the mantle is not as depleted as theory predicts. Although the latter notion probably applies to nickel, recent experiments suggest that it is not applicable to the precious metals and that some other explanation must be sought for the higher than expected concentrations of the latter in the mantle.

A clue as to why the mantle might be relatively enriched in siderophile metals lies in the fact that their abundance ratios (i.e. the abundance of one element relative to another, such as Au/Pt or Pt/Pd) are generally similar to chondritic abundance ratios as determined from analyses of meteorites that have fallen to Earth. The only way to explain this is by having a substantial proportion of the precious metals in the mantle derived from meteorites that impacted the proto-crust during the early stages of Earth evolution, but *after* the differentiation of core and mantle (Figure 1.7). This idea, known as the "late-veneer" hypothesis (Kimura *et al.*, 1974), suggests that much, if not all, the Au and Pt that is mined from ore deposits on the

Earth's surface today ultimately had an extraterrestrial origin and that the planet's own inventory of these metals is presently locked away in the core. Since both the meteorite flux itself and the subsequent distribution of this material through the mantle are likely to have been irregular, this hypothesis is also consistent with the heterogeneous distribution of precious metals over the Earth's surface.

As a footnote it is intriguing to note that precious metals may not have been the only valuable commodity introduced to Earth by meteorites. The enigmatic "carbonado" diamonds found only in 1500 Myr old metasediments of Bahia State in Brazil and the Central African Republic have mineralogical and isotopic characteristics unlike any diamond of terrestrial origin. Haggerty (1999) has suggested that carbonado diamonds are derived from the fall-back of a fragmented carbon-type asteroid that impacted the Earth's crust at a time when the relevant parts of Brazil and Africa formed a single continental entity. Although contentious, the notion of an extraterrestrial origin for certain constituents of the Earth's surface (and of life itself?) is one that is likely to continue attracting attention in the future.

1.3.2 Diamonds and the story they tell

The Earth's mantle, between about 35 and 2900 km depth, is the ultimate source of material that, over geological time, has contributed, either directly or by recycling, to formation of the crust. Considering that the mantle is essentially inaccessible it has, nevertheless, been the subject of numerous studies by both geologists and geophysicists and its structure and composition are now reasonably well known. One reason for studying the mantle is to understand the origin of diamond. This remarkable mineral, together with the magmas that bring it to the surface, has provided a great deal of information about the deep Earth, much of which is very relevant to understanding those properties of the mantle that also relate to the source of metals in other igneous ore deposits.

Most diamonds are brought to the Earth's surface by kimberlitic magmas (see section 1.2) or a compositionally similar melt known as lamproite. Most kimberlites and lamproites are barren, and diamondiferous magmas only intrude into ancient, stable continental crust that is typically older than 2500 Myr, but sometimes as young as 1500 Myr. The kimberlite magmas that transport diamonds to the surface, however, are typically much younger than the rocks they intrude, forming in discrete episodes in the Mesozoic and Cenozoic eras. Older intrusive episodes have also been observed in the Devonian, as well as at around 500 Ma and again at 1000 Ma (Haggerty, 1999). Diamondiferous kimberlites must also have been emplaced during the Archean, since the Witwatersrand conglomerates in South Africa, for example, are known to contain green detrital diamonds. To further complicate the story, the diamonds themselves tend to be much older than their kimberlitic host rocks and range in age from 1500 to 3000 Ma, indicating that they have resided in the mantle for considerable periods of time prior to their eruption onto the Earth's surface. Diamonds did not, therefore, crystallize from the kimberlite but were introduced to the Earth's surface as xenocrysts within the magma (Richardson et al., 1984). Diamond xenocrysts occur either as isolated single crystals in the kimberlitic matrix or as minerals within discrete xenoliths of either peridotite (P-type diamonds – the more common) or eclogite (E-type diamonds). The high pressure phase relations that characterize mineral assemblages in these mantle xenoliths indicate that diamonds are derived from zones of thickened, sub-cratonic lithosphere, at least 200 km thick, that extend beneath stable Archean–Proterozoic shield areas (Figure 1.8). These lithospheric keels comprise old, depleted, peridotite (i.e. from which mantle melts have already been extracted) as well as primitive, but younger, eclogite that has generally not had a melt fraction extracted and is, therefore, more fertile with respect to crust-forming elements (Haggerty, 1999).

It is now generally accepted that diamonds were generated from deep in the mantle, in the layer known as the Transition Zone between the lower and upper mantle at around 400 to 650 km depth. Because the upper mantle is relatively depleted in carbon (100 ppm compared with 1000–3700 ppm in the lower mantle; Wood et al., 1996) it is

Figure 1.8 Schematic diagram illustrating features pertinent to the formation of diamond and the fertilization of the Earth's mantle by plume-related magmas and their associated aqueo-carbonic fluids (after Haggerty, 1999). LILE refers to the large ion lithophile elements; FMQ refers to the fayalite–magnetite–quartz oxygen buffer.

unlikely to be a viable source for the primordial carbon that makes up diamond. The more fertile lower mantle is more likely to be the source of the carbon, and this is supported by the presence of very high pressure minerals occurring as tiny inclusions in many diamonds. However, the upper mantle is more reduced than the lower mantle, which, in addition to its high carbon contents, also contains substantially more water (500–1900 ppm compared to only 200 ppm in the upper mantle). The upper mantle is, therefore, more likely to preserve diamond because the mineral's long-term stability depends on the existence of a reducing environment. Carbon in the relatively oxidized, fluid-rich lower mantle would, despite the higher pressures, not occur as diamond at all, but as CO_2, CCO, or $MgCO_3$ (Wood et al., 1996). The model for diamond formation (Figure 1.8), therefore, suggests that plumes transfer melt and volatiles from the lower mantle, and precipitate diamond at higher levels either in the reduced environment represented by the Transition Zone or in the keels extending below thick, cratonic lithosphere. Thus, the more common P-type diamonds form when the relatively oxidized carbonic fluids dissolved in ascending plumes interact with reduced mantle at higher levels and precipitate elemental carbon. This mass transfer process is referred to as *metasomatism* and involves the movement of fluids and volatiles from deep in the Earth's mantle to higher levels. This process is turning out to be very relevant to the concepts of mantle fertilization and geochemical inheritance. The more rare E-type diamonds, by contrast, are considered to have crystallized directly from a magma intruded into or ponded below the keels (Haggerty, 1999).

Formation of the kimberlitic magma that transports diamond to the Earth's surface has also been attributed to plume activity and the metasomatic transfer of volatile constituents from a fertile lower mantle into depleted upper mantle. Evidence for this process comes from the observation that many of the major episodes of kimberlite intrusion mentioned above correlate with "superchron" events that are defined as geologically long time periods of unidirectional polarity in the Earth's magnetic field. Superchrons are caused by core–mantle boundary disruptions which increase the rate of liquid core convection, causing a damping of the geomagnetic field intensity but promoting plume activity and mantle metasomatism. Intrusion of diamondiferous kimberlites has also been linked in time to major geological events, such as continental break-up and flood basaltic magmatism (Haggerty, 1994). England and Houseman (1984) suggested that enhanced kimberlite intrusion could be related to periods of low plate velocity when uninterrupted mantle convection gave rise to partial melting and volatile production in the lithosphere, and the subsequent formation of plume activity. Accompanying epeirogenic uplift created the fractures that allowed kimberlite magma to intrude rapidly upwards and, in many cases, to extrude violently onto the Earth's surface. This explanation is certainly consistent with the geodynamic setting of kimberlites, such as their predominance in Africa during the Mesozoic still-stand (see Chapter 6). The relative rarity of kimberlite formation and penetration to the surface

BOX 1.1 Diamondiferous kimberlites and lamproites: The Orapa diamond mine, Botswana and the Argyle diamond mine, Western Australia

Diamond mining around the world was worth some US$7 billion in 2001, a substantial proportion of which was derived from exploitation of primary kimberlitic and lamproitic deposits. The biggest single deposit is at Argyle in Western Australia, which is hosted in lamproite and produces some 26 million carats per year. Most of the diamonds produced here, however, are of low value. The Orapa and Jwaneng deposits of Botswana, by contrast, produce less than half the number of carats per year, but their stones are much more valuable. Orapa and Jwaneng together are the richest diamond deposits in the world.

Kimberlites are by far the most important primary source of diamonds (see section 1.3.2) and there are over 5000 occurrences known world wide (Nixon, 1995). By contrast there are only some 24 known occurrences of lamproite. Both kimberlites and lamproites are emplaced into the Earth's crust as "diatreme–maar" volcanoes which are the product of highly overpressured, volatile-rich magma. Kimberlitic or lamproitic magma is injected into the crust, along zones of structural weakness, to within 2–3 km of the surface. At this point volatiles (H_2O and CO_2) either exsolve from the magma itself (see Chapter 2), or the magma interacts with groundwater, with the resulting vapor phase

causing violent phreatomagmatic eruption of magma and disruption of country rock. Figure 1 shows the anatomy of a diatreme–maar system that has applicability to the nature and geometry of both kimberlites and lamproites.

Kimberlites are richer in CO_2 than lamproites and since CO_2 has a lower solubility than water in silicate melts, kimberlite magmas will usually exsolve a volatile fraction at lower depths than lamproites (Nixon, 1995). Lamproite venting is quite often a function of magma interaction with groundwater, the availability and depth of which dictates the geometry of the crater. These factors account for the carrot-like shape of kimberlites compared to a broader, champagne glass shape for many lamproites.

The distribution of diamonds in any one kimberlite may be highly erratic and there seems to be little or no relationship between grade and depth (Nixon, 1995). Some hypabyssal dykes are very rich in diamonds, such as the Marsfontein mine in South Africa which has an average grade of 200–300 carats per 100 tons of ore mined. Diatreme facies kimberlites are often characterized by multiple injections of magma, some of which are barren and others economically viable. Kimberlitic pyroclastic sediments in crater facies are also often richer than

Figure 1 Idealized geometry of a diatreme–maar type volcano, showing the nature of the hypabyssal facies of magma emplacement along crustal weaknesses (after Smith *et al.*, 1979). Kimberlites around the world are seen as hypabyssal, diatreme, or crater facies, depending on the extent of preservation (or depth of erosion) of the bodies.

associated diatreme rocks, possibly due to enrichment of heavy minerals, including diamond, by wind (during eruption) or water (in the crater lake).

Argyle

The Argyle diamond mine occurs in a 1200 million year old lamproite diatreme that has intruded older Proterozoic sediments in the Kimberley region of Western Australia (Boxer *et al.*, 1989). It forms an elongate 2 km long body that varies from 100 to 500 m in width and is the result of at least two coalesced vents along a fault line. It is mined in the southern section where it has grades in excess of 5 carats per ton. Most of the body is made up of pyroclastic or tuffaceous material, with marginal breccia and occasional lamproitic dykes. The diatreme was formed when lamproite magma encountered groundwater in largely unconsolidated sediments, resulting in multiple phreatomagmatic eruptions and venting of lamproite at the surface.

Orapa

The Orapa diamond mine occurs in a mid-Cretaceous kimberlite in the north of Botswana, and is well known for the excellent preservation of its crater facies. The kimberlite was emplaced in two pulses that merge at about 200 m depth into a single maar. The diatremes, comprising tuffisitic kimberlite breccia, grade progressively into

Figure 2 Large boulder of country rock in tuffisitic and lacustrine maar sediments, Orapa Mine, Botswana.

crater facies made up of both epiclastic and pyroclastic kimberlite debris. All these phases are diamondiferous. At Orapa the northern diatreme is believed to have been emplaced first, followed by residual volatile build-up and explosive volcanic activity. This was shortly followed by a similar sequence of events to form the southern diatreme, with the subsequent merging of its crater facies into a single maar (Field *et al.*, 1997).

Figure 1.9 Schematic diagram illustrating the concept of mantle metasomatism and metal enrichment associated with subduction, and the subsequent inheritance of an enhanced metal budget by magmas derived from melting of metasomatized mantle. Metal abundances of the relevant rock types (in ppm) are from McInnes *et al.* (1999); the two analyses showing metal abundances for the magmatic products of subduction refer to basalt (b) and syenite (s).

is also consistent with this model, since magma formation requires that a number of coincidentally optimal conditions apply.

1.3.3 Metal concentrations in metasomatized mantle and their transfer into the crust

Although it has been evident for many years that there is an association between mantle metasomatism and diamond formation, a link to mantle fertilization with respect to other constituents, such as the base and precious metals, has only recently been suggested. A comparison of Re–Os isotopic ratios of epithermal Cu–Au ores from the giant Ladolam mine on Lihir Island, near Papua New Guinea, with peridotite xenoliths transported to the ocean surface by volcanic activity from the underlying mantle wedge, shows that the ore constituents are derived from the mantle. Although this is not unexpected, closer study of the peridotitic material involved reveals that some of this material has been extensively metasomatized to form a high temperature hydrothermal mineral assemblage comprising olivine, pyroxene, phlo-

gopite, magnetite, and Fe–Ni sulfides (McInnes *et al.*, 1999). Metasomatism is considered to be the result of dehydration of the oceanic slab as it moves down the subduction zone, yielding fluids that migrate upwards into the overlying mantle wedge. Metasomatized peridotite contains precious and base metal concentrations that are up to two orders of magnitude enriched relative to unaltered mantle (Figure 1.9).

Subduction of oceanic crust beneath an island arc, such as that of which Lihir Island is part, has resulted in the formation of alkaline basalt which builds up the arc and ultimately forms the host rocks to the Ladolam Cu–Au deposit. The deposit itself occurs at a high level in the crust by the circulation of metal-charged hydrothermal fluids, a process that is not relevant to the present discussion except for the fact that these fluids have dissolved the ore constituents that they carry from the immediate country rocks (i.e. the alkaline basalts). An interesting feature of the study by McInnes *et al.* (1999) is that basaltic and syenitic country rocks to the deposit (refer to b and s in Figure 1.9) were analyzed well away from the mineralization itself and also exhibit significant enrichments in their base and precious metal contents. The inference is, therefore, that although the ore metals resided originally in the mantle, they were redistributed, and their concentrations significantly upgraded, by the high temperature metasomatic processes observed in the mantle peridotite. Because it is the metasomatized peridotite that is likely to have been preferentially melted above the subduction zone (by virtue of its hydrous nature and lower solidus temperature), the resulting alkali basalt magma will have inherited a significant metal endowment, thus enhancing the chances of creating a substantial ore deposit during subsequent (hydrothermal) stages of ore formation. The Ladolam study illustrates three important features: first, that metasomatism and fluid flow are very important processes in redistributing and concentrating incompatible elements in the mantle; second, that partial melting is the main process by which matter is transferred from the mantle to the crust; and, third, that inheritance is critical to the nature and formation of igneous hosted ore deposits, as well as to whether subsequent fluid circulation is likely to form viable hydrothermal deposits.

1.3.4 I- and S-type granite magmas and metal specificity

As mentioned previously, the different types of granite, and more specifically the origins of felsic magma, can be linked to distinct metal associations. Of the many classification schemes that exist for granitic rocks one of the most relevant, with respect to studies of ore deposits, is the I- and S-type scheme, originally devised for the Lachlan Fold Belt in southeast Australia (Figure 1.10a) by Chappell and White (1974). In its simplest form the scheme implies that orogenic granites can be subdivided on the basis of whether their parental magmas were derived by partial melting of predominantly igneous (I-type) or sedimentary (S-type) source rock. In general, I-type granites tend to be metaluminous and typified by tonalitic (or quartz-dioritic) to granodioritic compositions, whereas S-types are often peraluminous and have adamellitic (or quartz-monzonitic) to granitic com-

positions. Also very important from a metallogenic viewpoint is the fact that I-type granites tend to be more oxidized (i.e. they have a higher magmatic fO_2) than S-type granites, whose magmas were originally fairly reduced because of the presence of graphite in their source rocks. An approximate indication of the oxidation state of granitic magmas can be obtained from their whole rock Fe_2O_3/FeO ratio (which effectively records the ferric/ferrous ratio). Blevin and Chappell (1992) have shown that an Fe_2O_3/FeO ratio of about 0.3 provides a useful discriminant between I- (with Fe_2O_3/FeO > 0.3) and S-type (with Fe_2O_3/FeO < 0.3) granites, at least for the Australian case (Figure 1.10 b and c). A classification of granites according to oxidation state was, in fact, made relatively early on by Ishihara (1977), who distinguished between reduced granite magmas (forming ilmenite-series granitoids) and more oxidized equivalents (forming magnetite-series granitoids). The metallogenic significance of this type of granite classification was also recognized by Ishihara (1981), who indicated that Sn–W deposits were preferentially associated with reduced ilmenite-series granitoids, whereas Cu–Mo–Au ores could be linked genetically to oxidized magnetite-series granitoids. Magnetite-series granitoids are equivalent to most I-types, whereas ilmenite-series granitoids encompass all S-types as well as the more reduced I-types.

Although now regarded as somewhat oversimplified, at least with respect to more recent ideas regarding granite petrogenesis, the S- and I-type classification scheme is nevertheless appealing because it has tectonic implications and can be used to infer positioning relative to subduction along Andean-type continental margins (see Figure 1.2). The scheme also has metallogenic significance because of the empirical observation that porphyry Cu–Mo mineralization (with associated Pb–Zn–Au–Ag ores) is typically associated with I-type granites, whereas Sn–W mineralization (together with concentrations of U and Th) is more generally hosted by S-type granites. Although this relationship is broadly applicable it, too, is oversimplified. Some granites, notably those that are post-tectonic or anorogenic, do not accord with the scheme, such as the alkaline granites of the Bushveld Complex, which are polymetallic and

Figure 1.10 (a) Simplified map showing the distribution of S- and I-type granites, and associated metallogenic trends, in the Lachlan Fold Belt of southeastern Australia (after Chappell and White, 1974). (b and c) Plots of Fe_2O_3/FeO versus Rb for granites of the Lachlan Fold Belt that are mineralized with respect to Sn–W and Cu–Mo–Au (after Blevin and Chappell, 1992).

contain both Sn–W and base metal mineralization (Robb *et al.*, 2000). A more accurate appraisal of the relationship between magma composition (including oxidation state) and metallogenic association is given by Barton (1996). Figure 1.11 shows Barton's scheme, which regards granites as a continuum of compositional types and their metal associations in terms of different intrusion-related ore deposit types.

Adjacent to Andean type subduction zones a clearly defined spatial pattern exists with respect to the distribution of I- and S-type granite intrusions, as well as associated metallogenic zonation (Sillitoe, 1976; Clark *et al.*, 1990). The leading edge (i.e. the oceanic side) of the subduction zone tends to correlate with the production of I-type granite magmas and is associated with the formation of porphyry Cu styles of mineralization. By contrast, the continental side of the subduction zone contains more differentiated granite types that are often S-type in character and with which Sn–W styles of mineralization are associated. Other examples of this type of regional zonation are seen

in the Cordilleran granites of the western United States and in the Lachlan Fold Belt of southeast Australia, where I- and S-type granites were originally defined (Figure 1.10a). Again, although exceptions and complications do exist, the recognition and delineation of these patterns is clearly important with respect to understanding the spatial distribution of different types of ore deposits hosted in granitoid rocks.

The Lachlan Fold Belt provides an excellent example of the relationships between magma type and metallogenic association and, as predicted, granite related mineralization is dominated by Sn–W in the mainly S-type granites to the west of the I–S line, whereas largely Mo with lesser Cu–Au ores are found in the I-type terrane to its east (Figure 1.10a). Another very important feature of the metal content of granites is, however, also apparent in the Lachlan Fold Belt. When the Fe_2O_3/FeO ratio (an indication of magmatic oxidation state) is plotted against Rb content (an indicator of degree of fractionation) for granites that are mineralized in terms of either Sn–W or Cu–Mo–Au

Figure 1.11 Generalized scheme that links granite compositions and magmatic oxidation state to metal associations and intrusion-related ore deposit types (modified after Barton, 1996). Ore deposit types referred to are "alkalic," "porphyry," and "lithophile" and are discussed in more detail in Chapter 2. Metals shown in bold reflect the more important associations.

(Figure 1.10b and c) it is clear that metal content is not simply a function of magma type alone. It is apparent that Cu–Mo–Au related intrusions typically have higher Fe_2O_3/FeO ratios than those associated with Sn–W mineralization, and are, therefore, preferentially associated with I-type granites. What is perhaps more clearly apparent, however, is that Sn and W mineralization is associated with intrusions that are *more highly fractionated* than those containing Cu–Mo–Au (Blevin and Chappell, 1992). Metal contents are, therefore, also a function of processes that happen as the magma cools and fractionates and these processes are discussed in more detail in section 1.4 below. In fact, mineralization in granites also involves hydrothermal processes that are quite distinct

from either geochemical inheritance or fractionation, and these are examined in Chapter 2.

1.4 PARTIAL MELTING AND CRYSTAL FRACTIONATION AS ORE-FORMING PROCESSES

The previous section discussed the various magma-forming processes and some of the reasons why they are variably endowed with respect to their trace element and mineral contents. This section examines how trace elements and minerals behave in the magma, both as it is forming and then subsequently during cooling and solidification.

Trace element abundances can be very good indicators of petrogenetic processes, during both partial melting and crystal fractionation. Since many magmatic ore deposits arise out of concentrations of metals that were originally present in very small abundances, trace element behavior during igneous processes is also very useful in understanding ore formation.

A trace element is defined as an element that is present in a rock at concentrations lower than 0.1 wt% (or 1000 ppm), although this limit places a rather artificial constraint on the definition. In general trace elements substitute for major elements in the rock forming minerals, but in certain cases they can and do form the stoichiometric components of accessory mineral phases (Rollinson, 1993). Many of the ores associated with igneous rocks are formed from elements (Cu, Ni, Cr, Ti, P, Sn, W, U, etc.) that originally existed at trace concentrations in a magma or rock and were subsequently enriched to ore grades by processes discussed in this and later sections.

When rocks undergo partial melting trace elements partition themselves between the melt phase and solid residue. Those that prefer the solid are referred to as compatible (i.e. they have an affinity with elements making up the crystal lattice of an existing mineral), whereas those whose preference is the melt are termed incompatible. Likewise, during cooling and solidification of magma, compatible elements are preferentially taken up in the crystals, whereas incompatible elements are enriched in the residual melt. Enrichment of trace elements and potential ore formation can, therefore, be linked to the concentration of incompatible elements in the early melt phase of a rock undergoing anatexis (see Box 1.2), or the residual magma during progressive crystallization (see Box 1.3). Compatible trace elements tend to be "locked up" in early formed rock-forming minerals and are typically not concentrated efficiently enough to form viable ore grade material. An exception to this is provided, for example, during the formation of chromitite layers, as discussed in section 1.4.3 below.

A brief description of how one can quantify trace element distribution during igneous processes is presented below, with an indication of how these processes can be applied to the understanding of selected ore-forming processes.

1.4.1 The conditions of melting

Despite the fact that temperatures in the upper mantle reach 1500 °C and more, melting (or anatexis) is not as widespread as might be expected because of the positive correlation that exists between pressure and the beginning of melting of a rock (i.e. the solidus temperature). The asthenosphere, which is defined as that zone in the mantle where rocks are closest to their solidus and where deformation occurs in a ductile fashion (which explains the lower strength of the asthenosphere relative to the elastically deformable lithosphere), is the "engine-room" where a considerable amount of magma is formed. Major magma-generating episodes, however, do not occur randomly and without cause, but are catalyzed by processes such as a decrease of pressure (caused, for example, by crustal thinning in an extensional regime such as the mid-ocean ridge) or addition of volatiles to lower the solidus temperature (such as during subduction and metasomatism). An increase in local heat supply is generally not important in the promotion of partial melting, although it is possible that mantle plumes might be implicated in this role.

Partial melting, so called because source rocks very seldom melt to completion, invariably leaves behind a solid residue. It is a complex process that is affected by a number of variables, the most important being the nature of the mineral assemblage making up the protolith, as well as local pressure, temperature and water/volatile content. Early experimental work on the progressive fusion of peridotite with increasing temperature (Mysen and Kushiro, 1976) helps to explain the process of partial melting in the asthenosphere, even though the description outlined below is probably not a particularly good indication of the very complicated processes actually involved.

In Figure 1.12 melting of peridotite starts just above 1400 °C with the formation of a small melt fraction in equilibrium with pyroxenes and olivine. Melting can continue without significant addition of heat until between 30 and 40% of the rock is molten and the clinopyroxene is totally consumed. Once the clinopyroxene is gone, further melting can only continue with addition of heat (the

Figure 1.12 The sequential melting behavior of peridotite in the mantle at 20 kbar pressure, (a) without water and (b) in the presence of some 2% water (after Mysen and Kushiro, 1976).

first inflection point on the curves in Figure 1.12), which, if present, would then promote the melting of orthopyroxene. Once orthopyroxene has been consumed, after some 50–60% of the rock has melted, a further input of heat is required (the second inflection point) if olivine is to be wholly included into the melt product. A small degree of partial melting of peridotite will, therefore, yield magma with a composition that is dominated by the melt products of clinopyroxene (an alkali basalt), with the residue reflecting the bulk composition of orthopyroxene + olivine. In reality melting processes are more complex and usually involve the fusion of more than just one mineral at a time. It is also pertinent to note that the presence of even a small amount of water in the system will catalyze the extent of melting and also allow anatexis to occur at lower temperatures.

Anatexis in the crust is better explained by considering the partial melting of a metasedimentary protolith, to form, for example, an S-type granite. If the sediment consisted only of quartz then the temperature would have to exceed 1170 °C (the melting temperature of SiO_2 at $P_{H_2O} = 1$ kbar) in order for it to start melting. If the sediment were

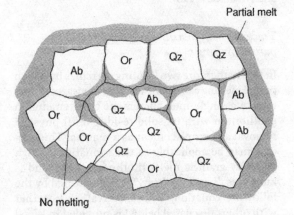

Figure 1.13 The pattern of grain boundary melting of an arkosic protolith subjected to temperatures of 700–800 °C at $P_{H_2O} = 1$ kbar (after Hall, 1996).

an arkose, however, made up of a recrystallized assemblage of quartz + orthoclase + albite (as shown in Figure 1.13), then melting would commence at much lower temperatures because of the depression of melting points that occurs for binary or ternary eutectic mixtures. Thus, where quartz + albite are in contact, melting would commence at temperatures around 790 °C and, where quartz + albite + orthoclase meet at a triple junction, melting could start as low as 720 °C. Disaggregation of the arkose protolith would, therefore, take place by small increments of partial melt forming along selected grain boundaries within the rock. The residue left behind during such a process is likely to be made up of fragmented minerals that cannot melt on their own at a given temperature. Melt and residue are also likely to have different compositions.

The extraction of a partial melt from its residue, whether it be from an igneous or sedimentary protolith, is a process which segregates chemical components and is referred to as fractionation. Partial melts can be considerably enriched in certain elements, but depleted in others, relative to the source rock. The mechanisms whereby melt is removed from its residue may differ, and this is discussed in more detail below. More detailed, quantitative descriptions of partial melt modelling are provided in Cox *et al.* (1979), Rollinson (1993), and Albarede (1996).

Trace element distribution during partial melting

In theory there are two limiting extremes by which partial melting can occur. The first envisages formation of a single melt increment that remains in equilibrium with its solid residue until physical removal and emplacement as a magma. This process may be applicable to the formation of high viscosity granitic melts (Rollinson, 1993) and is known as "*batch melting.*" It is quantified by the following equation, whose derivation (together with others discussed below) is provided in Wood and Fraser (1976):

$$C_{liq}/C_o = 1/[D_{res} + F(1 - D_{res})] \qquad [1.1]$$

where: C_{liq} is the concentration of a trace element in the liquid (melt); C_o is the concentration of trace element in parental (unmelted) solid; D_{res} is the bulk partition coefficient of the residual solid (after the melt is extracted); F is the weight fraction of melt produced.

A diagrammatic illustration of the extent of enrichment (or depletion) of an incompatible (or compatible) element in a batch partial melt is presented in Figure 1.14a, where the ratio C_{liq}/C_o is plotted as a function of the degree of melt produced (F) for a variety of values of D_{res}. Marked enrichments of highly incompatible elements (i.e. those with very small values of D_{res}) can occur in small melt fractions, with the maximum enrichment factor being $1/D_{res}$ as F approaches 0.

The second partial melt process is referred to as "*fractional melting*" and is the process whereby small increments of melt are instantaneously removed from their solid residue, aggregating elsewhere to form a magma body. This process may be more applicable to low viscosity basaltic magmas where small melt fractions can be removed from their source regions. The distribution of trace elements during fractional melting is quantified in terms of the following equation:

$$C_{liq}/C_o = 1/D_o(1 - F)^{(1/D_o - 1)} \qquad [1.2]$$

where: D_o is the bulk partition coefficient of the original solid (prior to melting); and the other symbols are the same as for equation [1.1].

The extent of trace element enrichment and depletion in a fractional partial melt is shown in Figure 1.14b. For very small degrees of melting the changes in trace element concentrations relative to the source material are extreme and vary from a maximum value of enrichment ($1/D_o$ as F approaches 0) to depletions in the magma as melting progresses. Unlike the batch melt situation, compatible element enrichment can also occur during fractional melting, but this is only likely to happen in the unlikely event of more than 70% partial melting. An example of incompatible element concentration in a granitic partial melt is provided in Box 1.2.

1.4.2 Crystallization of magmas

The melt sequence for peridotite described in Figure 1.12 can be used in reverse to illustrate the crystallization of an ultramafic magma as it cools (bearing in mind that in reality a magma derived from complete melting of a peridotitic protolith at around 1800 °C is unlikely ever to have existed).

BOX 1.2 Partial melting and concentration of incompatible elements: the Rössing uranium deposit

The Rössing mine in Namibia is one of the largest uranium deposits in the world, and certainly the largest associated with an igneous rock. This deposit is associated with leucogranite (locally termed "alaskite"). The ore occurs mainly in the form of disseminated uraninite (UO_2) distributed unevenly throughout the leucogranite, together with secondary uranium silicate and oxide minerals such as beta-uranophane and betafite. Rössing occurs in the central zone of the c.500 Ma Damaran orogen and the leucogranites are thought to be a product of partial melting of older basement comprising granite and supracrustal (metasedimentary) sequences. Upper amphibolite to granulite grades of metamorphism apply regionally and melts are considered to have been derived from depths not significantly greater than the actual level of emplacement, as indicated by the profusion of leucogranitic dykes in the region. The Rössing mine is located where several of the larger leucogranitic dykes have coalesced to form a significant mass of mineable material. The deposit comprises several hundred million tons of low grade uranium ore running on average at about 0.031% (or 310 ppm) U_3O_8. Although the deposit is low grade, a concentration of 310 ppm uranium in the leucogranite nevertheless represents a significant enrichment factor relative to the Clarke value (i.e. about 2.7 ppm for U; see Table 1.2). This degree of enrichment is consistent with what might be expected for a magma formed by a low degree of partial melting of an already reasonably enriched protolith.

This can be tested very simply in terms of the partial (batch) melt equation, given as equation [1.1] in section 1.4.1 of this chapter. If the protolith contained 10 ppm U and its bulk partition coefficient relative to the melt fraction was significantly less than 1 (i.e. D_{res} between 0.01 and 0.1) then a 5% batch melt would yield a magma that is enriched by factors of between 7 (for $D_{res} = 0.1$) and 17 (for $D_{res} = 0.01$), as shown in Figure 2. This process would have resulted in uranium concentrations in the leucogranite of between 70 and 170 ppm, which is at best only one-half of the observed average concentration. In order to achieve concentrations of around 300 ppm U by batch melting either the degree of melting would have to have been very low (i.e. <5%), or the protolith would itself have to have been significantly enriched, and have contained substantially more than 10 ppm U.

Figure 2 Simplified batch melt model showing the degree of enrichment expected for an incompatible element such as uranium (with D_{res} of either 0.1 or 0.01) after 5% melting (further details provided in section 1.4.1).

Figure 1 Two phases of leucogranite cutting through high-grade metasediments in the vicinity of the Rössing uranium mine, Namibia (photograph by Paul Nex).

Research by Nex *et al.* (2001) has shown that partial melting in the central zone of the Damaran orogeny was an episodic affair and that only one of several generations of leucogranite is significantly enriched in uranium. Since all are likely to have been generated by approximately the same degrees of partial melting, this would suggest that the single enriched episode was derived from a particularly fertile protolith. It is apparent that deposits representing enrichment of incompatible trace elements in rocks formed by small degrees of melting, like the Rössing leucogranites, are not very common in the Earth's crust. Another example might be the Johan Beetz uranium deposit in Quebec, Canada.

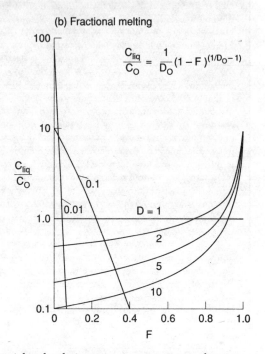

(a) Batch melting – liquids

$$\frac{C_{liq}}{C_O} = \frac{1}{D_{res} + F\,(1 - D_{res})}$$

(b) Fractional melting

$$\frac{C_{liq}}{C_O} = \frac{1}{D_O}(1 - F\,)^{(1/D_O - 1)}$$

Figure 1.14 The enrichment/depletion of a trace element in a partial melt relative to its concentration in the source rock (C_{liq}/C_o) as a function of increasing degrees of melting (F). (a) Batch melting using equation [1.1], and (b) fractional melting using equation [1.2] (after Rollinson, 1993).

The crystallization sequence would have commenced with olivine, followed by orthopyroxene and clinopyroxene. Together with plagioclase, this mineral assemblage and the crystallization sequence is typical for a basaltic magma.

The sequential crystallization of a mafic magma is, of course, another way of fractionating chemical components, since minerals of one composition are often physically separated from the compositionally different magma from which they form. Once minerals are removed from the magma (by a process such as crystal settling) there is little or no further chemical communication (or equilibration) between the solid and liquid components of the

chamber. This process is referred to as *fractional crystallization* or *Rayleigh fractionation*. The nature of fractional crystallization, and the geometry of cumulate rocks that form during these processes, are both very relevant to an understanding of ore deposits hosted in igneous rocks. It is, therefore, necessary to consider these processes in more detail and, in particular, their relationship to metal concentration and ore formation. It should also be emphasized at this stage that emplacement and crystallization of magma is generally accompanied by varying degrees of assimilation of country rock by the magma. Consequently, chemical trends reflecting fractionation processes are accompanied by the effects of magma contamination and this, too, has important implications for igneous ore-forming processes (see sections 1.4.3 and 1.6).

The form and internal zonation of igneous bodies

The emplacement mechanisms of magma into the Earth's crust and the resulting shapes of igneous intrusions is a complex topic and is reviewed in Hall (1996), Pitcher (1997), and Best (2003). Basaltic intrusions are typically quite different in shape and form from granitic batholiths. In addition, the mechanisms of crystal fractionation within a mafic magma chamber are also different to those applicable inside granite intrusions. These differences are relevant to ore formation in crystallizing magmas, as exemplified by the stratiform nature of chromitite seams in mafic intrusions such as the Bushveld Complex (see Box 1.4), compared to tin deposits in granites of the same Complex which tend to be concentrated in disseminated form toward the center of such intrusions (see Box 1.3).

Mafic intrusions   The viscosity of mafic magma is relatively low, as illustrated by the ease with which basaltic magmas flow on eruption. The densities of mafic minerals are typically greater than 3 g cm^{-3}, whereas mafic magma has a density of around 2.6 g cm^{-3}. The low viscosity of mafic magma and the high densities of minerals crystallizing from it imply that minerals such as olivine and the pyroxenes will typically sink in a magma at velocities of anywhere between 40 and 1000 m yr^{-1} depending on their composition and size (Hall, 1996). By contrast, less dense minerals, such as the felspathoids, might float in an alkaline magma as they have densities less than 2.5 g cm^{-3}. Plagioclase would float in a basaltic magma at pressures greater than about 5 kbar, but would sink in the same magma emplaced at high crustal levels (Kushiro, 1980).

The sequence of layered rocks that result from gravitationally induced crystal settling are referred to as cumulates and their compositions differ from that of the starting magma. Crystal settling is, therefore, a form of fractional crystallization and this process could explain the segregation of

chemical constituents and their possible concentration into either of the solid or liquid phases of the chamber. Trace elements that are readily incorporated (by substitution) into cumulus minerals are referred to as compatible elements. By contrast, trace elements which are excluded from the cumulate assemblage (because they cannot easily substitute into the crystal lattice sites of the major rock-forming minerals) are called incompatible elements and they will, naturally, become progressively enriched in the residual magma as the cumulate assemblage is formed.

Gravitationally induced settling of minerals in mafic intrusions would seem to be the most logical way of explaining the well layered internal structure so often observed in these bodies. Early models for explaining the crystallization and layering in mafic intrusions were derived from the classic work of Wager and Brown (1968) on the Skaergaard intrusion of Greenland. The latter is particularly well suited to petrogenetic study because it is considered to represent a single pulse of magma that crystallized to completion in a closed chamber without substantial addition or removal of magma during solidification. The sub-horizontal layers that form in mafic intrusions arise from the initial accumulation of early formed minerals (such as olivine and orthopyroxene), followed, in a stratigraphic sense, by accumulations of later formed minerals such as the pyroxenes and plagioclase. Minor oxide minerals such as chromite and magnetite are also observed to accumulate among the major silicate mineral phases. The Skaergaard intrusion is made up of a chilled marginal phase and a relatively simple internal zone made up of sub-horizontal rhythmic and cryptic (i.e. where the layering is not visually obvious but is reflected only in chemical variations) layers, ranging in composition upwards from gabbro to ferrodiorite and granophyre (Figure 1.15).

Although it is tempting to attribute the relatively ordered, sub-horizontal layering that is so characteristic of intrusions such as Skaergaard to simple gravitationally induced crystal settling, solidification of magma chambers, including Skaergaard, is a much more complex process (McBirney and Noyes, 1979). The temperature gradients and associated variations in magma density that form in cooling magmatic bodies

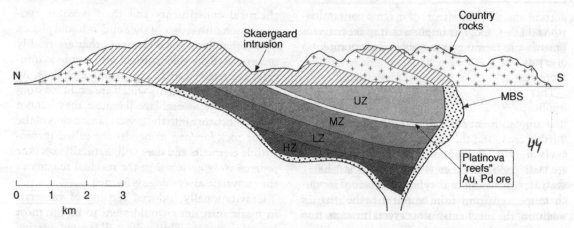

Figure 1.15 Schematic illustration showing the nature of layering in the Skaergaard intrusion, east Greenland (after Anderson *et al.*, 1998). The relative stratigraphic position of the Au- and Pd-bearing Platinova Reefs is shown in relation to the Marginal Border Series (MBS) and the Layered Series, which is subdivided into the Hidden Zone (HZ), Lower Zone (LZ), Middle Zone (MZ), and Upper Zone (UZ).

Figure 1.16 (a) Density variations in a fractionating magma similar in starting composition to that of the Bushveld Complex. (b) Contrasting behavior of a new magma injected into a density stratified magma chamber within which crystal fractionation has already occurred (after Campbell *et al.*, 1983; Naldrett and von Gruenewaldt, 1989).

have been shown to result in pronounced density stratification, with the formation of liquid layers through which elements diffuse in response to both chemical and temperature gradients (Huppert and Sparks, 1980; Turner, 1980; Irvine *et al.*, 1983; McBirney, 1985). Density variations over time in a magma chamber are also a product of crystal

fractionation itself. In Figure 1.16a it is apparent that during early stages of olivine crystallization the residual magma density decreases because the chemical components extracted by olivine have higher densities than that of the starting liquid. The trend changes, however, with the appearance' on the liquidus of a mineral such as plagioclase, which has a density lower than that of the magma. In such a situation it is possible, after an interval of crystallization, for a residual magma to become more dense than when it started solidifying.

This pattern of density variation has major implications for the behavior of crystals settling in a magma chamber, particularly when a new injection of magma takes place into an already evolved chamber. In Figure 1.16b two situations are considered. If the new magma has a density that is greater than the liquid residue in the chamber (as might be the case if the new magma was injected fairly early after crystallization had commenced), then a rather muted fountain-like feature will form and mixing between the new and evolved liquids will be limited to a layer along the base of the chamber. By contrast, if the new magma is injected late in the crystallization sequence, there is a possibility that its density will be less than that of the residual liquid and a more impressive plume-like feature would form (see Figure 1.16b) and the new magma would rise to its own density level, or to the very top of the chamber. In the latter scenario turbulent mixing between the new and residual liquids is likely to be more complete. Injection of a plume that reached and interacted with the roof of the magma chamber has been suggested for the Bushveld Complex (Schoenberg *et al.*, 1999). This plume has also been strongly implicated in the formation of both the chromite and PGE mineralization in the Bushveld (Kinnaird *et al.* 2002).

At a first glance, layered mafic intrusions such as Skaergaard may seem to be the products of relatively straightforward, gravitationally induced, crystal settling of minerals as they appear sequentially in the growth sequence. In detail, the nature of the layers may be quite complex and the normal, usually rather thick, cumulate assemblages are likely to be affected by complex processes involving the relative rates of thermal and chemical diffusion. In addition, convective currents in the magma chamber, as well as turbidity currents in which a crystal-laden flow of magma surges down a slope on the margins or floor of the chamber, add to the complexities of crystallization. Finally, the composition of the minerals crystallizing at any one time will be sensitive to perturbations in the chemistry of the magma and rapid changes

caused either by injection of new magma or contamination of existing magma by wall rock. The processes resulting in crystal fractionation, density variations and changes in magma composition are all critical to the formation of ore grade concentrations of chromite, magnetite, platinum group elements, base metal sulfides and even gold in layered mafic complexes. As the processes are better understood, such intrusions are increasingly attracting the attention of explorationists worldwide and even well studied bodies, such as Skaergaard, are now known to be mineralized. Although the presence of sulfide minerals at Skaergaard was recognized early on (Wager *et al.*, 1957), the recognition of a potentially significant Au and Pd resource only came much later (Bird *et al.*, 1991; Andersen *et al.*, 1998). The interaction between magmatic processes and the role that they play in mineralization are discussed in more detail below, and also illustrated in case studies.

Felsic intrusions Granite intrusions do not exhibit the well defined sub-horizontal layering that typifies large mafic intrusions. This is largely due to the fact that felsic magmas are several orders of magnitude more viscous than mafic ones (i.e. up to 10^6 Pa s for rhyolite compared to 10^2 Pa s for basalt at the same temperature; Hall, 1996). In addition, the density contrasts that exist in crystallizing mafic magma chambers are not as marked as they are with respect to quartz and felspars forming in felsic chambers. Crystal settling is inconsequential in all but a few granite plutons, such as the relatively hot, hydrous alkaline granites whose parental magmas were emplaced at shallow depths in the crust. It is nevertheless evident that substantial fractionation does occur in felsic intrusions and there are many recorded examples of internal zonation in granite plutons (Pitcher, 1997). Most plutons record a concentric zonation, with the outer zones preserving more mafic compositions (i.e. diorite, tonalite, granodiorite) and rock types becoming progressively more fractionated toward the center. Since many granite plutons intrude at shallow crustal levels and most of their heat is, therefore, lost to the sidewalls, this type of zonation is logically attributed to crystallization that commenced from the sides and roof of the magma chamber and progressed inwards. Although crystals are not being removed from the magma by the settling process applicable in mafic intrusions, they are effectively isolated from the residual melt by the crystallization front which advances in towards the center of the chamber. This process, referred to as *sidewall boundary layer differentiation*, can also, therefore, be regarded as a form of crystal fractionation and is characterized by concentration of incompatible elements in the center of the intrusion where the final increments of differentiated granite melt accumulate.

Trace element distribution during fractional crystallization

There are several ways by which crystallization can be modeled but the most appropriate would appear to be where crystals are removed from the site of formation with only limited equilibration between solid and liquid phases. In such a case trace element distributions can be described in terms of Rayleigh fractionation, in which:

$$C_{liq}/C_o = F^{(D-1)} \qquad [1.3]$$

for trace element concentration in the residual magma (liquid), and

$$C_{sol}/C_o = DF^{(D-1)} \qquad [1.4]$$

for trace element concentration in the crystallizing assemblage (solid), where: C_o is the original concentration of trace element in the parental liquid; D is the bulk partition coefficient of the fractionating assemblage; F is the weight fraction of melt remaining.

The extent of trace element enrichment and depletion during fractional crystallization of a magma is shown in Figure 1.17. The enrichment of an incompatible trace element in the residual melt relative to the original concentration in the parental magma is demonstrated in Figure 1.17a, where abundances can be seen to increase exponentially as crystallization proceeds (i.e. as the fraction of melt remaining, F, decreases). Compatible elements will, of course, continuously decrease

in the residual melt as they are extracted into the solid phases. Figure 1.17b shows, however, that the relative concentration of a compatible element in the crystallizing assemblage will start off as enriched only for rocks formed in the early stages of fractionation. Relative concentrations will decrease as crystallization progresses because the magma rapidly depletes itself of the compatible elements as they are withdrawn into the crystallizing assemblage.

Rayleigh fractionation equations apply reasonably well to low viscosity basaltic magmas where the effects of crystal fractionation are very evident. As mentioned previously, though, granitic magmas do not exhibit well defined igneous stratification and they tend to solidify by inward nucleation of a sidewall boundary layer. This *in situ* style of crystal fractionation, where the crystallizing front is spatially distinct from the magma residue, is akin to Rayleigh fractionation, but the equations that govern trace element distribution have to be modified, as shown below, to accommodate the melt fraction that is returned to the magma chamber as the solidification zone moves progressively into the chamber (Langmuir, 1989):

$$C_{liq}/C_o = (M_{liq}/M_o)^{[f(D-1)/(D(1-f)+f)]} \qquad [1.5]$$

where: M_{liq} is the mass of liquid remaining in the magma chamber; M_o is the initial mass of the magma chamber; f is the fraction of liquid in the solidification zone returned to the magma chamber; and the other symbols are as in equation [1.4].

The distribution trends of compatible and incompatible trace elements during this style of progressive inward solidification are essentially similar to Rayleigh fractionation (Figure 1.17) although the degrees of concentration, especially at low values of f, are not as extreme (Rollinson, 1993). This accords with observations that the effects of crystal fractionation in granites tend to be less evident than in mafic intrusions.

An example of trace element concentration during inward nucleation of a sidewall boundary layer in granite is provided by the Zaaiplaats Sn deposit in the granitic phase of the Bushveld Complex in South Africa (see Box 1.3). There

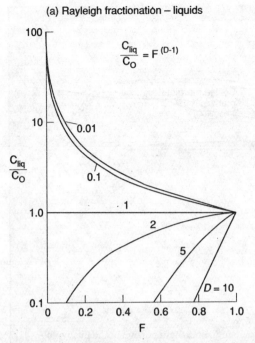

(a) Rayleigh fractionation – liquids

$$\frac{C_{liq}}{C_O} = F^{(D-1)}$$

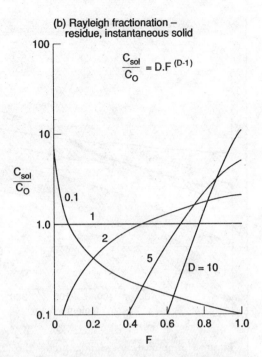

(b) Rayleigh fractionation – residue, instantaneous solid

$$\frac{C_{sol}}{C_O} = D.F^{(D-1)}$$

Figure 1.17 Trace element distribution during fractional crystallization. (a) The enrichment/depletion of a trace element in the residual magma relative to its concentration in the original melt (C_{liq}/C_o) as a function of the fraction of the remaining magma (F) using equation [1.3]. (b) The enrichment/depletion of a trace element in a crystallized assemblage (immediately removed from its melt) relative to its concentration in the original melt (C_{sol}/C_o) as a function of the fraction of the remaining magma (F) using equation [1.4] (after Rollinson, 1993).

BOX 1.3 Boundary layer differentiation in granites and incompatible element concentration: the Zaaiplaats tin deposit, Bushveld Complex

The granites of the Bushveld Complex, which overlie the better known layered mafic intrusion, occur as large sill-like intrusions and are also known to be strongly fractionated (McCarthy and Hasty, 1976; Groves and McCarthy, 1978). The granites of the Bushveld Complex are enriched in Sn and several deposits occur in the more highly fractionated parts of the suite. One of the better studied examples is the Zaaiplaats tin mine, which obtains the bulk of its tonnage from a zone of low-grade, disseminated cassiterite (SnO_2) mineralization that occurs within the central portion of the granite (Figure 1).

A cross section through the ore body, from diamond drill core, defines the low grade zone of disseminated cassiterite toward the center of the granite sheet. This is consistent

with the suggestion that solidification occurred from the margins inwards and that Sn was fractionated by processes akin to boundary layer differentiation. This type of crystal fractionation and its implications for ore-forming processes can be evaluated in terms of trace element distribution patterns. If boundary layer differentiation is modeled in terms of Rayleigh Fractionation (equations [1.3] and [1.4] in section 1.4.2), then the degree of crystallization required to concentrate Sn in the residual magma to the levels observed in the disseminated zone at Zaaiplaats can be calculated. Assuming that Sn is incompatible in the crystallizing granitic magma (i.e. D = 0.1) then some 96% crystallization is required in order to achieve an enrichment factor of 20 × (Figure 2). Coetzee and Twist (1989) have

Figure 1 Simplified cross section through the Zaaiplaats tin mine in the northern portion of the Bushveld Complex, South Africa (after Coetzee and Twist, 1989).

shown that unmineralized granite of the type that hosts tin mineralization in the Bushveld Complex contains between 8 and 14 ppm Sn, whereas mineralized portions of the suite, like the disseminated zone at Zaaiplaats, average around 270 ppm Sn. The disseminated mineralization at Zaaiplaats is, therefore, consistent with Sn concentration by crystal fractionation. After an advanced degree of solidification, it is suggested that the Sn content of the residual magma was sufficiently enriched to promote cassiterite crystallization. Other factors are also necessary in order to stabilize cassiterite in granites (Taylor and Wall, 1992), and these include fO_2 and magma composition (specifically the Na/K ratio). These factors, together with the degree of enrichment required, account for the fact that cassiterite is seldom seen as an accessory mineral in granites.

Figure 2 (*left*) Rayleigh fractionation model showing the degree of enrichment expected for an incompatible element (D = 0.1) such as Sn after 96% crystallization (further details provided in section 1.4.2).

are many examples of trace element concentrations in layered mafic intrusions and subsequent sections discuss some of the complex processes involved in accumulation of ore grade Pt, Cu, and Ni deposits such as those of the Bushveld Complex, Kambalda, and Sudbury (see Boxes 1.4, 1.5, 1.6, and 1.7). A case where crystal fractionation alone, without the added complication of features such as magma replenishment or contamination, has resulted in significant enrichment of Au, Pd, and S is provided by the Platinova Reefs of the Skaergaard Complex. Figure 1.15 shows that this zone of potentially ore grade precious element enrichment occurs toward the top of the Middle Zone and formed after a substantial proportion of the magma chamber had crystallized. The incompatible nature of Au, Pd, and S with respect to the early formed crystals (dominantly plagioclase, olivine, and pyroxene with lesser magnetite and apatite) resulted in a progressive enrichment of these metals in the residual magma (Anderson *et al.*, 1998). Once the concentration of sulfur had reached saturation levels (believed to be between 0.16 and 0.3 wt% in the Skaergaard magma) the metals precipitated out as a Au–Pd alloy to be further concentrated as inclusions within the sulfide minerals that now occur distributed interstitially among the normal cumulus mineral assemblage. The concentrations of Au and Pd that resulted from the progressive *in situ* crystal fractionation of the Skaergaard magma amounts to about 2 ppm for each metal and it has been estimated that some 90 million tons of potential ore grade material is available in the Platinova Reefs (Anderson *et al.*, 1998).

1.4.3 Fractional crystallization and the formation of monomineralic chromitite layers

Crystal settling, convective fluid flow, and diffusion-related chemical segregation across density stratified layers are the processes which give rise to the characteristically sub-horizontal, well ordered layering evident in most layered mafic intrusions. These processes do not, however, account for the occasional development of monomineralic layers of chromite or magnetite so spectacularly developed in many layered

mafic intrusions around the world. Nor do they explain the formation of the massive pods of chromitite that occur in the lithospheric portions of ophiolite complexes. This section provides some insight into the processes by which layers and pods of massive chromitite can form in mafic cumulate rocks.

There are many mafic intrusions that contain layers of near monomineralic chromite or (vanadium-rich) magnetite that are typically 0.5–1 meter in thickness and extend laterally for tens of kilometers, representing enormous reserves of Cr and Fe–V ore (see Box 1.4). Notable among these are the Bushveld Complex in South Africa and the Great Dyke in Zimbabwe. The formation of such layers, which might comprise up to 90% of a single mineral (chromite or magnetite), would appear to require that normal crystallization of silicate minerals (dominated by olivine, the pyroxenes, and plagioclase) be "switched off" and replaced by a brief interlude where only the single oxide phase is on the liquidus. A simple, but elegant, explanation of this process was provided by Irvine (1977) with respect to the formation of chromitite seams.

The Irvine model

The Irvine model refers to part of the phase diagram for a basaltic system in which only the olivine–chromite–silica end-members are portrayed in a ternary plot (Figure 1.18a). The normal crystallization sequence in a basaltic magma with starting composition at A (Figure 1.18b) would commence with olivine as the only mineral on the liquidus, settling of which would result in the formation of a dunitic cumulate rock. Extraction of olivine from the magma composition at A would result in evolution of the magma composition away from the olivine end-member composition and toward the cotectic phase boundary at B. At B a small amount of chromite (around 1%) would also start to crystallize together with olivine, and the magma composition would then evolve along the cotectic towards C. At C the SiO_2 content of the magma has increased to a level where olivine and chromite can no longer be the stable liquidus assemblage and orthopyroxene starts to

Figure 1.18 A portion of the ternary system quartz–olivine–chromite (a) showing the nature of crystallization in a mafic magma (b). Scenarios in which magma mixing (c) and magma contamination (d) occur as mechanisms for promoting the transient crystallization of only chromite are also shown (after Irvine, 1977).

crystallize to form a bronzitite cumulate rock. From this stage magma composition evolves toward D. Continued fractional crystallization will eventually lead to the appearance of plagioclase together with orthopyroxene on the liquidus, but felspar compositions are not reflected on the simplified phase projection shown here. This crystallization sequence *cannot* lead to the formation of a chromite seam and the latter mineral would only occur as an accessory phase in the early formed cumulates.

In order to make an ore deposit something unusual, or different from the norm, needs to take place. One way of disturbing the normal crystallization sequence is to introduce, at point D, a new magma with a composition at E (i.e. not as primitive as the original starting liquid), that is injected into the chamber and allowed to mix with the evolved liquid at F (Figure 1.18c). Mingling of the two liquids represented by D and E would result in a mixture whose composition must lie somewhere along the mixing line DE. Exactly where along DE this mixture would lie depends on the relative proportions of D and E that are mixed together. For most mixtures (at point F, for example, in Figure 1.18c) the magma composition would lie within the stability field of chromite and for a brief interval of crystallization (from F to G) only chromite would crystallize

from the mixture. Being relatively dense, chromite would settle fairly efficiently and a single, near monomineralic layer of chromite would form. In a very large magma chamber, such as the one from which the Bushveld Complex must have developed, the crystallization of such a layer could lead to the formation of an ore body with

BOX 1.4 Crystal fractionation and formation of monomineralic chromitite layers: the UG1 chromitite seam, Bushveld Complex

The Bushveld Complex is the world's largest layered mafic intrusion (Figure 1), covering an area of some 67 000 km². It also contains a substantial proportion (more than 75%) of the world's chromite reserves. Several major chromitite seams (at least 14 in number) occur within the Critical Zone of the Bushveld Complex and these are subdivided into three groups termed the Lower Group (LG1 to LG7), the Middle Group (MG1 to MG4), and the Upper Group

(UG1 to UG3). The LG6 chromitite seam is the most important in terms of production and reserves and can be traced for over 160 km in both the western and eastern portions of the complex.

In section 1.4.3 of this chapter the mechanisms by which monomineralic layers of chromitite could form in a layered mafic intrusion were discussed with specific reference to the Irvine model. The UG1 chromitite layer is

Figure 1 Simplified geological map and section through the Bushveld Complex. The distribution of chromitite layers or seams in the Critical Zone is shown in relation to the PGE-rich Merensky Reef and the vanadium-rich magnetite seams at the base of the Upper Zone. Also shown is the distribution of associated granite and rhyolite that overlies the layered mafic intrusion.

of particular interest because it is hosted essentially within anorthositic rocks (rather than olivine and orthopyroxene cumulates), and is also spectacularly well exposed in a gorge of the Dwars River in the eastern portion of the Bushveld Complex. The UG1 shows some intriguing features that require special explanation. One of the interesting aspects of the UG1 chromitite layer is the way in which the seam bifurcates. In some sections the seam splits into several thinner layers, whose cumulative thickness is similar to that of the single seam. Chromitite splits tend to occur in areas where anorthosite layers thicken into domal features, with the bifurcations opening out towards the core of the dome. Nex (2002) has explained this by suggesting that normal "sedimentation" of chromite (according to Irvine's model) was interrupted by liquefaction of the footwall crystalline assemblage to form a slurry of plagioclase feldspar and melt that erupted at the magma–cumulate interface. The bottom-up accumulation of the slurry is responsible for the formation of the domal features in the anorthosite and also serves to dilute the top-down settling of chromite grains. There is, therefore, a correlation between liquefaction of the footwall cumulates, doming

Figure 2 Bifurcating chromitite seams exposed at Dwars River in the eastern Bushveld Complex.

of the anorthosites, and splitting of chromitite layers. This type of feature, together with many other intriguing textures and relationships, indicates that crystallization processes in magma chambers can be very complex.

potentially vast Cr reserves. Experimental confirmation of these processes has been provided by Murck and Campbell (1986).

Once the magma composition reaches point G (after extraction of only chromite) on the cotectic, crystallization will again be dominated by olivine and the rocks that form in the hanging wall of the chromite seam will again contain only accessory amounts of chromite. It should also be mentioned that another way of forcing the magma composition into the chromite field is shown in Figure 1.18d, where the magma at point E (or anywhere along the cotectic for that matter) becomes contaminated with siliceous material (perhaps by assimilation of crustal material forming either the floor or the roof of the magma chamber). The contaminated magma would have a composition that lies somewhere along the mixing line joining E to the SiO_2 apex of the ternary diagram. This composition would also lie transiently in the chromite field and result in the formation of a monomineralic cumulate layer of chromite (between H and G). This is an indication of how important contamination of magma can be to igneous ore-forming processes.

Other mechanisms for the formation of chromitite layers or pods

Although the Irvine model very neatly explains many of the characteristics of chromitite layers it is unlikely to apply to all situations and there are several other mechanisms that might pertain to the accumulation of monomineralic layers or pods. Two of the most likely, since they have been confirmed experimentally, include changes in oxygen fugacity (fO_2) and total pressure (P_{Tot}) of the crystallizing magma.

An increase in fO_2 will promote the stability of chromite and possibly allow the mineral to crystallize alone for a period of time (Ulmer, 1969). Increasing fO_2 in the magma could be achieved by a devolatilization reaction such as [1.6] below (after Lipin, 1993).

$$4FeCO_3 \leftrightarrow 2Fe_2O_3 + 4CO + O_2 \qquad [1.6]$$

where CO_3^{2-} in solution breaks down to form carbon monoxide and free oxygen. However, because CO_2 and not CO is likely to be the dominant carbon species in basalt, it seems unlikely that oxidation of a magma will be easily achieved and the process is generally not called upon as an explanation for chromite accumulation.

By contrast, small increases in P_{Tot} of the magma have now been shown to occur readily in basaltic chambers. Observations in the Kilauea volcano (Hawaii) have shown that a pressure increase (of up to 0.25 kbar) can occur in the roof of the magma chamber as a result of CO_2 exsolution and expansion of the gas bubbles as they stream upwards in the magma (Bottinga and Javoy, 1990; Lipin, 1993). An increase in total pressure in the magma chamber will have the effect of shifting the phase boundary between olivine and chromite such that the field of the latter phase expands. This would have the same effect as that predicted in the Irvine model, in that chromite would crystallize alone until such time as the ambient pressure is restored (by egress of magma, volatiles or both). This mechanism has been proposed for the formation of chromitite layers in the Stillwater Complex (Montana), where it is suggested that CO_2 streaming and associated pressure increase accompanied ingress of a new magma pulse into the chamber (Lipin, 1993). Exsolution of volatiles and fluids from a magma is discussed in more detail in Chapter 2.

A note on podiform chromitites

Although not as large as the deposits in layered mafic intrusions, podiform chromitite ores in ophiolite complexes represent important resources in many parts of the world. The chromitite ores are typically found as irregular, stratiform to discordant, pods within dunitic and harzburgitic host rocks which themselves are often intensely deformed. In detail the ore textures, characterized by nodular and orbicular associations of chromite and olivine, suggest that the mingling of two magmas has given rise to crystallization of the chromitite ores. Ballhaus (1998) has suggested that the sites of chromite mineralization represent zones in the oceanic lithosphere where low viscosity, olivine-normative melt mingled with a more siliceous, higher viscosity magma. The two melt fractions remain segregated, at least for the time it takes to accumulate chromitite ore. For thermodynamic reasons chromite nucleates preferentially in the ultramafic melt globules, with crystals forming initially along the metastable liquid interface (where mixing takes place at a small scale and a situation akin to the Irvine model (Figure 1.18) pertains) and then progressively throughout the globule. Diffusion of chromium from the siliceous magma, where no chromite nucleation has occurred, across the liquid interface into the ultramafic melt globules, also takes place, with the result that the latter might ultimately be entirely replaced by chromitite. Because the siliceous magma acts as a chromium reservoir, the richest ores are considered to occur where the volume of the latter is high relative to that of the ultramafic globules within which accumulation of chromitite is occurring.

1.4.4 Filter pressing as a process of crystal fractionation

The separation of crystal phases from residual melt during the solidification of magma is generally attributed to gravitational segregation where crystals of either higher or lower density than the magma settle or float to form horizontally layered cumulate rocks. As mentioned previously, this is an oversimplification of the actual processes, which often involve complex density and chemical diffusive controls. Another mechanism by which crystal melt segregation can occur is the process known as filter pressing. The residual magma within a network of accumulating crystals in a partially solidified chamber can be pressed out into regions of lower pressure such as overlying non-crystalline magma or fractures in the country rock. The process is considered to apply even in more viscous granitic magma chambers where evolved, water-saturated melts are filter pressed into adjacent fractures created during hydrofracturing.

Anorthosite hosted Ti–Fe deposits

Large massif-anorthosite intrusions of Mesoproterozoic age, located in the Paleohelikian and Grenvillian orogenies extending from North America into the Sveconorwegian province, are the hosts to very important Ti and Fe deposits of magmatic origin (Force, 1991a; Gross et al., 1997). Well known examples of such deposits include Sanford Lake in the Adirondacks of New York state, USA, the Lac Tio deposit in the Allard Lake region of Quebec, Canada, and the Tellnes deposit in southern Norway. The deposits are typically thought to be related to large differentiated intrusive complexes made up mainly of anorthosite, gabbro, norite, and monzonite rocks emplaced in the late tectonic to extensional stages of the orogenic cycle. Although mineralogically variable, the more important category economically is the andesine anorthosite type (or Adirondack type), which contains ilmenite–hematite as the principal ore minerals. The Ti–Fe oxide ore accumulations occur as stratiform layers and disseminations within the intrusive complexes themselves, or as more massive, higher-grade, cross-cutting or dyke-like bodies.

These deposits are clearly a product of *in situ* crystal fractionation. Early extraction of a plagioclase-dominated crystal assemblage results in concentration of Fe and Ti in the residual magmas, which crystallize to form ferrogabbro or ferrodiorite. Titaniferous magnetite or hemo-ilmenite (depending on the magma composition) also crystallize with disseminated layers formed by crystal settling and accumulation on the chamber floor. The more massive discordant bodies are considered to be a product of the pressing out of an Fe–Ti oxide mineral slurry – the slurry concentrates to form an intrusive body often along the margins of the largely consolidated anorthosite complex, or into fractures and breccia in the host rocks. The Lac Tio orebody is an irregular, tabular intrusive mass some 1100 m long and 1000 m wide, whereas the Tellnes ores form part of a 14 km long dyke (Gross et al., 1997).

1.5 Liquid immiscibility as an ore-forming process

Liquid immiscibility is the segregation of two coexisting liquid fractions from an originally homogeneous magma. The two fractions may be mineralogically similar (silicate–silicate immiscibility) or be very different (silicate–oxide, silicate–carbonate or silicate–sulfide immiscibility). The phenomenon of immiscibility is best observed in extrusive rocks where rapid quenching prevents the segregated products from being rehomogenized. Philpotts (1982) noted two compositionally distinct glasses interstitial to cumulus minerals in a tholeiitic basalt. Their compositions were essentially granitic, on the one hand, and an unusual mafic assemblage, comprising pyroxene, magnetite–ilmenite, and apatite, on the other. The August 1963 eruption of the Kilauea volcano in Hawaii provided evidence of another form of liquid immiscibility in which a directly observable sulfide melt separated from a cooling, basaltic magma (Skinner and Peck, 1969). The Duluth Complex in Minnesota contains several small occurrences of massive Cu–Ni sulfide mineralization, as well as rare discordant bodies of ilmenite-magnetite–apatite (in oxide to apatite proportions of about 2:1) referred to as nelsonites. These occurrences are considered to provide evidence that both sulfide and Fe–Ti–P immiscible fractions separated from the Duluth magma and that these represent a compositional continuum of immiscible products (Ripley et al., 1998). Although its occurrence is difficult to prove, and despite the fact that it is not a major process during magma evolution, immiscibility is very important as an ore-forming process in mafic magmas and can lead to the formation of large and important deposits such as the PGE sulfide deposits of the Merensky Reef in the Bushveld Complex, South Africa (Box 1.6), the Ni–Cu sulfide ores at Kambalda in Western Australia (Box 1.5), and at Sudbury in Ontario (Box 1.7). Various types of immiscibility are discussed below, with special emphasis on silicate–sulfide immiscibility.

1.5.1 Silicate–oxide immiscibility

It is well known that unusual, discordant bodies of magnetite–apatite or ilmenite/rutile–apatite (nelsonite) are preferentially associated with some alkaline rocks, as well as with anorthosite complexes. Early experimental work showed that it is possible to create two immiscible liquids, one quenching to form a mixture of magnetite and apatite in proportions of about 2:1, and the other a

Figure 1.19 The nature of the "immiscibility gap" (shaded) that exists in felsic magmas under conditions of variable oxygen fugacity. The tie-lines indicate the coexisting liquid compositions (after Naslund, 1976).

The observation that oxidized iron-rich magmas can segregate into two immiscible liquids, one which is Fe-rich and the other a more normal silicate composition, has relevance to the formation of Fe- and Ti-rich magmatic segregations in nature. In slowly cooled plutonic rocks resorption reactions are largely responsible for the rehomogenization of segregated liquids, such that immiscibility is not often seen. In extrusive magmas, however, quenching can occur, or a more dense oxide liquid could separate from its silicate counterpart to be forcibly injected into a different part of the magma chamber, or into fractured country rock. Such an immiscible Fe- or Ti-rich fluid could also form a discrete magma or lava flow, a possibility that provides a theoretical basis for understanding the very important magnetite–hematite–apatite ores in, for example, the Kiruna district of northern Sweden (Freitsch, 1978). Another example of what appears to be a flow of immiscible magnetite lava that separated from andesitic lavas has been documented at the El Laco volcano in northern Chile (Naslund *et al.*, 2002). A word of caution though – in the cases of both Kiruna and El Laco there is considerable debate about the origin of the iron ores, and in the latter example in particular, a strong case has been made suggesting a hydrothermal origin for the Fe mineralization (Rhodes and Oreskes, 1999; Sillitoe and Burrows, 2002). The question of silicate–oxide immiscibility as a viable ore-forming process is still very contentious, despite the fact that the process has been proven experimentally.

1.5.2 Silicate–sulfide immiscibility

By contrast with the process of silicate–oxide immiscibility, where there is some controversy over its extent in nature, the existence of silicate–sulfide immiscibility in mafic magmas is widely accepted as a common feature of magma crystallization. Experimental data in the system SiO_2-FeO-FeS (MacLean, 1969) confirms that silicate liquid can coexist with sulfide liquid over a large volume of the system (Figure 1.20; two-liquid field). Magma at A in Figure 1.20, crystallizing Fe-rich olivine (fayalite), would evolve along A–A′ and eventually intersect the two-liquid phase

rock that is dioritic in composition (Philpotts, 1967). Further experimental studies showed that for a fairly broad range of rock compositions under conditions of high fO_2, an immiscible FeO melt will separate from a magma of felsic composition (Naslund, 1976). A large immiscibiity field exists, for example, in the system $KAlSi_3O_8$-SiO_2-FeO (Figure 1.19) at approximately atmospheric fO_2 conditions, but the gap is greatly diminished in a more reducing environment. The existence of immiscibility is also enhanced in magmas with high concentrations of P, Ti, and Fe, but the field diminishes with increasing Ca and Mg (Naslund, 1983).

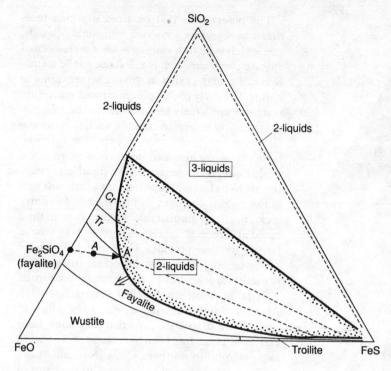

Figure 1.20 Phase equilibria established experimentally in the system SiO₂–FeO–FeS (after MacLean, 1969). The field of two coexisting silicate and sulfide liquids is shown by the stipple accentuated line. Oxidation of the magma would shift the phase boundary in the direction shown by the double arrow, and expand the field of two-liquids. A magma represented by composition A and crystallizing fayalite would evolve along the line A–A'. Silica phases are represented by tridymite (Tr) and cristobalite (Cr).

boundary where the residual melt would comprise conjugate silicate and sulfide melts.

Sulfur as sulfide is dissolved in magmas by displacing oxygen bonded to ferrous iron. Sulfide solubility is, therefore, a function of FeO activity in the magma, but is also controlled by oxygen fugacity (fO_2), decreasing as fO_2 increases (MacLean, 1969). Sulfide solubility, or the amount of sulfide dissolved in the magma at saturation, will vary as a magma progressively crystallizes and, at any point when saturation is reached, small immiscible globules of sulfide melt will form. Sulfide saturation can be achieved as solidification proceeds and magma temperature falls, or by an increase in fO_2, or by a decrease in the amount of ferrous iron in the magma (such as might occur during extraction of an Fe-rich phase; see Figure 1.20). As will be shown later, other factors, such as addition of externally derived sulfur, or ingress of new magma, can also promote saturation and the formation of an immiscible sulfide phase.

The immiscible sulfide melt that segregated from basaltic magma on the Kilauea volcano contained approximately 61% Fe, 31% S, 4% Cu, and 4% O. It subsequently solidified to form minerals such as pyrrhotite, chalcopyrite, and magnetite (Skinner and Peck, 1969). Segregated sulfide melts forming in this fashion clearly have enormous potential to host concentrations of metals with both chalcophile and siderophile tendencies, such as base (Cu, Ni, Co) and precious (Au, Pt) metal ores. There are many large and important ore deposits associated with the development of an immiscible sulfide fraction in mafic and ultramafic magmas (see Boxes 1.5, 1.6, and 1.7). Central to the formation of all these deposits are three fundamental steps:

• the appearance of a substantial fraction of immiscible sulfide melt;

• creation of conditions whereby the sulfide globules can effectively equilibrate with a large volume of silicate magma;

• effective accumulation of the sulfide globules into a single cohesive layer or spatial entity.

The processes whereby ore deposits are created during silicate–sulfide immiscibility are, therefore, complex and multifaceted, and are discussed in more detail in the following section.

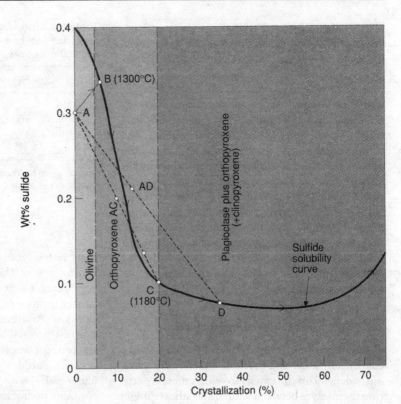

Figure 1.21 Variation in sulfide solubility as a function of progressive crystallization in a mafic magma such as that from which the Bushveld Complex formed (after Naldrett and Von Grünewaldt, 1989).

1.6 A MORE DETAILED CONSIDERATION OF MINERALIZATION PROCESSES IN MAFIC MAGMAS

1.6.1 A closer look at sulfide solubility

The question of whether an immiscible fraction will develop in a magma or not is related to the amount of sulfur required to achieve sulfide saturation. This concept is referred to simply as *sulfide solubility*. As mentioned previously, sulfide solubility decreases with increasing oxygen content in a magma because solution of sulfur appears to be controlled by the following equilibrium reaction (after Naldrett, 1989a):

$$FeO \text{ (melt)} + \frac{1}{2}S_2 \Leftrightarrow FeS \text{ (melt)} + \frac{1}{2}O_2 \qquad [1.7]$$

Sulfide solubility increases as a function of increasing temperature and FeO content of the magma, but decreases with increasing pressure and SiO$_2$ content. The data for sulfide solubility (reviewed in Naldrett, 1989a) have been used to construct a generalized solubility curve for a fractionating Bushveld type mafic magma and are shown in Figure 1.21. The sulfur content at sulfide saturation is seen to decrease from a maximum of about 0.4 wt% sulfide at the start of crystallization to below 0.1 wt% as olivine and orthopyroxene crystallize, but then levels off after plagioclase forms.

A magma with an original sulfide content of 0.3 wt% would initially be undersaturated and its position would plot below the curve in Figure 1.21. Extraction of olivine and pyroxene as cumulus minerals would cause the sulfide content to increase in the residual magma until the saturation limit was attained (i.e. after about 10% crystallization). At this point immiscible globules of homogeneous sulfide melt would form and the magma would remain saturated with respect to sulfide. The amount of sulfide remaining in the magma will, however, decrease as dictated by the solubility curve. If the high density sulfide globules are extracted from the magma by gravitational settling, then the distribution of trace elements between sulfide and silicate liquids can be modeled in terms of crystal fractionation mechanisms. After solidification the cumulate rocks that had formed during this stage of the crystallization sequence would contain minor disseminations of sulfide minerals (such as pyrrhotite, FeS, and chalcopyrite, $CuFeS_2$) among the olivine and orthopyroxene crystals. Alternatively, since the sulfide globules have a high density, they might also accumulate as a separate sulfide layer toward the base of the magma chamber. The decrease in sulfide solubility with progressive crystallization of a mafic magma, as well as the shape of the solubility curve shown in Figure 1.21, have important implications for the understanding of ore-forming processes in these rocks and this diagram is referred to again below.

1.6.2 Sulfide–silicate partition coefficients

The ability of an immiscible sulfide fraction to concentrate base and precious metals will obviously depend on the extent to which metals partition themselves between sulfide and silicate melts (i.e. the magnitudes of the relevant sulfide-silicate partition coefficients). All metals that have chalcophile tendencies are likely to partition strongly into the sulfide phase rather than remain in the silicate melt, and the data presented in Table 1.3 confirms that both base and precious metals are markedly compatible with respect to sulfide minerals. The partition coefficients indicate that although Cu, Ni and Co partition strongly into the sulfide phase, scavenging of platinum group elements (PGE)* by sulfide melt is even more efficient. Values of partition coefficients up to 100 000 for the PGE (Table 1.3) indicate that the presence of an immiscible sulfide fraction is potentially a very powerful concentrating mechanism.

In reality, however, even though the sulfide–silicate partition coefficients for the PGE are so

Table 1.3 Estimates of sulfide–silicate partition coefficients for base and precious metals in ultramafic and mafic magmas

	Ni	Cu	Co	Pt	Pd
Komatiite					
27% MgO	100	250–3000	40	10^4–10^5	10^4–10^5
19% MgO	175	250–2000	60	10^4–10^5	10^4–10^5
Basalt	275	250–2000	80	10^4–10^5	10^4–10^5

Source: from Naldrett (1989a), Barnes and Francis (1995), Tredoux *et al.* (1995).

high, one seldom finds economically viable concentrations of these elements in layered mafic complexes. One reason for this is that the original concentrations of PGE in magmatic reservoirs are very low. Another reason is that, even in magmas where immiscible globules of sulfide do form, the concentration mechanism may be diminished because sulfides are not able to communicate (chemically) with the entire magma reservoir that contains the metals. In the case of the Skaergaard intrusion, for example, sulfide disseminations occur mainly in the upper portions of the layered body and sulfide immiscibility is believed to have occurred relatively late in the crystallization sequence (Anderson *et al.*, 1998). The sulfide minerals at Skaergaard are depleted in Ni because a significant proportion of the latter metal was extracted by early formed olivine and orthopyroxene and was no longer available to be scavenged by the sulfide phase. On the other hand, the Skaergaard sulfide zone is cupriferous, and is also enriched in Au and Pd, as both these metals were concentrated into the residual magma as incompatible elements during crystal fractionation. The Skaergaard sulfides have only, therefore, equilibrated with the more differentiated parts of the magma chamber.

---

* Six elements make up the platinum group – they are platinum (Pt), palladium (Pd), and rhodium (Rh), collectively referred to as the Pd subgroup, and osmium (Os), iridium (Ir), and ruthenium (Ru), referred to as the iridium subgroup. Both the Pd and Ir subgroups have strong affinities with Fe–Cu–Ni sulfides, whereas the iridium subgroup is also often associated with chromite and olivine cumulates.

The effects of early removal of trace elements are demonstrated in Figure 1.17, where it is seen that partitioning of a highly compatible trace element (e.g. D = 10 in Figure 1.17b) leads to enrichments in the solid cumulates only for the first 20–30% of crystallization (i.e. for values of F from 1.0 to about 0.7) and, thereafter, the solids are increasingly depleted in that element. This is because a high-D trace element will comprehensively enter the early formed solids, leaving the residual magma strongly depleted. Later solids will have to equilibrate with a depleted reservoir and will likewise be depleted, irrespective of the magnitude of the partition coefficient. An immiscible sulfide melt within a silicate magma can also be regarded as a cumulus mineral phase and the same situation would, therefore, apply. In fact, the problem would be particularly acute for the PGE with respect to an immiscible sulfide fraction because their partition coefficients are so high, and the original abundances in the parental magma so low (generally only a few ppb), that all but the very first formed sulfide fraction will be depleted in these metals. One does, therefore, have to ask the very pertinent question as to how large and economically viable concentrations of low abundance metals actually form. Or, put another way, how do the enormous concentrations of PGE-bearing sulfide ores such as those of the Bushveld Complex form when early depletion of compatible metals apparently limits the extent to which viable concentrations of metals can be achieved?

1.6.3 The R factor and concentration of low abundance trace elements

If a globule of sulfide melt equilibrates with an *infinite* reservoir of magma then the concentration of a trace metal in that, or any other similar, globule is given simply by the product of the partition coefficient and the initial concentration of the metal in the coexisting silicate melt. In reality of course the sulfide globule is only likely to interact with a small, restricted mass of silicate melt, which is why the problem alluded to at the end of the previous section is very relevant. Clearly, the greater the proportion of silicate relative to

sulfide melt, the higher and more persistent the concentration of compatible trace metals in that globule is likely to be. Campbell and Naldrett (1979) quantified the problem by proposing that the concentrations of low-abundance trace elements, such as the PGE, into an immiscible sulfide phase should be calculated in terms not only of the original abundance in the magma and the relevant partition coefficients, but also of the silicate/sulfide liquid mass ratio, termed the "R" factor. An expression which incorporates the R factor into the normal distribution law is provided in equation [1.8] (after Campbell and Naldrett, 1979):

$$C_{sul} = C_o D(R + 1)/(R + D) \qquad [1.8]$$

where: C_{sul} is the concentration of a trace element in the sulfide fraction; C_o is the original trace element concentration in the host magma; D is the sulfide–silicate partition coefficient; and R is the mass ratio of silicate magma to sulfide melt.

Although the R factor is simply a mass fraction, it is a parameter that also effectively records the extent to which the immiscible sulfide fraction interacts with the silicate magma from which it is derived (and which also contains the metals that need to be concentrated if an ore deposit is to be formed). If a sulfide globule sinks through a lengthy column of magma (or is caught up in a turbulent plume) it is effectively interacting with a large volume of silicate liquid, and this can be equated to a high R factor (Campbell *et al.*, 1983; Barnes and Maier, 2002). Even though a sulfide globule may rapidly deplete the surrounding magma at any one instant of time by virtue of a very high sulfide–silicate partition coefficient, it may be provided with the opportunity to scavenge compatible elements by continuously moving through undepleted magma. A low R factor is analogous to a situation where a sulfide globule is static, or is removed early on from the magma, so that it is not able to efficiently scavenge compatible elements even though the partition coefficients may be very high.

The way in which the concentrations of compatible trace metals in sulfide melts vary as a function of both partition coefficient (D) and R is

Figure 1.22 (a) Plot showing the relationships between partition coefficients (D), the R factor (i.e. the mass ratio of silicate melt to sulfide melt), and the degree of enrichment (C_{sul}/C_o) of compatible trace elements in the sulfide phase (after Barnes and Francis, 1995). (b) Diagram showing the effect of variations in the R factor on the concentration of Ni and Pt in an immiscible sulfide fraction that is in equilibrium with a basaltic magma (after Naldrett, 1989b).

shown in Figure 1.22a (after Barnes and Francis, 1995). For cases where D is much larger then R, the enrichment factor (C_{sul}/C_o) approximates the value of the R factor (i.e. the sloped portions of the curves in Figure 1.22a). Conversely, when the R factor is much larger than D, then the enrichment factor is approximately the value of D (Figure 1.22a – the flat parts of the curves). Another way of emphasizing the importance of the R factor is to examine its influence on the concentrations in sulfide melt of two compatible trace elements, one with a moderately high partition coefficient (for example, Ni with D = 275) and the other with a very high partition coefficient (Pt with D = 100 000). Figure 1.22b shows that where the R factor is low (say 10^3) Ni concentrations in sulfide fractions are high (i.e. typical of most Ni-sulfide ores) because of the combination of high D and high initial Ni content (350 ppm) of the parental magma. By contrast, the Pt concentrations in the same sulfide fraction will be low because, despite the very large D, they have not had the opportunity of scavenging a substantial mass of the element from a magma that initially had a very small Pt abundance (5 ppb). By contrast, in situations where the R factor is high (say 10^6) the Ni concentrations of the sulfide fraction will not be significantly higher than the lower R

factor case, but the Pt contents will have increased substantially because of more extensive interaction between the immiscible sulfide fraction and the silicate magma.

Variations in the R factor have real implications for the grades of sulfide phases within individual mafic intrusions. In the Muskox intrusion of northern Canada, for example, disseminated Cu–Ni sulfides on the margins of the body contain only moderate concentrations of PGE, whereas the more voluminous interior of the intrusion contains sulfides with higher PGE grades (Barnes and Francis, 1995). This is attributed to a lower mass ratio of silicate to sulfide melt, and therefore a lower R factor, on the margins of the intrusion. Considerations such as this might be of considerable relevance to an exploration strategy for this type of deposit.

1.6.4 Factors that promote sulfide immiscibility

It is conceivable that situations in which sulfide saturation is attained relatively late in the crystallization history of a magma could be disadvantageous to the formation of, for example, Ni- or PGE-sulfide ores if the latter metals had already been extracted from the residual magma. It is also possible that late sulfide saturation could equate with a low R factor simply because the volume of residual silicate magma is low. A scenario whereby magmas become sulfide saturated relatively early in the crystallization history of an intrusion is considered to be advantageous for the development of a wide range of magmatic sulfide deposits. There are several processes by which sulfide saturation can be promoted and these are discussed below.

Addition of externally derived sulfur

Perhaps the simplest way of promoting saturation in a magma whose composition is sulfur undersaturated is to increase the global amount of sulfur in the melt by addition from an external source. Some of the komatiite-hosted Ni–Cu deposits, such as Kambalda in Western Australia (Box 1.5) and several examples in Zimbabwe and Canada, are hosted in lava flows that have extruded onto sulfide-bearing footwall sediments such as chert, banded iron-formation, or shale. The komatiitic host lava commonly cuts down into its footwall, a feature attributed to a combination of thermal erosion and structural dislocation. Good geological and geochemical evidence exists to suggest that the komatiitic magma arrived on surface undersaturated with respect to sulfur, and that saturation was achieved by a combination of crystal fractionation and assimilation of crustally derived sulfur derived from footwall sediments (Lesher, 1989). This concept is consistent with factors such as the localization of Ni–Cu ore within the footwall embayments created by extruded komatiitic lavas and is discussed in more detail in Box 1.5.

Injection of a new magma and magma mixing

As mentioned in section 1.3.2 above, large magma chambers are seldom the result of a single injection of melt and most witness one or more replenishments during the crystallization sequence. The Bushveld Complex and the Stillwater Complex in Montana contain important chromite deposits as well as PGE-enriched base metal ores associated with a sulfide-rich layer (the Merensky reef in the Bushveld and the J-M reef at Stillwater).

These two, economically important, layered mafic intrusions were both characterized by crystallization that was interrupted by periodic injections of new, less differentiated magma. The magma replenishment events broadly coincide, in both cases, with the development of PGE-enriched sulfide horizons. In the Bushveld Complex very detailed Rb–Sr and Re–Os isotopic measurements indicate that the new magma was more radiogenic (perhaps due to crustal contamination) but less differentiated than the magma remaining in the chamber at the time of injection (Kruger and Marsh, 1982; Lee and Butcher, 1990; Schoenberg et al., 1999). Further discussion on magma replenishment and its role in mineralization in other mafic intrusions is presented in reviews by Naldrett (1989a, b, 1997, 1999).

The sulfide solubility diagram in Figure 1.21 can be used to demonstrate how the mixing of new and residual magmas can promote sulfide saturation. Although the proportions of cumulus minerals being extracted from the magma, as well as the sulfur solubility curve itself, may not be universally applicable, the principles could be modified for application elsewhere. An initial magma composition represented by A in Figure 1.21, containing 0.3 wt% sulfide, would be undersaturated relative to sulfide (i.e. sulfide solubility at this stage is 0.4%). Extraction of olivine from the magma (A–B in Figure 1.21) would decrease its FeO content and result in sulfide saturation with formation of an immiscible sulfide fraction. With continued crystallization and segregation of sulfides the magma would remain saturated, following the solubility curve as shown in Figure 1.21. If after some 20% crystallization (at point C just prior to the appearance of plagioclase as a cumulus phase) the chamber is replenished with the injection of a new magma (similar to A) and mixing occurs, then the composition of the mixture would lie somewhere along the mixing line between A and C. If the mixture is at AC it would clearly be undersaturated again and any sulfide globules present would be resorbed back into the magma. If, however, the chamber is replenished with the injection of a new magma at point D (after 35% crystallization, and after the introduction of plagioclase as a cumulus phase), then a mixed magma

BOX 1.5 Silicate–sulfide immiscibility: the komatiite-hosted Ni–Cu deposits at Kambalda, Western Australia

An important category of magmatic Ni–Cu sulfide deposits is that related to mafic and ultramafic volcanic rocks (komatiites) in Archean greenstone belts. Deposits of this type occur in Canada (the Thompson Ni belt of Manitoba) and Zimbabwe (Trojan and Shangani mines), but the largest and richest occurrences occur in the Kambalda region of Western Australia. Although a great deal is now known about these deposits (Lesher, 1989) this case study focuses specifically on the source of sulfur in the immiscible globules of sulfide within the komatiitic lava flows that host the mineralization.

Komatiites are ultramafic extrusive rocks that were first described in the Barberton greenstone belt, South Africa, by Viljoen and Viljoen (1969). They comprise mainly olivine + clinopyroxene and typically contain MgO > 18 wt% and low alkalis. As indicated in section 1.2.2 of this chapter they are characterized by high Ni contents. Komatiites are extruded onto the Earth's surface as high temperature, low viscosity lava flows characterized by a variety of volcanic forms of which pillowed lava and bladed spinifex textures are the most diagnostic. Most komatiites are not mineralized and their Ni is resident mainly in cumulus olivine, suggesting that on extrusion these lavas were undersaturated with respect to sulfide.

Evidence from the Kambalda region indicates that voluminous eruption of hot, low viscosity komatiitic lava flows formed extensive sheet flows and gradient-controlled lava rivers or channels (showing many of the features seen in parts of present day Hawaii). Hot lava rivers are believed to have thermally eroded discrete channels into the previously consolidated footwall and some of the

Ni–Cu ores at Kambalda exhibit sulfide concentrations at the base of well defined, linear channelways (Figure 1). Another feature of this type of ore is that the mineralized channelways are devoid of interflow sediments even though such sediments occur laterally away from the ore zones at that level. These sediments comprise a variety of carbonaceous and sulfidic shales as well as sulfidic chert and banded iron-formation (Bavinton, 1981). The nature of these sediments has led to suggestions that they represented a source of sulfur and this is supported by S isotope studies showing similarities in the isotope ratios of ores and interflow sediments (Lesher, 1989). One implication of this idea is that assimilation of sediment by thermally eroding komatiitic lava channels enhanced the sulfide content within the magma and promoted local sulfide saturation and immiscibility.

Sulfur saturation and immiscibility of a sulfide fraction early in the magma crystallization history is the fundamental process responsible for mineralization in komatiitic lava flows. Chalcophile metals, in particular Ni and lesser Cu, were scavenged from the turbulent, flowing komatiite magma by the immiscible sulfide globules, which eventually accumulated as massive sulfide ore along the bottom of the channelways (Figure 1). The disseminated ore that overlies the massive sulfide ore reflects the static buoyancy contrast that existed between komatiitic crystal mush and massive sulfide. External derivation of sulfur has also been suggested for the promotion of sulfide saturation in the very large Noril'sk–Talnakh Cu–Ni–PGE deposits in the Russian Federation (Grinenko, 1985) and also for the Duluth Complex in Minnesota (Ripley and Al-Jassar, 1987).

Figure 1 The characteristics of komatiite-hosted Ni–Ci deposits in the Kambalda region, Western Australia (after Solomon *et al.*, 2000).

BOX 1.6 New magma injection and magma mixing: the Merensky Reef, Bushveld Complex

In addition to its huge chromite reserves, the Bushveld Complex also hosts the world's largest reserves of platinum group elements (PGE). About 80% of the world's PGE reserves are located in the complex, from three specific horizons, namely the Merensky Reef (where exploitation commenced and which itself contains about 22% of the world's total PGE reserves; Misra, 2000), the UG2 chromitite layer, and the Plat Reef. A simplified outline and section of the Bushveld Complex, showing the extent of the Merensky Reef, is presented in Box 1.4. This case study focuses specifically on the Merensky Reef as it was formed at the time when a major injection of new magma occurred into the chamber, and it also marks a regional mineralogical hiatus separating the Critical Zone from the Main Zone (Kruger and Marsh, 1985). It is typically represented by a 1 meter thick, coarse-grained (or pegmatoidal), feldspathic pyroxenite that extends along strike for about

250 km. The origin of the Merensky Reef is a contentious issue (Naldrett, 1989a) and arguments range from purely magmatic models to those involving interaction with magmatic-hydrothermal fluids (Cawthorn, 1999). There is ample evidence that the Merensky Reef and its contained PGE mineralization have been involved with a hydrothermal fluid, and this topic is discussed in more detail in Chapter 2. For the purposes of this discussion, however, it is accepted that the Merensky unit (i.e. the mineralized reef and the rocks immediately overlying it, called the Bastard unit) owes its origin to the turbulence and magma mixing that accompanied a magmatic replenishment event (Schoenberg et al., 1999).

Mineralization in the Merensky Reef is evident in the presence of disseminated base metal sulfides, mainly chalcopyrite and pyrrhotite–pentlandite, with which minor PGE sulfides (such as braggite, cooperite, laurite, and

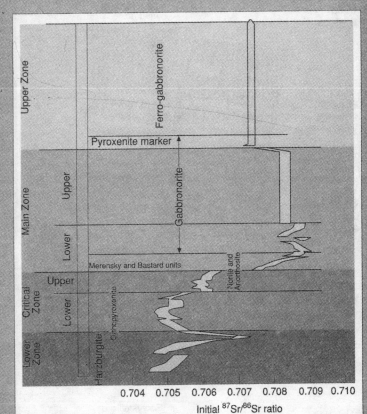

Figure 1 Sr isotope variations (in terms of the initial $^{87}Sr/^{86}Sr$ ratio or R_0) with stratigraphic height in the Bushveld Complex (after F.J. Kruger, personal communication).

Figure 2 The edge of a small pothole showing anorthosite in contact with pyroxenite. The Merensky Reef should occur at the contact between the two rock types.

moncheite) and PGE metal alloys are associated. As a general statement, magma replenishment and mixing are believed to have been responsible for the formation of an immiscible sulfide fraction, and the concentration of PGE into these sulfides, at the time of Merensky Reef formation (Naldrett, 1989a). It must be emphasized, however, that mineralization in the Merensky Reef, as well as in the UG2 chromitite and Plat Reef, is a very complex process and this is discussed in somewhat more detail in section 1.6 and also again in Chapter 2.

Evidence for a new magma pulse at the Merensky unit is most obvious in terms of mineral–chemical trends. The most convincing evidence for the input of a new magma, however, comes from a dramatic shift in the initial $^{87}Sr/^{86}Sr$ ratio (R_o) of rocks below and above the Merensky unit (Figure 1). Such a change cannot be achieved by crystal fractionation and must record the input of new magma. In this case the new magma had a higher initial $^{87}Sr/^{86}Sr$ ratio

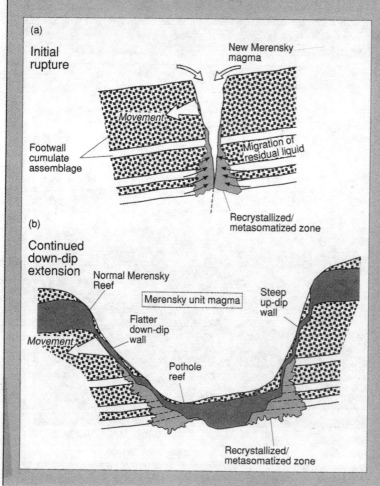

Figure 3 Schematic cross sections illustrating the progressive development of potholes in the Merensky Reef by syn-magmatic extension in the footwall cumulate rocks just prior to and during injection of a new magma (after Carr *et al.*, 1999).

than the original magma pulse, a trait that is attributed to crustal contamination of the new magma increment. Magma mixing, sulfide segregation, and mineralization in the same interval are also, therefore, likely to be related to this event. Recognition of replenishment events should be regarded as a useful criterion for the exploration of PGE mineralization in layered mafic intrusions.

Another intriguing feature of the Merensky Reef linked to injection of new magma is the presence of enigmatic potholes (Figure 2) that are well revealed in underground workings. Potholes are elliptical areas, 100–200 m in diameter, where the Merensky Reef cuts down into its footwall, often by as much as 20–30 m. They are of considerable inconvenience to mining operations and also reflect changes in the mineralogy of the PGE, in that metal alloys tend to dominate over PGE minerals (i.e. sulfides,

tellurides, etc.). Their origin is highly debated (see Buntin *et al.*, 1985) and has been attributed to either downward erosional processes (such as convective scouring or thermal erosion) or upward fluid/melt migration (involving focused vertical migration of filter-pressed interstitial magma or a hydrothermal fluid). A model that accommodates the Sr isotopic characteristics of the Merensky unit, however, envisages syn-magmatic extension of the footwall cumulus assemblage just prior to injection of the new magma (Carr *et al.*, 1999). The pull-apart rupture grows in a down-dip direction (perhaps due to subsidence and slumping) and is then filled by the new magma to form the Merensky unit, with the mineralized reef at its base (Figure 3). Potholes are another feature that illustrate just how complex ore-forming processes actually are when deposits are examined in detail.

composition at, for example, AD would be oversaturated with respect to sulfide. This would result in the segregation of an immiscible sulfide fraction, the mass of which exceeds the expected cotectic proportion. A period of enhanced sulfide production could be expected, therefore, to accompany the injection of a new magma at point D.

Magma mixing is, therefore, a process that can lead to the production of an immiscible sulfide fraction. The process seems to be linked with the formation of some very important PGE-sulfide bearing horizons such as the J-M Reef in the Stillwater Complex and the Merensky Reef in the Bushveld Complex. It is considered again in the context of a more holistic model in section 1.7 below.

Magma contamination

In the discussion on the formation of monomineralic chromitite seams (section 1.4.3 and Box 1.4) it was mentioned that one way of forcing a magma composition off its cotectic crystallization path into the stability field of chromite was to contaminate the magma with foreign material rich in SiO_2. The same process will also result in a lowering of the sulfur content required for sulfide saturation, thereby promoting the formation of an immiscible sulfide fraction. Figure 1.23 shows a 1200 °C isothermal section of the SiO_2-FeO-FeS system in which the silicate–sulfide immiscibil-

Figure 1.23 The ternary system FeO–SiO_2–FeS at 1200 °C showing how the addition of silica to a homogeneous, sulfide-undersaturated magma will force its composition below the solvus into the field of two liquids, one at Y (silicate-rich) and the other at X (sulfide-rich) (after Naldrett and MacDonald, 1980).

ity field is identified. The composition of a homogeneous magma undersaturated in sulfide at point A can be forced into the field of two liquids by the addition of SiO_2 (toward B). At B the two liquids in equilibrium will have compositions at Y (silicate rich) and X (sulfide rich). This process could have applied to the formation of the Ni–Cu ores at Sudbury (see Box 1.7) where contamination of

BOX 1.7 Magma contamination and sulfide immiscibility: the Sudbury Ni–Cu deposits

Figure 1 Simplified geological map of the Sudbury Complex showing the relationship between the main mass of the layered mafic intrusion and the Ni–Cu mineralized sublayer unit and offset dykes (after Prevec *et al.*, 2000).

Figure 2 Typical appearance of the Ni–Cu sulfide-bearing "sublayer" at Sudbury showing its heterogeneous and contaminated nature.

Ni–Cu mineralization associated with the Sudbury Complex in Ontario, Canada represents a fascinating and unique ore occurrence. Although small (only 1100 km²) in comparison to the Bushveld Complex, the Sudbury layered mafic intrusion has for a long time been the world's leading producer of nickel, and contains over 1.5 billion tons of ore at an average grade of some 1.2 wt% Ni, together with substantial Cu and PGE credits (Misra, 2000). It is even more fascinating for the widely held view that it is the product of a large meteorite impact that struck Earth about 1850 million years ago (Krogh *et al.*, 1984). The meteorite impacted into a composite crust containing Archean granite gneisses and the Paleoproterozoic volcano-sedimentary Huronian Supergroup.

The main mass of the Sudbury Complex is made up of a differentiated suite of norite, quartz gabbro, and granophyre. The Ni–Cu ores, however, are found in an enigmatic mafic unit at the base of the succession termed the sublayer (Figure 1). The interior of the structure is underlain by a chaotic sequence of brecciated debris and volcaniclastic material interpreted as the fall-back from the meteorite impact. The granitic and sedimentary floor to the structure also contains dramatic evidence for a violent meteorite impact in the form of breccia, pseudotachylite (frictional melt rock formed by very high strain rates), and shatter cones. A widely accepted model suggests that Sudbury magmatism was triggered by the meteorite impact event, or more specifically by partial melting of crustal source rocks, during the rebound and pressure release that immediately followed impact (Naldrett, 1989a).

Ni–Cu sulfides (mainly chalcopyrite and pyrrhotite-pentlandite) are found along the basal contacts of the sublayer as massive ore which grades upwards into more disseminated mineralization. Significant sulfide mineralization also occurs in the brecciated floor of the structure where sulfide melt percolated downwards into embayments and fractures. The offset dykes also contain steeply plunging pods of sulfide mineralization. An enigmatic feature of the Sudbury ores, however, is their high Ni contents relative to Cu. High Ni magmatic sulfide ores are generally associated with ultramafic rocks (see, for example, Box 1.5 for a description of the Kambalda deposits), with more differentiated rocks being characterized by higher Cu/Ni ratios. An important, and relevant, feature of the Sudbury ores in the sublayer is their intimate association with exotic ultramafic inclusions. These inclusions are now known to be the same age as the main Sudbury Complex itself and display no mantle isotopic or geochemical signatures (Prevec *et al.*, 2000). Their presence has important implications for the source of metals in the Sudbury deposits.

An intriguing aspect of the relationship between meteorite impact and Ni–Cu sulfide mineralization at Sudbury is the notion that the catastrophic impact was responsible

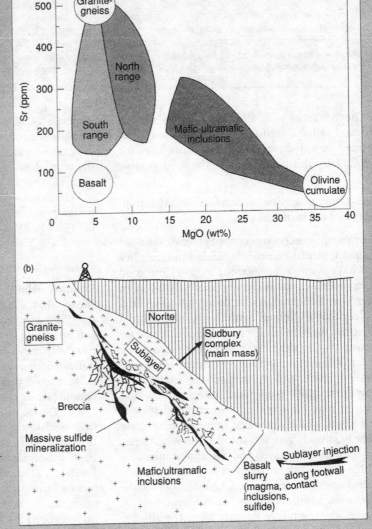

Figure 3 (a) Plot of Sr versus MgO showing the compositional fields of the mineralized sublayer from the north and south ranges of the Sudbury structure, and that of the mafic–ultramafic inclusions within the sublayer. The sublayer is a mixture of melts derived by near total melting of granite–gneiss and tholeiitic basalt of the Huronian Supergroup. The inclusions formed by olivine and pyroxene fractionation of a high-Mg melt at and differentiated toward lower MgO contents (after Prevec *et al.*, 2000). (b) Schematic and simplified cross section through a sublayer-hosted Ni–Cu sulfide orebody in the Sudbury Complex showing some of the features of the Prevec *et al.* (2000) model for the origin of the sublayer.

Force a magma to immiscibility, scavenges elements

for the extensive and widespread contamination of magma as it intruded into the dust and debris of the impact scar (Naldrett et al., 1986). The rocks of the Sudbury Complex are highly contaminated by crustal material and this is readily apparent in their high silica and potassium contents relative to normal continental basalts. One of the features of the Sudbury ores is that this type of contamination might have been responsible for the promotion of sulfide immiscibility and mineralization, as discussed in section 1.6.4 of this chapter. In detail, however, the picture is much more complex and the sublayer is now thought to have an origin that is different to the remainder of the intrusive complex (Prevec et al., 2000; Lightfoot et al., 2001). The main mass of intrusive magma is thought to have been derived by wholesale melting of granite–gneiss and volcano-sedimentary target rocks immediately after meteorite impact and elastic rebound. These crustally contaminated melts crystallized a dominantly plagioclase + pyroxene assemblage to form the bulk of the Sudbury

complex, from which the offset dykes were also tapped. The sublayer, however, is considered to have been derived by melting of a much higher proportion of Huronian basaltic target material such that its parental magma was more mafic than that of the main mass. It crystallized an assemblage dominated initially by olivine, forming ultramafic cumulate rocks at depth in the structure (Prevec et al., 2000). This particular magma was also sulfur saturated and segregated significant volumes of immiscible Ni–Cu sulfide melt, as well as accumulating sulfides from above. It was then emplaced along the brecciated footwall contact as a basaltic slurry, comprising magma, ultramafic inclusions, and sulfide melt, at a relatively late stage in the evolution of the complex. Although convoluted, a meteorite impact model would appear to best explain the complex geology of the Sudbury Complex and to accommodate the intricate processes of anatexis, crustal contamination, and sulfide segregation required to explain its contained ores.

the host magma with siliceous country rock is believed to have facilitated the formation of an immiscible sulfide fraction which scavenged Ni and Cu from the magma to form the ore deposits.

1.6.5 Other magmatic models for mineralization in layered mafic intrusions

The preceding sections described processes such as magma replenishment and sulfide immiscibility that have come to be regarded as providing good "first-order" explanations for mineralization in layered mafic intrusions. In detail, however, it is evident that additional mechanisms are required to explain the many differences that exist from one deposit type to the next, and also the enigmatic patterns of metal distribution evident from very detailed study and more rigorous exploration (Cawthorn, 1999; Barnes and Maier, 2002). Suggestions have been made, for example, that even in rocks as well mineralized as the Critical Zone of the Bushveld Complex, sulfide saturation might not have been achieved and the appearance of a sulfide melt was not the most important feature of the mineralization process. Instead, it is argued that, under conditions of low sulfur fugacity (fS_2), PGE might crystallize directly from the silicate magma in the form of various platinum group

minerals (PGM, such as braggite, laurite, malanite, moncheite, cooperite) or alloys. Although it is difficult to conceive how this might happen given the very low abundances of the PGE in the magma, a novel mechanism involving clustering of PGE ions has lent credibility to this as an alternative process to sulfide segregation (Tredoux et al., 1995; Ballhaus and Sylvester, 2000).

PGE clusters

Detailed studies of PGE mineralization have shown that these elements are heterogeneously distributed in rocks and minerals, even at a sub-microscopic level. The application of the relatively new field of *cluster chemistry* has indicated that the heavy transition metals in a magma will tend to coalesce by metal–metal bonding into clusters of 10 to 100 atoms (Schmid, 1994). Tredoux et al. (1995) have suggested that this mechanism might also apply to mineralization in natural PGE ores such as the Merensky Reef of the Bushveld Complex and the J-M Reef at Stillwater. Theory predicts that heavy transition metals form more stable clusters than light ones and that the PGE will therefore tend to cluster preferentially relative to Cu and Ni. Likewise, the heavy PGE (i.e. higher atomic numbers – Os, Ir, and Pt) will form more stable clusters than the light PGE (Ru, Rh, and Pd). Clustering may, therefore, provide a mechanism for fractionating metals in a magma chamber.

Clustering of atoms and molecules in magmas is a complex process and is controlled by variables such as temperature and composition. Figure 1.24 schematically illustrates the nature of PGE clustering in magma. Initial coalescence of metals occurs by metal–metal bonding, but the clusters are then stabilized by an envelope of ligands (see Chapter 3) such as sulfur or aluminosilicate species. Although there is no direct experimental evidence for PGE clusters in magmas (Mathez, 1999), circumstantial evidence comes from features such as light/heavy PGE fractionation and microbeam detection of minute PGE metal alloys in natural materials. It has also been noted that cumulus olivine- and chromite-rich rocks, such as the harzburgites and chilled margins of the Bushveld Complex, which show no association with sulfide segregations, are notably enriched in PGE relative to less mafic rocks (Davies and Tredoux, 1985; Ballhaus and Sylvester, 2000). Such an enrichment could be attributed to inclusion of PGE clusters into early formed cumulus phases such as olivine and chromite. Stability of PGE clusters and their precipitation from the magma as discrete platinum group minerals or metal alloys is likely to be promoted by a low fS_2 environment.

The existence of PGE clusters in mafic magmas has important implications for understanding the mineralization process. If PGE clusters do form then crystal-chemical considerations and partitioning behavior might be less important than mechanical concentration mechanisms involving trapping of clusters as micro-inclusions in any suitable cumulus phase, be it silicate, oxide, or sulfide. Figure 1.24 illustrates two options, one where PGE clusters are incorporated into sulfide globules and the other where they are trapped as micro-inclusions in either olivine or chromite (Tredoux *et al.*, 1995; Ballhaus and Sylvester, 2000).

Detailed analyses of PGE in minerals of the Merensky Reef indicate that cluster theory might well explain some of the metal distribution patterns not previously explained by conventional sulfide partitioning behaviour. Micro-inclusions of Os–Ir–Pt alloy are found in pyrrhotite and pentlandite, as are other discrete aggregates of Pt with lesser Pd and Au. In olivine and chromite, micro-inclusions are dominantly the Pt–Pd–Au type (Ballhaus and Sylvester, 2000). The latter category is particularly significant as it suggests that the Bushveld magma contained abundant Pt–(Pd–Au) clusters early on in its crystallization history and that concentration of these metals (by trapping them as inclusions in early cumulus phases) can be achieved without sulfide saturation having occurred at all. Admittedly, the concentrations of PGE in silicate phases have not as yet proved to be of economic interest, although the process should remain of interest to platinum explorationists in the future. Chromitite layers can, by contrast, contain very significant concentrations of PGE, as in the case of the huge reserves associated with the UG2 chromitite seam in the Bushveld Complex. This association is discussed in more detail below.

The role of chromite in PGE concentration

The very significant concentration of PGE in chromitite layers such as the UG2 in the Bushveld Complex suggests that mineralization processes other than sulfide scavenging must have played a role. The UG2 also contains a different assemblage of the PGE than the Merensky Reef, for example, and is relatively enriched in Ru, Os, and Ir, but with similar Pt contents (von Grünewaldt *et al.*, 1986). At a first glance this would seem to suggest that heavy PGE clusters had been preferentially concentrated as metal-alloy inclusions in cumulus chromite grains (similar to the process shown in Figure 2.24), a model first suggested by Hiemstra (1979). More detailed work, however, reveals the following characteristics of PGE mineralization in chromitite layers:

1 The chromitite layers do, in fact, contain minor sulfide minerals, both interstitially to the chromite grains and as inclusions (of which laurite RuS_2 is predominant; Merkle, 1992) within them.

2 Pyrrhotite is virtually absent from the chromitites probably because of reaction between sulfides

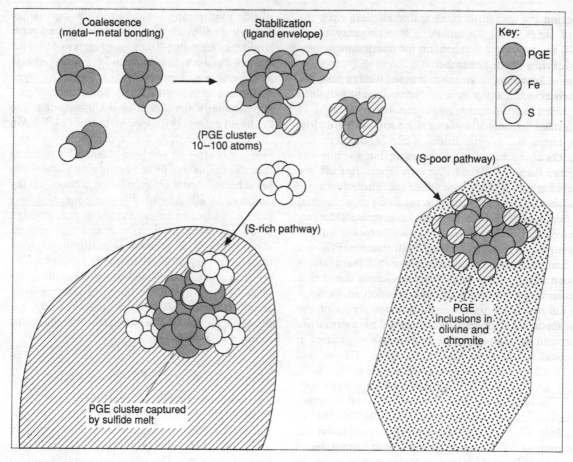

Coalescence
(metal–metal bonding)

Stabilization
(ligand envelope)

Key:
PGE
Fe
S

(PGE cluster
10–100 atoms)

(S-poor pathway)

(S-rich pathway)

PGE
inclusions in
olivine and
chromite

PGE cluster captured
by sulfide melt

Figure 1.24 Schematic diagram illustrating the formation of PGE clusters in a magmatic system and their eventual inclusion either in an immiscible sulfide fraction (S-rich pathway) or in a silicate or oxide cumulus phase such as olivine or chromite (S-poor pathway) (after Tredoux *et al.*, 1995; Ballhaus and Sylvester, 2000).

and chromite which partitions additional Fe into chromite and liberates sulfur (as shown in equation [1.9], after Naldrett and Lehmann, 1988):

$$4Fe_2O_3 \, (chr) + FeS \Rightarrow 3Fe_3O_4 \, (chr) + 0.5S_2 \quad [1.9]$$

3 The assemblage Pt–(Pd–Au) occasionally occurs as discrete metal-alloy inclusions in chromite (Ballhaus and Sylvester, 2000), indicating that the other PGE are associated with sulfide minerals, either as inclusions within, or interstitially to, chromite.

These characteristics led Barnes and Maier (2002) to suggest that an association between PGE con-

centration and chromitite layers could be related to both sulfide accumulation and metal clustering. In their model sulfide segregation under high R factor conditions leads to the accumulation of PGE-enriched sulfide cumulates together with the normal silicate minerals and chromite. The sulfide phase reacts with chromite consuming Fe and liberating S, resulting in a Cu–Ni rich residual sulfide assemblage that crystallizes minor chalcopyrite and pentlandite. The localized lowering of fS_2 that results from sulfide–chromite interaction promotes the direct crystallization of PGM or metal alloys from clusters in the magma so that PGE concentration in the immiscible sulfide fraction is dictated by clustering principles rather than strict partitioning behavior. The unusual PGE content of chromite-rich cumulate assemblages arises from the fact that Ru and, to a lesser extent, Rh partition strongly into the oxide phase whereas other PGE (Pd and Pt) are specifically excluded from the chromite lattice and remain in solution. Since Ru and Rh are fractionated into the chromite, the remainder of the PGE cluster (i.e. Os, Ir, and Pt) destabilizes and is likely to precipitate as PGM or metal alloys. The latter are scavenged by any interstitial sulfides present in and around the chromitite layer.

Application of composite models, as illustrated above, seems to provide an adequate explanation for several of the intriguing characteristics of PGE mineralization in both sulfide-rich and sulfide-poor environments. Detailed observations, in particular intricacies such as the location of PGE in different mineralogical sites, clearly provide the sort of constraints that are needed to improve our understanding of the relevant ore-forming processes.

Hiatus models

One of the tendencies of traditional models for the formation of magmatic deposits is to consider the processes in terms of accumulation of cumulus phases, be they silicate or oxide minerals, or sulfide melt. An intriguing thought by Cawthorn (1999) has suggested that the opposite, namely the lack of accumulation of cumulus minerals, might be the essential ingredient in the formation of PGE and base metal sulfide mineralization styles in certain types of deposits. The Merensky Reef, for example, represents a layer in the Bushveld magma chamber where a major injection of new magma occurred and where there is a pronounced mineralogical hiatus in the magmatic "stratigraphy" (see Box 1.6). Magma replenishment could create a zone of mixing where the liquidus temperature is substantially above that relevant to local crystallization, resulting in a transient stage when no silicate minerals formed. This would also result in a hiatus in the solidification process, equating to a period, at least in terms of simplified gravitative settling, with little or no accumula-

tion of minerals on the chamber floor. Sulfide accumulation and/or metal clustering could, nevertheless, have continued during this interval so that enrichment and mineralization was assisted by the absence of phases that might normally contribute to dilution of the PGE. The view of Ballhaus and Sylvester (2000) with respect to Merensky Reef formation is somewhat analogous. They suggest that PGE concentration occurred by metal clustering in the magma to form an *in situ* stratiform PGE anomaly. The anomaly was effectively "frozen in" at the hiatus created by magma replenishment and local sulfide saturation, as the sulfide globules scavenged PGE clusters from the magma and then settled into the underlying cumulate mush.

Fluid-related infiltration of PGE

There is abundant mineralogical evidence to suggest that many layered mafic intrusions, as well as their contained mineralization, have been effected by alteration related to hydrothermal fluids derived either from the evolving magma itself or from an external source. There is little doubt that such fluids have played a role in the remobilization of existing magmatic sulfide mineralization. A more pertinent question, however, relates to whether such hydrothermal processes may not in fact have been dominant in ore formation (Schiffries and Rye, 1990; Boudreau and Meurer, 1999). Discussion of this topic falls outside the confines of this chapter but it is revisited in Chapter 2.

1.7 A MODEL FOR MINERALIZATION IN LAYERED MAFIC INTRUSIONS

The Bushveld Complex in South Africa, together with the Great Dyke of Zimbabwe and the Stillwater Complex of Montana, represent the prime examples of chromite and PGE-sulfide ore formation in layered mafic intrusions. These examples have many features in common and the detailed work of researchers such as Irvine (1977), Naldrett (1989a, b), Naldrett and von Grünewaldt (1986), Naldrett and Wilson (1991), and Campbell *et al.* (1983), as well as many others, facilitates the compilation of a relatively simple model to explain the occurrence and formation of these very important deposits. The nature and origin of important Cu–Ni sulfide deposits such as Sudbury (Ontario), Noril'sk-Talnakh (Siberia), and Duluth (Minnesota) are somewhat different, but their formation can nevertheless be explained by some of the processes described below. The model described in this section represents a useful summary, but for ease of explanation is simplified, both conceptually and with respect to the actual nature of the ore deposits that it represents. Readers should be cautious in applying this model too rigorously to the real situation. Additional detail can be obtained from the original reference articles, in particular Naldrett (1989b, 1997).

Previous sections of this chapter have emphasized the following features as being important with respect to the formation of ores in igneous intrusions:

1 Crystal fractionation and gravity-induced crystal settling.

2 Density stratification of magma chambers and the ability of magmas to undergo density changes as crystallization proceeds.

3 Repeated recharge of chambers by injection of fresh magma.

4 The ability of fresh magma to find its own density level and to turbulently mix with the residual magma.

5 The existence of transient periods of crystallization when only a single phase such as chromite is on the liquidus.

6 The formation of immiscible globules of sulfide liquid once the magma becomes saturated or supersaturated with respect to sulfide.

7 The very high partition coefficients of siderophilic elements for the immiscible sulfide fraction.

These features are all used to construct the model in Figure 1.25, which shows a schematized layered mafic intrusion containing elements of mineralization representing well known deposits such as the PGE-sulfide bearing Merensky, J-M (Stillwater), and LSZ (Lower Sulfide Zone, Great Dyke) reefs, and the chromitiferous UG and LG (upper and lower groups respectively) seams of the Bushveld Complex. The UG2 chromitite is particularly important because it contains vast

reserves of Cr as well as PGE occurring together in the same, very extensive, horizon.

One empirical observation which has not been previously mentioned, but which turns out to be of considerable importance to understanding both the position and tenor of these ores, is the "stratigraphic" level in the layered intrusion where plagioclase first appears as a cumulus phase. This seemingly innocuous point in the evolution of an igneous intrusion (clearly marked in Figure 1.25) divides ore horizons which tend to be less PGE-enriched below it from those above it, which tend to be both more enriched and more substantial (at least in the Bushveld and Stillwater). In Figure 1.16a it is clear that an evolving magma will become more dense than when it started once significant plagioclase is extracted. This has important implications for the behavior of newly injected melt into the magma chamber and affects the formation of fountains and plumes (Figure 1.16b) as well as the magnitude of the R factor, which in turn controls metal concentration into the immiscible sulfide fraction (Figure 1.22). Thus, with reference to Figure 1.25, any new magma which is introduced into the chamber early in its crystallization sequence (*i.e. prior to the appearance of plagioclase on the liquidus*) will tend to behave as a fountain. The limited degree of mixing that does occur (point AC in the "Irvine model," Figure 1.25) will force the magma composition into the chromite field and give rise to a chromitite layer associated with ultramafic cumulates such as those, for example, of the Great Dyke. The magma composition at this stage will be undersaturated with respect to sulfide (point AC in the "Naldrett and von Grünewaldt model," Figure 1.25) and no sulfide ores will, therefore, form. As crystallization continues, however (A to B in the "Naldrett and von Grünewaldt model," Figure 1.25), saturation will be achieved and immiscible sulfides will segregate to form disseminations of sulfide ore in an orthopyroxene cumulate rock. The very high partition coefficients of Cu, Ni, and the PGE into the immiscible fraction will mean that even with limited buoyancy and mixing the earliest sulfides will be enriched in these elements.

As further sulfides exsolve, however, they will rapidly become depleted in low abundance metals because the residual magma in equilibrium with

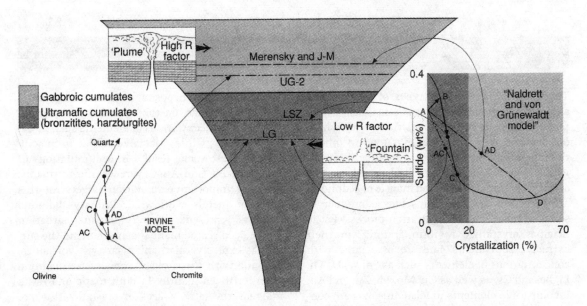

Figure 1.25 Generalized model showing the nature of igneous processes that give rise to some of the important styles of chromite and PGE–base metal sulfide deposits associated with layered mafic intrusions. LG and UG refer to the Lower and Upper Group (UG2 specifically) chromite seams of the Bushveld Complex; LSZ is the Lower Sulfide Zone of PGE mineralization in the Great Dyke; Merensky refers to the Merensky Reef of the Bushveld Complex and J-M is the J-M reef of the Stillwater Complex, both of which contain PGE–sulfide mineralization. The difference between ultramafic and gabbroic cumulates in this model is marked by the first appearance of cumulus plagioclase in the latter (modified after Naldrett, 1997).

these sulfides, which itself originally only had very low abundances of the PGE, becomes depleted (refer to Figure 1.22 for a quantification of this effect). This feature characterizes the Pt–Pd ores of the Lower Sulfide Zone of the Great Dyke, for example, where despite the existence of Cu–F sulfides over a 2–3 meter interval, the ores contain viable grades of PGE over only a few centimeters at the base of the mineralized zone.

By contrast, if a new injection of magma takes place *after the first appearance of plagioclase* then it will likely have a lower density than the residual magma and emplace itself in a turbulent, buoyant fashion at a relatively high level in the chamber. The more efficient mixing that occurs will again promote chromite precipitation (point AD in the "Irvine model," Figure 1.25). These chromite seams will be associated with either gabbroic or ultramafic cumulate rocks, depending on the relative proportions of liquids A and D that are mixed together, and it is also possible that

they will be better developed. Mixing of primitive magma A with an evolved liquid at D will also, in this case, result in a mixture that is sulfide over-saturated (point AD in the "Naldrett and von Grünewaldt model," Figure 1.25), resulting in the formation of a sulfide immiscible fraction. The plume effect that is created by the injection of the lower density primitive magma will result in buoyancy and a high degree of convective circulation of these sulfides, which translates into a high R factor. PGE are again strongly partitioned into the sulfide fraction but the grades will be higher and more evenly distributed because the sulfides have the opportunity of equilibrating with a much larger mass of the magma. This situation is applicable to the formation of the Merensky and J-M reefs, both of which are formed well above the first appearance of plagioclase cumulate rocks. It also applies to the formation of the UG2 seam where PGE-sulfides are intimately associated with a major chromitite layer.

SUMMARY

There are many different types of ore deposits associated with igneous rocks; there is also a wide range of igneous rock compositions with which ore deposits are linked. Magmas tend to inherit their metal endowment from the source area from which they are partially melted. Fertile source areas, such as metasomatized mantle or sedimentary rock, are usually themselves a product of some sort of metal concentration process. Felsic magmas crystallize to form granites, or their extrusive equivalents, and are associated with concentrations of elements such as Sn, W, U, Th, Li, Be, and Cs, as well as Cu, Mo, Pb, Zn, and Au. Incompatible elements in felsic magmas are concentrated into the products of very small degrees of partial melting or into the residual magma at an advanced stage of crystallization. Such processes do not, however, very often result in economically viable ore deposits. Crystal fractionation in mafic magmas, on the other hand, results in important concentrations of elements such as Cr, Ti, Fe, and V, while associated sulfide immiscibility in these rocks results in accumulations of PGE, Cu, Ni, and Au. Layered mafic intrusions are very important exploration targets for this suite of metals worldwide. Primary diamond deposits represent the very unusual situation where deep-seated mafic magma vents to the surface as explosive diatreme-maar type volcanoes, bringing with them older, xenocrystic diamond from fertilized mantle. In both mafic and felsic magmas the latter stages of crystallization are accompanied by the exsolution of a dominantly aqueous and carbonic fluid phase that ultimately plays a very important role in ore formation. It is this process that is the subject of Chapter 2.

FURTHER READING

For those readers wishing to delve further into magmatic ore-forming processes, the following references to books and journal special issues will help:

Economic Geology, volume 80 (1985) Special Issue on the Bushveld Complex.

Kirkham, R.V. *et al.* (eds) (1997) *Mineral Deposit Modeling*. Geological Association of Canada, Special Paper 40.

Misra, K.C. (2000) *Understanding Mineral Deposits*. Dordrecht: Kluwer Academic Publishers, 845 pp.

Naldrett, A.J. (1989) *Magmatic Sulfide Deposits*. Oxford Monographs on Geology and Geophysics. Oxford: Clarendon Press, 186 pp.

Naldrett, A.J. (1999) World-class Ni–Cu–PGE deposits: key factors in their genesis. *Mineralium Deposita*, 34, 227–40.

Taylor, R.P. and Strong, D.F. (eds) (1988) Recent advances in the geology of granite-related mineral deposits. *Canadian Institute of Mining and Metallurgy*, special volume 39, 445 pp.

Whitney, J.A. and Naldrett, A.J. (1989) Ore deposition associated with magmas. *Reviews in Economic Geology*, volume 4. El Paso, TX: Society of Economic Geologists, 250 pp.

CHAPTER TWO

Magmatic-hydrothermal ore-forming processes

TOPICS

CASE STUDIES

2.1 INTRODUCTION

In Chapter 1 emphasis was placed on the concentration of metals during the igneous processes associated specifically with magma formation and its subsequent cooling and crystallization. Little mention was made in the previous chapter of aqueous solutions (or hydrothermal fluids), even though it is well known that such fluids have often played a role in either the formation or modification of various magmatic deposits. The interaction between igneous and hydrothermal processes is an extremely important one for the

formation of a wide variety of ore deposit types, especially in near surface environments where magmas and fluids are spatially and genetically linked. This chapter introduces the concept of "magmatic-hydrothermal" fluids and concentrates on those fluids specifically derived from within the body of magma itself. Particular emphasis is given to the fluids derived from *granitic magmas* crystallizing in the Earth's crust.

There is little doubt that the majority of ore deposits around the world either are a direct product of concentration processes arising from the circulation of hot, aqueous solutions through the Earth's crust, or have been significantly modified by such fluids. A wide variety of ore-forming processes are associated with hydrothermal fluids and these can be applied to both igneous and sedimentary environments, and at pressures and temperatures that range from those applicable at shallow crustal levels to those deep in the lithosphere. Many different types of fluids are involved in hydrothermal ore-forming processes. The most primitive or "juvenile" of these are the magmatic-hydrothermal fluids that originate from magmas as they cool and crystallize at various levels in the Earth's crust, and a number of important ore deposit types are related to the concentration of metals that arise from circulation of such solutions. This chapter has particular relevance to ore deposits such as the large family of porphyry Cu and Mo deposits, as well as the "high-sulfidation" epithermal Au–Ag deposits that often represent the surface or volcanic manifestations of porphyry deposits. In addition, the formation of greisen-related Sn–W ores, polymetallic skarn mineralization, and pegmatite-related deposits are also explained in this chapter. Discussion of processes involved in the formation of hydrothermal ores that are not directly linked to magmatic activity follows in Part 2 of the book (Chapter 3).

2.2 SOME PHYSICAL AND CHEMICAL PROPERTIES OF WATER

Water (H_2O) is a liquid at room or standard temperature and pressure (STP). By contrast, other light molecules (CH_4, NH_3, H_2S, etc.) at STP exist as vapor and form gaseous hydrides. H_2O boils at a much higher temperature than the hydrides formed by other light elements. The main reason for this is that the hydrogen of a water molecule has a very strong affinity for oxygen such that

temporary hydrogen bonds are formed between it and the oxygen atoms of the neighboring water molecule (Figure 2.1). Water is, therefore, a liquid polymer at STP, and this is responsible for its many anomalous properties.

The physical properties of water that make it so important for chemical, biological, and geological processes include:

1 A high heat capacity, which means that it can conduct heat more readily than other liquids.

2 High surface tension implying that it can easily "wet" mineral surfaces.

3 A density maximum at temperatures just above the freezing point, which means that solid-H_2O (ice) will float on liquid-H_2O.

4 A high dielectric constant and, hence, an ability to dissolve more ionic substances, and in greater quantities, than any other natural liquid.

The last property is particularly relevant to the formation of ore deposits, since water is largely responsible for the dissolution, transport, and, hence, concentration of a wide range of elements and compounds, including metals, in the Earth's crust.

The chemical properties of water are dominated by its high dipole moment, a feature related to the fact that the water molecule is not symmetrical but comprises two hydrogen atoms that are not directly opposite one another but offset relative to the diametric axis of the single, much larger, oxygen atom (Figure 2.1). The H_2O molecule is, therefore, an electric dipole in which the center of positive charge does not coincide with the center of negative charge. Consequently, water

(a)   (b)

Figure 2.1 Idealized illustration of the water molecule and the nature of hydrogen bonding.

molecules can align themselves in an electrical field or orientate themselves around other charged ionic species. The clustering of water molecules around a dissolved ion is referred to as hydration, and this promotes the stability of ions in aqueous solution. The dielectric constant is a measure of a fluid's ability to separate ions or other dipoles and is a function of the number of dipoles per unit volume. The high dielectric constant of water also has the effect of enhancing dissolution and increasing solubility.

In nature water exists as three different phases, solid (or ice), vapor (or steam), and liquid (Figure 2.2a). H_2O-ice typically exists below about 0 °C and forms when water molecules are arranged in a hexagonal crystalline structure similar to many rock forming silicate minerals. When H_2O-ice melts only a small proportion of the hydrogen bonds are broken and H_2O-liquid retains a large measure of tetrahedral coordination. At temperatures close to the freezing point, this structure is more tightly knit than ice, which explains why the liquid form of water is more dense than its solid, and ice floats. The density of H_2O-liquid varies mainly as a function of temperature, but also pressure, as illustrated in Figure 2.2b. Density defines the difference between the liquid phase (typically around 1 g cm^{-3} at room temperatures) and its coexisting vapor (where densities are one to two orders of magnitude lower). Lines of equal density (or volume) in P–T space are referred to as isochores (Figure 2.2c). The phase boundary along which liquid and vapor are in equilibrium (i.e. between the triple point and the critical point in Figure 2.2a) defines the equilibrium or saturation vapor pressure, also known simply as the boiling point curve. On the Earth's surface, water effectively "boils" when equilibrium vapor pressure exceeds the prevailing atmospheric pressure and vapor can bubble off from the liquid.

As temperature rises and the density of H_2O-liquid decreases, the latter must coexist in equilibrium with a vapor whose partial vapor pressure (and density) is increasing. The boiling point temperature of pure water increases progressively with pressure until a maximum limit is reached, called the critical point, at 374 °C and 221 bar

(Figure 2.2a). The critical point is where it is no longer possible to increase the boiling point by increase of pressure and is effectively defined as the stage where there is no longer a physical distinction (i.e. a contrast in density) between liquid and vapor. The densities of liquid and vapor at the critical point have merged to a value of around 0.3 g cm^{-3} (Figure 2.2c). Since the terms "liquid" and "vapor" no longer have any meaning at the critical point, the term *"supercritical fluid"* (see section 2.3.3 below) is used to describe the homogeneous single phase that exists at pressures and temperatures above the critical point.

For an ideal gas which obeys the Gas Law, the relation between pressure (P), temperature (T), and volume (V) or density is expressed by the well known equation:

$$PV = RT \qquad [2.1]$$

where R is the gas constant.

Water only behaves as an ideal gas at very high temperatures and low pressures and equation [2.1] cannot, therefore, be used to predict aqueous phase relations under natural conditions in the Earth's crust. Consequently, many attempts have been made to introduce correction factors and modifications to the ideal gas equation such that it will more accurately reflect non-ideal behavior. The modified forms of the equation, of which there are many that have been derived by both empirical and theoretical means, are referred to as equations of state. The simplest, general form of an equation of state, which incorporates two corrective terms, is an expression known as van der Waals's equation:

$$P = [RT/(V-b)] - a(V) \qquad [2.2]$$

where a is the corrective term that accounts for the attractive potential between molecules, and b is a term that accounts for the volume occupied by the molecules.

A widely utilized equation of state for water at higher pressures and temperatures is the modified Redlich–Kwong equation, a more detailed discussion of which, together with its applicability to the chemical and thermodynamic properties

Figure 2.2 (a) Pressure–temperature phase diagram (not to scale) for pure H_2O showing the occurrences of the three phases (solid/ice, liquid water, water vapor/gas). The Triple Point, where solid, liquid, and vapor coexist, is at 0.008 °C and 0.06 bar. The Critical Point, beyond which there is no longer a physical distinction between liquid and vapor, is at 374 °C and 221 bar. The critical density is 0.322 g cm^{-3}.
(b) Schematic visual representation of H_2O fluid densities in relation to the boiling point curve and critical point, cp (after Helgeson, 1964).
(c) Part of the H_2O phase diagram showing actual variations of liquid and vapor equilibrium densities in pressure–temperature space (isochoral densities in g cm^{-3}).

of magmatic fluids, can be found in Holloway (1987).

2.3 FORMATION OF A MAGMATIC AQUEOUS PHASE

2.3.1 Magmatic water – where does it come from?

In the very early stages of the Earth's development there was probably very little water either in the atmosphere or on the surface of the planet. It seems likely that the incipient oceans developed as soon as the early crust had stabilized and rain water ponded on its surface. Substantial bodies of water (oceans or seas) existed by at least 3800 Myr ago as evident from the preservation of early Archean sediments and subaqueously deposited volcanic rocks. Some of this early water was derived from the degassing of volcanic magmas as they extruded onto the early crust, and is referred to as juvenile water. As plate tectonic processes progressively dominated Earth processes, water has been subjected to extensive recycling and it is likely that much of the fluid introduced by magmatic activity at the surface in more recent geological times is no longer juvenile, although it is still referred to as magmatic.

Subduction of oceanic crust that has been highly altered and hydrated by percolating sea water is a scenario that can be used to explain the H_2O contents of most arc-related andesitic and basaltic magmas. Arc-related magmas probably, therefore, contain dissolved water derived from mixing of primitive, mantle-derived fluids and sea water. A minor component from meteoric fluid (i.e. derived from the hydrosphere) is also possible. It is interesting to note that hydrous basaltic magmas that pond at the base of the crust, and whose heat is responsible for initiating anatexis of the lower crust to form granitic melts, may contribute their water to these melts. Whitney (1989) has suggested that underplating of a felsic magma chamber with a more dense mafic magma will result in diffusive transfer of elements and volatile species across the boundary layer.

Most of the water present in granitic magmas is, however, derived from the dehydration of minerals in the crust that were themselves melted to form the magma. The concept of "fluid-absent" or dehydration melting (i.e. where melting occurs without the presence of free water in the rock) is regarded as a realistic model for the generation of granites in the Earth's crust. The process can best be explained by considering the phase equilibria of essentially three minerals, namely muscovite, biotite, and hornblende. Although the detailed reactions are complex (see Clemens and Vielzeuf, 1987; Whitney, 1989; Burnham, 1997), the approximate conditions for dehydration melting of muscovite, biotite, and hornblende in relation to an average geothermal gradient are shown in Figure 2.3. The amount of H_2O contained within these three minerals decreases from around 8–10% in muscovite, to 3–5% in biotite and 2–3% in hornblende. Accordingly, the water activity in melts formed at breakdown of these hydrous minerals will vary considerably and a magma derived from anatexis of a muscovite-bearing precursor is likely to contain more dissolved water than one derived by melting of an amphibolite. Source material comprising dominantly muscovite and progressively buried along the 25 °C km^{-1} geotherm in Figure 2.3 will start to melt at point A. The water content of that first-formed magma will be 7.4 wt% (Burnham, 1997). If the source material contained mainly biotite as the hydrous phase, melting would begin at a significantly higher temperature and pressure, at point B, and in this case the first-formed melt would contain only 3.3 wt% H_2O. Likewise, dehydration melting of an amphibolitic source rock would only produce a melt at even higher P–T (point C, Figure 2.3), and this would contain 2.7 wt% H_2O. It is apparent, therefore, that granites of variable composition derived from different levels in the crust will *initially* contain very different H_2O contents.

It is clear that substantial volumes of magmatic water will be added to the Earth's crust as granite magmas progressively build the continents. It is relevant to point out that melting of a muscovite- or a muscovite + biotite-bearing source rock (represented in nature by rocks such as metasediments) is likely to yield peraluminous, S-type granite compositions (see section 1.3.4). The types of granites with which most Sn–W–U ore

Figure 2.3 Pressure–temperature plot showing the approximate conditions under which dehydration melting of muscovite-, biotite-, and hornblende-bearing assemblages would take place in relation to a 25 °C km^{-1} geothermal gradient. Melts formed at A, B, and C respectively are likely to contain different initial water contents. The solidus curves for granite and basalt are for water-saturated conditions (redrawn after Burnham, 1997).

assemblages are typically associated will, therefore, be relatively "wet," and contain high initial H_2O contents. S-type granites generally correlate with the relatively reduced "ilmenite-series" granites of Ishihara (1977), which inherit their low fO_2 character by melting of graphite-bearing metasedimentary material. By contrast, melting of biotite- or biotite + hornblende-bearing source material (represented by meta-igneous rocks) will yield metaluminous, I-type granite compositions. The porphyry Cu–Mo suite of ore deposits are associated globally with the latter and are typically relatively "dry" compared to S-type granites. Ishihara's "magnetite-series" granites are often, but not always, correlatable with I-type granites and these are characterized by higher fO_2 magmas (Ishihara, 1981).

2.3.2 H_2O solubility in silicate magmas

It is evident from the above discussion that magmas derived in different tectonic settings are likely to have had variable initial H_2O contents,

and that this is partly a function of the amount of water supplied by the source material during melting. There is, however, a maximum limit to the amount of H_2O that a given magma can dissolve, and this is defined by the solubility of water in any given magma. The solubility of H_2O in silicate magmas is determined mainly by pressure and to a lesser extent temperature. Figure 2.4a shows the results of experimental determinations of water content in melts of basaltic, andesitic, and granitic, or pegmatitic, compositions. The experiments suggest that water content is strongly dependent on pressure, with magmas at the base of the crust (circa 10 kbars) able to dissolve between 10 and 15% H_2O. It would also appear from Figure 2.4a that for any given pressure, felsic melts are able to dissolve more water than mafic ones.

When water dissolves in a magma it exists essentially as hydroxyl (OH) groups, although it is likely that at higher pressure and water contents discrete molecular water (H_2O) also exists (Stolper, 1982). The solubility of water in silicate

(a)

(b)

Figure 2.4 (a) Experimentally determined solubilities (in wt%) of H_2O in silicate melts as function of pressure. 1, basalt (at 1100 °C); 2, andesite (at 1100 °C); 3, granitic pegmatite (at 660–820 °C) (after Burnham, 1979). (b) Calculated estimates of the mole fraction of water (X_{H_2O}) (squared) in hydrous magmas at 1100 °C as a function of the water fugacity (f_{H_2O}) and pressure (after Stolper, 1982). H_2O-saturation is defined by the encompassing curve.

magmas is thought to be governed by the following equilibrium reaction:

$$H_2O_{(molecular)} + O^o \leftrightarrow 2OH \qquad [2.3]$$

where O^o refers to the oxygen that bridges or polymerizes the silicate structure of the magma. Low viscosity basaltic magmas comprise a smaller proportion of bridging O^o than more highly polymerized granitic melts. Basaltic melts may, therefore, accommodate fewer OH groups in O^o substituted sites, which could explain their inability to dissolve as much water as granite. At high pressures, however, water solubilities are essentially independent of magma composition. As a generalization, the mole fraction (squared) of water dissolved in any magma is proportional to the water fugacity (f_{H_2O} or the effective concentration in a non-ideal solution) of the magma and this is strongly pressure dependent. An indication of the amount of water dissolved in a hydrous melt as a function of pressure and water fugacity is provided in Figure 2.4b. At low pressures, where

total solubilities are low, OH groups are the dominant species of dissolved water in silicate magmas, whereas at higher pressures water solubility is dominated by molecular H_2O (Stolper, 1982).

2.3.3 The Burnham model

The importance of processes whereby zones of H_2O-saturated magma are formed and localized toward the roof of a granite intrusion, and their significance with respect to granitoid related ore deposits, was emphasized by the pioneering work of C. W. Burnham (1967, 1979, 1997). The concept has stimulated much fruitful research and continues to receive experimental and theoretical refinement through the work of Whitney (1975, 1989), Candela (1989a, b, 1991, 1992, 1997), Shinohara (1994), and many others.

When a granitic magma crystallizes the liquidus assemblage is dominated by anhydrous minerals and the concentration of dissolved incompatible constituents, including H_2O and other volatile species, increases by processes akin to Rayleigh

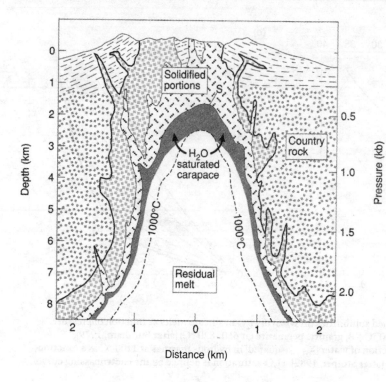

Figure 2.5 Section through a high-level granodioritic intrusion undergoing progressive crystallization and showing the hypothetical position in space of the H_2O-saturated granite solidus (S), as well as the zone (in gray) where aqueous fluid saturation occurs in the residual magma (after Burnham, 1979).

fractionation (see Chapter 1). At some stage, either early or late in the crystallization sequence, granitic magma will become water-saturated, resulting in the exsolution of an aqueous fluid to form a chemically distinct phase in the silicate melt. This process is called H_2O-saturation, but it is also often referred to as either *"boiling"* or *"vapor-saturation."* These terms often lead to semantic confusion and the footnote* should provide some clarity on the issue. Because the aqueous fluid has a density that is considerably lower (usually less than or around 1 g cm^{-3}, see Figure 2.2c) than that of the granitic magma (which is typically around 2.5 g cm^{-3}) it will

tend to rise and concentrate in the roof, or carapace, of the magma chamber. Although some of the original OH$^-$ in the magma may be utilized to form hydrous rock-forming minerals (such as biotite and hornblende), the amount of magmatic-hydrothermal water formed in this way can be very substantial.

The concept of the formation of a zone of H_2O-saturated magma in a high-level granite intrusion (2 km depth) which initially contained some 2.7 wt% H_2O is schematically illustrated in Figure 2.5. At these shallow depths H_2O-saturation is achieved after only about 10% crystallization, when the water content of the residual magma

---

* Unless the pressure, temperature, and composition of a magmatic aqueous solution are specified, one cannot say whether it exists as liquid or vapor, or a homogeneous supercritical phase (see Figure 2.2). In such a case it should be referred to by the generic term *"H_2O fluid."* Since the magmatic aqueous phase is so much less dense than the silicate melt from which it was derived, and because it may contain other low solubility volatile species such as CO_2 or SO_2, it is often referred to as the "vapor" or "volatile" phase. In addition, a homogeneous supercritical fluid is one that would effectively fill its container, and in this sense should be regarded as a gas or vapor, even though its density might be much higher than a gas as we might envision one at the Earth's surface. Accordingly, in this book the terms H_2O-saturation, boiling, degassing, and vapor-saturation are used interchangeably. The concepts are discussed again in section 2.4.4.

reaches 3.3 wt%. At low pressures such as those pertaining in Figure 2.5, the fluid does in fact boil, since the equilibrium vapor pressure equals that of the load pressure on the magmatic system and bubbles of gas (i.e. water vapor plus other volatiles such as CO_2) vesiculate. The process whereby vapor-saturation is achieved by virtue of decreasing pressure (i.e. because of upward emplacement of magma or mechanical failure of the chamber) is called "*first boiling*" and is particularly applicable to high level systems. As mentioned earlier, it is also possible to achieve saturation with respect to an aqueous fluid by progressive crystallization of dominantly anhydrous minerals under isobaric conditions, and this process is referred to specifically as "*second boiling.*" Second boiling generally occurs in more deep-seated magmatic systems and occurs only after a relatively advanced stage of crystallization. As shown later, the differences between first and second boiling, and more specifically the timing of H_2O fluid saturation relative to the progress of solidification of the magma, is very important in understanding how different granite related ore deposits form (see sections 2.6 and 2.7).

In addition to the strong dependence of boiling on pressure, it is obvious that fluid saturation will also be a function of the original water content of the initial melt. Melts that are more enriched in water and volatiles will achieve saturation earlier (relative to the progression of crystallization) than those that are poorer in these components. Experimental studies have confirmed the effects of pressure and initial water content on fluid saturation. Figure 2.6 compares the attainment of H_2O-saturation in a typical granite melt at high and low pressures, and in terms of crystallization sequences and initial H_2O content. In a situation deep in the Earth's crust (i.e. 8 kbar), where the original granite melt contained 2 wt% H_2O, crystallization would have commenced with nucleation of plagioclase at temperatures around 1100 °C, followed by the appearance of K-feldspar and quartz on the liquidus at lower temperatures (A–A'–A", Figure 2.6a). H_2O-saturation is achieved at temperatures that are just a few degrees above the solidus (at A') and only after over 80% of the melt had crystallized. The solidus is intersected

at 650 °C, at which point the granite has totally solidified. In the unlikely event that this granite was initially H_2O saturated at 8 kbar it would have contained at least 12 wt% H_2O and, as illustrated by the crystallization path B–B' (Figure 2.6a), would not have started to crystallize plagioclase until the melt temperature had cooled to around 750 °C. In this case solidification would have progressed quite rapidly between 750 and 650 °C and entirely in the presence of H_2O fluid.

At shallower levels in the crust (2 kbar) the situation is quite different (Figure 2.6b). The same granite magma composition would be saturated in water if it originally contained only 6–7 wt% H_2O and in this situation (path D–D') crystallization in the presence of H_2O fluid would take place over a wider temperature interval than at greater depth. The same crystallization path at 8 kbar would have existed over much of its temperature range in the H_2O undersaturated field. A granitic melt at 2 kbar with low initial water content (2 wt%; path C–C'–C" in Figure 2.6b) would also crystallize over a significant temperature interval in the undersaturated field, as with deeper in the crust, but in this case H_2O-saturation would be achieved at a higher temperature (around 700 °C at C') and after only some 60–70% crystallization.

These experimental data reinforce the concept that an aqueous fluid will exsolve from a granitic melt as a normal consequence of its crystallization. The Burnham model has great relevance to the formation of a wide range of ore deposit types. The porphyry Cu–Mo suite of deposits, epithermal precious metal ores, and polymetallic skarn type deposits are all examples of deposits whose origins are related to the processes conceptualized in this model. More detailed discussion of these deposit types is presented in later sections.

A note on the mechanical effects of boiling

An aqueous fluid constrained to the roof zone of a granite magma chamber will have limited effect on the concentration of metals unless it has the opportunity to circulate efficiently in and around the intrusive complex from which it is derived. The appearance of an exsolved H_2O fluid within a magma is, however, also accompanied by the

(a)

P = 8 kb

(b)

Figure 2.6 Plots of temperature versus H_2O content showing the crystallization sequences for granitic melts cooling and solidifying at (a) deep crustal levels (8 kbar) and (b) shallower crustal levels (2 kbar). The bold lines in both cases refer to the H_2O-saturation curve, and also the liquidus and solidus (after Whitney, 1989). Pl, plagioclase; Q, quartz; Af, alkali feldspar; L, melt; V, H_2O fluid. Crystallization paths refer to hypothetical situations where the granite was either initially oversaturated in H_2O (B–B′ and D–D′) or markedly undersaturated in H_2O (A–A′–A″ and C–C′–C″).

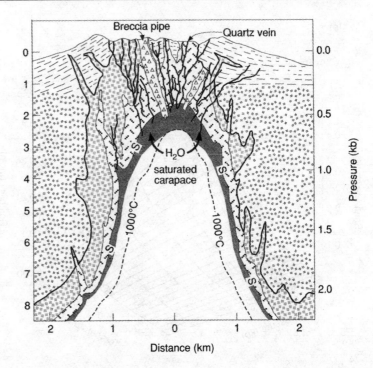

Figure 2.7 Section through a high-level granodioritic intrusion showing the nature of hydrofracturing and breccia pipe formation that could form around the apical portion of a granite body (after Burnham, 1979).

release of mechanical energy, since the volume per unit mass of silicate melt plus low density H_2O fluid is greater than the equivalent mass of H_2O saturated magma (Burnham, 1979). At shallow levels in the crust the volume change accompanying H_2O fluid production may be as much as 30% (at P_{total} of 1 kbar). This results in overpressuring of the chamber interior and can cause brittle failure of the surrounding rocks. The *hydrofracturing* that results from this type of failure usually forms fractures with a steep dip, because expansion of the rock mass takes place in the direction of least principal stress, which is usually in the horizontal plane. Hydrofractures tend to emanate from zones of H_2O fluid production in the apical portions of the granite body and may propogate into the country rock and even reach surface. This concept is schematized in Figure 2.7.

Experimental work has confirmed that high level granite emplacement enhances the possibility of brittle failure, both in the intrusion itself and in the surrounding country rocks (Dingwell *et al.*, 1997), thereby providing excellent ground

preparation for the efficient circulation of ore-bearing fluids. The factors that help to promote brittle failure in high level granite-related ore-forming systems include volatile saturation, which increases magma viscosity because of dehydration, bubble vesiculation, and rapid cooling.

2.4 THE COMPOSITION AND CHARACTERISTICS OF MAGMATIC-HYDROTHERMAL SOLUTIONS

2.4.1 Quartz veins – what do they tell us about fluid compositions?

Quartz veins are the products of precipitation of silica from hot aqueous solutions percolating through fractures in the Earth's crust. As pressure and temperature increases, water becomes an increasingly powerful solvent and can dissolve significant quantities of most rock-forming minerals. The solubility of quartz in water increases to about 8 wt% at temperatures of 900 °C and pressures up to 7 kbar (Anderson and Burnham, 1965). When dissolved in water, silica exists in

Figure 2.8 The variation of quartz solubility in aqueous solution as a function of (a) pressure and temperature and (b) temperature and pH (after Rimstidt, 1979).

the form H_4SiO_4. This is a typical constituent of hydrothermal solutions, and explains the common occurence of quartz in veins. The variation of quartz solubility in aqueous solution is, however, quite complex (Rimstidt, 1997) and other parameters in addition to P and T, such as pH and salinity, play an important role. The combined effects of P, T, and pH on quartz solubility in aqueous solutions is shown in Figure 2.8.

2.4.2 Major elements in magmatic aqueous solutions

In addition to silica, water can dissolve significant amounts of other major elements, such as the alkali metals. In a now classic experiment, Burnham (1967) reacted granite with pure water under a variety of conditions and showed that at high pressures and temperatures (10 kbar and 650 °C) the total solute content of the solution was about 9 wt% and comprised Si, Na and K *in proportions that are approximately the same as the granite eutectic* (or minimum melt) composition (Figure 2.9). This indicated that material precipitating from an aqueous solution at high P–T could have the same composition and mineralogy as granite that crystallized from a silicate melt (i.e. quartz + plagioclase + K feldspar in approximately equal proportions). At progressively lower pressures and temperatures, however, the total solute content of the solution decreased (to a minimum of about 0.7 wt% at 2 kbar), with the alkali metals (i.e. Na + K) also decreasing relative to silica (Figure 2.9). Close to the surface, therefore, the products precipitating from an aqueous hydrothermal solution comprise mainly silica.

In addition to their ability to dissolve cationic species (i.e. electron acceptors) such as Na^+, K^+, and Si^{4+}, magmatic aqueous solutions can also transport significant amounts of Ca^{2+}, Mg^{2+}, and Fe^{2+}, as well as a variety of anionic substances, in particular Cl^-. The anions are referred to as ligands (electron donors) and there are several others which are also commonly found in aqueous solutions, including HS^-, HCO_3^-, and SO_4^{2-}. These additional components are important in ore-forming processes and are discussed in more detail below. Further discussion of solution chemistry,

and of the ability of hydrothermal fluids to transport different metals, is presented in Chapter 3.

2.4.3 Other important components of magmatic aqueous solutions

Rocks are mainly made up of some ten major element oxides that are used to form the more abundant rock-forming minerals. Any given rock sample also comprises most other known elements, albeit for many of them in vanishingly small quantities. Their detection, for the most part, depends on the barriers imposed by analytical technology. To a certain extent, the same is true of the solute content of aqueous solutions in the Earth's crust, which, although dominated by a few highly soluble species, contain a wide range of other constituents, some of which are easily detectable, with the remainder occurring in only minute quantities. The trace constituents of an aqueous solution cannot simply be dismissed, especially in an ore-forming context, as it is these ingredients that distinguish an ore-forming fluid from one that is likely to be barren.

The typical composition of a magmatic aqueous solution in the Earth's crust is probably best obtained by direct analysis of waters produced adjacent to active volcanoes or geothermal springs. Although it is now known that such fluids are not entirely magmatic in origin (most have significant contributions from meteoric waters), their composition gives a reasonable indication of the types and quantities of dissolved components in aqueous solutions. Table 2.1 shows the chemical compositions of volcanic and geothermal fluids from a variety of places around the world. The data show that these natural fluids are variable in composition and this reflects the different rocks through which they have been circulating, and also, possibly, contamination by other types of fluid. Typically the solute content of magmatic fluids is dominated by the alkali and alkali-earth metal cations and by chlorine as the major ligand, although exceptions do occur (e.g. Rotorua; Table 2.1).

A few additional comments are relevant. There is often a significant amount of carbon dioxide associated with magmatic fluids and this is

Figure 2.9 Normalized compositions of aqueous fluid in equilibrium with a granitic pegmatite at pressures varying from 2 to 10 kbar (pressure shown next to each point on the diagram) and temperatures between 600 and 900 °C. The auxiliary diagram on the left shows the approximate variation in total solute content of the aqueous solutions as a function of pressure (after Burnham, 1967).

discussed again below. The amount of sulfur in magmatic fluids is generally low, but this may reflect the fact that at high crustal levels SO_2 partitions into the vapor phase on boiling. The oxidized and reduced forms of sulfur are essentially mutually exclusive and exist either as the SO_4^{2-} complex (with S^{6+}), or as the reduced HS^- complex (with S^{2-}). Relatively oxidized I-type magmatic fluids tend to comprise sulfur as SO_4^{2-}

which fractionates into the aqueous liquid phase. Porphyry Cu and Mo type deposits, therefore, are associated with abundant sulfide minerals in the form of pyrite and chalcopyrite. S-type magmas, which are more reducing because of equilibration with graphite-bearing metasediments, exsolve aqueous fluids that contain mainly H_2S or HS^- and have lower total sulfur contents. The presence of reduced sulfur species promotes the stability of

Table 2.1 Typical solute concentrations (in mg kg^{-1} or ppm) of the main components that comprise natural aqueous solutions from a variety of geothermal and volcanic fluids

Location	pH	Na$^+$	K$^+$	Ca^{2+}	Mg^{2+}	Fe^{2+}	Cl$^-$	HCO$_3^-$	SO$_4^{2-}$
White Island	1.1	8630	960	2010	3200	6100	7300	<1	6600
Mahagnao	5.8	20 340	4840	2900	95	<0.1	46 235	20	138
Rotorua	6.8	147	20	8	1	<0.1	13	560	<5
Sea water	–	10 560	380	400	1270	–	18 900	140	2710

Sea water is shown for comparison.
Source: after Giggenbach (1997).

sulfide minerals down to lower temperatures, such that the Sn and W oxide minerals (cassiterite and scheelite) associated with S-type granites tend to form early in the mineralizing sequence of these systems (Burnham, 1997).

It is important to point out that Table 2.1 illustrates the *major* dissolved components of natural aqueous solutions. The concentrations of ore metals, which should be regarded as trace constituents in hydrothermal fluids, are usually considerably lower than those shown in the table. Recent analytical developments have allowed measurements of magmatic ore-forming fluids *directly* from the tiny volumes of fluid trapped in individual fluid inclusions and this has provided some important new insights into the compositions of both the aqueous liquid and vapor phases in granite ore-forming systems.

Magmatic fluid compositions from fluid inclusion analysis

Ore-forming fluids can perhaps best and most directly be studied by examining the fluid inclusions (typically 5–30 μm in diameter) that exist particularly in quartz, but also in many other rock- and ore-forming minerals. Studies of porphyry Cu and Mo systems have shown that the early generation of fluid trapped in primary fluid inclusions is characterized by high temperatures and high salinities, and also provides evidence of liquid–vapor phase separation, or boiling (Roedder, 1984). The high salinities of these ore-forming fluids are confirmed by the fact that their associated fluid inclusions often contain daughter

crystals (i.e. tiny minerals that precipitated from the fluid on cooling after it was trapped within the inclusion; see inset microphotograph in Figure 2.10a). The majority of these daughter crystals are identified as halite (NaCl) and, to a lesser extent, sylvite (KCl), and confirm the fact that magmatic fluids contain significant amounts of K, Na, and Cl. A plot of fluid compositions derived from microthermometric homogenization experiments on individual fluid inclusions for a wide range of porphyry Cu deposits is shown in Figure 2.10a. A more detailed description of these data and their significance can be found in Roedder (1984).

A much more accurate and complete assessment of porphyry Cu-related ore fluid composition, however, is obtained from the quantitative analysis of individual fluid inclusions by laser-ablation inductively coupled plasma mass-spectrometry (LA-ICP-MS). This remarkable technique allows recognition and analysis of a wide range of cationic species in the tiny volume of inclusion fluid, and down to levels of about 1 ppm. Figure 2.10b shows the results of LA-ICP-MS analysis of two coexisting fluid inclusions in quartz from the Bajo de la Alumbrera porphyry Cu–Au deposit (Ulrich et al., 2001). The two coexisting fluid inclusions, one a vapor-rich inclusion and the other a hypersaline liquid-rich inclusion containing several daughter crystals, indicate that the ore fluid was boiling as it was trapped. Their analysis reflects the extent to which elements were partitioned between liquid and vapor, as well as the metal abundances in each. The plot shows that the majority of elements analyzed partition preferentially (by a factor

(a)

(b)

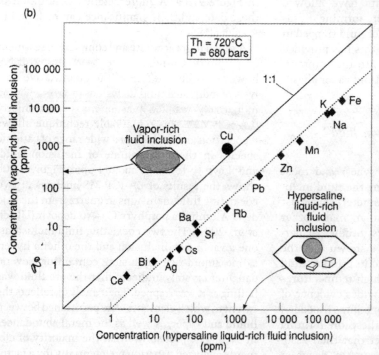

Figure 2.10 (a) Plot of the system H_2O–$NaCl$–KCl showing the compositional range of fluids in fluid inclusions from a variety of different porphyry Cu deposits (after Roedder, 1984). Inset microphotographs show (top) a hypersaline (containing a vapor bubble, saturated brine, and a daughter crystal) fluid inclusion, and (bottom) a trail of vapor-rich fluid inclusions. (b) Plot of element concentrations (obtained by laser-ablation ICP-MS analysis) in a vapor-rich fluid inclusion versus element concentrations in a related hypersaline liquid-rich fluid inclusion. Schematic illustrations of the nature of the two fluid inclusions analyzed in order to create the plot are shown next to the respective axes. The data pertain to the Bajo de la Alumbrera porphyry Cu–Au deposit in Argentina. The plot is redrawn after Ulrich *et al.* (2001).

of about 10 to 20 ×) into the liquid phase rather than the vapor (Figure 2.10b). As expected, the Na and K contents of the ore fluid are high, but so is the Fe content. The liquid also contains significant quantities of Mn, Cu, Pb, and Zn in solution. Interestingly, Cu behaves differently to the other metals in that it is preferentially fractionated into the vapor phase, a feature also previously noted by Lowenstern *et al.* (1991) and Heinrich *et al.* (1999).

2.4.4 Carbon dioxide in magmatic fluids

After water, CO_2 is the most common gas emanating from volcanic eruptions and its presence is important in a variety of ore-forming processes, albeit in a more obscure way than for H_2O. Many different studies have confirmed that the solubility of CO_2 in magmas is typically an order of magnitude lower than that of H_2O. It dissolves as molecular CO_2 in normal felsic or mafic melts, but in alkaline magmas it also exists as carbonate ionic complexes in solution (Lowenstern, 2001). As an indication, rhyolite and basalt melts at 3 kbar will normally contain between 1000 and 2000 ppm dissolved CO_2 compared to values at least 4–5 times higher in a leucitite melt. CO_2 solubilities, therefore, increase as a function of pressure and magma alkalinity.

Because CO_2 solubilities are much lower than those of H_2O, it follows that CO_2 will exsolve early such that vapors generated at an early stage of solidification will tend to be more CO_2-rich than those forming later. Carbon dioxide will partition preferentially into the vapor phase and it is probable that many normal magmas, both felsic and mafic, will be vapor-saturated at significant crustal depths, even to the mid-crust (Lowenstern, 2001). Other low solubility gases are also likely to be associated with the vapor phase created by early CO_2 saturation or effervescence. Volatiles that are generated in systems that have undergone protracted differentiation, or reach shallow crustal levels, will tend to be H_2O-dominated since the relatively insoluble gases like CO_2, as well as N_2 and others, will already have bubbled away. It is, therefore, possible for magmas to become volatile-saturated before, and independently of, H_2O fluid saturation. The presence of CO_2 in an evolving aqueous fluid within a crystallizing granite will promote immiscibility between vapor and saline liquid phases of the solution. Such processes can be very important during ore-forming processes since they promote the precipitation of metals from solution (Lowenstern, 2001). Effervescence of CO_2 from the fluid will also promote certain types of alteration in the host rocks and increase pH in the remaining fluid, further influencing ore-forming processes (see Chapter 3 for more discussion of these and related topics). Thus, although CO_2 does not appear to play a direct role in the transport and concentration of metals in hydrothermal solutions, it nevertheless has a role to play in the distribution and precipitation of metals, especially via the volatile or vapor phase.

2.4.5 Other important features of magmatic fluids

An important characteristic of magmatic aqueous solutions at low pressures is that they tend to segregate into two phases of differing densities and composition. This feature of hydrothermal solutions is often overlooked, and it also further complicates the description of these fluids. It is evident that the so-called boiling-point curve (Figure 2.2) is actually part of a solvus which separates low density H_2O from high density H_2O. As emphasized above, this distinction becomes meaningless in P–T space above the critical point (or the solvus) where densities of liquid and vapor have merged and only a single "fluid" phase exists. The critical point of pure water, at 374 °C, 220 bar, and 0.322 g cm^{-3}, migrates towards higher temperatures and pressures as dissolved salts (usually in the form of alkali chloride complexes) are added to water. A representation of the critical points for hydrothermal solutions of differing salinities and the effect on fluid densities (isochores) is shown in Figure 2.11a. The locus of critical points, as a function of increasing salinity, represents a solvus boundary which governs the existence or otherwise of immiscible behavior in aqueous solutions.

The phase relationships of magmatic aqueous solutions (brines) are also, therefore, dependent

Figure 2.11 (a) Boiling point (liquid–vapor) curves for pure water and for two aqueous solutions containing 10 and 25 wt% NaCl, showing the shift of critical point to higher temperatures and pressures with increasing salinity. Selected isochores, with relevant densities (in g cm^{-3}), are also shown for each of the three cases. The diagram is redrawn after Roedder and Bodnar (1980). (b) A projection of the system H$_2$O–NaCl showing the solvus curves, for a variety of pressures between 500 and 1750 bars, that define whether a homogeneous aqueous solution will segregate into two immiscible phases or not (after Bodnar *et al.*, 1985).

on this solvus which, depending on the pressure, temperature, and composition of the fluid, dictates whether a single homogeneous phase exists above the critical point, or two immiscible phases below it. Figure 2.11b shows a projection of the H$_2$O–NaCl system onto the T–X plane in which the solvus curves for various pressures are shown. The phase relationships show that, for a granite at

600 bar in which an exsolved H$_2$O fluid has formed with a composition at point A, the fluid exists below the relevant solvus. Such a fluid must segregate into two phases, a small proportion of brine containing 78 wt% NaCl (A″) and a more voluminous low density fluid (A′) containing only 1 wt% NaCl (Burnham, 1997). The same granite at 1 kbar (point B, Figure 2.11b) would also

exsolve two aqueous solutions, but with different compositions. The brine would in this case contain 53 wt% NaCl (B″), whereas the remaining fluid would have 2 wt% NaCl (B′). The granite at 2 kbar (point C), however, would exist above the solvus (which falls off the diagram in Figure 2.11b) and would exsolve a *single*, homogeneous fluid phase containing about 12.5 wt% NaCl. It should be noted that the presence of CO_2 in the fluid will promote immiscibility to much higher pressures and, as mentioned above, this is one of the important roles that this common gas has to play in ore-forming processes. These features of an H_2O fluid exsolving from a granite magma are extremely important to the understanding of ore-forming processes because metals partition themselves differently between the high solute content brine and the more pure H_2O phase. This topic is discussed in more detail in section 2.6 below.

The discussion of magmatic-hydrothermal fluids and ore-forming processes in the preceding sections has given rise to some confusing terminology. As a summary, and before we proceed further, the following definitions are presented in order to clarify some of the concepts referred to thus far.

• **H_2O-saturation.** At some stage, either early or late in the crystallization sequence, granitic magma will become water saturated, resulting in the formation of a chemically distinct, aqueous phase in the silicate melt.

The magmatic aqueous phase can exist as a liquid, vapor, or homogeneous supercritical fluid. In the last case it should also be regarded as gas since it is a substance that would fill its container. For this reason the magmatic aqueous fluid is often simply referred to as the "*vapor phase.*"

• **Vapor-saturation**, also referred to as boiling, occurs when the equilibrium vapor pressure of the magma equals that of the load pressure on the system and bubbles of gas (i.e. steam or water vapor, CO_2, N_2, SO_2, H_2S, etc.) nucleate in the magma. Vapor-saturation of low solubility volatiles such as CO_2 may be unrelated to, and can precede, H_2O-saturation.

The process of H_2O-saturation can be achieved in two ways, either by progressive crystallization of magma, or by decreasing the pressure of the system:

• **First boiling** refers to the case where vapor-saturation is achieved by virtue of decreasing pressure (i.e. because of upward emplacement of magma or mechanical failure of the chamber) and is particularly applicable to high level systems. It reflects the fact that solubilities of volatile phases in a melt increase as a function of pressure.

• **Second boiling** refers to the achievement of H_2O fluid saturation by progressive crystallization of dominantly anhydrous minerals under isobaric conditions. It pertains to more deep-seated magmatic systems and occurs only after a relatively advanced stage of crystallization.

• **Immiscibility** refers to the tendency for brine solutions at low pressures, or in the presence of CO_2, to segregate into two phases, one a dense, more saline brine and the other a lower density, low salinity aqueous solution.

2.5 A NOTE ON PEGMATITES AND THEIR SIGNIFICANCE TO GRANITE-RELATED ORE-FORMING PROCESSES

Pegmatites are commonly regarded as rocks derived from magma that *may* have crystallized in the presence of a magmatic aqueous fluid. They are defined as very coarse-grained rocks, typically associated with granites and comprising the major granite rock-forming minerals. The large crystals of quartz, feldspar, and muscovite that make up the bulk of most pegmatites are often extracted for industrial purposes. In addition, they can comprise a wide variety of minor minerals of more exotic and semi-precious character, such as tourmaline, topaz, and beryl. Pegmatites also contain concentrations of the large ion lithophile and high field strength elements, such as Sn, W, U, Th, Li, Be, B, Ta, Nb, Cs, Ce, and Zr. Their origin is a topic that provides a fruitful area of research because of the clues they provide for ore-forming processes and igneous petrogenesis in general.

Although there are several classification schemes for pegmatites, the model by Cerny (1991) is particularly convenient because it separates them into characteristic metal assemblages that have an implied genetic connotation. Two families of pegmatites are recognized, the Nb–Y–F suite associated with sub-alkaline to metaluminous (largely I-type) granites and the Li–Cs–Ta suite, also enriched in boron, and typically associated with peraluminous (dominantly S-type) granites. Some pegmatites clearly form as the result of small degrees of partial melting and form minor dykes and segregations in high grade metamorphic terranes. Other pegmatites are spatially associated with the cupola zones of large granite intrusions and may be genetically linked to the most highly differentiated, water-saturated portions of such bodies. Many pegmatites, on the other hand, are almost certainly not the products of water-saturated granite crystallization. The origin of pegmatites is one of the more fascinating problems in igneous petrology and, even though the processes are now well understood, they remain complex and somewhat contentious. Both the early and later developments in the understanding of these rocks are instructive to ore-forming processes, and are discussed below.

2.5.1 Early models of pegmatite genesis

Prior to the classic paper by Jahns and Burnham (1969), pegmatites were viewed as the products of extreme crystal fractionation of mainly granitic magmas. Experimental work, however, suggested that pegmatites were distinguished from "normally textured" granite by crystallization in the presence of an exsolved H_2O fluid phase. More specifically, Jahns and Burnham (1969) suggested that the transition from granite to pegmatite marked the point at which H_2O fluid saturation occurred in the crystallization sequence and that pegmatites, therefore, formed in the presence of an immiscible H_2O + volatile fraction. The existence of H_2O fluid in the magma was used to explain the large crystal size of pegmatites, the latter growing, because of extended crystallization due to either volatile-related depression of the granite solidus, or more efficient diffusion of major elements into low viscosity H_2O fluid-saturated magma. Mineral zonation in pegmatites was attributed largely to the separation of relatively dense silicate melt from the low density H_2O fluid phase, and the attendant segregation of alkalis such that Na remained in the silicate

melt and K partitioned in the aqueous phase. In addition, it was envisaged that precipitation of dissolved constituents from the H_2O fluid phase could explain the pockets of exotic minerals (including gemstone-quality crystals formed in an open space or vug from fluids enriched in Li, B, Cs, Be, etc.) so often characteristic of pegmatites. The Jahns and Burnham model was particularly attractive because it was supported by experimental evidence demonstrating that an aqueous fluid at high temperatures and pressures is capable of dissolving very significant proportions of solute (see Figure 2.9).

2.5.2 More recent ideas on the origin of pegmatites

The Jahns–Burnham model represented a major advance in the understanding of pegmatite genesis, as well as the crystallization and mineralization of granites generally. More recent work, however, has shown that there are other factors, in addition to H_2O-saturation, which need to be considered in order to fully understand the formation of these rocks and their associated ore deposits. The research of D. London and co-workers (1990, 1992, 1996) in particular has shown that it is possible to generate pegmatites from H_2O under-saturated granitic melts by *undercooling* the magma below its normal liquidus temperature. They have demonstrated experimentally that kinetic delays in the initiation of crystallization in felsic magmas that are rapidly undercooled means that melts persist in a metastable condition and result in non-equilibrium crystal growth. Many of the features of pegmatites, including mineral zonation, large grain size, variable textures, and highly fractionated chemistry, can be replicated experimentally in terms of the slow crystallization response to undercooling of granitic melts. This work has enabled pegmatites to again be explained by magmatic crystal fractionation process (as had been suggested prior to the Jahns–Burnham model) rather than to silicate melt–H_2O fluid exsolution and alkali element segregation. The London model has removed a fundamental difficulty always faced by the Jahns–Burnham model, namely how to explain the symmetric mineral zonation typical of so many pegmatites in terms of segregation mechanisms that, being gravitationally induced, should have been intrinsically asymmetric. It also provided a rather neat explanation for why pegmatitic textures are uncommon in more mafic rocks. Mafic melts nucleate crystals much more readily than their felsic equivalents, resulting in a tendency toward equilibrium crystallization conditions and the formation of more uniform textures.

It should be emphasized, however, that more recent work on pegmatites has not, by any means, precluded the important role of water in the formation of these rocks. A fluid inclusion study of the Tanco Li–Cs–Ta pegmatite in Manitoba, Canada, showed that it crystallized from a mixture of alumina–silicate melt plus H_2O (with minor CO_2) fluid over a temperature interval that extended from about 700 °C down to below 300 °C (Thomas et al., 1988). These observations were, in fact, interpreted as support for the Jahns–Burnham model. The processes are further complicated when one takes into account the major influence of other volatile species, such as B, F, and P, on pegmatite formation (London, 1996). These three elements, individually and collectively, lower the granite solidus temperature to below 500 °C and increase the range of temperatures over which magmatic crystallization occurs. They also dramatically increase the solubility of H_2O in the melt and promote the crystallization of quartz. In a study of the Ehrenfriedersdorf Sn–W–B–F–P-rich pegmatites of the Erzgebirge in southeast Germany, it has been shown that fluid inclusions are made up of coexisting silicate-rich H_2O-poor and silicate-poor H_2O-rich melts (Thomas et al., 2000). On progressive reheating from 500 to 700 °C at 1 kbar pressure, the latter inclusions become poorer in H_2O, whereas the former undergo a steady increase in water content (Figure 2.12). At just above 700 °C the two inclusion populations are effectively identical, with both containing about 20 wt% H_2O. This indicates that the silicate-rich H_2O-poor and silicate-poor H_2O-rich melts were in fact derived from a single, originally homogeneous, melt. Even at low pressures (the Ehrenfriedersdorf pegmatites crystallized at about 1 kbar) these

Figure 2.12 Plot of H_2O content versus temperature for rehomogenized (at 1 kbar) silicate-rich H_2O-poor (A) and silicate-poor H_2O-rich (B) melt inclusions from the Ehrenfriedersdorf pegmatite. The curve defines a solvus with a critical point (above which there is no longer a distinction between the two melts and they are miscible) at about 700 °C and 20 wt% H_2O content (after Thomas et al., 2000).

B–F–P-rich pegmatitic magmas exhibit complete miscibility between silicate melt and aqueous fluid such that water can be regarded as infinitely soluble in this melt. On cooling below 700 °C, however, immiscibility occurs to form two coexisting melts. One of these is a silicate melt with low H_2O content, while the other is a silicate melt with very high H_2O content. The latter, however, has a density, viscosity, and diffusivity that is more akin to an aqueous solution than to a silicate melt. Although its properties are water-like, it is by definition different from the exsolved H_2O fluid envisaged to have formed in the Jahns–Burnham model.

It is apparent, therefore, that a magmatic aqueous phase has to be represented by a fluid that is more complex than simply exsolved H_2O. At high pressures and temperatures water can contain significant quantities of dissolved silica and alkalis which, on cooling, will yield precipitates with bulk compositions not dissimiliar to a granite. At lower pressures H_2O fluid will exsolve from a normal granitic magma, such that crystallization will occur in the presence of an aqueous phase. At low pressures and in the presence of significant concentrations of elements such as B, F, and P, granite melt solidus temperatures are significantly depressed and H_2O solubility increases to such an extent that H_2O-saturation might not occur at all. In this case two immiscible melts form, one of which is H_2O-rich and has physical properties akin to an aqueous solution with high solute content. Pegmatites could conceivably form in all these situations.

2.6 FLUID–MELT TRACE ELEMENT PARTITIONING

The rise of magma to shallow levels of the Earth's crust will inevitably result in saturation with respect to an aqueous fluid or vapor phase. Even though the diffusivity of H_2O is relatively low in most felsic magmas, the buoyant, low density H_2O-fluid, together with entrained melt and crystals, will move to the apical portions of the magma chamber (Candela, 1991). In an equilibrium situation, trace components of the magma must then partition themselves between melt, crystals, and H_2O-fluid. The extent to which trace components, such as metals, distribute themselves between these phases is a process that is potentially quantifiable in terms of partition coefficients. It is possible to derive equations that express the partitioning of trace constituents between melt and H_2O-fluid in exactly the same way as was discussed for the partitioning of trace elements between melt and crystals in section 1.3.4 of Chapter 1. However, considerations of melt–fluid partitioning are complicated by the fact that it is necessary to consider partitioning behavior prior to water saturation, and also because the sequestration of incompatible constituents by the H_2O-fluid depends on solubilities of both the fluid and the magma from which it is derived. A detailed account of the quantification of melt–fluid partitioning behavior is provided by the work of Candela and co-workers, summarized in Candela and Holland (1984, 1986), Candela (1989a, b, 1992), and Candela and Piccoli (1995). Before the results of this work are discussed in more detail, brief mention will first be made of

some of the classic experimental work that provided initial insights into why hydrothermal fluids are such efficient scavengers of metals and, therefore, so important in ore-forming processes. Again, more details on this topic are provided in Chapter 3.

2.6.1 The classic experiments of H. D. Holland and others

In a now classic set of experiments, Holland (1972) showed that the solubilities of many metals in a magmatic H_2O-fluid are strongly dependent on its Cl^- concentration, in addition to other parameters such as temperature and pH. When experimentally reacting an aqueous solution with a granitic melt it was observed that metals such as Zn, Mn, Fe, and Pb are strongly partitioned into the H_2O-fluid and that the ratio of metal concentration between melt and fluid is exponentially proportional to the Cl^- concentration (Figure 2.13a and b). These experiments demonstrated quite clearly that certain metals will only readily dissolve in an aqueous solution if the latter contains appreciable amounts of the chloride anion (Cl^-). Furthermore, metals will exhibit different magnitudes of partitioning into H_2O-fluid according to their variable abilities to bond, or form complexes, with Cl^-.

Figure 2.13b also shows that the total Fe content of the H_2O-fluid varies as a function of temperature, and is higher for any value of Cl^- at 750 °C than it is at 650 °C. This confirms the intuitive notion that solubility normally increases as a function of temperature. The diagram also shows that the Al content of the fluid remains constant (because the total Fe content changes in the same way as does the total Fe/Al ratio) and that it is not affected by the Cl^- concentration of the aqueous fluid. This indicates that not all metals will have their solubilities controlled by Cl^- concentrations in the fluid (although they may still be affected by the presence of other ligands) and that some metals may not even choose to partition into the aqueous phase at all.

The dependence of metal solubility on Cl^- concentrations presupposes that the ligand itself will partition effectively into the H_2O-fluid phase. Kilinc and Burnham (1972) and Shinohara *et al.*

Figure 2.13 (a) The ratio of the concentration of Zn in H_2O-fluid $[Zn]^f$ to that in a granitic melt $[Zn]^m$ as a function of the Cl^- concentration; experiments carried out at various temperatures between 770 and 880 °C and pressures between 1.4 and 2.4 kbar (after Holland, 1972). (b) The total Fe content (left ordinate) and the total Fe to Al ratio (right ordinate) in H_2O-fluid that equilibrated with a granitic melt as a function of the Cl^- concentration; experiments carried out at temperatures of 650 and 750 °C and a pressure of 2.0 kbar (after Burnham, 1967).

(1989) have confirmed experimentally that chloride partitions strongly into the magmatic aqueous phase, according to the reaction:

$$Cl^- \text{ (melt)} + OH^- \text{ (melt)} \Rightarrow HCl \text{ (fluid)} + O^{2-} \text{ (melt)} \quad [2.4]$$

Reaction between granitic melt and a chloride-bearing aqueous fluid showed that the Cl^- ion partitions strongly into the fluid, but that the value of the partition coefficient varies in a complex fashion (Figure 2.14). At low pressures where the

H_2O-fluid phase segregates into two immiscible fractions (one vapor-rich and the other liquid-rich), the partitioning of Cl^- into the H_2O-fluid phase is fixed by the saturation of Cl^- in the coexisting vapor-rich phase. At higher pressures the partitioning of Cl^- into a homogeneous H_2O-fluid phase (i.e. above the critical point) is controlled by the concentration (or activity) of Cl^- in the melt, but increases with increasing pressure.

The early experiments of Holland and others showed how important the composition, and more specifically the nature and content of the ligand

Figure 2.14 Variations in the concentration of Cl⁻ in a silicate melt with that in an exsolved H_2O-fluid for a variety of different pressures. Cl⁻ is seen to be partitioned strongly into the aqueous phase relative to the melt. At low pressures, where liquid–vapor immiscibility occurs (0.6 and 1.2 kbar), the concentration of Cl⁻ is fixed by the saturation of Cl⁻ in the coexisting vapor-rich phase; at higher pressures, for any given concentration of Cl⁻ in the melt a homogeneous H_2O-fluid phase will contain more Cl⁻ at higher pressures (after Shinohara *et al.,* 1989).

species, of the aqueous fluid phase is to metal solubility in aqueous solutions. Metal contents of aqueous solutions are not, of course, only dependent on the Cl⁻ concentration and many other factors affect the ability of hydrothermal fluids to transport metals. A more complete discussion of this topic is presented in section 3.4 of Chapter 3. In the section below, a more detailed consideration is given to the partitioning of metals between silicate melt and an exsolved magmatic H_2O-fluid in the light of recent theoretical and experimental work.

2.6.2 Complications in the fluid–melt partitioning of metals

The partitioning of metals between a silicate melt and an exsolved H_2O-fluid is a complex matter. The extent to which metals are partitioned between melt and fluid is variable and is largely

controlled by the Cl⁻ (and other ligand) concentration of the fluid which, in an evolving system, itself changes continuously. In addition, however, factors such as temperature, pressure, the amount of water exsolved relative to the amount of water remaining in the silicate melt (i.e. when H_2O-fluid saturation is achieved during crystallization), and the oxygen fugacity (fO_2) of the silicate–fluid system also influence metal partitioning. This means that a partition coefficient cannot be regarded as a constant because it pertains only to a very specific, transient, set of conditions. Melt–fluid partition coefficients, therefore, show wide variations as the magmato-hydrothermal system evolves.

Candela (1989) pointed out that the metal content of an exsolved H_2O-fluid will depend to a large extent on when in the crystallization sequence water saturation is achieved. This is because crystal–melt partitioning can be as efficient a means of distributing and concentrating trace metals in a magma as can H_2O fluid–melt partitioning. It is particularly important to distinguish between "first boiling" (when vapor-saturation is caused by pressure decrease) and "second boiling" (when crystallization of a dominantly anhydrous assemblage causes the H_2O content of the residual melt to rise to the saturation water content for a given level of emplacement). First boiling processes are simpler to model mathematically and pertain to ore-forming processes associated with high level granite intrusions such as those associated with porphyry Cu and Mo deposits. Second boiling requires a more complicated mathematical model since the metals have to partition among melt, crystal, and H_2O fluid phases.

Fluid–melt partitioning during "first boiling"

Candela (1989) has provided equations that quantify the distribution of a trace component between H_2O fluid and silicate melt for a first boiling situation. These particular equations are applicable to those components whose partitioning does not change as a function of the ligand concentration of the fluid. They are somewhat similar in form to the exponential equations applicable to fractional melting and crystallization presented in Chapter 1, and are expressed as:

$$C_{fluid}^i = D_{fluid/melt}^i C_O^i (1 - [(1 - F)C_O^{water}])^{D_{fluid/melt}-1}$$

[2.5]

where: C_{fluid}^i is the concentration of a component (i) in the H_2O fluid at any instant in the evolution of the aqueous phase; $D_{fluid/melt}^i$ is the H_2O fluid/silicate melt partition coefficient for the component (i); C_O^i is the initial concentration of the component (i) in the silicate melt (defined at the instant of water saturation); C_O^{water} is the initial concentration of water in the silicate melt (defined at the instant of water saturation); and F is the ratio of the mass of water in the silicate melt (at any given instant after water saturation) to the initial mass of water in the silicate melt.

The concentration of the component (i) in the associated silicate melt (C_{melt}^i) is simply given by:

$$C_{melt}^i = C_{fluid}^i / D_{fluid/melt}^i$$

[2.6]

where C_{fluid}^i is the value obtained from equation [2.5].

Knowing the magnitude of the partition coefficient ($D_{fluid/melt}^i$), which changes as a function of pressure and, hence, saturation water content, the concentrations of a component such as chloride in an evolving aqueous phase, as well as in the associated silicate melt, can be calculated. Diagrammatic representations of Cl concentration trends in an evolving silicate melt–H_2O-fluid system are shown in Figure 2.15. The appearance of a magmatic aqueous fluid will typically result in depletion of the volatile component in the melt (Figure 2.15b) and this will be accompanied by a concomitant decrease of the same component in the H_2O-fluid (Figure 2.15a), as the system evolves toward complete solidification. The efficiency with which the aqueous phase extracts components, such as chlorine or other chloride-complexing metals, from the melt is effectively measured by the ratio of the total or integrated amount of the component in the H_2O-fluid to the amount initially present in the melt at the time of water-saturation (Candela, 1989). The efficiency

Figure 2.15 Calculated concentrations of chlorine in (a) an aqueous fluid exsolved from a granitic magma, and (b) the residual magma itself, both as a function of the proportion of water remaining in the melt. The calculations were carried out for a situation where water saturation is achieved in a "first boiling" scenario with a magma rising adiabatically upwards from 5.4 km depth (where water content at saturation is 5 wt%) to the surface (after which 1 wt% water remains in the rock). C_O^{Cl} is assumed to be 4000 ppm and $D_{fluid/melt}^{Cl}$ is calculated to vary from 39 at the point of water saturation to 1 as the magma reaches the surface (after Candela, 1989b).

factor will be dependent not only on obvious criteria such as $D_{fluid/melt}^i$, but also on parameters such as F (the ratio of the mass of water in the silicate melt at any given instant after water saturation to the initial mass of water in the silicate melt). Note that not all volatile components will act in the same way, as is the case for fluorine, whose concentration in the melt is predicted to remain relatively constant during first boiling (Figure 2.15b).

Calculation of fluid–melt partitioning is more complex for components such as Cu or Zn, whose behavior not only varies as a function of pressure, but is also strongly controlled by the Cl⁻ concentration of the fluid phase. Likewise, the partitioning of metals into the aqueous fluid phase in a situation where "second boiling" has taken place also involves many additional assumptions and a more complex mathematical derivation. The detailed discussion of both of these situations is beyond the scope of this book, and the interested reader is referred to Candela (1989) for more detail. It is pertinent to note, however, that any metal which bonds strongly with Cl⁻ in an aqueous solution (such as Cu) will tend to exhibit partitioning behavior that is similar to that shown in Figure 2.15. In the case of metals such as copper, therefore, the maximum concentration into the aqueous fluid occurs immediately after water-saturation has been achieved. By contrast, metals such as molybdenum, which do not bond strongly with Cl⁻, and are not, therefore, controlled by concentrations of this ligand, partition differently and may be most efficiently concentrated in the very last portions of the evolving H_2O-fluid phase. The contrasting behavior of Cu and Mo in the magmato-hydrothermal environment, suggested by these theoretical calculations, has been confirmed by direct experimental evidence and this is discussed in the following section.

2.6.3 Experimental confirmation of Cu, Mo, and W partitioning behavior

In a series of experiments run at 750 °C and 1.4 kbar, Candela and Holland (1984) were able to measure the extent to which Cu and Mo partition between granitic melt and a coexisting aqueous fluid containing both Cl⁻ and F⁻. The results of these experiments are shown in Figure 2.18 and clearly demonstrate that Cu is a metal whose partitioning behavior is strongly controlled by the Cl⁻ concentration of the fluid phase, whereas Mo remains unaffected by the latter. The value of $D^{Cu}_{fluid/melt}$ varies from about 1, for low salinity fluids, up to about 50 at high salinities (Figure 2.16a) and is determined by the relationship $D^{Cu}_{fluid/melt} = 9.1[Cl^-]$. By contrast, although Mo is also preferentially

partitioned into the H_2O-fluid ($D^{Mo}_{fluid/melt} = 2.5$), its partition coefficient is fixed and remains constant irrespective of the Cl⁻ concentration (Figure 2.16b). It is interesting to note that the partitioning behavior of both Cu and Mo is unaffected by the presence of F⁻ in the aqueous solution. This is because fluorine tends to partition more strongly into the silicate melt ($D^F_{fluid/melt} = 0.2{-}0.3$) than into the aqueous fluid and is, therefore, generally not present as a complexing agent for metals in the fluid phase.

The fluid–melt partitioning behavior of W is not as well constrained as that for Cu and Mo, although experiments do suggest that its properties are similar to those for Mo, but that its partition coefficient is even lower ($D^W_{fluid/melt} \approx 1$: Manning and Henderson, 1984; Keppler and Wyllie, 1991). However, it is also known that W behaves as an incompatible element in terms of its *crystal–melt* partitioning behavior in relatively reduced (i.e. S-type) granitic magmas solidifying at some depth in the Earth's crust. By contrast, Mo behaves in a more compatible manner in the same magma types such that fractionation will tend to result in increasing W/Mo ratios (Candela, 1992). The efficiency of metal extraction by an aqueous phase exsolving late in the crystallization sequence of such a granite will, therefore, favor concentration of W over Mo, despite the lower $D_{fluid/melt}$ values. The crystal–melt partitioning behavior of W also contrasts with that of copper, which tends to act as a compatible element in virtually any magma composition (Candela and Holland, 1986). A value of $D^{Cu}_{crystal/melt} = 3$ was calculated for a crystallizing basaltic magma composition and is likely to be >1 for a granite too, since Cu is able to substitute very efficiently into accessory sulfide phases and, to a lesser extent, into biotite and magnetite.

It is apparent that both fluid–melt and crystal–melt partition coefficients play an important role in the distribution of metals in and around crystallizing granite plutons. These parameters, when coupled with considerations of granite type, depth of emplacement, and the timing of water-saturation relative to the crystallization sequence, can be used to explain the nature and

Figure 2.16 (a) The relationship between H_2O fluid/silicate melt partition coefficient for Cu ($D_{Cu}^{f/m}$) and the Cl^- concentration of the aqueous fluid. (b) The relationship between the H_2O fluid/silicate melt partition coefficient for Mo ($D_{Mo}^{f/m}$) and the Cl^- concentration of the aqueous fluid (after Candela and Holland, 1984).

origin of many different magmatic-hydrothermal ore deposit types. A model that summarizes some of the features discussed in this chapter is presented in section 2.8 below as an explanation for the characteristics of granite-related Cu, Mo, and W deposits.

2.7 WATER CONTENT AND DEPTH OF EMPLACEMENT OF GRANITES – RELATIONSHIPS TO ORE-FORMING PROCESSES

Many of the ore deposits associated with granites, such as porphyry Cu and epithermal Au–Ag ores, are related to magma emplacement at high levels of the crust where H_2O-fluid production and hydrofracturing can take place. These types of deposits are commonly located in the volcanic or subvolcanic environment and have formed as much from the action of surface-derived (or meteoric) water as they have from the circulation of magmatic waters. Other deposit types, such as porphyry Mo and granitoid hosted Sn–W deposits, are generally associated with magmas emplaced at deeper levels in the crust. The depth of emplacement of a granite magma, together with related parameters such as magma composition and initial water content, plays a very important role in determining the nature and origin of ore deposits associated with felsic igneous rocks, and these topics are discussed below.

Section 1.3.1 described how granitic magmas derived from the melting of different source materials, at different pressures and temperatures in the crust, would contain variable initial amounts of water. A melt derived by anatexis of a rock comprising mainly muscovite, for example, would contain in the region of 7–8 wt% H_2O. By contrast, dehydration melting of an amphibolitic source rock could only produce a melt at higher pressure and temperature (i.e. deeper in the crust) and this would contain only 2–3 wt% H_2O (Figure 2.3). It was suggested on this basis that S-type granite magmas would initially contain more water than I-type granite magmas. In terms of this model the drier I-type granite magmas would be derived from the deep crust (possibly with contributions from the upper mantle), whereas S-type granites come from material melted in the mid- to lower-crust. Several workers have used these concepts to develop models that link granite emplacement depths with their metallogenic characteristics (Hyndman, 1981; Strong, 1981).

Figure 2.17a shows the same P–T diagram as that in Figure 2.3 but inverted to reflect the surface (i.e. low pressures) at the top of the diagram. Hypothetical zones of melting are shown for each of three cases where the water required to initiate melting is supplied by the breakdown of muscovite, biotite, and amphibole. If sufficient melt is allowed to accumulate and then to rise upwards in the crust along an adiabatic cooling path, it is apparent, at least theoretically, that each of these

magmas would crystallize at different levels in the crust. Adiabatic upward movement of magma (i.e. where conductive heat loss to the wall rocks is ignored) would involve cooling at a rate of about 1.5 °C kbar⁻¹ and in P–T space would approximately follow the steep curves that define mineral phase boundaries. Conceptually, therefore, magmas could rise upwards in the crust until they intersect the water-saturated granite solidus, by which time they would have become completely solid and could not intrude any further. In reality crystallization is likely to have occurred prior to this level because of heat loss to the wall rocks and the water-saturated solidus effectively represents the depth above which a magma is unlikely to be emplaced. These considerations suggest that S-type granite magmas would be emplaced at mid-crustal depths (4–5 kbar), as dictated by intersection of the muscovite breakdown curve with the water-saturated granite solidus. By contrast, intersection of the biotite or amphibole breakdown curves with the water-saturated granite solidus indicates that an I-type magma could move to much shallower crustal levels (1 kbar or less) before completely solidifying (Figure 2.17a).

Figure 2.17b is a schematic crustal profile showing the relationships between depth of emplacement and the metallogenic character of various granite-related deposit types. I-type magmas generated deep in the lithosphere usually form adjacent to subduction zones and commonly receive a contribution from mantle-derived mafic melts. Forming at high temperatures (1000 °C or more) and being relatively dry (H_2O contents < 3–4 wt%) they will rise to shallow levels of the

Figure 2.17 (*Opposite*) Strong's model showing the relationship between level of granite emplacement and metallogenic character. (a) Pressure–temperature plot showing the approximate conditions where fluid-absent melting of amphibolite- (I), biotite- (II), and muscovite-bearing (III) protoliths would occur, and the expected levels in the Earth's crust to which melt fractions would rise adiabatically, as a function of the water-saturated solidus. (b) Schematic diagram illustrating the emplacement style and metallogenic character of granites formed under each of the conditions portrayed in part (a) (after Strong, 1988).

(a)

Volatile depressed solidus

Water-saturated granite solidus

Muscovite solidus

Biotite solidus

Amphibolite solidus

Granite melt (8.4% H_2O)

Granodiorite melt (3.3% H_2O)

Diorite melt (2.7% H_2O)

(b)

GRANOPHILE DEPOSITS
(Sn, W, U)

PORPHYRY/EPITHERMAL DEPOSITS
(Cu, Mo, Au)

(Ground water)

Connate water

Veins

Metamorphic water

Pegmatites

Partial melts

Second boiling

(Barren)

First boiling

	Muscovite (−biotite) granitoid
	Biotite granitoid
	Amphibole (−biotite) granitoid

crust and may even extrude to form substantial volcanic structures. Such magmas will typically exsolve a magmatic vapor phase by first boiling, an event that will also promote hydrofracturing, brecciation, and the widespread circulation of hydrothermal solutions in and around the sites of magmatic activity. These are the environments in which porphyry Cu, as well as epithermal Au–Ag deposit types, occur.

By contrast, S-type magmas are generated in the mid- to lower-crust by partial melting of a source rock that comprises a substantial proportion of metasedimentary material. These melts will form at relatively low temperatures (around 700 °C) and will initially comprise significant H_2O dissolved in the magma. Such a magma type will crystallize in the mid-crust, not too far from its site of generation, and will typically be barren. If substantial crystal fractionation occurs, however, incompatible trace elements will become concentrated in residual melts, and in those rocks representing the crystallized products of differentiated magma (see Box 1.3, Chapter 1). H_2O-fluid saturation will also eventually occur in the residual magma by second boiling, to form pegmatites and related deposits. The concentration of volatiles,

BOX 2.1 Magmatic-hydrothermal fluids associated with granite intrusions: 1 La Escondida porphyry copper deposit, Chile

Chile is the world's leading copper producer, with an output in 2000 of about 4.6 million tons of fine copper, or 36% of global production (Camus and Dilles, 2001). Northern Chile in particular contains several giant porphyry copper deposits, including world-renowned mines such as Chuquicamata, El Teniente, and El Salvador. The porphyry deposits of this huge metallogenic province formed during five discrete magmatic episodes extending from the Cretaceous to the Pliocene. The most prolific of these is the late Eocene–Oligocene period of magmatism, during which time at least 10 major porphyry copper deposits were formed, including the two biggest copper mines in the world, La Escondida and Chuquicamata. La Escondida was discovered as recently as 1981 and in 1999 produced over 800 000 tons of fine copper from a reserve base of more than 2 billion tons of ore at 1.15 wt% copper (Padilla Garza et al., 2001).

La Escondida, together with other giant porphyry systems such as Potrerillos, El Salvador, Chuquicamata, El Abra, and Collahuasi to its north and south, lies on the Domeyko fault system (Figure 1). This faulting was dominantly transcurrent during Eocene–Oligocene magmatism. Locally developed areas of transtension and dilation are considered to have created an environment conducive to high level ascent of magma and accompanying magmatic-hydrothermal mineralization (Richards et al., 2001). The Escondida district actually comprises six separate deposits (of which La Escondida is the largest) contained within a system of left-lateral strike-slip faults. Mineralization is associated with quartz monzonite (adamellite) and granodiorite intrusions within which alteration evolved from early potassic to sericite–chlorite and quartz–sericite. These assemblages have been overprinted by a younger

Figure 1 Simplified map showing the position, in northern Chile, of the Domeyko fault system and the six giant porphyry copper deposits located on it.

Figure 2 contains three stacked sections:

(a) Lithology — Pit outline 1997, Rhyolitic dome, Andesite, Escondida stock, with fault markers (f).

(b) Alteration — Chl-Ser (Bt), Qz-Ser, Advanced argillic, Epid-Chl., Chl-Ser (Bt), Kfel-Chl-Ser.

(c) Mineralization — Leached capping, Chalcocite blanket (supergene), Primary Cu-Fe sulfides (hypogene).

Figure 2 North–south sections through La Escondida showing the lithologies, alteration zonation, and mineralization characteristics (after Padilla Garza *et al.*, 2001).

advanced argillic alteration assemblage, and both hypogene sulfide and supergene sulphide + oxide ores occur (Padilla Garza *et al.*, 2001).

Cross sections through La Escondida (Figure 2) show that the system is related to a multiphase, 38 Myr old, intrusion, the Escondida stock, that cuts through Paleocene andesites. This was capped, 35 million years ago, by a rhyolite dome. Three phases of sequential alteration are recorded in the deposit. The earliest stage involves potassic alteration (K-feldspar + biotite) with associated silicification and propylitic (chlorite–sericite) alteration, and is linked to magnetite, chalcopyrite, and bornite. This was followed by phyllic alteration (sericite–chlorite–quartz) with which chalcopyrite, pyrite, and molybdenite are associated. The final hydrothermal alteration stage involves acid-sulfate or advanced argillic alteration (quartz–pyrophyllite–alunite). Precipitation of the hypogene sulfide assemblages, mainly during the first two stages of alteration, is attributed to a drop in temperature as the magmatic system cooled and was uplifted, as well as to progressive dilution of magmatic fluids by meteoric solutions (Padilla Garza *et al.*, 2001).

An important aspect of the ore-forming system at La Escondida is the development of supergene mineralization (see Chapter 4 and Box 4.2) in areas where the three stages of hydrothermal alteration overlap (i.e. where maximum sulfides were concentrated). Supergene processes were active between 18 and 15 Ma and were responsible for 65% of the total copper resources of the mine (Figure 2).

The upper portions of the supergene zone comprise a leached cap characterized by low Cu and Mo contents and limonite, hematite, and goethite. This is underlain by a supergene-enriched sulfide blanket containing mainly chalcocite, with lesser covellite and digenite. The best grades (up to 3.5 wt% Cu) occur in the thickest parts of the supergene zone, and also coincide with zones of intense vein stockwork and overlapping hydrothermal alteration. Copper "oxide" minerals such as chrysocolla, brochantite, and atacamite also occur, mainly in late fractures.

Figure 3 View of the Escondida open pit showing the nature of altered host rocks (photo courtesy of Rio Tinto)

as well as elements such as boron and phosphorus, will, together with exsolved water in the residual magma, depress the temperature of the water-saturated granite solidus to lower temperatures (500–600 °C) such that the magma could continue its upward migration to higher levels in the crust (Figure 2.17b). Fluid pressures would probably not be sufficient to fracture rock at these depths, but other structural controls would nevertheless promote fluid circulation and it is these environments in which Sn greisen deposits, porphyry Mo deposits, polymetallic skarn ores, and mesothermal veins might form.

2.8 MODELS FOR THE FORMATION OF PORPHYRY-TYPE CU, MO, AND W DEPOSITS

Considerable progress has been made in understanding the processes that occur in a crystallizing granite intrusion in order to form genetically associated base metal deposits (Candela and Holland, 1984, 1986; Candela, 1989, 1991, 1994; Candela and Piccoli, 1995). As a generalization, porphyry Cu–Mo deposits are associated with arc-related "calc–alkaline" or I-type magmas generated adjacent to Andean type subduction zones. Sn–W deposits are more often associated with S-type granites that are derived by partial melting of continental crust that would normally include a significant proportion of metasedimentary material. In certain settings the latter deposits are also regarded as "porphyry-type" even though they may differ significantly in their geological characteristics from the Cu–Mo types. Each of these deposit types is considered in turn below.

2.8.1 The origin of porphyry Cu–(Mo) and porphyry Mo–(Cu) type deposits

The family of deposit types known as porphyry Cu–Mo ores can be subdivided into two groups, one in which Cu is the dominant exploitable metal (together with minor Mo and occasionally Au), and the other where Mo is the dominant exploitable metal (with minor Cu and sometimes W). The two groups are referred to below as the Cu–(Mo) and the Mo–(Cu) porphyry types, respect-

ively. Porphyry deposits are the world's most important source of both Cu and Mo and, especially in the circum-Pacific region, there are many world-class deposits that exploit these metals. A description of one of the world's great porphyry Cu–(Mo) deposits, La Escondida in Chile, is provided in Box 2.1.

As illustrated in Figure 2.18, both types are associated with the generation of oxidized I-type granite magmas associated with melting processes adjacent to subducted oceanic crust. Porphyry Cu–(Mo) can be explained in terms of a body of magma with a relatively low initial H_2O content (inherited from the fluid absent melting of an amphibolitic protolith) rising to high levels in the crust before significant crystallization takes place. It is considered likely that some melt fractions from this high level magma chamber will be tapped off and extrude on the surface. These fractions will crystallize to form volcanic and subvolcanic (porphyry) suites of rocks whose compositions will not be highly differentiated (i.e. granodioritic or rhyodacitic) because of the low degree of fractionation that has taken place prior to extrusion. Because the magma is emplaced at low load pressures the saturation water content will be relatively low and probably not significantly different from the initial water content. Vapor-saturation will, therefore, occur *early* in the crystallization sequence, essentially due to "first boiling." Even though Cu is a compatible element in a crystallizing granitic melt (sequestration of Cu into accessory sulfide phases and biotite result in $D^{Cu}_{crystal/melt} > 1$), the lack of crystallization means that very little of the metal will have been removed from the melt by the time water-saturation occurs. The vapor phase, by contrast, is characterized by high Cl^- concentrations and it will, therefore, efficiently scavenge Cu from the silicate melt.

In this setting, however, the situation with respect to Mo is different. Mo is an incompatible element in a crystallizing granitic melt ($D^{Mo}_{crystal/melt} < 1$) but, because of the low degree of crystallization, its concentration in the residual magma will not have increased significantly prior to water saturation. On saturation, Mo will partition into the H_2O-fluid phase but, because its

Figure 2.18 Schematic model for the origin and formation of porphyry-type Cu, Mo, and W deposits. Detailed descriptions are provided in the text (modified after the models of Candela and Holland, 1984; 1986; Strong, 1988; Candela, 1992).

partition coefficient is relatively small and unaffected by the Cl$^-$ concentration ($D^{Mo}_{fluid/melt} = 2.5$) it will never attain very significant concentrations in the fluid phase. In this setting, therefore, a high level granodioritic I-type magma will exsolve an aqueous fluid phase that is highly enriched in Cu, but only moderately so in Mo, and form a typical porphyry Cu–(Mo) deposit.

A different scenario can be constructed for the formation of Mo–(Cu) porphyry deposits, where it is envisaged that the parental I-type magma might originally have contained a slightly higher initial water content (perhaps due to the fluid absent melting of a biotite-bearing protolith) than the Cu-dominant situation. As shown in Figure 2.18, this magma would not normally rise to the same

shallow crustal levels as its drier equivalent. The saturation water content of the magma is also significantly higher in this situation and, consequently, a greater degree of crystallization needs to take place before water-saturation is achieved (in this case vapor-saturation might occur by second boiling). As the magma crystallizes so will Cu be extracted from the melt and end up distributed somewhat evenly throughout the rocks representing the marginal zones of the pluton. This Cu will not, of course, be available for partitioning into the aqueous fluid once saturation is achieved. Mo, on the other hand, is incompatible and its concentration will continue to increase in the residual melt. When saturation does occur, Mo will be concentrated even further into the H_2O-fluid phase because of its favorable partition coefficient. Despite the fact that Cu will be strongly partitioned into the highly saline H_2O-fluid, its abundance in the melt is now significantly depleted due to earlier crystal–melt sequestration and the vapor phase will not be significantly concentrated in Cu. The extraction of a melt fraction from a more deep-seated magma chamber will give rise to a pluton that is less likely to reach the surface and whose composition is more highly differentiated due to the greater degree of crystal fractionation prior to extraction. Porphyry-style mineralization associated with the circulation of a magmatic hydrothermal fluid in and around such an intrusion may well have Mo concentrations in excess of Cu, giving rise to Mo–(Cu) porphyry-type mineralization.

2.8.2 The origin of porphyry W-type deposits

The above model can also be used to explain some of the characteristics of W-dominated, porphyry-type ore deposits that are associated with many magmatic arc settings. Candela (1992) has emphasized the relationship that exists between W-rich porphyry-type deposits and the more reduced, ilmenite-bearing, S-type granites that crystallize at relatively deep levels of the Earth's crust and whose setting is illustrated under (3) in Figure 2.18. Under oxidizing conditions, such as those applicable to the I-type, magnetite-bearing granites discussed above, the efficiency of extracting W from a magmatic-hydrothermal system into an ore body is relatively low and this metal is not a normal component of porphyry Cu–Mo deposits. Under reducing conditions, however, W behaves as an incompatible element in terms of its crystal–melt partitioning behavior and its concentration will increase during crystal fractionation. When a magma forms from the partial melting of a metasedimentary precursor, the melt formed will be relatively hydrous and will tend to crystallize relatively deep in the crust. Such a melt is also likely to be peraluminous and relatively reduced since it will have equilibrated with metasedimentary material that might have contained organic carbon. The saturation water content under these conditions will be high and a significant degree of crystallization will occur before saturation is attained (by second boiling). Because W is incompatible under these conditions its concentration will rise in the residual melt, whereas Mo concentrations will tend to decrease because it behaves in a more compatible way under reducing conditions. When the H_2O-fluid phase does exsolve it will interact with a highly differentiated melt that is significantly enriched in W. The fluid phase will scavenge some W but the relatively low partition coefficient ($D^W_{fluid/melt} \approx 1$) will ensure that most of the concentration is achieved prior to water saturation. The deposits that form in this setting will be associated with deep-level, highly differentiated S-type granites with metal concentrations dominated by W and only minor Mo.

2.9 FLUID FLOW IN AND AROUND GRANITE PLUTONS

Discussion has focused in this chapter thus far on the mechanisms by which a magmatic aqueous fluid phase is formed and its role in the transport of metals derived essentially from the melt. Of equal importance with respect to the formation of magmatic-hydrothermal ore deposits are considerations of the flow patterns in and around the intrusion that forms the fluid source, and also the length of time that magmatic-hydrothermal fluids can remain active subsequent to magma emplacement. Fossilized fluid flow pathways are revealed by recognizing the effects of alteration and mineralization that a hydrothermal solution imposes on the rocks through which it circulates (see Chapter 3). The prediction of where such fluids have circulated, however, is best achieved by modeling the thermal effects of an evolving fluid phase in terms of both conductive and convective heat loss in and around a theoretical intrusion. There have been many attempts to model fluid flow around granite plutons and these have proven useful in predicting where optimal fluid flux, and hence mineralization, should be located in relation to the intrusion.

Cathles (1981) used a thermal modeling approach to demonstrate that intrusions cool very rapidly,

Figure 2.19 Models illustrating the thermal and fluid flow characteristics in and around a cooling igneous intrusive body. (a) Plot of the time taken for the temperature of an intrusion to fall to 25% of its initial temperature ($T_{25\%}$) as a function of the intrusion dimensions (a in km and defined in the inset diagram). Two situations, one where heat is lost by conduction alone (steep slopes) and another where a combination of conduction and convective heat loss occurs (shallow slopes), are shown. Permeabilities (in millidarcy, md) are shown for the two cases (after Cathles, 1981). (b) Thermal model showing fluid flow and temperatures in and around an intrusion some 20 000 years after emplacement. For clarity, streamlines (quantified in terms of the stream function ψ) are shown on the left and isotherms on the right hand side, although the model is symmetric about the intrusion. The intrusion was initially at 750 °C with a permeability of 0.07 md and the country rocks at 0 °C with a permeability of 0.13 md. (c) Similar model for the situation 100 000 years after emplacement. Parts b and c are after Norton and Cathles (1979).

at least in terms of a geological time scale. In Figure 2.19a model curves are plotted which relate the time for an intrusion to cool to 25% of its initial temperature, and the size and geometry of the intrusion. The models can be erected for cases where heat is lost either by conduction alone, or by a combination of conduction and convective fluid flow. For the case where a small (1–2 km wide) intrusion cools by conduction of heat to the wall-rocks, solidification will be complete and magmatic-hydrothermal fluid circulation effectively over in about 10^5–10^6 years. If cooling is ac-

companied by convective heat loss caused by the circulation of a hydrothermal fluid through a permeable network of fractures (such as would be the case if hydrofracturing had occurred; see section 2.3.3 and Figure 2.7) then such a pluton could be reduced to 25% of its initial temperature within as little as 10^4 years. Thus, in a highly permeable system where fluid flow is maximized by fluid exsolution and hydrofracturing, heat loss will be very rapid and a single intrusion will not be able to sustain a geologically long-lived period of hydrothermal circulation. This feature could work against the development of a viable ore body, if it is considered that only magmatic fluids are responsible for ore formation. It should, however, be noted that mineralization in and around magmatic intrusions can also be the result of externally derived fluids and that these can circulate in response to other factors besides thermal gradients.

Norton and Cathles (1979) have been able to model the evolution of hydrothermal fluid flow with time in and around a granite intrusion. Figure 2.19b and c illustrate the isotherms and fluid flow streamlines that are likely to exist around a granite intrusion at two discrete periods (i.e. 2×10^4 and 10^5 years after magma emplacement and fluid saturation) for situations where heat is lost by both conduction and convection. Soon after intrusion of even a small granite body (Figure 2.19b) a substantial thermal anomaly is created for up to 2 km around the intrusion and an active system of circulatory fluid flow is set up from both the sides and top of the body. Aqueous solutions establish a convective cell where flow is upwards from the intrusion, and circulates back downwards at some distance away. These solutions could incorporate waters from the surrounding country rocks as well as the magmatic fluid derived from the cooling pluton itself. An indication of the fluid flux around the intrusion is obtained in the diagrams from the gradients of the stream function which defines the streamlines (i.e. the closer together the streamlines, the greater the fluid flux). The demise of the hydrothermal fluid cell is demonstrated in Figure 2.19c, where it is clear that the thermal anomaly providing the energy for fluid circulation, as well as the fluid convection itself, has diminished to insignificant proportions within 10^5 years of magma emplacement and fluid saturation. This again reinforces the view that ore-forming events are likely to be short-lived in and around small granite intrusions representing just a single pulse of magma. Likewise, the ore bodies that form under these sorts of conditions are also likely to be small and perhaps sub-economic. Larger, multi-episodic intrusions are required in order to create a system where a substantial magmatic-hydrothermal ore body will form.

A good example of where the nature of fluid flow in and around a granite intrusion contributes greatly to understanding the distribution of magmatic-hydrothermal mineralization is provided by the polymetallic (Sn–W–Cu–Pb–Zn) deposits of the Cornubian batholith in Cornwall and Devon, southwest England. In this classic mining district mineralized veins occur along the margins of individual granite plutons, but also extend out into the surrounding metasedimentary country rocks. Mineralization is also characterized by a pronounced regional zonation in the distribution of metals. These patterns can be explained in terms of the nature of fluid flow in and around individual granite plutons, as well as the shape of the intrusions and the extent to which they have been exhumed. A description of mineralization and metal zoning in the Cornubian batholith is provided in Box 2.2.

BOX 2.2 Fluid flow in and around granite intrusions: polymetallic mineralization associated with the granites of Cornwall, southwest England

The Cornubian granite batholith, emplaced at around 280–290 Ma during the Carboniferous to Permian Variscan Orogen, is associated with one of the classic polymetallic mining districts of the world. The batholith outcrops as a series of five major plutons, in addition to a host of minor granite bodies and related dykes, in the counties of Cornwall and Devon, southwest England (Figure 1). The batholith is believed to have been emplaced in response to subduction caused by convergence of Laurasia and Africa (the assembly of Pangea), with similar granites and styles of mineralization also evident elsewhere along the orogenic belt, notably in Spain, Portugal, France, and the Czech Republic in Europe, and New Brunswick–Newfoundland in North America. In southwest England mining can be traced back to the Bronze Age, but the peak of activities occurred in the nineteenth century. Historically, the district has been a predominantly Sn (2.5 million tons of cumulative metal production) and

Figure 1 Distribution of the major exposed plutons in Cornwall and Devon making up part of the Cornubian granite batholith, and the distribution of Sn, Cu, and Pb–Zn mineralization in and around these plutons (after Atkinson and Baker, 1986).

Cu (2 million tons of cumulative metal production) producer, although other metals such as Fe, As, Pb, Zn, W, U, and Ag have also been extracted (Alderton, 1993). Presently the district is still a major producer of kaolinite (China clay) for the ceramics industry (see section 4.4.1 of Chapter 4).

The Cornish granite, as with many similarly mineralized bodies elsewhere along the Variscan belt, is peraluminous in composition, enriched in Rb, Li, F, B, and Be, and can be classified as an S-type granite (Willis-Richards and Jackson, 1989). Mineralization in the granite is related to the early exsolution of a voluminous aqueous phase from the magma which is responsible for widespread alteration of pluton margins and much of the mineralization (Jackson et al., 1989). Alteration is typically zoned and characterized by the sequence tourmaline – potassic alteration (K-feldspar and biotite) – sericite – chlorite as one progresses away from mineralization. Magmatic-hydrothermal fluids are also responsible for the formation of mineralized quartz veins that are both endo- and exogranitic. Particularly characteristic of the Cornubian mineralization is the presence of sheeted, greisen-bordered vein sets which generally represent the sites of preferential

Sn–W mineralization. These veins consist essentially of quartz and tourmaline with variable cassiterite and wolframite, and a greisen alteration halo comprising quartz, muscovite, Li-mica, and topaz. These vein systems often extend for several kilometers out into the surrounding country rock and record a well defined metallogenic zoning or paragenetic sequence. The ore mineral zonation progresses from an early oxide-dominated assemblage (cassiterite and wolframite together with tourmaline) to a later sulfide assemblage comprising chalcopyrite, sphalerite, and galena, together with fluorite and chlorite. The zonation pattern is evident both vertically within a single vein system and laterally away from a granite body as shown in Figures 1 and 3. Although metal zonation is complex (Willis-Richards and Jackson, 1989), the progression from Sn–W to Cu to Pb–Zn reflects an ore fluid that evolved, in terms of both cooling and chemical changes due to fluid–fluid and fluid–rock interactions.

Computerized numerical simulations of the fluid flow in and around the Cornubian granites have provided useful insights into the distribution of mineralization, as well as the controls on metal zonation that is such of feature of the district. One of the characteristics of the Cornubian batholith is that mineralization is preferentially distributed along one margin of the exposed granite pluton, such as the northern margin of the Carnmenellis pluton and the southern margins of the St Austell and Bodmin plutons (Figure 1). Two of the factors that influence the pattern of magmatic-hydrothermal fluid flow in and around granite plutons are the shape of the body and its depth of emplacement (Sams and Thomas-Betts, 1988). Maximum fluid flow tends to be concentrated on the more gently dipping margins of a granite body, which accounts for the asymmetry in distribution of mineralization. In addition, progressive unroofing of a granite by erosion will cause the locus of convective fluid flow to migrate outwards into the surrounding sediments. A model for the southeastern margin of the St Agnes–Cligga Head granite (Sams and Thomas-Betts, 1988), much of which is under the sea, illustrates how progressive unroofing of the body causes the locus of vertical fluid flow to move progressively away from the pluton margins. Thermal and chemical evolution of the mineralizing solutions over the time interval represented by unroofing could account for the successive increments of metal deposition and the regional zonation of metals observed.

Figure 2 (*left*) Sheeted Sn–W-bearing, greisen-bordered veins exposed at Cligga Head, Cornwall.

Figure 3 The regional pattern of metal zonation around the southeast margin of the St Agnes–Cligga Head granite (a). Numerical simulation of fluid flow in and around the granite as a function of progressive unroofing of the granite with time (b and c; both diagrams after Sams and Thomas-Betts, 1988).

Figure 2.20 Plot of SiO_2 versus $[FeO + Fe_2O_3 + CaO + Na_2O]/K_2O$ showing the relationship between the composition of igneous intrusions and the dominant metal in various skarn deposits (after Meinert, 1992).

2.10 SKARN DEPOSITS

The word "skarn" is an old Swedish term that originally referred to the very hard rocks composed dominantly of calc–silicate minerals (i.e. Ca-rich garnet, pyroxene, amphibole, and epidote) that identify the rather unusual alteration assemblages associated with magnetite and chalcopyrite deposits in that country. It is now widely used to refer to the metasomatic replacement of carbonate rocks (limestone and dolomite) by calc–silicate mineral assemblages during either contact or regional metamorphic processes. Mineral deposits associated with skarn assemblages are referred to as skarn deposits, and are typically the product of contact metamorphism and metasomatism associated with intrusion of granite into carbonate rocks. A wide variety of deposit types and metal associations are grouped into the category of skarn deposits, and these include W, Sn, Mo, Cu, Fe, Pb–Zn, and Au ores. The different metals found in skarn deposits are a product of the differing compositions, oxidation state, and metallogenic affinities of the igneous intrusion, as described in Chapter 1 (Einaudi *et al.*, 1981; Misra, 2000). A simple diagram relating granitoid

composition to skarn deposit type is shown in Figure 2.20. As a general rule Fe and Au skarn deposits tend to be associated with intrusions of more mafic to intermediate compositions. Cu, Pb, Zn, and W are linked to calc–alkaline, magnetite-bearing, oxidized (I-type) granitic intrusions, and Mo and Sn with more differentiated granites that might be reduced (S-type) and ilmenite-bearing. It should be noted that there are exceptions to this general trend.

Skarn deposits can be classified into calcic or magnesian types, depending largely on whether the host rock is a limestone or dolomite. They are also described as either endo- or exo-skarns, depending on whether the metasomatic assemblage is internal or external to the intruding pluton. Most of the large, economically viable skarn deposits are associated with calcic exoskarns. Tungsten skarns produce the bulk of the world's W production and are typically associated with intrusion of calc–alkaline intrusions, emplaced relatively deep in the crust. Examples include the King Island mine of Tasmania and the MacTung deposit in the Yukon territory of Canada (see Box 2.3). Copper skarns, by contrast, are often associated with high level porphyry-style intrusions

BOX 2.3   Magmatic-hydrothermal fluids associated with granite intrusions: 2 The MacTung tungsten skarn deposit, Yukon, Canada

The northern Cordillera of Canada, extending from British Columbia into the Yukon Territory, is a highly prospective zone that contains several major porphyry, SEDEX, and VMS base metal mines, as well as gold deposits. In addition, several large W–Cu–(Zn–Mo) skarn deposits occur in the region, including the world's largest known deposit in the Macmillan Pass area. The deposit, known as MacTung, has yet to be mined but contains ore reserves of some 63 million tons at 0.95 wt% WO_3, with minor copper (Misra, 2000).

The MacTung deposit occurs in Cambrian–Ordovician clastic and carbonate sediments deposited on a continental margin in a platformal shelf setting (Atkinson and Baker, 1986). The sequence is characterized by alternating siltstones, carbonaceous shales, and limestones. It is intruded by the 90 Myr old Cirque Lake stock, a biotite- and garnet-bearing quartz monzonite of probable S-type affinity. This granite is implicated in the mineralization process, although the actual source of the magmatic-hydrothermal fluids associated with alteration and metal deposition is believed to be a hidden intrusion at depth to the south of the deposit (Figure 1). Two distinct zones of skarn mineralization are evident at MacTung. The lower zone is hosted within a folded limestone breccia, whereas the upper zone straddles three separate lithological units, namely a lower limestone breccia, an intermediate pelitic unit, and an upper unit comprising alternating shale and limestone. Prograde hydrothermal alteration varies as a function of the host sediment composition and reactivity with fluids. Non-reactive and less porous shales are characterized mainly by quartz veining with narrow bleached halos and low concentrations of scheelite. Highly reactive and porous limestones are the main hosts to skarn mineralization, and are pervasively altered. A distinct zonation is evident and alteration progresses from marginal limestone cut by occasional garnet–pyroxene veins, to a pervasively altered intermediate zone comprising extensive limestone replacement by garnet–pyroxene skarn, and finally a core of pyroxene and pyroxene–pyrrhotite skarn. Ore grades improve progressively from the margins to the core, where WO_3 and Cu concentrations are better than 1.5 and 0.2 wt% respectively (Atkinson and Baker, 1986).

Figure 1 Generalized geology of the MacTung deposit and a cross section of the ore zone showing mineralized lithologies and the possible location of a hidden intrusion suggested to be the source of the ore-bearing magmatic-hydrothermal fluids (after Atkinson and Baker, 1986).

Retrograde alteration is minimal at MacTung and is characterized by late quartz and calcite veins with coarse grained scheelite, and minor amphibole formation representing hydration of the pyroxene skarn.

The pattern of alteration zonation, which is discordant to the Cirque Lake stock contact, as well as the distribution of quartz veins, suggest that fluids migrated up-dip and toward the stock. For these reasons the source of magmatic-hydrothermal fluids involved in skarn formation is believed to be a hidden intrusion at depth to the south of the mineralization, as suggested in Figure 1. It is not known whether such an intrusion is merely part of the Cirque Lake stock or an unrelated event.

Figure 2 The Cirque Lake stock intruding Cambrian–Ordovician clastic and carbonate sediments in the vicinity of the MacTung skarn deposit.

and many porphyry copper systems that intrude carbonate host rocks have copper skarns associated with them. A classic example is the Bingham district of Utah, USA, which contains not only a huge porphyry Cu deposit, but also the world's largest Cu skarn deposit. In addition, the non-porphyry ores at Bingham contain economically viable Pb–Zn–Ag ores in limestones that are distal to the copper mineralization (Einaudi, 1982). It is interesting to note that the world's largest gold mine, at Grasberg in the Ertsberg district of West Papua, also exhibits a porphyry–skarn association and actually produces gold as a by-product of the copper mining process (Meinert, 2000). Gold skarns associated with porphyry Cu mineralization are associated with emplacement of high level, oxidized, magnetite-bearing granitoids. Other gold-specific skarn deposits, where Au occurs in association with a Bi–Te–As metal assemblage, are linked to more reducing, ilmenite bearing granitoid intrusions (Meinert, 2000). Fe skarns, which occasionally form large, economically viable magnetite deposits, such as at Sverdlovsk and Sarbai in Russia, are associated with more mafic gabbroic to granodioritic intrusions, and are typified by endoskarn alteration and sodium metasomatism (Einaudi et al., 1981). Tin skarns are generally associated with highly differentiated S-type (or ilmenite-bearing) granitoids, a good

example of which is the Renison Bell mine in Tasmania.

Even though there are so many different metal associations in skarn deposits, the processes by which they form are similar, namely granitoid emplacement and magmatic-hydrothermal activity, albeit at different levels in the crust. An association with granite intrusion cannot always be demonstrated, but is usually inferred. Skarn deposits typically form as a result of three sequential processes (Einaudi et al., 1981; Meinert, 1992). These are isochemical contact metamorphism during early stages of pluton emplacement and crystallization, followed by open system metasomatism and alteration during magmatic fluid saturation, and, finally, draw-down and mixing with meteoric fluids (for a definition see Chapter 3) during cooling of the pluton.

Prograde – isochemical contact metamorphism (Figure 2.21a)

As the granite pluton intrudes the country rock sediments are subjected to contact metamorphism and the formation of a variety of hornfelsic textures. The mineral assemblages that form at this stage reflect the composition of the lithotypes within which they form. Contact metamorphism is largely a thermal effect although fluids

(a)

(b)

Figure 2.21 The evolution of intrusion-related skarn deposits showing the three sequential stages of formation. (a) Prograde stages, and (b) retrograde stage (modified after Corbett and Leach, 1998).

are likely to circulate during this process and are largely a product of prograde metamorphic reactions and, therefore, comprise mainly H_2O and CO_2 (see Chapter 3 for a description of metamorphic fluids). In dolomitic units metamorphic mineral zonation approximates the sequence garnet–clinopyroxene–tremolite–talc/phlogopite, reflecting increased distance and progressively more hydrous assemblages away from the intrusion. In limestone units the mineral zonation is garnet–vesuvianite + wollastinite–marble. There is no mineralization associated with this stage, although the process of dehydration close to the

pluton margins may be important for increasing porosity of the source rocks and facilitating fluid flow during later episodes of mineralization.

Prograde – metamorphism and replacement (Figure 2.21a)

The second stage in the formation of skarn deposits involves H_2O-fluid and vapor-saturation of the intruding magma (as a function of either first or second boiling or both) and the egress of the fluid phase into the surrounding contact metamorphic halo. At deeper crustal levels fluid flow is likely to be concentrated along discrete structural or bedding parallel conduits, whereas at higher levels fluid flow will be more pervasively distributed, perhaps due to hydrofracturing, in a broad halo in and around the granite cupola. Metasomatic mineral assemblages will be similar to those formed during contact metamorphism but alteration will be more pervasive and coarser-grained, and will replace earlier formed assemblages. Si, Al, and Fe, as well as other components, will be introduced into the calcareous sediments by the aqueous magmatic fluid, while Ca, Mg, and CO_2 are locally derived and also introduced into the metasomatic system. Sulfide mineralization does not form at this stage, although magnetite and scheelite (in W skarns) do precipitate in the waning stages of prograde metasomatism.

Retrograde – meteoric fluid influx and main metal precipitation (Figure 2.21b)

All magmatic-hydrothermal systems undergo progressive cooling and decay of the high temperature magmatic fluid system. As fluids become progressively dominated by shallow meteoric waters, a series of complex retrograde reactions takes place, as well as the precipitation of the main stages of base and precious metal, sulfide-related mineralization (Einaudi *et al.*, 1981). The retrograde alteration assemblages are superimposed onto earlier metamorphic and metasomatic minerals and, typically, this process is recognized by paragenetically late formation of epidote, biotite, chlorite, plagioclase, calcite, quartz (all after various garnet types), tremolite–actinolite, and talc (after pyroxenes) and serpentine (after olivine). Sulfide ore minerals, as well as magnetite and hematite, occur as disseminations, or veins, that cut across prograde assemblages. Assemblages such as pyrite–chalcopyrite–magnetite characterize proximal settings, whereas bornite and sphalerite–galena are typically more distal in occurrence. The paragenetically late precipitation of most skarn-related ores suggests that metal precipitation is related to decreasing temperature of the ore fluids (and a resulting drop in solubilities), fluid mixing, or neutralization of the ore fluid by reaction with carbonate lithologies.

Mixing of the magmatic ore fluid with the late meteoric component, and related redox reactions in the fluid, may be additional controls on the ore formation process. A more detailed description of precipitation mechanisms in hydrothermal solutions is provided in Chapter 3.

2.11 NEAR-SURFACE MAGMATIC-HYDROTHERMAL PROCESSES – THE "EPITHERMAL" FAMILY OF AU–AG–(CU) DEPOSITS

Exploration for gold in the circum-Pacific region, especially since the 1970s, has led to the discovery of a large number of world-class gold deposits associated with either active or geologically recent volcanic environments. These deposits are now regarded as an important and very prospective category of gold deposit type, termed epithermal deposits. The term "epithermal" is derived from Lindgren's (1933) classification of ore deposits and refers to those that formed at shallow crustal levels (i.e. the epizone). Many studies of this ore-forming environment, and in particular comparisons with active, modern analogues such as the Taupo volcanic zone on the north island of New Zealand, have shown that epithermal deposits typically form at temperatures between 160 and 270 °C and pressures equivalent to depths of between 50 and 1000 m (Cooke and Simmons, 2000; Hedenquist *et al.*, 2000).

There are two contrasting styles of mineralization that are now recognized in epithermal deposits, and these are referred to as *high-sulfidation* and *low-sulfidation* types. These terms refer specifically to the oxidation state of sulfur in the ore fluid, the chemistry and pH of which also relates to the nature of alteration associated with each type.

Unfortunately, the geological literature contains a confusing plethora of synonyms for these two types. Table 2.2 attempts to summarize these terms and also illustrates the main characteristics of each. Note that the two terms do not relate to the abundance of sulfur, as this is highly variable in each deposit type, but in some publications "high sulfur" and "low sulfur" have been equated with high-sulfidation and low-sulfidation respectively.

Table 2.2 Characteristics of high- and low-sulfidation epithermal deposits

High-sulfidation	Low-sulfidation
Oxidized sulfur species (SO_2, SO_4^{2-}, HSO_4^-) in ore fluid/vapor	Reduced sulfur species (HS^-, H_2S) in ore fluid/vapor
Also referred to as	
Gold–alunite, acid–sulfate, alunite–kaolinite	Adularia–sericite, hotspring-related
Fluids	
Acidic pH, probably saline initially, dominantly magmatic	Near-neutral pH, low salinity, gas-rich (CO_2, H_2S), dominantly meteoric
Alteration assemblage	
Advanced argillic (zonation: quartz–alunite–kaolinite–illite–montmorillonite–chlorite)	Adularia–sericite (zonation: quartz/chalcedony–calcite–adularia–sericite–chlorite)
Metal associations	
Au–Cu (lesser Ag, Bi, Te)	Au–Ag (lesser As, Sb, Se, Hg)

High- and low-sulfidation epithermal deposits can be viewed as end-members of processes related to fluid evolution and circulation in and around volcanoes. High-sulfidation deposits occur in proximal settings and are commonly found within or close to the volcanic vent itself. The fluids involved with mineralization are derived directly from the magma as a product of vapor- and fluid-saturation and are usually boiling in the ore-forming environment. The fluids are very acidic (pH of 1–3) and oxidized, carrying the oxidized S^{4+} or S^{6+} species as SO_2, SO_4^{2-}, or HSO_4^- in solution. As this fluid boils and SO_2 and CO_2 are partitioned into the vapor phase, the remaining liquid carries a surplus of H^+ which makes it very acidic (pH = 1; Hedenquist *et al.*, 2000). This acidic fluid is also capable of leaching most of the major elements from the host volcanic or volcano-sedimentary rocks through which it circulates, resulting in vuggy textures and an advanced argillic style of alteration (see Table 2.2 and also the more detailed account of hydrothermal alteration in Chapter 3). By contrast, low-sulfidation deposits are associated with fluids that are similar to those involved with hotsprings and other geothermal manifestations in areas of enhanced heat flow. These fluids have equilibrated with their host rocks and generally comprise a dominantly meteoric component, although it is likely that this will have been mixed with an evolved magmatic fluid if active volcanism is located nearby. Consequently, low-sulfidation deposits may form within the volcanic edifice, especially during the waning stages of magmatic activity when draw-down of meteoric fluids is perhaps more likely. More typically they may form at locations that are somewhat removed from the focus of volcanism. The fluid involved is near-neutral and has low salinities, but as with high-sulfidation environments, it is also likely to have boiled in and around the zone of ore formation.

The characteristics of high- and low-sulfidation deposits are shown schematically in Figure 2.22. This diagram suggests that a spatial and genetic link exists between the two types, but it should be emphasized that this may not be the case. Many gold districts contain either low-sulfidation epithermal deposits (such as the major deposits in Nevada, USA, including Round Mountain, Comstock Lode, Midas, and Sleeper) or high-sulfidation deposits (such as many of the Andean deposits, including Yanacocha, Pierina, and El Indio–Tambo). There is, however, an increasing number of cases where spatial and genetic links are evident. One area where both high- and low-sulfidation epithermal deposits occur in fairly close proximity to one another is in Kyushu, the southernmost island of Japan (Box 2.4). It is evident in Figure 2.22 that there should also be a genetic link between porphyry Cu–(Mo–Au) deposits formed in the sub-

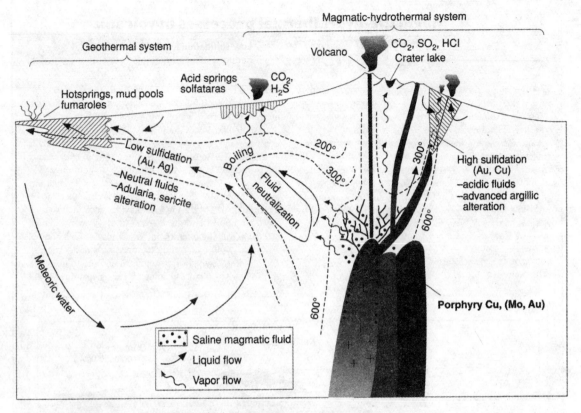

Figure 2.22 The geological setting and characteristics of high-sulfidation and low-sulfidation epithermal deposits. A genetic link between high-sulfidation epithermal Au–Cu and sub-volcanic porphyry type Cu–Au deposits is also suggested (after Hedenquist *et al.*, 2000).

volcanic environment and high-sulfidation Au–Cu deposits at surface. This link can be demonstrated in the case of the Lepanto epithermal Au–Cu and the Far Southeast porphyry Cu–Au deposits on Luzon in the Phillipines. These two deposits are adjacent to one another in late Pliocene rocks, with the mineralization in both occurring over a brief 300 000 year time period at around 1.3 Ma (Arribas *et al.*, 1995). It is also pertinent to note that low-sulfidation Au–Ag mineralization is located within a few kilometers of the Lepanto–Far Southeast system, indicating that spatial and genetic links between high- and low-sulfidation epithermal and porphyry styles of mineralization are likely. The fact that their coexistence is only rarely documented is, at least partially, therefore, a function of erosion and lack of preservation.

2.11.1 Gold precipitation mechanisms in epithermal deposits

The detailed mechanisms of gold precipitation in high- and low-sulfidation deposits are complex and vary depending on the geological setting and nature of fluids involved (Cooke and Simmons, 2000). The following section briefly considers gold precipitation mechanisms as applicable to epithermal deposits, although the principles discussed here also apply to other gold deposit types. The reader is encouraged to read the relevant sections on metal solubility and precipitation mechanisms in Chapter 3 (sections 3.4 and 3.5) before continuing with this section.

Anionic species, or ligands, of chloride (Cl^-) and sulfide (specifically HS^-) are regarded as being

BOX 2.4 Magmatic-hydrothermal processes in volcanic environments: the Kasuga and Hishikari epithermal Au–Ag deposits, Kyushu, Japan

Kyushu, the southernmost major island of the Japanese arc, is the country's principal gold producing region. Late Cenozoic volcanic activity in this region has given rise to several epithermal Au–Ag deposits, all related to either extinct or waning magmatic-hydrothermal systems arising from this volcanism. Both styles of epithermal gold mineralization are preserved on Kyushu, namely high-sulfidation (or acid–sulfate) mineralization represented by the Nansatsu type ores of which Kasuga is an example, and low-sulfidation (or adularia–sericite) mineralization represented by the very rich Hishikari deposit.

Kasuga

The Nansatsu district in the southern portion of Kyushu

has been the site of calc–alkaline volcanism for the past 10 million years. Several deposits occur in the district, including Akeshi, Iwato, and Kasuga. Kasuga is a small deposit that produces about 120 000 tons of ore annually at an average Au grade of about 3 g t^{-1}. The ore body is associated with a residual high-silica zone in andesites of the Nansatsu Group, which overlies basement metasediments of the Cretaceous Shimanto Supergroup (Hedenquist *et al.*, 1994). Alteration in the open pit is characterized by a central quartz-rich zone in which the volcanic host rock has been almost entirely leached of all elements except Si (Figure 1a). The quartz body is surrounded by a zone of advanced argillic alteration (comprising alunite, dickite, and kaolinite), which in turn grades out into a propylitic zone (chlorite + illite). Ore minerals consist mainly of pyrite

Figure 1 (a) Cross section through the Kasuga deposit showing the nature and geometry of the alteration zoning (after Hedenquist *et al.*, 1994). (b) Cross section through the Hishikari deposits illustrating the concentration of mineralization at one particular elevation (after Izawa *et al.*, 2001).

Figure 2 Gold and silver rich Hosen vein photographed underground at the Hishikari mine, Kyushu.

and enargite with later native sulfur, covellite, and goethite. The Au–Ag (electrum) is largely contained within the quartz body in the center of the alteration halo, although considerable remobilization into late oxidized phases also occurs. Mineralization is linked to the exsolution of a metal charged fluid phase from the host andesite, with subsequent segregation into vapor and liquid phases. Highly acidic vapors are implicated in the leaching of volcanic rocks to form the porous quartz body. The metal charged fluid phase subsequently percolated through the porous rock and precipitated Cu, Ag, and Au. Progressive mixing of this fluid with meteoric waters was probably the main precipitation mechanism, and was also responsible for

the zonation in the alteration halo and the late oxidation of pre-existing assemblages (Hedenquist *et al.*, 1994).

Hishikari

The Hishikari deposit, discovered in 1981, is a very rich low-sulfidation epithermal deposit containing about 260 tons of mineable gold (Izawa *et al.*, 2001). It is located some 20 km to the northwest of the recently active Kirishima volcano in south-central Kyushu. The deposit occurs as a series of vertical, en-echelon veins largely within the Cretaceous Shimanto Supergroup basement, but also extending short distances into overlying Pleistocene andesites. The veins consist mainly of quartz and adularia, with lesser smectite clay. Vein formation and mineralization is believed to be linked to volcanism that started about 1.6 Ma and terminated at about 0.7 Ma. Vein related adularia, however, has been dated at between 1.15 and 0.60 Ma, suggesting that the geothermal system and mineralization commenced about 0.5 Myr after volcanism (Izawa *et al.*, 2001). The spectacularly rich Hosen No. 1 vein (which averages over 3000 g t^{-1} Au and 2000 g t^{-1} Ag!) records evidence of three phases of vein deposition. Each consists mainly of quartz, adularia, and electrum. Minor pyrite and chalcopyrite also occur but only during the early phases of deposition. The high grade ores at Hishikari are restricted to a specific elevation, extending over about 200 m of vertical extent (Figure 1b), and veins either terminate or become sub-economic above and below this range. This, together with fluid inclusion evidence, suggests that boiling of a dominantly meteoric fluid was responsible for the precipitation of gold and silver from solution.

essential in order to solubilize gold in aqueous solutions (Seward and Barnes, 1997). In reduced, near-neutral pH, aqueous solutions Au is likely to be transported as the $Au(HS)_2^-$ complex and this is also likely to be the preferred medium for the movement of gold in low-sulfidation environments. By contrast, at higher temperatures (>300 °C) and for solutions that are both more acidic and saline, gold is preferentially transported as the $Au(Cl)_2^-$ complex, and this mode of transport probably applies to high-sulfidation environments. Since the mechanism whereby gold is transported could be fundamentally different in the two epithermal deposit types, it follows that the chemical and physical controls that precipitate the gold from the hydrothermal fluids are also likely to differ.

For low-sulfidation deposits gold precipitation is relatively straightforward and is linked to one, or both, of the two processes that characterize fluid evolution in this environment, namely boiling and fluid mixing. Boiling of an ore fluid in this case will result in loss of H_2S to the vapor phase, which causes destabilization of the $Au(HS)_2^-$ complex and precipitation of Au, as described in equation [2.7] (after Cooke and Simmons, 2000):

$$Au(HS)_2^- + H^+ + 0.5H_2 \leftrightarrow Au + 2H_2S \qquad [2.7]$$

Mixing of an oxidized meteoric water with the same ore fluid would also have the effect of precipitating gold, as shown in equation [2.8]:

$$Au(HS)_2^- + 8H_2O \leftrightarrow Au + 2SO_4^{2-} + 3H^+ + 7.5H_2 \qquad [2.8]$$

Evidence for boiling-induced Au precipitation is provided from modern geothermal systems that exploit steam to drive electricity-generating turbines, such as at Broadlands in New Zealand (Cooke and Simmons, 2000). It is well known in these power stations that the siliceous scale that plates the inside of pipes and accompanies the flashing of water to steam is often enriched in both Au and Ag. In actual low-sulfidation deposits the narrow vertical interval over which vein-hosted mineralization occurs (such as at Hishikari; Box 2.4) is another indication that boiling acts as a fundamental control on ore precipitation. Although it is clear that fluid mixing also plays a role, in deposits such as Creede in Colorado, the evidence for a widespread role for this mechanism is less clear (Cooke and Simmons, 2000).

For high-sulfidation deposits the Au deposition mechanisms are less well understood and more complex, since it is feasible to transport gold, not only as a $Au(Cl)_2^-$ complex, as suggested above, but also as a bisulfide complex ($Au(HS)$) in fluids with a high sulfur activity. It is also considered possible that Au is transported together with Cu in the vapor phase (see section 2.4.2 above). If gold is transported as a bisulfide complex in high-sulfidation environments then the precipitation mechanisms are also likely to be related to boiling and fluid mixing, as for low-sulfidation systems. If, on the other hand, gold is transported as a chloride complex, then boiling and extraction of oxidized sulfur species (SO_2 or SO_4^{2-}) into the vapor phase will have little effect on its stability. Fluid mixing, between a hot, acidic and saline $Au(Cl)_2^-$ bearing ore fluid and a cooler, neutral meteoric solution, could, however, be an important precipitation mechanism, since it will have the effect of increasing pH and decreasing salinity (by dilution) of the ore fluid. Studies at Lepanto, for example, indicate that fluid mixing did occur with variations in the ratio of magmatic to meteoric fluids ranging from 9:1 to 1:1 over the ore deposit (Hedenquist et al., 1998).

Arribas et al. (1995) have provided a model for the formation of high-sulfidation epithermal systems that reflects the complexities related to possible variations of gold speciation in this environment. The model envisages two stages of ore formation. The first involves degassing of hot, acid rich magmatic vapors that are responsible for intense leaching of the host rock to form the porous vuggy quartz zone in the fumarolic conduit and the advanced argillic alteration halo around it (Figure 2.23a). The vapor phases could also mix with meteoric waters to form an acid sulfate fluid that has a low Au solubility, but is also implicated in the alteration process. The secondary porosity and permeability created during this alteration process is considered to be a necessary preparatory stage for the influx of later metal-bearing fluids. Subsequent ore deposition can occur in one of two ways. A hot, acidic, and saline ore fluid, carrying gold as a $Au(Cl)_2^-$ complex, could be derived directly from the subjacent magma and move directly up into the alteration zone. Ore precipitation would occur as a result of mixing and dilution of this fluid by cooler meteoric waters (Figure 2.23b). Alternatively, it is suggested that Cu and Au are initially removed from the magma in the vapor phase and that these metal charged gases mix with heated ground waters circulating around the intrusion to form a low salinity fluid in which gold is transported as $Au(HS)$. This fluid would then precipitate metals by boiling in the near surface environment, or mixing with meteoric waters, or both (Figure 2.23b).

2.12 THE ROLE OF HYDROTHERMAL FLUIDS IN MINERALIZED MAFIC ROCKS

Much of this chapter has concentrated on the relationships between felsic magmas and the fluids that exsolve from them. As mentioned at the beginning of this chapter, however, it is also feasible for a mafic melt to exsolve a magmatic fluid phase, although the resultant mass fraction of exsolved water may be lower than in felsic melts. In mafic rocks the role of a magmatic fluid in ore-forming processes is commonly overlooked, even though it is now apparent that such fluids may be important in the concentration of metals such as Cu, Ni, and the platinum

Figure 2.23 Two stage model for the formation of high-sulfidation epithermal deposits (after Arribas *et al.*, 1995). (a) Initial stage where a dominantly magmatic vapor phase is responsible for leaching of the country rock and development of an advanced argillic alteration halo around the main fumarolic conduit. (b1) Ore deposition stage, in this case where gold is transported as a chloride complex; and (b2) ore deposition stage where gold is transported as a bisulfide complex.

group elements (PGE) in layered mafic intrusions (Mathez, 1989a, b).

The solubility of H_2O in a melt is higher than that of CO_2 and it follows, therefore, that the latter will exsolve before the aqueous species. The first fluids to form from a crystallizing mafic melt are rich in CO_2 (as well as CO in more reduced environments), but they will evolve to more H_2O-rich compositions as crystallization progresses. In addition the fluid will also contain appreciable chlorine (as HCl or $FeCl_2$) and sulfur (as HS^- or SO_4^{2-} depending on fO_2). The change in fluid composition from CO_2 to H_2O-dominated occurs quite rapidly in fluids derived from mafic melts and is marked by the precipitation of C (graphite) from the fluid. These fluids are, therefore, unlikely, *at least initially*, to be able to dissolve much metal, but this would change as the proportion of water in the solutions increases.

Considerations of metal concentration in mafic rocks, such as those discussed at some length in Chapter 1, assume that distribution patterns of Cu, Ni, and PGE reflect crystal–melt or melt–melt partitioning during progressive crystallization or silicate–sulfide immiscibility. These assumptions presuppose that the ore deposits observed

have not re-equilibrated with a vapor phase and that the metal distribution patterns are genuinely magmatic and not overprinted by hydrothermal processes. This is not always the case and mineralogical observations in serpentinites from eastern Australia, for example, show that certain of the PGE (in particular Pd, Pt, and Rh) tend to be readily redistributed by hydrothermal solutions, whereas others (specifically Os, Ir, and Ru) remain unaffected by such processes (Yang and Seccombe, 1994). The rare cases where nuggets, overgrowths and dendrites of PGE are found in placer deposits, and in laterite enrichments, also indicate that under certain conditions these metals are labile and can be put into solution even at low temperatures (see Chapter 4).

In the case of the PGE it is apparent, with the possible exception of palladium (Pd), that these metals tend to exhibit *low solubilities* in magmatic-hydrothermal fluids at high temperatures and under fairly reduced (low fO_2) conditions. In the case of Pd it appears that this metal is fairly soluble in saline solutions at elevated temperatures (Sassani and Shock, 1990). In general, however, the presence of ligands such as Cl^- enhances PGE solubilities only slightly and significant dissolution of these metals is only feasible under highly oxidized, acidic conditions (Wood et al., 1992). Hydroxide (OH^-) complexation is also regarded as unlikely to contribute toward PGE solubility in hydrothermal solutions, although it may be important in surficial waters and PGE–OH^- complexes may be implicated in placer and laterite deposits. Likewise, bisulfide (HS^-) complexes result in very low (ppb) quantities of Pt and Pd being transported in most geologically pertinent solutions. These observations tend to support the conventional view that metal concentrations in mafic rocks have not been markedly modified by hydrothermal processes. However, under conditions of very low fS_2 (where the metal and not the metal sulfide is stable) it appears that PGE solubilities in a highly saline brine might be high (10^2–10^3 ppb), mainly because PGE complexation with Cl^- is not detrimentally affected by the presence of sulfide ligands. Under such conditions, a fluid could play an important role in the redistribution of these metals.

2.12.1 The effects of a magmatic fluid on PGE mineralization in the Bushveld Complex

In the Bushveld Complex the grades of platinum group element (PGE) mineralization and the relative proportions of these elements remain uniform over tens of kilometers of strike, in both the Merensky Reef and the UG2 chromitite seam (Cawthorn et al., 2002). By contrast the mineralogy of the PGE varies markedly. The normal stratiform reef is generally dominated by PGE sulfide minerals such as cooperite, braggite, and laurite. Atypical situations, represented by mineralized potholes (see Box 1.6) and unusual discordant Pt-rich dunite pipes, are characterized by PGE–Fe alloys and tellurides. The general consensus is that the sulfide-dominated mineralogy of normal reefs is the product of magmatic processes, as discussed in Chapter 1, but that the sulfur-deficient PGE mineralogy in potholes and pipes reflects areas where a volatile-rich fluid phase has interacted with the magmatic ores, resulting in localized low fS_2 conditions.

The Bushveld Complex contains several unusual rock types such as iron-rich ultramafic pipes,

as well as iron-rich pegmatites (with concentrations of Pb, As, Sb, and Bi) and plagioclase–amphibole–phlogopite veins, that have been used as evidence for vapor- or fluid-saturation in the late stages of crystallization of the Bushveld magmas. Schiffries (1982) regarded the Fe- and Pt-rich dunite pipes as metasomatic in origin and implicated an aqueous magmatic brine that reacted with the country rocks at around 600 °C and 3.5 kbar. More recent work has indicated that these bodies are probably discrete magmatic intrusions, but that they did act as channelways for later, lower temperature hydrothermal fluids (Cawthorn et al., 2000). The sulfide-poor, Pt-dominated mineralogy of these bodies is considered to represent re-equilibration of an original magmatic sulfide assemblage by later hydrothermal fluids.

One of the still contentious issues concerning the Bushveld Complex, however, is the extent to which the major mineralized horizons, such as the Merensky Reef and the UG2, owe their PGE and base metal mineralization to hydrothermal rather than magmatic processes. Detailed mineralogical studies have shown that in certain environments magmatic fluids must have played a role in redistribution of sulfur and recrystallization of the PGE. Where the UG2 chromitite horizon is cut by a dunite pipe, for example, it contains the same distinctive Pt–Fe alloy and Pt–arsenide (sperrylite) phases as the pipe itself. By contrast, the UG2 horizon well removed from such bodies comprises the normal, magmatic PGE–sulfide minerals such as braggite and cooperite (Peyerl, 1982).

In addition, the Merensky Reef itself often exhibits the same sort of variations in PGE mineralogy as does the UG2, but in this case the occurrence of sulfide-deficient PGE minerals is usually related to the formation of "potholes" and not necessarily to cross-cutting dunite replacement pipes (Figure 2.24). The Merensky Reef potholes were described in Chapter 1 (see Box 1.6) and are attributed to syn-magmatic faulting of the footwall cumulates just prior to injection of a new magma pulse, with accompanying metasomatism of rocks within the pothole structure by hydrothermal fluid. The occurrence of desulfidized PGE mineral assemblages in the potholes is consistent both with this process and with the

	Normal	Contact	Pothole
Pt-Fe alloys + base metal sulfides	0.1	0	92.6
Pt-Pd sulfides	89.0	11.5	0
Laurite Ru(Os,Ir)S₂	0.1	87.0	0.4
Tellurides and Cu–Au alloy	10.8	1.5	7.0

Figure 2.24 Schematic illustration showing the nature of "potholes" in the Merensky Reef of the Bushveld Complex and the distinctive mineral assemblages of these features relative to normal reef (after Kinloch, 1982; Mathez, 1989b).

fact that potholes were probably also the sites of fluid-saturation and enhanced circulation. The presence of saline, but relatively oxidized, fluids is considered to have been responsible for modifying the primary magmatic ore mineralogy, destabilizing the dominant base metal and PGE sulfide phases, with the resultant loss of sulfur and reaction between PGE and Fe to form alloys or telluride and arsenide minerals (Kinloch, 1982). It is important to note that, during the hydrothermal overprint, PGE and base metals do not appear to be redistributed and the metal budget, therefore, remains constant (Cawthorn *et al.*, 2002). There seems little evidence for a solely hydrothermal origin for the base and precious metal ores of the

Merensky Reef, or any other major mineralized part of the Bushveld Complex, although it is clear that magmatic fluids have reacted extensively with the rocks of this layered mafic intrusion.

In summary, it would appear that in contrast to granitoid-related systems, magmatic fluids in mafic melts have played a relatively small role in the mineralization processes that accompany the crystallization of these rock types. Vapor-saturation does occur but its influence as a mineralizing agent would generally appear to be limited to re-equilibration of existing magmatic PGE and base metal sulfides, in rocks where metasomatism is clearly demonstrable, such as potholes, Fe-rich dunite pipes, pegmatites, and veins.

SUMMARY

All magmas contain the constituents that, on crystallization, combine to exsolve discrete fluid and vapor phases. Most magmas will exsolve substantial quantities (up to several wt%) of water, as

well as an order of magnitude or so less of carbon dioxide, and these are the two dominant magmatic-hydrothermal fluids. Water in particular has the ability to dissolve significant quantities of anionic substances, in particular Cl⁻, which in turn promotes the dissolution of other alkali and transition metal cations. The magmatic aqueous phase can exist as a liquid, vapor, or homogeneous supercritical fluid. The process of H_2O-saturation can be achieved in two ways, either by decreasing the pressure of the system (called first boiling) or by progressive crystallization of magma (second boiling).

H_2O-saturation is particularly relevant to ore-forming processes during the emplacement and crystallization of granitic magmas at moderate to shallow crustal levels. This environment gives rise to the formation of a wide variety of important ore deposit types including porphyry Cu and Mo deposits, polymetallic skarn ores, granite-related Sn–W deposits, and the family of volcanic-related epithermal Au–Ag–(Cu) deposit types. Many metals will partition strongly into the liquid or vapor that forms on H_2O-saturation and, in such cases, mineralization accompanies the alteration of host rocks, both within and external to the intrusion. The formation of either Cu-dominant or Mo-dominant porphyry deposits reflects a subtle interplay between the depth of intrusion of a granitic body (itself a function of the original water content), the timing of H_2O-saturation relative to the progress of crystallization, and the behavior of metals during melt–fluid partitioning. Egress of fluids and vapor from the magma and their subsequent circulation are dependent on the permeability of the surrounds, and may be modified by boiling-related hydrofracturing. Polymetallic skarn deposits reflect the interaction between the exsolved magmatic fluids from different types of granite and calcareous sediments. H_2O-saturation and boiling in volcanic environments, producing significant volumes of volatile-rich vapor, is conducive to the formation of epithermal deposits. High- and low-sulfidation epithermal deposits reflect end-members in a continuum of magmatic-hydrothermal processes that progressively incorporate more non-magmatic waters as the volcanic system wanes, or as one moves away from the volcanic center. Many ore deposit types are the product of fluids that are unrelated to a magmatic source and these are the subject of Chapter 3.

FURTHER READING

For those readers wishing to read more about magmatic-hydrothermal ore-forming processes, the following references to books and journal special issues will be useful.

Corbett, G.J. and Leach, T.M. (1998) *Southwest Pacific Rim Gold–Copper Systems: Structure, Alteration and Mineralization*. Special Publication 6. El Paso, TX: Society of Economic Geologists, 237 pp.

Geochemistry of Hydrothermal Ore Deposits, ed. H.L. Barnes. 1st edn, 1967. Holt, Rinehart and Winston Inc., pp. 34–76. 2nd edn 1979. John Wiley and Sons, pp. 71–136. 3rd edn, 1997. John Wiley and Sons, pp. 63–124 and 737–96.

Misra, K.C. (2000) *Understanding Mineral Deposits*. Dordrecht: Kluwer Academic Publishers, 845 pp.

Pirajno, F. (1992) *Hydrothermal Mineral Deposits*. New York: Springer-Verlag, 709 pp.

Reviews in Economic Geology, Volume 2: Berger, B.R. and Bethke, B.M. (eds) (1985) *Geology and Geochemistry of Epithermal Systems*. El Paso, TX: Society of Economic Geologists, 298 pp.

Reviews in Economic Geology, Volume 4: Whitney, J.A. and Naldrett, A.J. (eds) (1989) *Ore Deposition Associated with Magmas*. El Paso, TX: Society of Economic Geologists, 250 pp.

Reviews in Economic Geology, Volume 13: Hagemann, S.G. and Brown, P.E. (eds) (2000) *Gold in 2000*. El Paso, TX: Society of Economic Geologists, 559 pp.

Seltmann, R., Lehmann, B., Lowenstern, J.B. and Candela, P.A. (eds) (1997) High-level silicic magmatism and related hydrothermal systems. Special issue, *Journal of Petrology*, 38(12), 1617–807.

Taylor, R.P. and Strong, D.F. (eds) (1988) *Recent Advances in the Geology of Granite-related Mineral Deposits*. Canadian Institute of Mining and Metallurgy, Special Volume 39, 445 pp.

Thompson, J.F.H. (ed.) (1995) *Magmas, Fluids and Ore Deposits*. Mineralogical Association of Canada, Short Course Handbook, 23, 525 pp.

PART TWO

Hydrothermal Processes

CHAPTER TWO

Hydrothermal
Processes

CHAPTER THREE

Hydrothermal ore-forming processes

3.1 INTRODUCTION

This chapter extends the concept of hydrothermal mineralization to deposits related to fluids derived from sources other than magmatic solutions. Such fluids include those formed from metamorphic dehydration reactions, from the expulsion of pore fluids during compaction of sediment, and from meteoric waters. It also considers sea water

as a hydrothermal fluid with specific reference to the formation of base metal deposits on the ocean floor. Unlike the previous chapter, which was mainly concerned with granite-related ore deposits, the present chapter discusses a much broader range of ore-forming processes and environments.

Hydrothermal ore-forming processes are ubiquitous and there is scarcely an ore deposit anywhere on Earth that has not been formed directly from hot aqueous solutions flowing through the crust, or modified to varying degrees by such fluids. This view is supported by the example in section 2.12 of Chapter 2, where a compelling case for hydrothermal precipitation of PGE mineralization in the potholes of the Merensky Reef,

Bushveld Complex, traditionally regarded as igneous in origin, is presented. Likewise, the Au–U ores of the Witwatersrand Basin can no longer be regarded simply as paleoplacer deposits and hydrothermal processes have clearly played a significant role in their formation (see section 3.9 below). Similarly, oil and gas deposits (see Chapter 5) have migrated to their present locations in the presence of hot water, during processes akin to those discussed below for hydrothermal solutions. Many of the giant ore deposits of the world owe their origins to the flow of hydrothermal fluids in the Earth's crust and the ability of aqueous solutions to effectively scavenge, transport, and concentrate a wide range of economically important components.

Over the past few decades in particular, a great deal of research has been directed toward better understanding the complexity of hydrothermal processes. Concepts such as the source of hydrothermal solutions, their passage through the Earth's crust, and the precipitation mechanisms involved in the formation of ore bodies are now relatively well understood. The three editions of Barnes's *Geochemistry of Hydrothermal Ore Deposits* (1967, 1979a, 1997) provide an account of the progress of this research over several decades. There are, of course, some features of hydrothermal ores about which we understand very little, and these include the ages and duration of ore-forming processes, the detailed recognition of ancient fluid pathways, and the depths of fluid flow in the crust, as well as the relationship between global tectonics and metallogeny (Skinner, 1997). The last topic is a particularly important one (see Chapter 6) that applies not only to hydrothermal ores, but to the entire range of mineral deposit types. Finally, the role of microorganisms in the formation of ore deposits is a topic that is beginning to attract attention and may turn out to be much more important than previously thought.

It will be evident that the separation of "magmatic-hydrothermal" and "hydrothermal" processes into two sections (Chapters 2 and 3 respectively) is not so much a conceptual necessity as a requirement of the organization and structure of the book. The two chapters should be seen as covering a spectrum of processes ranging from magmatic fluid flow to shallow level meteoric infiltrations. In order to emphasize the continuum, this chapter is terminated with a summary diagram that attempts to relate the sources of hydrothermal solutions to ore deposit types, and applies to both Chapters 2 and 3.

3.2 OTHER FLUIDS IN THE EARTH'S CRUST AND THEIR ORIGINS

Figure 3.1a shows that, in addition to magmatic fluids, there are four other major water types on or near the Earth's surface. Although they may all have had similar origins, each of these fluid reservoirs is different in terms of its composition and temperature and will, therefore, play different roles in the formation of ore deposits. The major water types are defined as sea water, meteoric water, connate water and metamorphic water, listed typically in order of increasing depth (and temperature) in the crust. A fifth fluid reservoir, where waters are derived from a mixing of two or more other water types, is also described below, specifically because mixed fluids can be very important in certain ore-forming environments.

In their present settings each of these fluids can be identified because the environment from which the fluid came is known. In the geological past, however, where only indirect manifestations of fluid flow are apparent, it is much more difficult to determine the origin of a particular water type. Fortunately, the hydrogen and oxygen isotope characteristics of water are reasonably diagnostic of its source and can be used to deduce the origins of an ancient reservoir. Figure 3.1b is a plot of δD versus $\delta^{18}O$ that shows trends and fields which serve to fingerprint the major fluid reservoirs on or near the Earth's surface. The origins of the various water types and their stable isotopic characteristics are briefly described below.

3.2.1 Sea water

The oceans collectively represent the largest fluid reservoir on the Earth's surface (Figure 3.2), covering some 70% of the surface and containing about

(a)

(b)

Figure 3.1 (a) The major types of liquid water that exist at or near the Earth's surface; magmatic water was specifically discussed in Chapter 2, while the other fluids are discussed in this chapter. (b) Plot of hydrogen (δD permil) and oxygen (δ^{18}O permil) isotopic ratios for various water types (after Taylor, 1997). Standard Mean Ocean Water (SMOW) is defined to be zero for both δD and δ^{18}O. Some ore-forming environments are clearly related to mixed fluid reservoirs; in the cases shown (see A and B) mixing of meteoric and connate fluids has taken place.

98% of its free water. As mentioned in Chapter 2, the Earth's surface has been covered by substantial volumes of water since very early in Earth history. Sea water is relatively well mixed at a global scale, and is weakly saline because of reaction with both continental and oceanic erosion products over time. The principal dissolved constituents in sea water are the cations Na^+, K^+, Ca^{2+}, and Mg^{2+} and anions Cl^-, HCO_3^-, and SO_4^{2-}, which typically occur at a total concentration (or salinity) of around 35 g of solids per kg of sea water (3.5 wt%).

Sea water is extensively circulated through the oceanic crust and is responsible for widespread alteration and metal redistribution in this portion of the Earth's crust. The drawdown of sea water into major faults associated with the mid-ocean ridges and its subsequent emergence from exhalative vents or "black smokers" is a major oceanographic discovery that has revolutionized the understanding of volcanogenic massive sulfide (VMS) deposits (see section 3.8 below). VMS deposits occur in many different parts of the world, and in rocks of all ages, confirming the

Figure 3.2 Simplified diagram illustrating the water budget on or close to the surface of the Earth (after Berner and Berner, 1996). Precipitation fluxes are in 10^6 km^3 yr^{-1} and reservoir volumes in 10^6 km^3.

Table 3.1 Representative concentrations (in ppm) of major ionic species in natural meteoric waters

Species (ppm)	Sea water	Black smoker sea water (at 100–300 °C)	Rain water	Meteoric spring water (at 6 °C)	Meteoric geothermal water (at 300 °C)
Na$^+$	10 000	6000–14 000	1.0	23	187
Cl$^-$	20 000	15 000–25 000	1.1	3.1	21
SO$_4^{2-}$	2700	0	1.5	11	103
Mg^{2+}	1300	0	0.2	2.4	0
Ca^{2+}	410	36	0.4	5.1	0.5
K$^+$	400	26	0.5	1.0	27
Si^{4+}	0.5–10	20	1.2	17	780
Metals (Fe, Cu, Zn, Mn, etc.)	depleted	enriched	depleted	depleted	enriched

Source: after data in Krauskopf and Bird (1995), Scott (1997).

importance of sea water as a hydrothermal fluid source. Table 3.1 illustrates the concentrations of major ionic species in sea water and compares this to fluids exhaled from black smoker vents, where significant concentrations of metals have taken place due to interaction between hot sea water and oceanic crust. Sea water is also compared to rain water and meteoric derived groundwaters, which again have higher dissolved solute contents at higher temperatures.

3.2.2 Meteoric water

Meteoric water has its immediate origin within the hydrological cycle and has, therefore, been in contact with the atmosphere. In a geological context it refers to groundwater that has infiltrated into the upper crust, through either rainfall or seepage from standing or flowing surface water. In this sense sea water infiltrating into the crust should also be regarded as a source of meteoric groundwater. Groundwater is the second largest reservoir of liquid water (Figure 3.2) and generally exists close to the surface in the interstitial pore spaces of rocks and soil. It does not refer to the water that forms part of the crystal structure of hydrous minerals, nor does it refer to the micrometer-sized fluid inclusions that occur within many of the rock-forming minerals of both the crust and mantle. Meteoric fluid can nevertheless penetrate along fractures to deep levels in the crust and is, therefore, involved in widespread circulation throughout the crustal regime. It is responsible for the formation of many different types of hydrothermal ore deposits, but especially those characterized by relatively low temperature transport and precipitation, such as sandstone-hosted and surficial uranium ores (see section 3.11 and Chapter 4).

The oxygen and hydrogen isotope compositions of meteoric waters, both on the surface and as groundwater, vary systematically over the entire globe as a function of latitude and elevation. The linear relationship between δD and $\delta^{18}O$ values (the meteoric water line in Figure 3.1b) exists because deuterium and hydrogen, as well as ^{18}O and ^{16}O, are systematically fractionated between liquid water and water vapor during the evaporation–condensation processes of the hydrological cycle, and this fractionation increases as a function of temperature (Craig, 1961). Thus, most meteoric waters have δD and $\delta^{18}O$ values that vary along a straight line ($\delta D = 8 \times \delta^{18}O + 10$; Figure 3.1b) and which help to broadly identify the climatic conditions or latitude from where the water came.

3.2.3 Connate water

Water that is included within the interstitial pore spaces of sediment as it is deposited is referred to as connate or formational water. Originally this water is either meteoric or sea water, but it undergoes substantial modification as the sediment is buried, compacted, and lithified. The various stages of diagenesis that result in the transformation from uncompacted particles of sediment to lithified sedimentary rock produce aqueous solutions that evolve with time and depth. Such fluids invariably move through the sequence and are often involved in the formation of ore deposits.

The progressive burial of sediment to depths of around 300 meters results in a rapid reduction of porosity and the initial production of a substantial volume of water. Shales are initially very porous and the early stages of burial can result in the production of up to 3500 litres of water for each cubic meter of sediment deposited (Hanor,

1979). Over 75% of the interstitial pore fluid is likely to be expelled from a shale by the time it is buried to 300 meters depth and its porosity will, accordingly, decrease rapidly at this early stage. By contrast, uncompacted sandstones are initially less porous than shales and will release only 700 litres of water for each cubic meter of sediment deposited (Hanor, 1979). Calculated average rates of water release for shales and sands are shown as a function of depth of burial in Figure 3.3a.

An additional source of formation water is the "structural" or "bound" water that occurs either as loosely bound H_2O or OH^- molecules within clay mineral particles in argillaceous sediments. Such water is able to leave the host mineral once temperatures of 50–100 °C have been reached. This is shown as the episodic peak-like increases in the rate of release of water from the sediment in the depth profiles of Figure 3.3a. The nature and volume of bound water release will obviously vary from one situation to the next and depend on factors such as the local geothermal gradient and the type and proportions of clay host minerals. The two main stages of connate fluid production (i.e. pore fluid and bound water) are also schematically illustrated in Figure 3.4, where they are compared to the production of metamorphic fluids that occurs at somewhat higher temperatures and greater burial depths.

The temperature of connate fluids increases with depth in the sedimentary sequence, with the exact rate of increase being a function of the local geothermal gradient. The latter varies typically between 15 and 40 °C km^{-1}. Fluid pressures will also increase with depth, although the nature of pressure variation with progressive burial is likely to be complex and depend on the amount of pore fluid present in any given sedimentary unit and the interplay between hydrostatic and lithostatic pressure gradients. A more detailed description of the relationships between hydrostatic and lithostatic pressure is presented in section 3.3.2 below, where its significance with respect to the movement of hydrothermal fluids in sedimentary sequences is discussed. Figure 3.3b illustrates the way fluid pressure varies with depth in the Gulf Coast sediments of the southern USA and points

(a)

Release of interstitial
water on compaction

Episodic release of
"bound" water from clays

Shales

Sands

Rate of water release (l m⁻¹ of burial)

Depth (km)

(b)

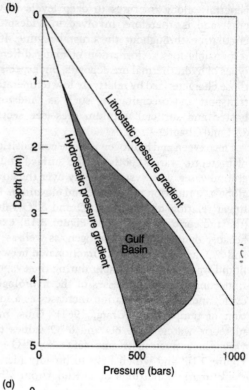

Lithostatic pressure gradient

Hydrostatic pressure gradient

Gulf
Basin

Pressure (bars)

Depth (km)

(c)

Gulf
Basin   Alberta   Michigan

Density (g cm⁻³)

Depth (km)

(d)

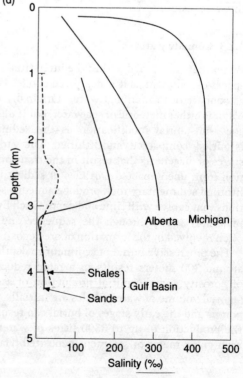

Alberta   Michigan

Shales

Sands   } Gulf Basin

Salinity (‰)

Depth (km)

to significant deviations above the hydrostatic gradient (i.e "overpressuring") caused by low permeability horizons within the sequence which impede the expulsion of fluids so that pore water supports the weight of the overlying strata and high fluid pressures result (Hanor, 1979). Zones of overpressured fluids dictate the nature of fluid flow and mass/heat transfer, which has important implications for the migration of oil brines (see Chapter 5) and the formation of a variety of sediment-hosted hydrothermal ore deposits.

Connate fluids also undergo increases in density and salinity with depth, as illustrated in Figure 3.3c and d. The density increases are related to increases in pressure and salinity, although there is a limit to such a trend since temperature is also augmented and this has an inverse effect on density. Deep basinal waters are commonly saline to the extent that they are generally unpotable. The increase in salinity is sometimes related to interaction of connate waters with evaporitic horizons which contain easily dissolvable minerals such as halite, sylvite, gypsum, and anhydrite. Salinity increases are also, however, apparent in sedimentary sequences which do not contain evaporites and in such cases the process of "membrane-" or "salt-filtration" probably applies. In argillaceous layers, where clay particles are strongly compacted, the interaction of the net negative charge (caused by atomic substitutions within the crystal lattice) around each particle creates what is termed a "Gouy layer" (Berner, 1971). The latter acts as a semipermeable membrane or filter which serves to reject anions in solutions passing through the shale layer. Since anions are excluded from the filtrate then so too must be cations, in order to maintain electroneutrality. The result is that any solution passing through the compacted

clay will emerge with a lower salinity. Upwardly migrating brines will, therefore, become less saline, whereas the dissolved salt content of deeper residual waters will increase. Although doubts have been expressed about the efficacy of forcing solutions upwards in a sedimentary sequence across semipermeable shale layers, the process of salt filtration is generally regarded as a feasible explanation for the widespread existence of subsurface connate brines. The topic is of considerable importance to ore genesis, as the availability of ligands in hydrothermal fluids, especially Cl^-, is crucial to increasing the solubility and transport efficiency of metals in solution (see Chapter 2 and section 3.4 below).

The salinity characteristics of connate waters will vary from one sedimentary basin to another, as seen in Figure 3.3d. Likewise, the δD and $\delta^{18}O$ characteristics of such fluids will also vary depending on the climatic characteristics and latitude of the host basin. Since the original trapped pore fluids in most sedimentary sequences will be either meteoric or sea water, their hydrogen and oxygen isotope compositions will initially reflect either the appropriate point along the meteoric water line or SMOW (Figure 3.1b). As the fluids evolve, through both temperature increases and interaction with the host rocks, their stable isotope characteristics will also change and define trends that typically deviate from a position on the meteoric water line along paths of shallower slope. Fluids will tend to reflect higher $\delta^{18}O$ values as their temperatures and salinities increase in sedimentary sequences (Taylor, 1997). In Figure 3.1b, for example, the low latitude Gulf Coast formational waters define a trend that is quite distinct from the fluids in the high latitude Alberta Basin of Canada.

Figure 3.3 (*Opposite*) The formation and characteristics of connate waters. (a) Depth profile illustrating the rate of water release due to initial compaction and porosity reduction followed by dehydration of clay minerals such as montmorillonite. (b, c, and d) Depth profiles showing typical pressures, fluid densities, and fluid salinities, respectively, in a compacting sediment pile. Different profiles refer to the Michigan, Alberta, and Gulf basins in the USA (after Hanor, 1979).

3.2.4 Metamorphic water

As rocks are progressively buried and temperatures exceed about 200 °C, the process of diagenesis evolves to one of metamorphism. Metamorphism is a multifaceted process but essentially involves the transformation of one mineral or mineral assemblage to another whose stability is more in equilibrium with the prevailing conditions at

Figure 3.4 The relationship between connate fluid production during diagenesis and metamorphic fluid production due to systematic dehydration reactions involving the breakdown of one mineral assemblage to another containing less water. The conditions pertaining here were calculated specifically for the Witwatersrand Basin (after Stevens *et al.*, 1997).

higher pressure and temperature. Of importance in this discussion is the transformation of hydrous silicate and carbonate minerals to newly formed assemblages that contain lesser volatiles than before. Dehydration and decarbonation reactions during prograde metamorphism are, therefore, very important processes that produce substantial volumes of metamorphic water in the mid- and lower-crust. An example from the Witwatersrand Basin in South Africa (Figure 3.4) shows that at around 300 °C a metamorphic reaction involving the breakdown of kaolinite to pyrophyllite will result in the production of metamorphic water. The latter arises from the fact that kaolinite contains more water than does pyrophyllite so that the excess water liberated by the phase transformation has to be expelled into the sedimentary sequence. This reaction is followed at around 400 °C by the transformation of muscovite and chlorite to biotite, when more fluid will be produced. Both H_2O and CO_2 (the latter specifically when the breakdown reactions involve carbonate minerals), as well as volatiles such as CH_4 and sulfur species, are produced as metamorphic fluids during prograde reactions of this type.

Fluids produced in low to medium grade metamorphic terranes are dominated compositionally by H_2O, CO_2, and CH_4 in approximately that order of abundance. High grade rocks tend to be dominated by dense CO_2 with lesser amounts of associated water and methane. Most metamorphic fluids have low salinities and low concentrations of reduced sulfur. Fluids of this nature are globally implicated in the formation of orogenic gold deposits, which represent a very important category of gold deposit types (Phillips *et al.*, 1994; see Box 3.2). Although it has not been mentioned before, it is clear that CO_2 may be an important component of hydrothermal solutions, not only in those originating through metamorphic devolatilization but also in magmatic waters.

Carbon dioxide is, after water, the most abundant component in hydrothermal solutions and its phase equilibria relative to those of water are briefly considered below. It is a larger molecule than water and is non-polar (see Chapter 2), which accounts for its lower melting and critical points. It is of little importance as a solvent other than for non-anionic species such as the hydrocarbons, especially CH_4.

A part of the phase diagram for pure CO_2 is shown in Figure 3.5a and when compared to a similar diagram for H_2O (Figure 2.2c) is seen to have remarkably similar densities and phase transition characteristics to water, except that it has lower melting ($-56.6\,^\circ C$) and critical ($31.1\,^\circ C$) points. At high temperatures H_2O and CO_2 are completely miscible and form a single fluid phase where the one compound is dissolved in the other. At lower temperatures H_2O and CO_2 become

(a) **CO₂**

(b) **H₂O–CO₂**

Figure 3.5 (a) Part of the phase diagram for CO_2 showing the variations in fluid density (i.e. isochores in g cm^{-3}) as a function of pressure and temperature. The diagram is similar to that for H_2O (see Figure 2.2c) except for the lower melting and critical points. (b) Various solvus curves for the system H_2O–CO_2; the solvus (i.e. the curve which defines where in P–T–X space H_2O and CO_2 unmix) moves to higher temperatures with decreasing pressure and increasing salinity of the mixture (compilations after Brown, 1998).

Figure 3.5 (cont'd) (c) Microphotograph showing the typical appearance of a H_2O–CO_2-bearing fluid inclusion. Prior to entrapment this fluid was a homogeneous mixture of mutually soluble H_2O and CO_2. On cooling it subsequently exsolved to form immiscible fractions of H_2O (outer fluid wetting the walls of the inclusion) and CO_2 (inner globule of fluid). A vapor bubble occurs within the inner CO_2 globule.

immiscible (like oil and water) and exist as two separate phases (usually as H_2O liquid and CO_2 supercritical fluid). This relationship is shown in Figure 3.5b, where the solvus (i.e. the curve which defines where unmixing of the single phase mixture occurs) for pure H_2O–CO_2 at 2 kbar identifies a plateau at around 250–300 °C, above which the two compounds occur as a single miscible phase. As the temperature falls the single phase fluid progressively unmixes until at room temperature H_2O and CO_2 are essentially immiscible. This phenomenon is clearly illustrated in fluid inclusions that have trapped single phase H_2O–CO_2 mixtures above the relevant solvus. When viewed in a laboratory at room temperature, these fluid inclusions are typically characterized by a so-called "double bubble." The larger "bubble" is actually a globule of immiscible CO_2 fluid within liquid H_2O, whereas the smaller inner "bubble" comprises a mixture of H_2O and CO_2 vapor (Figure 3.5c). The widespread occurrence of H_2O- and CO_2-bearing fluid inclusions in the rock record attests to the ubiquity of aqueo-carbonic fluids especially in the deep crust.

Metamorphic waters are characterized by relatively high $\delta^{18}O$ values (+10 to +30 permil) which are typically quite distinct compared to both

meteoric and connate waters, but which may overlap to a certain extent with magmatic waters (Figure 3.1b). The reasons for this are complex and related to the variable nature of metamorphic protoliths and the ubiquitous effects of fluid–rock interaction during regional metamorphism (Taylor, 1997).

3.2.5 Waters of mixed origin

Although the previous discussion has emphasized the nature and characteristics of different individual fluid reservoirs in the Earth's crust, it is unreasonable to expect that in nature such waters would necessarily retain their integrity with time. In the upper crust especially, it is expected that fluids will undergo mixing and effectively become hybrids with more than just a single source or origin. It is apparent that the mixing of ore-bearing hydrothermal fluids may be an important consideration in the precipitation of metals from such solutions. Magmatic and meteoric waters, for example, often undergo mixing at the volcanic to subvolcanic crustal levels associated with porphyry copper and epithermal Au–Ag ore-forming environments. Mixing of connate and meteoric waters is also a process known to characterize sedimentary basins forming in rapidly filled continental rift environments. The major effect of fluid mixing is to promote the precipitation of metals from ore-forming solutions and, consequently, this topic is discussed in more detail in section 3.5.1 below.

3.3 The movement of hydrothermal fluids in the Earth's crust

In order to be effective as a mineralizing agent, hydrothermal fluids need to circulate through the Earth's crust. The main reason for this is that they need to interact with large volumes of rock in order to dissolve and transport the metals required to form hydrothermal ore deposits. The flow of an ore fluid should preferably be focused so that the dissolved constituents can be concentrated into an accessible portion of the Earth's crust that has dimensions consistent with those of a potential ore body. The study of hydrothermal fluid movement has received a great deal of impetus from the oil and gas industry, where it is particularly important to understand the pathways of hydrocarbon-bearing brines in sedimentary sequences in order to explore for these types of deposits (see Chapter 5, section 5.4). Exploration for metallic hydrothermal ores has also benefited over the past few years from a better understanding of fluid flow in the Earth's crust, especially with respect to Archean lode gold ores and Mississippi Valley type Pb–Zn deposits (see Boxes 3.2 and 3.7 respectively).

In Chapter 2 the nature and duration of hydrothermal fluid flow associated with magmatic intrusions was briefly discussed. The present section looks at hydrothermal fluid flow in the Earth's crust in more general terms and also at a variety of scales. It emphasizes the role that deformation and the resulting structural features play, in terms of both movement and focusing of fluid flow in the crust. It is these features that are of particular importance to the formation and location of metallic hydrothermal ores.

3.3.1 Factors affecting fluid flow at a crustal scale

The question of how large volumes of fluid can move around at deep levels in the Earth's crust, where rocks are highly compacted and have low intrinsic permeabilities, is one that has long taxed researchers in a variety of disciplines. Movement of fluid is typically a response to either a thermal or a pressure gradient in the Earth's crust. The latter, in particular, is often related to deformation which causes both stress and strain to vary in the rocks being deformed. Deformation is widely regarded as having played a major role in controlling fluid flow throughout the crust (Sibson *et al.*, 1975; Oliver, 1996) and its effects are discussed in more detail in section 3.3.3 below. Since crustal deformation is invariably linked to global tectonic processes it is clear why the latter are so intimately related to the formation of hydrothermal ores (see Chapter 6).

Another question that is pertinent to understanding the nature of fluid movement in the Earth's crust is that of pervasive as opposed to channelized flow. The two scenarios can be described in terms of "intrinsic permeability," where fluids infiltrate pervasively along grain boundaries and microcracks in a rock, and "hydraulic permeability," where fluid flows along major cracks that are sufficiently interconnected to allow a distinct fluid channelway to develop (Oliver, 1996). Pervasive fluid flow can take place in porous rocks at relatively shallow levels in the crust, a situation that allows convective fluid movement to occur. Figure 3.6 illustrates a variety of tectonic scenarios at a crustal scale and the nature and distribution of major fluid flow vectors associated with each. At relatively shallow crustal levels pervasive fluid flow, along a porous aquifer, for example, often occurs in response to a gravity-driven hydraulic head formed by uplifted topography (Figure 3.6a). This is believed to be the dominant type of groundwater flow in continental regions and flow rates of between 1 and 10 m yr^{-1} could develop depending on the permeability of the aquifer (Garven and Raffensperger, 1997). A similar style of long-range fluid flow is now known to be associated with periods of orogenic compression which effectively squeeze the fluid out of one package of rock into channelways (thrusts?) or high permeability aquifers in another (Figure 3.6b). Orogeny-driven fluids have been implicated in the formation of the major Mississippi Valley type Pb–Zn ore province of the southeast USA (see Box 3.7).

In oceanic crust fluids are believed to flow in response to thermal gradients formed because of the high heat flow that characterizes the mid-ocean ridges (Figure 3.6c). Sea water is forced down into the crust along faults and, although essentially channelized, flows largely in response to convection, reappearing close to the zones of maximum heat flow. Thermally driven convective fluid flow can occur, as mentioned in Chapter 2, in close proximity to high level magmatic intrusions. It can also occur in deep intracratonic rift basins where high heat flow or fluid density gradients result in convective flow, but only in aquifers where permeabilities are sufficiently high (Figure 3.6d).

Large-scale flow of fluid at a crustal scale can also occur in association with the dilatancy (i.e.

Figure 3.6 Various tectonic scenarios illustrating the mechanisms by which major fluid movements in the Earth's crust take place. (a) Gravity-driven fluid flow in response to the creation of a hydrostatic head in an area of uplift. (b) Orogeny-driven fluid flow in response to rock compaction in a fold and thrust belt. (c) Thermally driven fluid flow in the ocean crust in response to high heat flow at mid-ocean ridges. (d) Thermally driven fluid flow in a permeable unit within a basin or rift. (e) Dilatancy- or fault-driven fluid flow along major, seismically active structural features by seismic pumping and fault valve mechanisms (modified after Garven and Raffensperger, 1997).

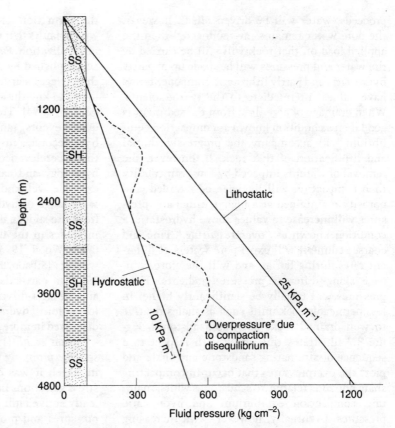

Figure 3.7 Plot of depth versus fluid pressure to illustrate the difference between hydrostatic and lithostatic pressure gradients. The dashed line shows the excesses in hydrostatic pressure (i.e. overpressure) that can accumulate in low permeability shale horizons (shown as SH relative to sandstone (SS) layers in the column on the left hand side) because of the inability of these rocks to efficiently drain off pore waters on compaction (after Hunt, 1979).

change in volume) of a rock mass that accompanies faulting and seismic rupture (Figure 3.6e). Orogeny-driven fluids may be partially associated with this process, but more typically dilatancy accompanies faulting and shearing and this particular process is considered in more detail in section 3.3.3 below.

3.3.2 A note on hydrostatic versus lithostatic pressure gradients

As mentioned previously, one of the main factors which controls fluid migration pathways is the existence of a pressure differential in the host rock. In a completely dry rock the pressure at any depth is effectively provided by the weight of the mass of rock above that point and is known as *lithostatic pressure*. In Figure 3.7 the lithostatic pressure gradient is demonstrated by the line of slope 25 kPa m^{-1}, and reflects the average density

(i.e. about 2.5 g cm^{-3}) of the rock sequence over that interval. The distribution of stress (i.e. force per unit area) in a rock at any point along a depth profile at lithostatic gradients will vary with orientation, and will be maximized in a vertical sense and minimized horizontally. By contrast, the pressure on a rock located at the bottom of the ocean will be given by the *hydrostatic pressure* gradient (Figure 3.7), which has a slope of about 10 kPa m^{-1}, reflecting the lower density of water relative to rock (i.e. about 1.0 g cm^{-3}). Stresses under hydrostatic pressure are distributed equally in all directions, which accounts for the relative "weightlessness" of objects immersed in water.

Uncompacted sediment on the ocean floor containing abundant pore water that is still in direct contact with the overlying ocean water column will also be pressurized along the hydrostatic gradient. As the sediment is buried and compaction proceeds, water will be driven off. If, however, the pore water remains interconnected then the applied load on that rock will still be carried by the water and pressures will be made up of partly hydrostatic and partly lithostatic components and have values intermediate to the two gradients. When drainage of pore fluid from the sediment is good then a condition known as compaction equilibrium will accompany the progressive burial and lithification of that rock. If, however, the removal of water is impeded by low permeability then compaction will likewise be retarded (and porosity maintained at a higher value) and pressures will increase to values above hydrostatic, a condition known as "overpressuring." Fine and coarse sediment will expel pore waters at different rates during burial, and will therefore compact along different pressure gradients. Fluid pressures will usually be significantly higher in less permeable rock units such as shales relative to well drained rocks such as sandstones. Figure 3.7 illustrates this effect with respect to a sequence of alternating sandstone and shale and plots the overpressures that occur in compacting shale horizons relative to sandstones which maintain compaction equilibrium and hydrostatic pressures. Eventually, however, with increasing depth in normal crustal profiles pore fluid pressures increase from hydrostatic to lithostatic (so that fluid pressure equals rock pressure) and this occurs at between 5 and 10 km depth depending on the nature of the rocks. The nature of hydrostatic and lithostatic pressure gradients in the Earth's crust, and the deviations from these end-member scenarios, are critical to understanding the nature of fluid flow in all rock types.

3.3.3 Deformation and hydrothermal fluid flow

At progressively deeper levels in the crust, rock porosity is reduced and so is the fluid volume contained within that rock. It is also more difficult for fluids to move pervasively through a rock and under these conditions fluid migration can only take place along channelways represented by structural discontinuities that form during deformation. Most of the fluid movement that occurs at deeper crustal levels, and is relevant to

the formation of mineral deposits, is located within faults that may, as a result, become loci for mineralization. Fault displacements are generally accomplished by increments of rapid movement that trigger earthquake events, usually in the upper 15 km (the seismogenic regime) of the crust (Sibson, 1994). The relationships between earthquake events, fault propagation, and fluid flow have become a major and important area of study that has relevance not only to ore genesis but to hydrology and earthquake prediction. It is, for example, well known that seismic events trigger a wide range of hydrological events that can vary from the sudden drying up of wells to significant increases in the flow of rivers adjacent to faults (Muir Wood, 1994). The work of Sibson and coworkers (Sibson, 1986, 1987; Sibson et al., 1975, 1988) in particular has emphasized the importance of fault-driven fluid flow (Figure 3.6e) to the formation of hydrothermal ore deposits and this is discussed in more detail below.

Sibson et al. (1975) first introduced the term seismic pumping to describe a theoretical model in which it was envisaged that the cyclicity of stress variations in and around a rupturing, seismically active fault system would affect local fluid pressures and promote the flow of fluids along the fault (Figure 3.8a). Prior to a seismic event friction between the opposing faces of a fault prevents rupture such that shear stress increases and the adjacent rock undergoes dilation (Figure 3.8a and b). The dilatant strain that develops in the rock around the fault causes cracks to form, into which fluids flow. Consequently, fluid pressures are predicted to fall in the build up to fault failure. At the instant the fault ruptures and an earthquake occurrs, however, shear stress drops significantly ($\Delta\tau$ in Figure 3.8b) but fluid pressure increases, resulting in the upward expulsion of fluids along the fault. As frictional forces are reinstated and shear stresses increase again, the entire cycle could repeat itself, causing episodic fluid flow along fault-related channelways in the crust. The seismic pumping model provided an explanation and a mechanism for moving fluids through the crust related to cyclical variations in both the stress and strain state of rocks around faults.

Figure 3.8 Early model explaining the episodic flow of fluid along a seismically active fault zone. (a) Block diagram illustrating the geometry of a fault generated seismic pumping system. (b) Explanation of the changes in tectonic shear stress and fluid pressure with time before and after a seismic event, and the accompanying fluid flow direction around the dilatant zone. Maximum outflow of fluid from the zone of dilatancy occurs as the seismic failure event occurs and fractures close (after Sibson *et al.*, 1975).

In reality the factors controlling channelized movement of hydrothermal solutions through the Earth's crust are more complex than the mechanisms outlined in the Sibson *et al.* (1975) model. The model is also somewhat unrealistic since there seems to be little or no evidence to substantiate the sort of crack propagation in rocks adjacent to faults that was envisaged in the model (Sibson, 1994). It is nevertheless still apparent that stress/strain cycling in rocks in and around faults is a major control of crustal fluid movement. The relevance of such processes to the formation of mesothermal lode-gold deposits has,

for example, been demonstrated by Sibson *et al.* (1988). These types of deposits (see Box 3.2) are typically located within high angle (i.e. subvertical) reverse faults (Figure 3.9a). Such faults are an enigma since compressive stresses in the Earth's crust generally form thrust faults that are shallowly inclined (i.e. 25–30° to a horizontal maximum principal compression). Friction theory suggests that reactivation of high angle faults in a horizontal compressive stress regime can only occur when the local fluid pressure reaches or exceeds the lithostatic load. The subsequent model proposed by Sibson *et al.* (1988) envisages

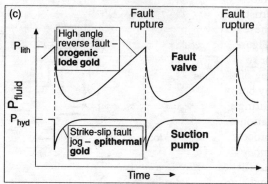

Figure 3.9 Models explaining the nature of hydrothermal fluid flow in (a) high angle reverse faults in a horizontal compressive stress regime considered to be applicable to the formation of mesothermal lode-gold deposits such as the Mother Lode in California and in many Archean greenstone belts; and (b) en echelon strike-slip fault arrays associated with extensional stresses and considered applicable to some shallow level epithermal gold deposits. (c) Plot of fluid pressure with time showing the cyclic fluctuations envisaged for the fault valve model (applicable to high angle reverse fault-related mesothermal lode-gold deposits) and the suction pump model (applicable to strike-slip related fault jogs and shallow level epithermal gold mineralization). The diagrams are after Sibson (1987) and Sibson *et al.* (1988).

that sites of mesothermal lode-gold mineralization are located in structures where fault rupture has been caused by the attainment of lithostatic fluid pressures. Figure 3.9c illustrates how fluid pressure in a seismically active fault builds up to levels approaching the lithostatic load because the upper crust represents an impervious cap to the fluid reservoir beneath. Fault rupture occurs as fluid pressures reach the lithostatic equivalent and the seismic event is accompanied by dilatancy and the development of a fracture permeability upwards and along the fault (Sibson *et al.*, 1988). As the fault fails and shear stresses are substantially reduced, fluids are also discharged into the open space created by the fault rupture itself. The dramatic decrease in fluid pressure (back toward hydrostatic values) that results from

the creation of open space could promote the precipitation of dissolved constituents within the hydrothermal solution, causing the fault to reseal itself. Once this has happened fluid pressures are likely to increase again. This crack–seal mechanism is now known as the *"fault valve model"* and appears to explain many of the characteristics of mesothermal lode-gold deposits (Figure 3.9a and c).

A slightly different mechanism of fluid movement is envisaged with respect to strike slip faulting associated with extensional stresses. Dilational. fault jogs are commonly found between the end of one rupture plane and the beginning of another in extensional en echelon fault arrays (Figure 3.9b), and such sites are particularly favorable for epithermal gold mineralization at high crustal levels (Sibson, 1987). Fault jogs are typically characterized by the development of extensional fractures which are preserved as a network of quartz veins. Fault jog related quartz vein arrays may also be mineralized, an example of which is the Martha Hill (or Waihi) gold deposit of the Coromandel Peninsula in New Zealand (Brathwaite and Faure, 2002). The development of extensional fractures in the fault jog results from the transfer of fault slip from one en echelon fault segment to the other during seismic activity along the fault trace. The opening up of open space at high crustal levels and the discharge of fluid into these spaces results in a rapid fluid pressure drop (Figure 3.9c) which could, at least within 2–3 km or so of the surface, also be accompanied by boiling of the fluid. The mechanical energy released by boiling would result in further hydraulic fracturing and brecciation, with enhanced fluid circulation and mineral precipitation. This particular process is referred to as the "*suction pump model*" (Sibson, 1987) and appears to have applicability to strike slip fault systems and epithermal fluid flow at shallow crustal depths (Figure 3.9b and c).

There is no doubt that deformation-controlled fluid movement along major fault systems in the Earth's crust is of major importance to the formation of hydrothermal ore deposits over a considerable range of crustal depths. This is confirmed by the fact that many hydrothermal ores are located within structural discontinuities and also that exploration companies frequently target structural features in their quest for mineral deposits.

3.3.4 Other factors affecting fluid flow and mineral precipitation

Previous discussion has centered on fluid movement in large-scale structures such as faults that are tens to hundreds of kilometers in length. This section considers smaller-scale fluid migration as evident at mesoscale (as individual quartz veins) or microscale (as fluid inclusion traces in individual minerals) levels. At these scales effective flow of fluid through a rock is determined by hydraulic conductivity, or the extent to which fractures along which fluids might flow are interconnected (Odling, 1997; Cox *et al.*, 2001). In a rock containing very few fractures or cracks, and where poros-

Figure 3.10 The small scale considerations of fluid flow in a rock depend on the creation of permeability and a percolation threshold, which is in turn a function of connectivity and fracture density. The percolation threshold is reached when one cluster of fractures becomes large enough to span the sample region (after Odling, 1997).

ity is low, permeability may be effectively zero and little or no fluid will flow through the rock (Figure 3.10). As the fracture density increases, so too does the probability of two cracks interconnecting. Eventually a point is reached, termed the *percolation threshold*, where permeability suddenly increases dramatically and fluid flow across a finite volume of rock becomes possible (Figure 3.10; Odling, 1997). The attainment of a percolation threshold, at any scale in a rock mass, is clearly necessary if effective fluid circulation is to take place.

How do we know that a fluid had passed through a rock?

The evidence that a fluid had once flowed through a rock mass is provided either by alteration (see section 3.6 below) or by the presence of veins that

Figure 3.11 Schematic diagram showing a convecting pore fluid circulating in a porous sandstone and the contrasting behavior of mineral precipitation and dissolution. In this model it is assumed that quartz solubility decreases, but calcite solubility increases, as fluid temperatures decrease (after Bjørlykke, 1994).

are typically filled with quartz or a carbonate phase (i.e. calcite, dolomite, siderite, etc.), together with other less common gangue minerals. Veins are formed by an assemblage of minerals that precipitate from hot aqueous solutions as they passed through a fracture, effectively fossilizing and preserving the fluid conduit in the rock record. Fracture fill will develop in one of two ways (Bjørlykke, 1994):

1 By diffusion of solids from the surrounds and precipitation within a fracture or open space (i.e. a vug). Since a mineral such as quartz has a lower solubility in aqueous solution at lower pressures and temperatures (see section 2.4.1 in Chapter 2), it follows that it is likely to precipitate in a fracture because the open space will exist under hydrostatic pressure gradients compared to the fracture walls which carry higher pressure lithostatic loads.

2 By precipitation of minerals from fluids flowing through a fracture. In this case material can be brought in from a distant source and will precipitate in the open space as a function of many different processes (see section 3.5.1 below), such as temperature decrease, rock alteration, solubility decrease, and boiling.

The factors controlling precipitation of minerals are varied and complex and this topic is discussed in more detail with respect to ore-forming constituents in sections 3.4 and 3.5 below. Minerals also precipitate from fluids flowing pervasively through a porous rock mass and this is the mech-

anism responsible for diagenesis, whereby sedimentary particles are cemented together and lithified (i.e. turned into rock). Assuming equilibrium between pore fluid and host rock, the volume of minerals precipitated from a fluid circulating through a rock mass can be calculated from the relation (after Bjørlykke, 1994):

$$V_m = Ftsin\,\beta(dT/dZ)\alpha_T/\rho \qquad [3.1]$$

where V_m is the volume of mineral precipitated; F is the fluid flux; t is time (seconds); β is the angle between direction of flow and isotherms in the rock; dT/dZ is the geothermal gradient; α_T is a function which reflects solubility in terms of temperature, and ρ is the density of the mineral being precipitated.

A schematic illustration of mineral precipitation, and conversely of mineral dissolution, is shown in Figure 3.11, where pore fluid is considered to be convecting freely through a porous sanstone. Because the solubility of quartz is reduced down a temperature gradient it will tend to be precipitated along a cooling path, but dissolved along a heating path. The volumes of quartz precipitated in such a situation can be calculated from equation [3.1] above. Conversely, a mineral such as calcite exhibits retrograde solubility (its solubility decreases as a function of increasing temperature) and will, therefore, behave in the opposite sense to quartz, tending to dissolve at the sites of quartz precipitation and vice versa

(Figure 3.11). Different types of mineral precipitates in a sandstone aquifer can, therefore, provide information about the nature and hydrology of fluid flow. In this type of environment calculations will show that the precipitation of even small volumes of quartz or calcite requires huge fluid fluxes, so that mass transfer becomes effective only when sediments have high permeabilities, or fluid fluxes are very focused (Bjørlykke, 1994). Although cooling is important, precipitation of minerals from circulating fluids is not only temperature-dependent and many other factors control the formation of ore constituents from hydrothermal solutions (see section 3.5 below).

3.4 FURTHER FACTORS AFFECTING METAL SOLUBILITY

Solubility is defined as the "upper limit to the amount of dissolved metal that a hydrothermal fluid can transport" (Wood and Samson, 1998). In Chapter 2 the concept of metal solubility in hydrothermal aqueous solutions was introduced and mention made of Holland's (1972) classic experiments in which the solubility of metals such as Pb, Zn, Mn, and Fe was found to vary as an exponential function of the chloride ion (Cl^-) concentration of the fluid. This work emphasized the fact that efficient transport of metals by hydrothermal fluids in the Earth's crust can be achieved only if aqueous solutions contain other dissolved ingredients with which the metals can bond, thereby promoting metal dissolution. For example, the solubility of a mineral such as galena (PbS) in pure water, even at high temperatures, is extremely small. Wood and Samson (1998) calculated that the amount of Pb that could be dissolved in an aqueous solution (with 10^{-3} molal H_2S and in equilibrium with galena at 200 °C) would be a trivial 47.4 ppb. If 5.5 wt% NaCl were added to this solution, however, the solubility of Pb at the same temperature would increase significantly to 1038 ppm.

In addition to Cl^-, a variety of different ligands (electron donors or electronegative ions with lone pairs of valence electrons) will affect the solubility of metals in solution. The ligand combines with a metallic ion by the formation of a coordinate bond, which is a type of covalent bond in which the shared electron pair is provided by one of the participating molecules (the ligand in this case) rather than the normal situation where the shared electrons are supplied from each of the two participating components. A ligand that promotes the formation of complexes by coordination bonding will typically increase the solubility of metals in aqueous ore-forming solutions.

Considerations of how metals go into solution in hydrothermal fluids can be made with respect to the concept of Lewis acids and bases. In the latter concept the conventional definition of acids and bases (i.e. substances capable, respectively, of contributing H^+ ions to, or taking up H^+ ions from, a solution) is expanded to situations where H^+ ions are not present, and this has particular relevance to geological situations (Gill, 1996). A Lewis acid is defined as an atom or molecule that can accept a lone pair of valence electrons, whereas a Lewis base can donate an electron pair to a bond. "Hard" Lewis acids are strongly electropositive metals (with high charges and/or small atomic radii) such as the alkali and alkaline earth metals (e.g. Na^+, K^+, Mg^{2+}, Ca^{2+}) that form ionic bonds with strongly electronegative elements like oxygen (O^{2-}). "Soft" Lewis acids have an abundance of easily accessible electrons in their outer shells and prefer to form covalent bonds with soft bases. Soft acids are typified by the chalcophile metals (i.e. those that have an affinity with sulfur, such as Cu, Pb, Zn, Ag, Bi, Cd) which tend to form covalent bonds with ligands of low electronegativity, such as S^{2-}. The principle stating that in a competitive situation hard metals (acids or electron acceptors) will tend to complex with hard ligands (bases or electron donors), and soft metals with soft ligands, is commonly referred to as *Pearson's Principle*, and underpins the solubility behavior of metals in hydrothermal solutions. A classification of metals and ligands in terms of the hard–soft breakdown and applicable to ore-forming processes is presented in Table 3.2. The "borderline" category is added to accommodate the fact that some metals (such as Fe and Pb) can complex readily with both hard and soft ligands, forming a range of minerals such as sulfides (pyrite FeS_2, galena PbS)

Table 3.2 Classification of some metals and ligands in terms of Lewis acid/base principles

HARD METALS	BORDERLINE	SOFT METALS
$Li^+ Na^+ K^+ Rb^+ Cs^+$	Divalent transition metals	$Au^+ Ag^+ Cu^+$
$Be^{2+} Sr^{2+} Ba^{2+} Fe^{3+}$	$(Zn^{2+} Pb^{2+} Fe^{2+}$ etc.)	$Hg^{2+} Cd^{2+} Sn^{2+} Pt^{2+} Pd^{2+}$
$Ce^{4+} Sn^{4+} Mo^{4+} W^{4+} V^{4+} Mn^{4+}$		$Au^{3+} Tl^{3+}$
$As^{5+} Sb^{5+} U^{6+}$		
$\Downarrow$	$\Downarrow$	$\Downarrow$
HARD LIGANDS	BORDERLINE	SOFT LIGANDS
NH_3	Cl^- Br^-	HS^- I^- CN^- H_2S $S_2O_3^{2-}$
OH^- F^- NO_3^- HCO_3^- CH_3COO^-		
CO_3^{2-} SO_4^{2-}		
PO_4^{3-}		

The major ligands in natural hydrothermal solutions are shown in bold. Caution is required in the application of the hard–soft model since the structure of water changes at higher temperatures and metal–ligand interaction will, likewise, change (Seward and Barnes, 1997).
Source: after Pearson (1963).

and carbonates (siderite $FeCO_3$, cerrusite $PbCO_3$). Likewise Cl^- can be an effective complexing agent for both hard and soft metals, and therefore promotes the solubility of a wide range of metals in hydrothermal aqueous solutions.

The classification of aqueous ionic species into hard and soft Lewis acids/bases assists considerably in understanding the nature of metal–ligand complexation, and, therefore, the controls on solubility, in hydrothermal solutions (Seward and Barnes, 1997; Wood and Samson, 1998). In addition, however, it is well known that temperature plays a very important role in determining the degree to which metals enter solution. In most cases stabilities of metal–ligand complexes such as $PbCl^+$ and $ZnCl^+$ will increase by several orders of magnitude as temperature increases from ambient values to 300 °C (Seward and Barnes, 1997). This is illustrated, together with data for other metal–chloride complexes, in Figure 3.12. By contrast, an increase in pressure will have the opposite effect to temperature and the stabilities of metal–ligand complexes will tend to decrease because of bond dissociation and the formation of free metal ions. In general, however, the effect on solubilities of pressure increases are minimal and more than offset by the significant changes associated with temperature increases (Seward and Barnes, 1997).

3.4.1 The important metal–ligand complexes in hydrothermal solutions

Wood and Samson (1998) have provided an excellent summary of solubility data for a wide variety of metal–ligand complexes. These data are described below in terms of hard, borderline, and soft metals. The summary given below provides an indication of the most likely metal–ligand complex that will exist in a natural fluid as a function of variables such as oxidation state, pH, temperature, and fluid composition. However, it cannot and should not be used to try to simply predict the nature of metal speciation in any situation where the many parameters that control solubility are imperfectly known. The concept of hard–soft Lewis acids and bases is an idealized scenario predicated on the assumption that there is competition between metals and a variety of ligands. In natural situations metals may, for example, complex with the most suitable available base and the formation of actual metal–ligand complexes and their solubilities will be quite different to those predicted on theoretical grounds.

Hard metals

Tungsten (W) Tungsten tends to occur in nature as the hexavalent aqueous cation W^{6+}, although

Figure 3.12 Plot of the effective stability of a metal complex (expressed in terms of β_1, which is the equilibrium formation constant) versus temperature (after Seward and Barnes, 1997). The stabilities of metal–chloride complexes shown increase by several orders of magnitude as temperature increases, as will their solubilities in aqueous solution.

the pentavalent form W^{5+} can also occur under more reducing conditions. These ions are hard Lewis acids and are likely to complex with hard bases such as O^{2-}, OH^-, F^-, and CO_3^{2-}, although the chloride ion is relatively unimportant as a complexing agent under most geological conditions. The majority of dissolved tungsten species in hydrothermal solutions occur as tungstates and have the forms WO_4^{2-}, HWO_4^-, and H_2WO_4. The stabilities of these tungstate species are obviously dependent on hydrogen ion concentration (i.e. on pH), such that H_2WO_4 is only stable under acidic conditions, whereas WO_4^{2-} is stable at alkaline pH. Significant quantities of tungsten can be carried in solution by these tungstate complexes and no other species are required to form most scheelite and wolframite deposits.

Molybdenum (Mo) Molybdenum tends to be more easily reduced in nature than tungsten and typically occurs in a variety of aqueous valence states as Mo^{6+}, Mo^{5+}, Mo^{4+}, and Mo^{3+}. It is also a hard Lewis acid and like tungsten will complex with hard bases, in particular, O^{2-} and OH^-. Chloride complexing takes place only under very acidic conditions and typically it is the oxyhydroxide complexes (such as MoO_2^+ and $Mo(OH)_3^+$) that are the most likely to occur in natural aqueous solutions.

Uranium (U) Uranium is characterized by two valence states in nature, as the quadrivalent uranous ion, U^{4+}, and the hexavalent uranyl ion, U^{6+}. The uranous ion is generally characterized by very low solubilities in aqueous solutions and most fluid-related transport takes place as U^{6+}. As a hard acid, U^{6+} will complex with hard bases such as O^{2-}, OH^-, F^-, HCO_3^-, and CO_3^{2-}.

Borderline metals

Arsenic (As) The trivalent cation As^{3+} dominates the valence state of arsenic in nature and in solution the neutral H_3AsO_3 complex is known to be stable over wide ranges of temperature (above 200 °C), Eh, and pH. Other less protonated arsenate complexes are also stable at higher pH values (as for tungsten) and generally chloride complexes do not play a role in fluid transport. Under conditions of high sulfide concentration and at low temperatures, As–sulfide complexes (such as $AsS_2(SH)^{2-}$) may become more important, although their exact stoichiometric proportions are unclear.

Antimony (Sb)   The aqueous geochemistry of antimony is similar to arsenic, with Sb^{3+} predominating and $Sb(OH)_3$ occurring as the main stable complex in low-sulfide aqueous solutions. In the presence of high concentrations of reduced sulfide species in the fluid a number of thioantimonite complexes (such as $HSb_2S_4^-$) are also likely to be stabilized and contribute to increasing antimony solubility.

Iron (Fe)   The majority of iron transported in aqueous solution through the Earth's crust is in the ferrous or divalent form (Fe^{2+}), while ferric iron (Fe^{3+}), which forms under relatively oxidizing conditions, is much less soluble. With its intermediate Lewis acid properties, iron does not exhibit a preference for either hard or soft bases and a variety of metal–ligand complexes are implicated in the dissolution of ferrous iron in aqueous solutions, including Cl^-, OH^-, and HCO_3^-. Most experimental studies indicate that $FeCl^+$ and $FeCl_2$ are the main complexes involved in the hydrothermal transport of ferrous iron, especially at high temperatures and salinities. The free hydrated ion itself, Fe^{2+}, is also implicated in fluid transport where hydrolysis has taken place, as are Fe–bicarbonate complexes under more alkaline conditions. Fe–bisulfide complexes are generally not involved in the transport of iron in hydrothermal solutions although they may be important in ocean floor exhalative environments (i.e. black smokers).

Manganese (Mn)   Manganese is also a borderline Lewis acid and, like iron, Mn^{2+} complexation in hydrothermal solutions is likely to be dominated by the chloride ligand (i.e. $MnCl^+$ and $MnCl_2$), with hydroxide and bicarbonate complexes also contributing to Mn solubility.

Tin (Sn)   Tin is a metal that exhibits both hard acid quadrivalent (as Sn^{4+}) and borderline divalent (as Sn^{2+}) traits such that it can be solubilized by complexation with a number of different ligands. Under oxidizing conditions it has been found that the Sn^{4+}–hydroxychloride complex, $Sn(OH)_2Cl_2$, is the dominant species, but that its solubility is low. Under more reducing conditions both Sn^{4+} and Sn^{2+} can complex with the simple chloride ion, forming very soluble complexes of the form $SnCl_n^{X-n}$ (i.e. where X is the valence state, either 2 or 4, and n is the ligation number for the chloride complex). The divalent Sn^{2+}–chloride complexes, formed under more reducing conditions, exhibit much higher solubilities than the quadrivalent Sn^{4+}–hydroxychloride complex that exists in a more oxidized state. Sn–hydroxide complexes ($Sn(OH)_4$ and $Sn(OH)_2$) are very stable under alkaline, lower temperature conditions but their solubilities are again much lower than those exhibited by the dominant Sn–chloride complexes formed at higher temperatures and lower pH. Contrary to expectation, tin does not complex significantly with fluorine despite its association with highly fractionated fluorite/topaz-bearing granites.

Zinc (Zn)   The dominant divalent zinc cation, Zn^{2+}, is a borderline Lewis acid that complexes with a variety of ligands, including Cl^-, HS^-, OH^-, HCO_3^-, and CO_3^{2-}. At relatively low temperatures and high pH, and in fluids with high bisulfide concentrations but low salinities, a variety of Zn^{2+}–bisulfide complexes are stable, including $Zn(HS)_2$, $Zn(HS)_3^-$, and $Zn(HS)_4^{2-}$. In contrast, at higher temperatures and under more acidic conditions, a host of chloride complexes predominate, including $Zn(Cl)^+$, $Zn(Cl)_2$, $Zn(Cl)_3^-$, and $Zn(Cl)_4^{2-}$.

Lead (Pb)   Lead is the softest of the borderline Lewis acids and forms stronger bonds with Cl^- and HS^- ligands than with OH^- or HCO_3^-. The valence state and complexing behavior of lead is very similar to that of zinc. Pb^{2+}–bisulfide complexes are more stable than chloride complexes in low temperature, neutral to alkaline, low salinity solutions. Different Pb^{2+}–bisulfide complexes form as a function of pH, and these include $Pb(HS)_2$ under acidic conditions and $Pb(HS)_3^-$ at higher pH (i.e. >6). At higher temperatures and lower pH, however, a variety of Pb^{2+}–chloride complexes form and these include $Pb(Cl)^+$, $Pb(Cl)_2$, $Pb(Cl)_3^-$, and $Pb(Cl)_4^{2-}$. Pb^{2+}–carbonate or Pb^{2+}–bicarbonate complexes can form in CO_2-bearing fluids but their solubilities are typically low and they are unlikely, therefore, to have relevance in ore-forming processes. There is, however, compelling evidence that lead, and to a lesser extent zinc, are transported by organo-metallic complexes (see section 3.4.2 below), especially in relatively low temperature environments such as those related to the formation of Mississippi Valley type Pb–Zn deposits (see Box 3.7), where hydrothermal fluids are known to contain hydrocarbons. The acetate ligand (CH_3COO^-) is one organic molecule that has been implicated in base metal transport, although there are others, such as thiols or sulfur-bearing organic compounds, that may also be important.

Soft metals

Copper (Cu) In nature, copper occurs in both Cu^+ and Cu^{2+} valence states, although the monovalent state is predominant in most hydrothermal fluids. It is a relatively soft acid and forms stable Cu^+–chloride and Cu^+–bisulfide complexes, as well as Cu^+–hydroxide complexes if other ligands are not available. Movement of copper in hydrothermal solutions under a wide range of conditions is most likely to take place by Cu^+–chloride complexation in the form $CuCl_2^-$. Although copper–bisulfide complexes will form in high-sulfur environments, they are not likely to play a significant role in most hydrothermal ore-forming environments.

Gold (Au) Gold is the softest metal ion considered in this summary and prefers complexation with soft ligands such as the bisulfide ion, rather than chloride. Gold typically occurs in a monovalent state (Au^+) in aqueous solutions and will form the complex AuHS at low pH and $Au(HS)_2^-$ under weakly acidic to basic conditions. The bisulfide complexes predominate in most hydrothermal fluids and are stable over a wide temperature range. Under very oxidizing, saline, and acidic conditions, it is possible to form both Au^+– and Au^{3+}–chloride complexes in the form of $Au(Cl)_2^-$ and $Au(Cl)_4^-$ respectively. The former complex might prevail in certain high temperature environments such as porphyry coppers, whereas the latter is only likely to be important at low temperatures in near surface settings. Au does form very soluble complexes with cyanide ($Au(CN)_2^-$), which is the reason why cyanidation is used so effectively at low temperatures to recover gold from ore. The cyanide molecule is, however, unstable at higher temperatures and the complex has no relevance to hydrothermal gold transport.

Silver (Ag) Silver is also a soft metal ion, but not as soft as gold. It is, therefore, more likely to form complexes with a borderline ligand such as chloride than gold is, although solution chemistry will again be dominated by Ag^+–bisulfide bonding. The predominant complexes are AgHS and $Ag(HS)_2^-$ under acidic and neutral to alkaline conditions respectively. Several Ag^+–chloride complexes are known to be stable over a wide range of conditions pertaining to hydrothermal fluid flow and these include $AgCl$, $Ag(Cl)_2^-$, and $Ag(Cl)_3^{2-}$.

Mercury (Hg) Mercury, occurring predominantly as Hg^{2+} in aqueous solutions, is a soft metal ion and will complex preferentially with bisulfide ligands. Most mercury transport under neutral to alkaline and moderately reducing conditions is likely to take place by the formation of complexes such as $Hg(HS)_2$, $HgS(HS)^-$, and HgS_2^{2-}. Harder ligands probably do not play much of a role in most hydrothermal fluids. Of interest and related to its low boiling point, however, is the fact that mercury can be transported as a vapor, or as elemental Hg in either aqueous solutions or hydrocarbon-bearing fluids.

In summary, it is apparent that the borderline chloride ion is the most important ligand that promotes the dissolution and transport of metals in hydrothermal fluids, followed by bisulfide. A variety of other ligands such as OH^-, HCO_3^-, CO_3^{2-}, F^-, SO_4^{2-}, NO_3^-, NH_3, and CH_3COO^- are of lesser importance because they are either stable under abnormal conditions or exist at very low concentrations in natural fluids. In addition to its ability to complex with a wide range of both hard and soft metal cations, Cl^- is also the major anionic species in most natural fluids. This ensures that many natural fluids are very capable of transporting large quantities of metal in solution and it is for this reason that the circulation of hydrothermal solutions in the Earth's crust is such an important ore-forming process. Even though metal–ligand complexes may be readily stabilized in natural aqueous solutions, it is nevertheless apparent from both direct analysis and theoretical calculation that the actual concentrations of metals dissolved in most hydrothermal fluids are very low. This means that the formation of a viable ore deposit still requires large volumes of fluid passing through a highly focused point in the Earth's crust (i.e. high fluid/rock ratios), as well as efficient precipitation mechanisms to take metals out of solution and concentrate them in the host rock. The compilation shown in Figure 3.13 shows the minimum concentrations of precious and base metals (i.e. the vertical dashed lines) estimated to be necessary for the formation of a deposit, and also the ranges shown for several examples where such data are available. Solutions that deposit Au and Ag typically contain much lower concentrations, in the range 1 ppb to 1 ppm, than those associated with Cu, Pb, and Zn ores. In the latter case massive sulfide deposits are formed from fluids that typically carry 1–100 ppm of metal, whereas the fluids associated with MVT and porphyry deposits are relatively enriched with concentrations in the range 100–1000 ppm.

3.4.2 A brief note on metal–organic complexes

A number of different hydrothermal ore types that are hosted in intracratonic and rift-related sedimentary sequences are known to have formed from fluids containing significant amounts of dis-solved organic compounds. It is also well known that crude oil and bitumen invariably contains minor amounts (<1%) of inorganic material that includes dissolved metals. It is not surprising, therefore, that considerable attention has recently been given to the roles that metal–organic complexes might have played in hydrothermal ore forming processes, especially in Mississippi Valley-type (MVT) Pb–Zn and stratiform, red-bed or shale-hosted base metal ores (see Parnell, 1994; Gize, 1999).

Organic compounds in connate waters tend to occur either as neutral hydrocarbon molecules (alkanes, aromatics, etc.) or as charged anionic species such as the carboxylic acids (acetic acid, oxalic acid, etc.). Most neutral hydrocarbons (with the exception of methane, CH_4) have only limited aqueous solubility and this decreases exponentially as the hydrocarbon molecule gets bigger and more complex. Organic acid anions, on the other hand, may have very high solubilities in water and the dominant aqueous anion, acetate (CH_3COO^-), can exist at concentrations up to $2000\,mg\,l^{-1}$ (Hanor, 1994). Organometallic complexes (i.e. those in which a metal is covalently bonded to the carbon of an adjacent hydrocarbon molecule) only rarely occur in nature, whereas metal–organic complexes, in which a metal cation is attached to the electron-donor atom (such as oxygen, sulfur, or nitrogen) of an organic ligand, are widely stable in natural aqueous solutions, as well as in ore fluids (Giordano and Kharaka, 1994).

In ore fluids metal–organic complexes will only exist if they are sufficiently stable to be able to compete with the normal inorganic complexes discussed previously. Modeling has shown that Pb and Zn can be transported as metal–organic complexes involving acetate or oxalate ($C_2O_4^{2-}$) ligands (e.g. $Zn(CH_3COO^-)_2$ and $Pb(C_2O_4^{2-})_2^{2-}$) in reduced fluids with greater than 10^{-5} molal H_2S or HS^-. In more oxidized fluids, such as those more applicable to red-bed related stratiform base metal deposits, Pb and Zn would be transported predominantly as metal–chloride complexes, but Pb– and Zn–acetate complexes could still account for up to 5% of metal transport (Giordano and Kharaka, 1994).

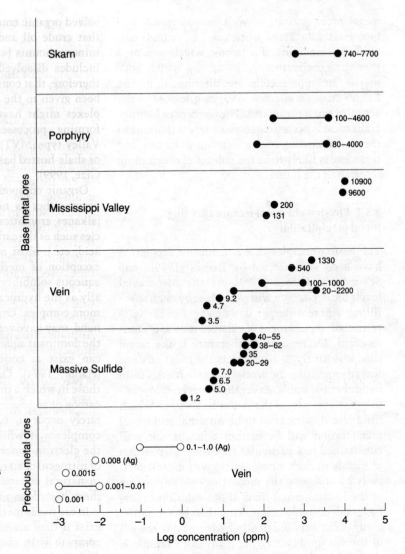

Figure 3.13 Base and precious metal concentrations in ore-forming hydrothermal solutions, in each of five major categories of deposit type. Base metals include Cu, Pb, and Zn (filled dots), and precious metals comprise Au, Ag, and Hg (open circles). The numbers next to individual points or ranges refer to average concentrations or ranges in a variety of different situations, and are all after Seward and Barnes (1997).

3.5 PRECIPITATION MECHANISMS FOR METALS IN SOLUTION

The previous section has shown that it is possible to stabilize many different metal–ligand complexes under wide ranging conditions in natural hydro-thermal solutions, thereby promoting the kind of solubility levels required to make effective ore-forming fluids. Once a metal is in solution, how-ever, it then needs to be extracted from that fluid

and concentrated in a portion of the Earth's crust that is sufficiently restricted and accessible to make an economically viable ore body. It is obvious that a wide range of precipitation mechanisms are likely to be effective since any mechanism that will destabilize a metal–ligand complex and, therefore, reduce the metal solubility, will cause it to be de-posited in the host rock through which the hydro-thermal solution is passing. The following sections examine the physical and chemical controls on metal precipitation, as well as adsorption and biologically mediated processes. The latter is particularly important as it is now widely accepted that the geochemical pathways by which both metals and non-metals are distributed in the Earth's crust are affected to varying degrees by the action of microorganisms. The concept of biomineralization is becoming increasingly important to the understanding of ore-forming processes and this topic is likely to be the subject of much more research in the future.

3.5.1 Physico-chemical factors affecting metal precipitation

The basic principles that control ore deposition have been summarized by Barnes (1979b) and Seward and Barnes (1997). At shallow crustal levels ore deposition will take place by open space filling, whereas deeper down where porosity is restricted, replacement of existing minerals tends to occur. Decrease in temperature is the factor that, intuitively, is regarded as the most obvious way of promoting the precipitation of metals from hydrothermal fluids. At depth, however, temperature gradients across the structures within which fluids are moving tend to be minimal and metal precipitation will be neither efficient nor well constrained to a particular trap zone. Deposition of metals in such a case is achieved more effectively by changing the properties or composition of the hydrothermal fluid. If ore solution occurs by metal–chloride complexing then precipitation could occur very efficiently by increasing the pH of the ore fluid (see Figure 3.14). An example is provided by the reaction of an acidic ore solution with a carbonate host rock and where precipitation is promoted by digestion and replacement of the host. Two coupled reactions illustrate the process in terms of calcite dissolution by an originally acidic, Zn^{2+}–chloride-bearing ore solution:

$$CaCO_{3(SOLID)} + 2H^+ \Leftrightarrow Ca^{2+} + H_2CO_{3(AQUEOUS)}$$
[3.2]

and subsequent sphalerite precipitation caused by increase of pH in the fluid as hydrogen ions are consumed:

$$ZnCl_n^{2-n} + H_2S_{(AQUEOUS)} \Leftrightarrow ZnS_{(SOLID)} + 2H^+ + nCl$$
[3.3]

It is apparent from reactions 3.2 and 3.3 that precipitation of metal–chloride complexes could also take place by increasing the H_2S concentration of the fluid (perhaps by fluid mixing or bacterial sulfate reduction) or by decreasing the Cl^- concentration (again perhaps by mixing of the ore fluid with dilute groundwater). As another option to calcite dissolution, an increase in fluid pH could also be brought about by boiling of the fluid, which results in acidic volatiles being partitioned preferentially into the vapor phase. There are, therefore, a number of ways of reducing the solubility of metal–chloride complexes and promoting metal precipitation.

The factors that promote precipitation of metal–sulfide complexes may be somewhat different to those for chloride complexes (Barnes, 1979b). Although fluid mixing (or dilution) and temperature decreases will promote metal precipitation, it is oxidation of the ore fluid (see Figure 3.14) that is particularly effective in decreasing the solubilities of metal–sulfide complexes. Oxidation (or loss of electrons) causes a decrease in the pH and also the total sulfide concentration, thereby promoting metal precipitation, as shown in reaction 3.4:

$$Zn(HS)_3^- + 4O_{2(AQUEOUS)} \Leftrightarrow ZnS_{(SOLID)} + 3H^+ + 2SO_4^{2-}$$
[3.4]

Precipitation of ores from metal–sulfide complexes are controlled by oxidation, decreases in pH (or acidification), and decreases in sulfide concentration in the fluid, all tendencies that are opposite to those controlling metal–chloride disassociation. A more detailed discussion of the actual geological processes that affect ore deposition controls is presented below, together with different scenarios where they might apply. An understanding of the geological factors relating to metal deposition is obviously very important to the exploration geologist who needs to have a firm grasp of the concepts that control where and why hydrothermal ore bodies form.

Temperature

Since the stabilities of many metal–ligand complexes increase as a function of temperature (Figure 3.12) it is clear that cooling of a fluid will generally have the effect of promoting ore deposition. Temperature decrease is particularly effective for destabilizing metal–chloride complexes because their solubilities are much more sensitive to temperature changes than are those of equivalent sulfide complexes. As mentioned previously, however, at deep crustal levels where fluid and rock are in equilibrium and exist at the same temperature, thermal gradients are minimal and cooling is a slow and ineffectual process. Under these circumstances the concentration of metals and the formation of hydrothermal ores are generally not mediated by temperature decreases.

In the near surface environment, however, rapid decreases in the temperature of an ore fluid are much more likely to happen and in such environments cooling is likely to play an important role in ore formation. The ocean floor undoubtedly represents the prime example of where a dramatic reduction in the temperature of ore-forming fluids plays the dominant role in controlling metal deposition. Volcanogenic massive sulfide deposits typically form at sites where hot (up to 350 °C) brines with very high metal contents are vented onto the ocean floor as black smokers (see section 3.8.1 and Box 3.3). Precipitation of base metals (mainly Cu and Zn transported as chloride complexes; Scott, 1997) and, in certain cases, precious metals (Au transported as a gold–bisulfide complex; Scott, 1997) is virtually instantaneous as the ore fluids mix with an essentially infinite volume of very cold (2–4 °C) sea water. In this environment it is the very rapid cooling through virtually 350 °C that causes a highly efficient precipitation of metal in the immediate vicinity of the exhalative vent. Black smokers are probably the most dramatic and efficient example of hydrothermal ore deposition anywhere on Earth.

The volcanic settings which give rise to the deposition of epithermal Au–Ag deposits (see Chapter 2, section 2.11 and Box 2.4) are also characterized by steep geothermal gradients and high conductive and convective heat loss by fluids to the surrounding rocks. Cooling may, therefore, play a role in controlling metal solubilities although in such environments it is more likely to be the decrease in pressure and associated phase separation (i.e. boiling and effervescence; see below) that plays the dominant role in ore deposition.

Pressure

Pressure variations do not dramatically effect the solubilities of metal–ligand complexes although it is clear that pressure increases will lead to a volume reduction which, in turn, promotes the dissociation of complexes to ionic species (Seward, 1981). In effect a decrease in pressure tends to favor an increase in solubility and, therefore, works in the opposite sense to temperature. Pressure reduction is not a process that, on its own, is typically associated with ore formation. A major exception occurs, however, when pressure reduction is accompanied by an event such as boiling or effervescence. These specific processes are very important in ore deposition and are generally promoted by decreases in pressure. In this sense pressure only has an indirect influence on ore formation.

Phase separation (boiling and effervescence)

Although one might intuitively expect that boiling is promoted by an increase in temperature, there is no doubt that, in the upper levels of the Earth's crust, the transformation from liquid to vapor usually occurs because of a decrease in fluid pressure (see trend A–A′ in Figure 3.5a). At deeper levels in the crust a decrease in fluid pressure could also be accompanied by effervescence, or the transition from a single phase H_2O–CO_2 mixture to one where H_2O and CO_2 unmix (see Figure 3.5c). Both these processes are potentially very important as mechanisms of precipitating metals from ore-forming solutions because they dramatically change the prevailing conditions under which metal–ligand complexes are stable.

In section 3.3.3 the relationships between fluid flow and deformation were discussed and the fault-valve and suction-pump models were described with reference to the formation of mesothermal lode-gold and epithermal Au–Ag deposits respectively. The metamorphic fluids generally attributed to formation of mesothermal lode-gold deposits are characterized by single phase H_2O–CO_2 mixtures and it is possible that the episodic decreases in fluid pressure accompanying crack–seal processes in a fault or shear (Figure 3.9a and c) could promote precipitation of ore components. This is because there is a tendency for the H_2O–CO_2 solvus to move to higher temperatures with decreasing pressure (Brown, 1998). A typical mesothermal lode-gold fluid comprising H_2O + CO_2 at 350 °C and with 2.6% NaCl, for example, will initially exist as a single homogeneous liquid just above the relevant solvus (shown as point A; Figure 3.5b). A pressure decrease will have the effect of moving the solvus plateau to higher temperatures, so that the fluid enters the immiscible, or two phase, field segregating CO_2 and H_2O. CO_2 effervescence will undoubtedly affect the prevailing fluid properties and likely promote precipitation of both gangue and ore components, as suggested in the fault-valve model.

Similarly, in the near surface environment where en echelon strike slip faulting results in fault jog formation, the resulting rupture-related dilation will instantaneously reduce pressure (Figure 3.9c) to such an extent that a fluid could move from a liquid to the vapor state. Boiling will, of course, only occur if the pressure reduction traverses the boiling point curve for the relevant hydrothermal fluid composition (refer to phase diagrams in Figure 2.2). The boiling away of an aqueous vapor from a hydrothermal fluid will result in the residual enrichment of solute, as well as partitioning of other volatile species into the gas phase, with probable increase of pH in the remaining fluid. Such processes will dramatically modify prevailing fluid properties and the pH increase will, as mentioned previously, be particularly effective in precipitating metal–chloride complexes from solution. When accompanied by temperature decreases, prolonged boiling will likely bring about solubility reduction of most dissolved species. As suggested by Sibson (1987) with respect to epithermal ore-forming environments, boiling is likely to be a very efficient mechanism for ore deposition at shallow crustal levels.

Fluid mixing/dilution

The mixing of two fluids is widely regarded as another important mechanism for reducing solubility in ore-forming solutions and promoting metal precipitation. This is particularly the case when a relatively hot, metal-charged ore fluid mingles with a cooler, more dilute solution. Mixing of the two fluids would result in cooling of the hotter with modification of the prevailing ore fluid properties and destabilization of existing metal–ligand complexes. There are several examples that point to the importance of fluid mixing during ore deposition. In a classic stable isotope study, Sheppard et al. (1971) demonstrated that precipitation of chalcopyrite at the interface between the potassic and phyllic alteration zones associated with porphyry copper deposits (see Box 2.1, Chapter 2) coincides with the zone where fluids of dominantly magmatic origin mingled with those derived from a meteoric source. A similar situation is known to exist with respect to precipitation of Au and Ag ores in epithermal deposits (Box 2.4, Chapter 2). Hedenquist and Aoki (1991) showed that magmatic fluids venting directly from a volcano without any mixing or dilution below the surface are less conducive to the formation of economically viable deposits since ground preparation (or alteration) is minimized and the resultant ore accumulations at the surface have a low preservation potential. By contrast, systems characterized by mixing of magmatic waters with a meteoric water carapace 1–2 km below the surface will more likely be associated with the formation of economically viable mineralization. This is because mixing of a hot, saline, metal-charged magmatic fluid with a cooler, more dilute meteoric water promotes acid leaching of the host rocks, increases their permeability, and forces the fluids to condense and precipitate their dissolved metal solute. Hedenquist and Aoki (1991) suggested that interaction of magmatic fluids with a meteoric fluid blanket near the surface of active

BOX 3.1 Fluid mixing and metal precipitation: the Olympic Dam iron oxide–copper–gold deposit, South Australia

The Olympic Dam deposit, some 500 km north of Adelaide in South Australia, was discovered in 1975 beneath 350 m of sedimentary cover. It represents one of the most spectacular discoveries of modern times, containing around 2 billion tons of Cu, U, Ag, and Au ore (Solomon and Groves, 1994). The ore body is hosted in a breccia complex within the apical portions of the 1588 Myr old (Creaser and Cooper, 1993) Roxby Downs granite, the latter being a K-, U-, and Th-enriched A-type or anorogenic granite. Mineralization is generally attributed to mixing of two entirely different fluids, one of possible magmatic derivation, and the other an oxidized meteoric fluid (Reeve *et al.*, 1990; Oreskes and Einaudi, 1992; Haynes *et al.*, 1995).

The breccias that host the ore comprise a variety of fragments, the majority of which are either granitic or hematitic, together with volcanic fragments, sedimentary rocks, and massive sulfide ore. The breccias are extremely iron rich and themselves comprise a huge iron resource made up of

hematite and minor magnetite. Polymetallic mineralization, in the form of chalcocite, bornite, chalcopyrite, pitchblende, argentite, gold, and a variety of rare earth element (REE) minerals, is most closely linked to the hematitic breccia. All breccias are cut by mafic and felsic dykes that are approximately the same age as the Roxby Downs granite, indicating that magmatism, brecciation, and mineralization were broadly coeval (Johnson and Cross, 1991).

Ore genesis at Olympic Dam (Solomon and Groves, 1994) was initiated by the high level intrusion of fertile A-type granite, with accompanying fluid exsolution and boiling, which gave rise to explosive volcanic activity and an early phase of brecciation. The fluid involved here is inferred to be of magmatic origin and moderately oxidizing. It was also clearly Fe-rich and precipitated an early generation of magnetite as well as REE-bearing minerals. Cooling of the magmatic system subsequently led to draw-down of groundwater (perhaps derived from a saline

Figure 1 Simplified, subsurface geological map of the Olympic Dam ore deposit (after Haynes *et al.*, 1995).

(a) Geological setting

Playa lake

Dykes

Olympic Dam breccia complex

v Basalt

+ Roxby Downs granite

(b) Fluid mixing

Oxidizing meteoric water

Hotter, magmatic fluid

Ore precipitation

Ore leaching

Figure 2 Geological model for the formation of the Olympic Dam deposit (after Haynes *et al.*, 1995). The geological setting and the distribution of a lower, hotter, moderately oxidizing fluid of possible magmatic derivation, and an upper, saline, highly oxidizing meteoric fluid, is shown in (a). Drawdown of meteoric fluid together with uprising plumes of hotter water promote mixing of the fluids and metal precipitation, as shown in (b).

playa lake above the deposit; Haynes *et al.*, 1995) that in turn led to phreatic explosive activity, further brecciation, and hematite precipitation. The spatial association between hematite breccia and polymetallic mineralization indicates that a low temperature, highly oxidizing, meteoric fluid was implicated in the dissolution and transport of substantial amounts of Cu, Fe, and U, possibly from the granite, or overlying volcanic rocks, or both. This fluid encountered and mixed with the less oxidized magmatic solutions (containing reduced sulfur species), destabilizing metal–ligand complexes and causing precipitation of metal sulfides together with iron oxides. Figure 2 illustrates a model showing the existence of two fundamentally different fluid types at different crustal levels, with ore precipitation occurring at the interface between the fluids. It is envisaged that fluid circulation and mixing continued episodically for a considerable period of time, perhaps in part stimulated by the high radioelement (K, U, Th) content of the granite and the resultant heat generated by radioactive decay. The longevity of the ore-forming process is consistent with the complexity and enormous size of the ore deposit.

volcanic regions may be an important prerequisite to the formation of viable epithermal Au–Ag mineralization.

In another example demonstrating the importance of mixed fluids in ore formation, it has been suggested that sediment-hosted ore deposits associated with continental rifts environments are the product of the mixing of meteoric and connate fluids. Using the active mineralizing systems of the Salton Sea geothermal system (see section 3.7 below) as an analogue, McKibben et al. (1988) have suggested that the mixing of upwelling high-salinity brines of essentially connate origin with descending meteoric waters of lower temperature and salinity may be a viable mechanism of promoting metal precipitation from the former. It has been suggested that this type of model might apply to the formation of several sediment-hosted ore deposits such as the stratiform Cu–Co ores of the central African Copperbelt, and the sedimentary exhalative (SEDEX) Zn–Pb ores of Mount Isa and Broken Hill in eastern Australia (McKibben et al., 1988; McKibben and Hardie, 1997).

Mixing of two fluids with distinct temperature, pH, and redox characteristics is a process that is likely to have widespread applicability to ore genesis in a variety of crustal settings. Another important is the Olympic Dam described in Box 3.1.

Fluid/rock reactions (pH and Eh controls)

A widespread manifestation of hydrothermal mineralization processes is the development of alteration mineral assemblages in and around the fluid conduit. Alteration is caused by the reaction between fluids and their wall rocks and is a complex process that has been extensively studied, both in ore genesis research and for the understanding of metamorphic and metasomatic (mass transfer) processes in the crust. The interaction that occurs between a fluid and its wall rock promotes metal precipitation because it is yet another process that changes the prevailing fluid properties, especially in terms of acidity (pH) and redox state. Reactions describing the factors controlling metal precipitation were presented in section 3.5.1 above. Quantification of the effects of changes in pH and redox state on, for example, gold solubility is demonstrated in Figure 3.14, where calculated gold solubility contours for the dominant $Au(HS)_2^-$ complex, as well as for the less important $AuCl_2^-$ complex, in a fluid at 200 °C are shown. A reduced, neutral fluid like that at A, subject to an oxidation event akin to the one in reaction [3.4] above, would have its $Au(HS)_2^-$ solubility dramatically reduced, as shown by the oxidation trend in Figure 3.14. This would almost certainly result in significant precipitation of Au from the fluid. Similarly, a decrease in fluid pH from around 7 to 3 would also result in a reduction of gold solubility and deposition of the metal. As described earlier, the precipitation of ores from metal–chloride complexes may occur under different conditions altogether. In Figure 3.14 it is clear that the precipitation of Au from an oxidized, acidic fluid like that at B, in which the $AuCl_2^-$ complex is stable, will best be achieved by increasing pH (perhaps by consumption of H^+ during alteration) or by reduction (perhaps caused by sulfate reduction to sulfide).

The relationship between alteration and hydrothermal ore-forming processes is a very important one and for this reason the topic is covered in more detail in section 3.6 below. In this section the link between fluid/rock reactions and the precipitation of metals from ore fluids is also discussed.

3.5.2 Adsorption

Although metal precipitation is generally considered to have been instigated by changes to the prevailing fluid properties and accompanying reduction in equilibrium solubility, it is evident that ores can also form by adsorption of metal onto an existing mineral surface. Metal deposition by adsorption can occur from fluids whose concentrations are below their saturation levels and the process may, therefore, be important in certain ore-forming environments. Adsorption is defined as the adherence of an ion in solution to the surface of a solid (or mineral) with which it is in contact. The process occurs because a mineral surface will inevitably contain charge inbalances

Figure 3.14 Log fO_2–pH diagram showing the stability of iron oxide and sulfide minerals in relation to gold solubility contours for $Au(HS)_2^-$ and $AuCl_2^-$ complexes in a fluid at 200 °C (also at saturated water vapor pressure, with $\Sigma S = 0.01$ and $a_{Cl^-} = 1.0$). Oxidation of fluid A across the pyrite–hematite phase boundary will result in a four order of magnitude decrease in the solubility of the $Au(HS)_2^-$ complex and likely precipitation of gold. The same result would occur if the fluid became more acidic and pH decreased by some 5 units. The converse would apply with respect to $AuCl_2^-$ in fluid B. In this case Au precipitation would occur in response to an increase in pH (neutralization) or reduction of the fluid (perhaps caused by an increase in the activity of H_2S). Phase diagram and contours from Wood (1998) and S. Wood, personal communication.

created by the fact that metal cations will not always be fully coordinated with anions such as O^{2-} or S^-. Sites of high charge density (either positive or negative) on a mineral surface represent the locations where adsorption of oppositely charged ions is likely to occur. Zones of high charge density are represented by features such as lattice defect sites, fracture planes, and trace element substitution sites. In general, a mineral surface in contact with an acidic solution (i.e. a high activity of H^+) will contain an abundance of positive charge and is likely to adsorb anionic complexes. Conversely, a mineral surface in contact with an alkaline solution (with a high activity of OH^-)

will show a tendency for a surplus negative charge and will adsorb cations.

Experiments have shown that adsorption of many different metals onto the surface of a range of silicate, oxide, and sulfide minerals can be an efficient way of forming an ore deposit. A variety of parameters affect adsorptivity and the most important of these are the surface area and surface properties of the adsorbent, as well as the pH of the solution (Rose and Bianchi-Mosquera, 1993). Temperature tends to have an inverse effect on adsorption and for this reason it is typically a low temperature phenomenon. Fine grained clay particles, as well as other materials with a high

(a)

(b)

(c)

(d)

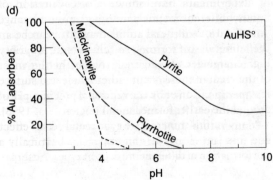

surface area to volume aspect such as diatomaceous earth, are very efficient adsorbers and are widely used in filtration and the removal of toxic matter from industrial effluent. With respect to ore deposition, however, it is the oxide and sulfide minerals that appear to play an important role in the concentration of metals from hydrothermal fluids. Since most metals form cationic species in nature, it follows that adsorption will be promoted by an increase in solution pH. This trend is demonstrated in Figure 3.15a, where the experimentally derived adsorption efficiency of Cu onto goethite (FeO(OH)) is plotted for oxidizing and reducing conditions. Under oxidizing conditions, such as those applicable to the formation of red-bed hosted stratiform copper deposits (see Box 3.6), Cu will be adsorbed very efficiently from a CuCl$^+$-bearing solution at pH greater than 6 (Rose and Bianchi-Mosquera, 1993). Under more reducing conditions Cu is only efficiently adsorbed under more alkaline conditions. Similar behavior to Cu is exhibited by other metals such as Pb, Zn, Co, and Ni (Figure 3.15b), although it is clear that the onset of efficient adsorption takes place at different pH values. Under the specific oxidizing conditions of the experiment, metals adsorb in the order Cu, Pb, Zn, Co, Ni with increasing pH. In a hydrothermal solution that is evolving along an acid neutralization trend caused, for example, by wall-rock alteration (see section 3.6 below) this sequence could account for any zonation evident in an ore deposit.

Metal adsorption efficiency is clearly very sensitive to pH, which is, in turn, mediated by the

Figure 3.15 (*left*) Plots of percentage adsorption versus pH for (a) copper as CuCl$^+$ onto goethite under oxidizing and reduced conditions and (b) a variety of transition metals onto goethite. Solutions in both cases are at 25 °C and 1 M NaCl, and data are from Rose and Bianchi-Mosquera (1993). (c) Plots of percentage adsorption versus pH for different metals with respect to various mineral sulfide substrates (after Jean and Bancroft, 1986). (d) Percentage adsorption for gold as AuHS onto different sulfide minerals as a function of pH. Solutions are at 25 °C and 0.1 M NaCl (after Widler and Seward, 2002).

Figure 3.16 Diagram showing the steps involved in adsorbing metal ions onto a mineral surface (after Jean and Bancroft, 1985; Knipe *et al.*, 1992). This case considers a gold–ligand (Au–L) complex that adheres initially by physical adsorption to a negatively charged sulfide mineral surface by weak Van der Waals forces and subsequently by chemical adsorption and covalent-like bonding to form a stronger attachment. Adsorbed gold ions can diffuse along the surface to form clusters such as that shown in the adjacent SEM image (inset; after Jean and Bancroft, 1985). Further growth of the site of metal accumulation can result in the formation of discrete gold particles that adhere onto sulfide grains such as pyrite or arsenopyrite.

presence of surface OH⁻-related charge distribution. Experimental data suggest the existence of an adsorption edge where an increase from low to virtually complete adsorption occurs over a narrow range of pH increase. Adsorption efficiency is not, on the other hand, much affected by the type of mineral surface. In addition to goethite, which is a good adsorbent under oxidizing conditions (Figure 3.15a and b), sulfide minerals also attract metals to their surfaces in more reducing environments. Sulfide minerals are typically characterized by an intrinsic negative surface charge usually attributed to the presence of S^{2-} (Shuey, 1975). Jean and Bancroft (1986) demonstrated that comprehensive adsorption of metals like Hg, Pb, Zn, and Cd can take place under alkaline conditions onto phases such as pyrite, pyrrhotite, and sphalerite (Figure 3.15c). Mercury is, in fact, readily adsorbed onto sulfide mineral surfaces over almost the entire pH range.

Interestingly, the role of adsorption of gold (as AuHS) from solution by sulfide minerals exhibits the converse pattern of behavior to the base metals. Widler and Seward (2002) showed that the most efficient adsorption of Au onto phases such as pyrite and pyrrhotite occurs under acidic conditions, with a marked decrease in adsorbence at neutral to alkaline pH ranges (Figure 3.15d). The

reason for this particular trend is that the AuHS complex is itself only stable at low pH, whereas under neutral to alkaline conditions the negatively charged $Au(HS)_2^-$ complex is stable. Since a negatively charged complex will be repulsed by a negatively charged mineral surface, adsorption will drop dramatically as pH increases.

The actual process by which metal adsorption occurs is very complex. Jean and Bancroft (1985) and Knipe *et al.* (1992) have suggested a two-stage process that is schematically illustrated in Figure 3.16. It is envisaged that adsorption is initiated by physical adsorption where the metal–ligand complex is loosely held at the mineral surface by weak van der Waals forces. There is no charge transfer at this initial stage. The second stage of the process is chemical and is promoted by reduction, or electron gain, and formation of covalent-like bonds between the metal ion and mineral substrate. Adsorbed metal atoms may diffuse across the mineral surface to form clusters at sites of high charge density (Figure 3.16). Further growth of the cluster could occur either by electrochemical precipitation or by conventional precipitation around the earlier formed metal nuclei.

Many sulfide minerals are good metal adsorbents and this fact clearly has an important bearing on the formation of different ore deposit types. Adsorption as a metal-depositing process in ore-forming environments may have been widely underestimated in terms of its importance. Adsorption of toxic metals onto a variety of different substrates is also likely to become increasingly important in combating pollution and for this reason also warrants much closer study in the future.

As a final point, it should be noted that the charge imbalances on mineral surfaces give rise to the fact that many natural materials act as semiconductors. Sulfide mineral surfaces, for example, exist as both n-type (negative or electron saturated) and p-type (positive or electron depleted) semiconductors (Shuey, 1975) and this influences metal precipitation onto these surfaces in much the same way as described above.

3.5.3 Biologically mediated processes of metal precipitation

It is well known that the evolution of all higher life forms since the end of the Precambrian is characterized by the ability of cells to interact chemically with inorganic metals such as silicon, calcium, and phosphorus to form shells, teeth, and bones. The interaction of microorganisms with a variety of other metals is also important for the formation of authigenic mineral phases during diagenetic and hydrothermal processes. The concept of biomineralization is increasingly being recognized as a significant process in ore formation, especially with respect to deposit types such as banded iron-formations, VMS-SEDEX ores, phosphorites, and supergene enrichments of Cu and Au. The following section briefly considers the basic principles of biomineralization and its significance to ore-forming processes.

The fundamental subdivision of life into prokaryotes and eukaryotes came about with an improvement in the understanding of cell microbiology in the mid-twentieth century (Patterson, 1999). Prokaryotes are the more primitive microorganism and the ancestral life form on Earth, developing at some stage between 4650 Ma and about 3500 Ma when they first appear in the fossil record. They are single celled microorganisms that can be subdivided into two kingdoms,

namely Bacteria (or Eubacteria) and Archaea (or Archaebacteria). Archaea exist in extreme environments, such as volcanic hot-springs and ocean floor hydrothermal vents (thermophiles) or hypersaline evaporitic waters (halophiles), and utilize strange metabolic pathways, involving the energy derived from hydrogen- and sulfur-based chemical reactions, to nourish themselves. Bacteria include a huge variety of microorganisms that occupy virtually every ecological niche on Earth. Bacteria perform many different functions: some are fermentative (*Escherichia coli*) whereas others either contain the enzymes for oxygen metabolism (i.e. they are aerobic) or lack such enzymes (anaerobic).

Eukaryotes evolved from prokaryotes and contain much more complex cellular structures, including a discrete nucleus, chromosomes, and characteristic cycles of cell division (mitosis and meiosis) and sexual reproduction. They probably appeared during Paleoproterozoic times although they could also have formed somewhat earlier (Patterson, 1999). They are almost all aerobic and metabolize oxygen in discrete packages within the cell called mitochondria, which are semi-autonomous chemical entities, containing DNA that is different from that of its own cell nucleus and more akin to prokaryotic DNA. This has led to the suggestion that more advanced cellular structures evolved by symbiotic inclusion of aerobic bacteria (i.e. mitochondria) into primitive eukaryotic entities. All higher life forms (the Animalia, Plantae, Fungi, and Protista kingdoms) consist essentially of eukaryotic cells.

Biomineralization

A capacity to chemically interact with metals is an inherent characteristic of most microorganisms. Mediation by microorganisms in the formation of a variety of authigenic mineral phases is referred to as "biomineralization" and the process has important implications for ore formation. The major animal phyla incorporated biomineralization as a "lifestyle" soon after their formation during the Cambrian explosion. It is this process that allowed the more advanced life forms to develop an exoskeleton and teeth and, eventually, internal bones (the vertebrates). It is, however, apparent that biomineralization occurred much before the Cambrian Period and it has been suggested that the formation of magnetite in bacteria (the so-called magnetotactic bacteria) might represent an ancestral template for unraveling the genetics of this process in higher life forms (Kirschvink and Hagadorn, 2000). It is the bacterial kingdom that is implicated in many of the processes linked to biologically mediated precipitation of metals during ore formation.

Biomineralization occurs in two ways (Lowenstam, 1981; Konhauser, 1998, 2003). The first is termed "biologically induced biomineralization" and refers to situations where minerals form as a consequence of the activity of microorganisms on their immediate environment. The second process is "biologically controlled biomineralization," in which the microorganism directly controls the uptake of inorganic material, either within the cell (where elements diffuse through the cell wall) or at the interface between the cell and its surrounds. These two processes are briefly described below with respect to iron, which is particularly relevant to many ore-forming environments.

Biologically induced biomineralization is controlled by the same equilibrium principles that govern metal precipitation in inorganic chemical systems. The metabolism of microorganisms effects the properties (i.e. pH, Eh) of aqueous solutions in their immediate environment and can promote the precipitation of authigenic minerals as a function of their solubility products. More importantly, ionized cell surfaces can induce mineral nucleation in much the same way as discussed in the previous section on adsorption. A wide range of different minerals can be biologically induced because the phases that form reflect the composition of the aqueous solution in which the microbe exists. Ferric hydroxide (or ferrihydrite $Fe(OH)_3$) is one of the most common biominerals, forming in a variety of different environments, and is often upgraded during diagenesis to more stable phases such as goethite and hematite. Precipitation of iron occurs in progressive

stages, from Fe-staining of the cell walls, to nucleation of small (<100 nm) ferric hydroxide grains and eventual replacement of bacterial colonies by the inorganic authigenic phase (Konhauser, 2003). There are a number of bacteria that passively induce ferric iron precipitation onto their cell walls to form ochreous accumulations, a common one being *Leptothrix ochracea*, as well as the *Crenothrix, Clonothrix,* and *Metallogenium* genera. Marine hydrothermal vent sites are characterized by abundant iron-depositing microbial populations. It has also been suggested that Precambrian oceans were characterized by bacteria capable of binding both ferric iron and silica and that this biologically mediated process contributed to the formation of banded iron-formations (see Chapter 5). In the present-day surface environment, the bacterium *Thiobacillus ferrooxidans* is capable of oxidizing ferrous iron, creating low pH solutions that have environmental implications during the formation of acid mine drainage from sulfide mineral-bearing ore deposits and mines. The fundamental problem associated with acid mine drainage is the production of sulfate and toxic labile metals in very acid solutions, as expressed in terms of reaction [3.5]:

$$FeS_2 + 8H_2O \leftrightarrow Fe^{2+} + 2SO_4^{2-} + 16H^+ \qquad [3.5]$$

This problem can, however, also be remediated by bacterial activity, as discussed in the section on sulfate-reducing bacteria (SRB) below.

Biologically controlled biomineralization is characterized by the creation of an area internal to the cell into which ions specific to the requirements of the microorganism are diffused, thereby creating localized conditions where concentrations are increased until saturation is reached. Minerals are thus able to form even though the aqueous milieu surrounding the microbe would not be able to precipitate the same phase. This process is responsible for the formation, for example, of linear arrays of magnetite crystals within magnetotactic bacteria, which enables them to navigate to preferred redox environments. The initial uptake of metal in this case is as ferric iron, with subsequent reduction to the

Figure 3.17 Microphotographs of (a) bacterial cell with amorphous ferric hydroxide replacing the cell walls, and (b) magnetotactic spirillum bacteria showing a chain of magnetite crystals developed along the longitudinal axis of the microorganism (photographs courtesy of Kurt Konhauser and Dennis Bazylinski).

ferrous state within the cell, but prior to transport into the magnetite bearing membrane. Fossil magnetotactic bacteria have been recognized from the 2000 Ma Gunflint Iron Formation, and this represents the oldest evidence for controlled biomineralization.

In terms of ore formation, the role that many bacteria play is to catalyze the oxidation of soluble metals to insoluble oxide phases. One particular group of anaerobic bacteria, the so-called "sulfate-reducing bacteria" (SRB), contribute to ore formation in a different way. SRB, such as *Desulphovibrio desulphuricans*, oxidize organic molecules by using sulfate as an electron acceptor, a process that generates dissolved sulfide (HS$^-$ or H$_2$S). On diagenesis the sulfide reacts with other metals or minerals to form sulfide phases that are either directly implicated in mineralization, or form the precursors to later ore-forming processes. These low temperature processes can result in the formation of many different sulfide minerals, including pyrite (via mackinawite and greigite) as well as nickel, lead, and zinc sulfides (Konhäuser, 2003). In a modern setting SRB can be useful in the microbial treatment of pollution and acid mine drainage. With reference to reaction [3.5] above, SRB would catalyze the reduction of

the sulfate to form sulfide, which in turn reacts with and stabilizes labile toxic metals. A bicarbonate ion (HCO^{3-}) is also commonly produced during these reactions, which has the effect of neutralizing the previously acid waters. This type of biological remediation of aqueous pollutants forms the basis for many operations that have to treat both acidic and metal toxic waters.

Biomineralization is a process that has considerable applicability to many other ore-forming environments in addition to those involving iron. Manganese is another redox-sensitive element that is biogenically precipitated in much the same way as iron. Manganous oxides such as birnessite and vernadite are the main phases formed in the presence of bacteria. Bacterial concentrations of Mn and Fe on the ocean floor have been implicated in the formation of manganese nodules (see Chapter 5). The formation of phosphate-rich sediments has also been linked, at least in part, to biogenic mediation, with apatite overgrowths having been observed replacing the remains of cyanobacteria. Large-scale phosphate deposits (phosphorites; see Chapter 5) forming along the eastern seaboard of Australia have been attributed to the progressive assimilation of sea water phosphorus by benthic bacteria (Konhauser, 2003). The amorphous silica that forms the characteristic siliceous sinters above epithermal gold deposits is also attributed to the presence of a diverse range of bacterial genera, the filaments of which act as nucleation sites for silicification. The siderophile metals (Au and Pt) are also amenable to biogenically mediated concentration, particularly with respect to the formation of nuggets in placer and lateritic environments (Watterson, 1991; see Chapter 4). One of the most spectacular demonstrations of the role of bacteria in the concentration of metals is derived from sulfur and lead isotopic determinations of sphalerite and galena ores from the world-class Navan deposit in Ireland. Although also characterized by replacement and epigenetic textural characteristics, the observation of pyritized worm tubes from a related deposit at Silvermines (Boyce et al., 1999) has shown that the Irish-type Zn–Pb–Ba ores are SEDEX types and related, at least in part, to syngenetic hydrothermal venting on the sea floor (see section 3.8.2). Isotopic studies indicate that some 90% of the sulfides at Navan were derived by the bacterial reduction of Carboniferous sea water sulfate (Fallick et al., 2001). It is argued that without an ample supply of reduced sulfur the Navan deposit might not have formed to the size that it is, emphasizing the importance of biologically mediated ore-forming processes.

Bacterial biomineralization is an extremely important process that has wide implications for the origin and evolution of life itself, and also for the formation of a wide variety of authigenic minerals in diagenetic and hydrothermal environments. In terms of ore-forming processes its role has probably been underestimated and this is likely to be a fruitful area of research in the future.

3.6 MORE ON FLUID/ROCK INTERACTION – AN INTRODUCTION TO HYDROTHERMAL ALTERATION

The passage of hydrothermal solutions through the Earth's crust is invariably accompanied by alteration. Alteration of a rock by the fluid passing through it is marked by the development of a mineral assemblage that is different from the original one and reflects the rock composition, as well as the properties and amount of fluid that has traversed the system. Zones of alteration mark the pathways of hydrothermal fluids through the crust and may represent useful guides for the exploration of many ore deposit types. The nature of hydrothermal alteration also provides an indication of the fluid properties associated with ore formation and there is commonly a close relationship between the chemical reactions involved in alteration and those responsible for metal deposition. It is, therefore, appropriate that a summary of the characteristics of hydrothermal alteration accompanies any description of ore-forming processes. The subject is, however, a complex one and the following section is necessarily brief. More detailed accounts documenting the evolution of ideas regarding hydrothermal alteration are provided in the relevant chapters of the three editions of H.L. Barnes's *Geochemistry of Hydrothermal Ore Deposits* (namely Meyer and Hemley, 1967; Rose and Burt, 1979; Reed, 1997).

Traditionally, alteration has been regarded as a process that, in its simplest form, involves both the hydrothermal fluid itself (essentially water with its dissociated components H^+ and OH^-) and the dissolved constituents of the aqueous solution. The low to moderate degrees of pervasive, isochemical alteration that characterize almost any rock evolving in the presence of a fluid can largely be explained by *hydrolysis* or *H^+ ion metasomatism* (see also Chapter 4, section 4.2.2). This process can be depicted in terms of simple chemical equilibria, or reactions, although it must be remembered that these are likely to be simplifications of actual alteration processes. For example, one of the most common forms of alteration recognized in nature is the reaction of K-feldspar with water to form muscovite or sericite. This reaction can be expressed as follows:

$$^3/_2 KAlSi_3O_8 + H^+ \Leftrightarrow$$
$$\text{(k-fel)}$$
$$^1/_2 KAl_3Si_3O_{10}(OH)_2 + 3SiO_2 + K^+ \qquad [3.6]$$
$$\text{(musc)} \qquad \text{(qtz)}$$

The hydrolysis of K-feldspar to muscovite in terms of this reaction requires nothing more than the presence of H^+ ions in an aqueous solution.

The reaction is isochemical and no new ingredients need to be added to the system. If the reaction proceeds to the right, H^+ ions are consumed and the fluid will become more basic, and will continue to do so until the K-feldspar is used up. The reaction will also produce quartz as part of the alteration assemblage, as well as K^+ ions dissolved in the aqueous solution.

If the products of reaction [3.6] are permitted to further react with H^+ ions in solution such that the system undergoes an increase in fluid/rock ratio, then muscovite would react to form kaolinite, as follows:

$$KAl_3Si_3O_{10}(OH)_2 + H^+ + {}^3/_2H_2O \Leftrightarrow$$
(musc)
$${}^3/_2Al_2Si_2O_5(OH)_4 + K^+ \qquad [3.7]$$
(kaol)

This reaction illustrates the way in which increasing fluid/rock ratios will change the alteration mineralogy by continued reaction with the rock after one set of mineral buffers have broken down (i.e. by consumption of K-feldspar in the case of reaction [3.6]). Alteration does not, however, necessarily result in the formation of only one mineral reactant, but generally forms an assemblage of phases. Plagioclase, for example, occurring in the same rock that originally contained the K-feldspar, might also react with H^+ ions in solution to form pyrophyllite, as follows:

$$2NaAlSi_3O_8 + 2H^+ \Leftrightarrow Al_2Si_4O_{10}(OH)_2 + 2SiO_2 + Na^+$$
(plag)   (pyroph)   (qtz)   [3.8]

Thus, reaction of a simple mineral assemblage with nothing but water could result in a multi-component alteration assemblage, even if the system remains isochemical.

If consideration is now given to an open chemical system where the dissolved constituents of an aqueous solution are also involved in alteration, then the processes and their products will be still more complex. The isochemical reactions above ([3.6], [3.7], and [3.8]) describing hydrogen ion metasomatism pertain to situations where reactants and products have similar bulk compositions. All three reactions also reflect acid–base

exchange because an aqueous H^+ ion is consumed and replaced by cations from the reactants. The accumulation of aqueous base cations in the evolving fluid will have an effect on the nature of downstream alteration, as they may themselves react with wall-rock. This type of alteration process is known as *cation metasomatism*. A wide variety of alteration products can form by cation metasomatism, examples of which are:

$$2NaAlSi_3O_8 + 4(Mg,Fe)^{2+} + 2(Fe,Al)^{3+} + 10H_2O \Rightarrow$$
(plag)
$$(Mg,Fe)_4(Fe,Al)_2Si_2O_{10}(OH)_8 + 4SiO_2 + 2Na^+ + 12H^+$$
(chl)   (qtz)   [3.9]

and

$$3CaMg(CO_3)_2 + 4SiO_2 + 6H^+ + 4H_2O \Rightarrow$$
(dol)
$$Mg_3Si_4O_{10}(OH)_2 + 6H_2CO_3 + 3Ca^{2+} \qquad [3.10]$$
(talc)

In reaction [3.9] the presence of Mg, Fe, and Al cations in a fluid which equilibrates with plagioclase will result in the chloritization of that mineral, with accompanying precipitation of quartz and significant H^+ production. This type of reaction will result in the fluid becoming more acidic during progressive alteration, which is contrary to the case for hydrolysis reactions. Reaction [3.10] demonstrates the sort of process which takes place when a cation-bearing aqueous solution interacts with a carbonate mineral, such as dolomite, to form a silicate mineral, such as talc. These processes are relevant to the formation of skarn ore deposits where fertile granites intrude carbonate country rocks, and are referred to as silication (see section 3.6.1 below).

More recent considerations of alteration processes have suggested that they should be regarded not only in terms of chemical equilibria, but also as dynamic systems that evolve with time. Given the time scale of most geological events, the attainment of equilibrium between rock and fluid is generally feasible, at least on a local scale. In dynamic systems, however, it is likely that kinetic considerations predominate over those of steady state equilibrium. The mineral assemblages that form as a result of hydrothermal alteration vary as a function of five factors (Reed, 1997), namely:

- temperature;
- pressure;
- host rock composition;
- fluid composition; and
- the ratio of fluid to rock in the alteration process (termed the *fluid/rock ratio*).

In nature these five factors interact in a complex way to create alteration assemblages that reflect all of them. The stabilities of mineral assemblages are dictated largely by temperature and pressure, whereas the host rock composition controls, to a certain extent, which ingredients are available to make up a particular alteration assemblage. Fluid composition and temperature have a strong influence on the nature and extent to which the host rock is dissolved by the aqueous solution, as well as the nature and concentration of new constituents introduced into the system by the fluid. The fluid/rock ratio is considered to be the "master variable" (Reed, 1997) in alteration processes because it dictates the extent to which reactions will move to completion.

Reed (1982, 1997) has shown that, because hydrothermal fluids migrate along pathways that represent evolving chemical gradients, alteration should be viewed in a dynamic sense as a function of changing fluid/rock ratio. This concept is schematically illustrated in Figure 3.18a, showing a fracture along which a hydrothermal fluid is flowing and adjacent to which alteration is taking place by diffusion-related reactions between fluid and country rock. At any instant in time, alteration pinches out downstream along the fracture because of the progressively diminishing ability of the fluid to react with the country rock as its enthalpy and its dissolved ingredients are effectively "used up" (e.g. an originally acidic fluid may become progressively neutralized as its H^+ ions are consumed by acid–base exchange; see below). The sequence of alteration minerals outwards or downwards of the fracture or vein reflects the sequence of reactions that relate to decreasing fluid/rock ratios (Figure 3.18a). The upstream portion of the vein has effectively "seen" more

fluid (and is, therefore, characterized by a higher fluid/rock ratio) than the distal sections of the system, and this is reflected in a variable alteration assemblage.

The evolution of alteration assemblages in a dynamic hydrothermal system can be modeled by reacting a fluid of known initial composition, pH, and temperature with a rock, using constraints imposed by established thermodynamic, chemical, and equilibrium data (Reed, 1997). The fluid composition and pH is then changed as the constituents of chemical reactions are consumed (i.e. as a mineral buffer system breaks down). Figure 3.18b shows how the alteration assemblage changes in a rock of andesitic composition subject to reaction with a hydrothermal solution. The scenario is modeled in terms of a system with high initial fluid/rock ratios and an acidic (low pH) fluid, evolving to lower fluid/rock ratios and alkaline (high pH) conditions. The plot shows that an acidic fluid circulating with high fluid/rock ratios through the andesite will be characterized by an alteration assemblage comprising quartz + pyrophyllite + alunite, also referred to as an *advanced argillic* alteration assemblage (Figure 3.18b). As the alteration systematics evolve, the same rock, now infiltrated by a more alkaline fluid circulating at a lower fluid/rock ratio, would be altered, initially to a sericite + chlorite assemblage and then to a chlorite + epidote + muscovite + albite assemblage. The latter assemblage is termed *propylitic* alteration and also matches the typical greenschist facies metamorphic assemblage. The expected distribution of ore minerals in the evolving system is shown in Figure 3.18c.

Viewing alteration assemblages in terms of dynamic fluid/rock interaction offers many advantages to the understanding of alteration processes, as well as to explaining the relationship between fluid rock interactions and ore deposition. The implication of time into the models of Figure 3.18 provides a good explanation for zonation and paragenetic sequence, two hallmark characteristics of hydrothermal ore deposits, discussed in more detail below. An evolving alteration system that moves from high to low fluid/rock ratios

Figure 3.18 Models illustrating the dynamic nature of fluid/rock interaction and hydrothermal alteration as a function of changing fluid/rock ratio. (a) Conceptual model showing one side of a diffusion-related alteration halo around a fracture through which fluid is passing from left to right. As fluid reacts with its host rock it changes composition and, through time, alteration assemblages evolve both along and outward of the fracture system (i.e. with decreasing fluid/rock ratios). (b) The occurrence and relative proportions of the principal alteration minerals forming when a relatively oxidized aqueous solution (of magmatic derivation at 300 °C and with initial pH = 1) reacts with a rock of andesitic composition, as a function of changing fluid/rock ratio (ser, sericite; chl, chlorite; ca, calcite; act, actinolite; micr, microcline; ab, albite; ep, epidote; par, paragonite; mus, muscovite; pyro, pyrophyllite; al, alunite; py, pyrite; anh, anhydrite; qz, quartz). (c) The precipitation sequence of some of the major ore minerals as a function of changing fluid/rock ratio for the same setting as in (b) (po, pyrrhotite; mt, magnetite; hem, hematite; bar, barite; sl, sphalerite; cp, chalcopyrite; gn, galena). (d) The evolution of fluid pH, as well as concentrations of certain key ligands in the fluid, as a function of changing fluid/rock ratio (also for the same setting as b). All figures after Reed (1997).

(i.e. from left to right in Figure 3.18) reflects a change from cation to hydrogen ion metasomatism, and from fluid-dominated to rock-dominated environments. The evolving system also dictates the compositional changes that occur in the fluid itself, such as the stepwise increase in fluid pH as H^+ ions are consumed by wall-rock reaction and stabilization of successive mineral assemblages (Figure 3.18d). The redox state of the fluid also changes as the alteration system evolves. Figure 3.18d shows that with decreasing fluid/rock ratio the concentration of SO_4^{2-} in the fluid decreases as the HS^- content increases. This is because SO_4^{2-} is reduced by reaction with ferrous wall-rocks, resulting in the precipitation of hematite in the alteration zone and fractionation of sulfide into the evolving aqueous solution (Reed, 1997). Sulfate reduction is an important source of sulfide in many hydrothermal ore-forming systems and promotes base metal sulfide precipitation. It is the changes in pH and redox state of the fluid that are so important in promoting the precipitation of metals from ore fluids.

There are many examples of situations where reaction between a hydrothermal fluid and its wall rocks is the main cause of ore precipitation. This process can be recognized, for example, in samples that reveal textures illustrating the replacement of primary minerals in the host rock by ore minerals. Such a texture is distinct from situations where ore minerals are precipitated into open spaces such as fractures or vugs, where other mechanisms of ore deposition, such as fluid mixing or boiling, might have prevailed. Skarn deposits (see section 2.10, Chapter 2) are a particularly good example of where alteration of carbonate rocks by acidic, metal-bearing solutions yields Ca–Mg silicate minerals accompanied by significant polymetallic mineralization. Carbonate rocks do, of course, have the ability to neutralize acidic solutions and the pH increases that arise from fluid/rock reactions in this environment promote efficient precipitation of metal sulfides (Reed, 1997). Likewise, greenstone belt hosted mesothermal lode-Au deposits are typically accompanied by extensive zones of quartz–albite–carbonate–muscovite–pyrite alteration in and around the shear zone or fault along

which fluids were focused (see section 3.9.1 below and Box 3.2). A common Au precipitation mechanism in these environments is the reaction of a H_2O–CO_2, sulfide-rich fluid with ferrous host rocks (commonly basalt or banded iron-formation) to form pyrite (Phillips, 1986). This causes destabilization of the dominant $AuHS_2^-$ complex and precipitation of native Au together with the sulfide minerals.

The intimate association between alteration and hydrothermal ore-forming processes is well established. The recognition of alteration styles and parageneses is now a standard tool in the array of techniques utilized by exploration geologists and has important bearing on the nature of the ore deposit itself.

3.6.1 Types of alteration and their ore associations

This section outlines some of the characteristics and ore associations of the main alteration styles associated with a variety of hydrothermal environments.

Potassic alteration

Potassic (or K-silicate) alteration is characterized by the formation of new K-feldspar and/or biotite, usually together with minor sericite, chlorite, and quartz. Accessory amounts of magnetite/hematite and anhydrite may occur associated with the potassic alteration assemblage. It typically represents the highest temperature form of alteration (500–600 °C) associated with porphyry Cu-type deposits, forming in the core of the system and usually within the granite intrusion itself. A degree of K^+ (cation) metasomatism in addition to hydrolysis is considered to have taken place during the formation of potassic alteration assemblages because studies of bulk compositions on a volume basis suggest that potassium has been added to the system. A variation of potassic alteration involving substantial addition of Na and Ca (called sodic and calcic alteration and characterized by abundant albite, epidote and actinolite) is documented in some porphyry systems such as Yerington, Nevada, USA.

BOX 3.2 Alteration and metal precipitation: the Golden Mile, Kalgoorlie, Western Australia – an Archean orogenic gold deposit

The "Golden Mile" is a zone of exceptional gold mineralization located immediately to the east of the twin cities of Kalgoorlie–Boulder in Western Australia. Gold was discovered here in 1893 and well over 1200 tons of gold has been won from the area since then. Until 1975 mining was carried out in several underground operations, a situation which led to a steady decline in production due to increasing depths and decreasing grades. This situation was reversed in the late 1980s when ownership was amalgamated and plans initiated to open a huge, low-grade open-pit operation known as the Fimiston or Super Pit. This is now the largest gold mining operation in Australia, producing well over 800 000 oz of gold per year.

The Golden Mile is located in the Norseman–Wiluna greenstone belt of the Yilgarn Craton. Auriferous mineralization is structurally controlled and hosted mainly in steeply dipping shear zones or lodes that are centered on the Golden Mile Fault (Figure 1a). Hundreds of subsidiary lodes are concentrated in and around this system and are hosted by a 2675 Myr old ferruginous tholeiitic intrusion (sill) called the Golden Mile dolerite. Although the initial high-grade, largely underground, workings were concentrated on the individual shear zones themselves, the system is accompanied by an extensive alteration halo of low grade mineralization which now forms the bulk of the ore in the Super Pit. It is the alteration of doleritic host rock by mineralizing, aqueo-carbonic hydrothermal solutions that is believed to be the main cause of the pervasive gold

Figure 1 (a) General geological outline of the Golden Mile, east of Kalgoorlie, Western Australia, and the approximate position of the "Super Pit," currently Australia's largest gold mining operation. (b) The nature of hydrothermal alteration in the Golden Mile dolerite. The East Lode was originally mined as a high grade underground deposit through the Lake View Shaft. The entire alteration zone now forms the bulk of the ore for the high tonnage–low grade operation in the Super Pit. Both diagrams are after Phillips (1986).

mineralization in this deposit (Phillips, 1986) and this is discussed in more detail below.

A schematic indication of the regional geology of the Golden Mile, and the approximate position of the Super Pit, is shown in Figure 1(a). The nature of the alteration halo around quartz–pyrite–gold mineralized shear zones (such as the East Lode at the Lake View mine, which has now been subsumed by the Super Pit) is shown in Figure 1(b). The Golden Mile dolerite was regionally metamorphosed to a dominantly actinolitic assemblage prior to and during folding and ductile deformation of the Norseman–Wiluna greenstone belt. Metamorphism was superseded by introduction of a reduced, low-salinity aqueo-carbonic fluid that percolated along hundreds of shear zones cutting preferentially through the relatively competent Golden Mile dolerite, progressively altering the host rock in and around them. Alteration is markedly zoned around individual shear zones, as well as on a broader scale, and is characterized by a paragenetic sequence that commences with early (metamorphic) actinolite and then progresses successively to chlorite-, carbonate-(siderite), and eventually pyrite-dominated assemblages (Phillips, 1986). Chlorite (with lesser carbonate, albite, and quartz) alteration forms a pervasive halo extending for several hundred meters around zones of shearing, and overprints the regional metamorphic assemblage. Carbonate assemblages reflect a more intense manifestation of alteration (i.e. higher fluid/rock ratio) and occur closer to individual shear zones (i.e. in halos extending up to 5 m away from the shear) or in more ferruginous parts of the differentiated dolerite sill. The shear zone itself is demarcated by a pyrite–quartz–muscovite–carbonate assemblage with which high-grade

gold mineralization occurs. Phillips (1986) has argued that the alteration paragenesis is a product of a single metamorphic fluid that introduced CO_2, K, S, and Au into the system, and that alteration and mineralization were synchronous. Precipitation of gold is considered to have been facilitated by the interaction of a reduced auriferous fluid with Fe-rich host rocks, such as in the following reactions:

$$FeCO_3 + 2H_2S + 1/2O_2 \Rightarrow FeS_2 + CO_2 + 2H_2O$$
(i.e. siderite replaced by pyrite)

and

$$FeCO_3 + Au(HS)_2^- \Rightarrow FeS_2 + CO_2 + H_2O + Au$$
(gold bisulfide complex destabilized by pyrite formation)

This model emphasizes the role that host rock alteration plays on metal precipitation, as described in section 3.5.1 of this chapter. Although the process is undoubtedly very important in the formation of many hydrothermal ore deposits, it seldom takes place in isolation. At Golden Mile, for example, it is now recognized that the late-stage, high grade gold–tellurium–vanadium ores that characterize very rich vein systems such as the Oroya shoot were the product of the mixing of a (possibly magmatic) oxidized, SO_2-bearing fluid with the more reduced metamorphic fluid that was responsible for the pervasive alteration described above (J. Walshe, www.agcrc.csiro.au/projects). Fluid mixing processes also appear to be broadly coincidental with the transition from a ductile to a brittle deformational regime, a changeover that is commonly associated with significant mineralization in orogenic gold systems.

Phyllic (or sericitic) alteration

This alteration style is very common in a variety of hydrothermal ore deposits and typically forms over a wide temperature range by hydrolysis of feldspars to form sericite (fine-grained white mica), with minor associated quartz, chlorite, and pyrite (see reaction [3.6] and Figure 3.18). Phyllic alteration is associated with porphyry Cu deposits, but also with mesothermal precious metal ores and volcanogenic massive sulfide deposits in felsic rocks.

Propylitic alteration

Propylitic alteration is probably the most widespread form of alteration in that it is essentially

indistinguishable from the assemblages which form during regional greenschist metamorphism. It comprises mainly chlorite and epidote, together with lesser quantities of clinozoisite, calcite, zoisite, and albite. It is a mild form of alteration representing low to intermediate temperatures (200–350 °C) and low fluid/rock ratios (see Figure 3.18). This style of alteration tends to be isochemical and forms in response to H^+ metasomatism. It characterizes the margins of porphyry Cu deposits as well as epithermal precious metal ores.

Argillic alteration

This alteration style is commonly subdivided into intermediate and advanced categories depending on the intensity of host mineral breakdown. Intermediate argillic alteration affects mainly plagioclase feldspars and is characterized by the formation of clay minerals kaolinite and the smectite group (mainly montmorillonite). It typically forms below about 250 °C by H^+ metasomatism and occurs on the fringes of porphyry systems. Advanced argillic alteration represents an extreme form of base leaching where rocks have been stripped of alkali elements by very acidic fluids active in high fluid/rock ratio environments (see Figure 3.18). It is characterized by kaolinite, pyrophyllite, or dickite (depending on the temperature) and alunite together with lesser quartz, topaz, and tourmaline. It is commonly associated with near surface, epithermal precious metal deposits where alteration is associated with boiling fluids and condensation of volatile-rich vapors to form extremely acidic solutions.

Silication

Silication is the conversion of a carbonate mineral or rock into a silicate mineral or rock (see reaction [3.10] above) and necessarily involves introduction of additional components into the system (cation metasomatism). It is the main process which accompanies the prograde stage in the formation of polymetallic skarn deposits which develop when a fertile, acidic, magmatic fluid infiltrates a carbonate host rock. Carbonate rocks are a particularly efficient host for metal deposition from hydrothermal solutions because of their ability to neutralize acidic fluids and their "reactivity," which enhances permeability and fluid flow. Skarn reactions and the formation of "calc–silicate" mineral assemblages are very complex and develop over an extended temperature range. Fluid/rock ratios also develop to very high values in skarn systems and these factors result in the precipitation of a diverse, polymetallic suite of ores.

Silicification

Silicification should not be confused with silication and refers specifically to the formation of new quartz or amorphous silica minerals in a rock

during alteration. Minor silicification develops in the alteration halos associated with many different ore deposit types and is usually a by-product of isochemical hydrolysis reactions where Si is locally derived (see reactions [3.6] and [3.8] above). The majority of fractures through which hydrothermal fluids have passed are at least partially filled with quartz to form veins. The Si in these settings is usually derived by leaching of the country rocks through which the fluids are circulating. Intense silicification, however, forms as a result of cation metasomatism, where substantial addition of Si^{4+} in solution is added to the system. This type of alteration is characteristic of the sinter zones in high level epithermal precious metal ore deposits.

Carbonatization

Carbonatization refers to the formation of carbonate minerals (calcite, dolomite, magnesite, siderite, etc.) during alteration of a rock and is promoted by fluids characterized by high partial pressures of carbon dioxide (P_{CO_2}) and neutral to alkaline pH. Archean greenstone belt related lode-gold deposits represent an ore deposit type where carbonate alteration is virtually ubiquitous and is accompanied by an assemblage comprising quartz, muscovite, biotite, albite, and chlorite. It forms when reaction occurs between a low-salinity, CO_2-rich fluid and its host rock. The carbonate mineral that forms is a function of the composition of the host rock and could be dolomite in association with amphibolite, siderite in a banded iron-formation, or calcite in a granitic host.

Greisenization

The formation of a greisen is specific to the cupola zones of highly differentiated (S-type) granites that contain Sn and W mineralization, as well as significant concentrations of other incompatible elements such as F, Li, and B. Greisens represent an alteration assemblage comprising mainly quartz, muscovite, and topaz, with lesser tourmaline and fluorite, usually forming adjacent to quartz–cassiterite–wolframite veins.

Hematitization

Alteration that is associated with oxidizing fluids often results in the formation of minerals with a high Fe^{3+}/Fe^{2+} ratio and, in particular, hematite with associated K-feldspar, sericite, chlorite, and epidote. In the magmatic-hydrothermal environment, occurrences such as the granitoid-hosted, Olympic Dam-type Cu–Au–Fe–U deposit in South Australia are characterized by this style of alteration. It also typifies other ore bodies, including the stratiform, sediment-hosted Cu–Co ores of the Central African Copperbelt. This style of alteration appears to be related to redox processes where highly saline, oxidizing fluids come into contact with a more reduced host rock environment, or mix with more reduced fluids.

3.7 METAL ZONING AND PARAGENETIC SEQUENCE

A characteristic feature of many hydrothermal ore deposits is the occurrence of a regular pattern of distribution, or *zoning*, of metals and minerals in space. Zoning can be observed at many different scales, ranging from regional patterns of metal distribution (at a scale of hundreds of kilometers), through a district scale, to individual ore-body related variations and even down to the level of a single vein or hand specimen (Smirnov, 1977; Guilbert and Park, 1986; Pirajno, 1992; Misra, 2000). A good example of regional metal zonation is the Andes metallogenic province, where the distributional pattern of ore deposits is related to continental scale subduction along the western margin of South America. At a district scale, however, the distribution of metals is more tightly constrained and better defined, and commonly characterized by a consistent pattern that is reproduced in other ore-forming environments. District scale zoning is well exemplified by the Sn–W–Cu–Pb–Zn–Ag–Sb–U sequence of ores associated with the Cornubian batholith in southwest England (see Box 2.2, Chapter 2), a pattern that is reproduced in other granite-related ore-forming systems. Zonation at this and smaller scales is clearly related to the systematic evolution of a hydrothermal fluid (i.e. alteration) and

the sequential precipitation of its contained metal budget by the types of processes discussed in section 3.6 above. Although the processes controlling metal precipitation are complex and varied, the relatively consistent pattern of metal zonation in so many different ore-forming environments means that the process should be amenable to rational and unified explanation.

Although there is still some ambiguity in its use, the term *paragenesis* is now widely applied to the association of minerals and metals that characterizes a particular ore type and, therefore, has a common origin (Guilbert and Park, 1986; Kutina *et al.*, 1965). Because both space and time need to be considered in the understanding of zonation, the phrase *paragenetic sequence* is now used to describe the distribution in time of a set of genetically related minerals or metals. The recognition and significance of parageneses and paragenetic sequences in hydrothermal ore deposits came from early observations of ore-forming environments by some of the founders of modern economic geology, notably Waldemar Lindgren (1933). On the basis of these empirical observations Emmons (1936) devised the concept of a "reconstructed vein." This was an idealized composite vein that extended from deep in the crust up to the surface and contained a paragenetic sequence of ore components that is typical of the zoning patterns observed in many different hydrothermal ore deposit types. The "Emmons reconstructed vein," revised by Guilbert and Park (1986), is summarized in Table 3.3.

Observations suggest that metals such as Mo, W, and Sn will precipitate early (or at deep levels) from a high temperature hydrothermal solution. Such solutions are sometimes referred to as *hypothermal.* They are followed, in the ideal precipitation sequence, by Cu, and then Zn, Pb, Mn, and Ag, as the fluid infiltrates upwards in the crust and cools to form *mesothermal* solutions. The precious and volatile metals such as Au, Sb, and Hg are typically observed to represent the latest stages of the sequence, forming from still cooler *epithermal* solutions circulating near the surface. Extensive studies of hydrothermal ore deposits leave little doubt that the Emmons sequence shown in Table 3.3 has general applicab-

Table 3.3 The "Emmons Reconstructed Vein" concept showing empirical observations that relate to typical patterns of zonation and paragenetic sequences in many hydrothermal ore deposits

Vein	Metal	Ore mineralogy (in bold), and related alteration assemblages
Surface (epithermal)	Barren	Chalcedony, quartz, barite, fluorite, and carbonate minerals
	Mercury	**Cinnabar**: chalcedony, quartz, barite, fluorite, and carbonate minerals
	Antimony	**Stibnite**: quartz
	Gold–silver	**Gold, electrum, acanthite**: quartz, chalcedony, adularia, alunite, carbonate minerals, silicification, some potassic, phyllic, and propylitic alteration
	Barren	Quartz and carbonate minerals
	Silver–manganese	**Acanthite, rhodochrosite**: quartz and carbonate minerals, some phyllic, argillic, propylitic alteration
Intermediate (mesothermal)	Lead	**Galena**: quartz with minor carbonate minerals
	Zinc	**Sphalerite**: quartz with occasional carbonate minerals, advanced argillic alteration
	Copper–arsenic–antimony	**Chalcopyrite, tennantite–tetrahedrite**: quartz, phyllic, propylitic, argillic alteration
	Copper	**Chalcopyrite**: quartz, phyllic alteration
	Molybdenum–tungsten–tin	**Molybdenite, huebnerite, scheelite, cassiterite**: quartz, potassic alteration
Deep (hypothermal)	Barren	Potassic alteration, anhydrite, carbonate minerals

Source: after Guilbert and Park (1986).

ility. Many exceptions, however, do exist and there is little doubt that the scheme can be much improved and extended in the light of modern observations and theory.

The wide ranging applicability of the Emmons sequence suggests that the secular precipitation of metals might simply be related to the decline in solubility that generally accompanies temperature decrease. Sections 3.5 and 3.6 above, however, have shown that metal solubilities and precipitation are controlled by a variety of complexly interacting variables that are related to both the fluid itself and its surrounds. Barnes (1975) first showed that if metals are considered to have been transported as *metal–sulfide* complexes then the relative stabilities of these complexes, when corrected for differing concentration of metals in solution, closely match the Emmons precipitation sequence. On this basis he identified the following paragenetic sequence:

$$Fe - Ni - Sn - Cu - Zn - Pb - Ag - Au - Sb - Hg$$

By contrast, if metal transport occurs by *metal–chloride* complexation then the above sequence no longer applies and a subset of these metals is more likely to be precipitated according to the sequence:

$$Cu - Ag - Pb - Zn$$

This suggests that paragenetic sequences are likely to be controlled by more than just a single variable. Susak and Crerar (1981) demonstrated that paragenetic sequences need to be considered in terms of classes of metals that are grouped in terms of mineral stoichiometry and the valence state of the aqueous metal species. They went on to show that the precipitation sequence of metals from *within one particular class* will be controlled essentially by the Gibbs free energies of the associated minerals. The precipitation of metals from different classes would, however, be controlled by the environment within which the metal-bearing solution occurs, and this could be a

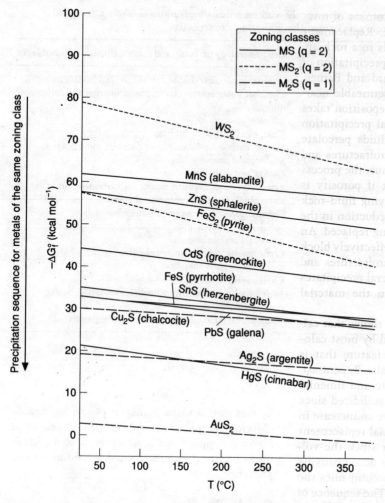

Figure 3.19 Plot of Gibbs free energy versus temperature for a variety of sulfide minerals categorized according to their stoichiometry (where M is metal and S is sulfide) and the valence state of the dissolved metal species (q). The precipitation sequence for metals in solution from the same zoning class is predicted in terms of decreasing values of free energy (after Susak and Crerar, 1981).

more complex, multivariable process. Thus, a simple and reproduceable zonation pattern or paragenetic sequence is likely to apply only to hydrothermal ore-forming environments that consist of metals from the same zoning class. Any exceptions and reversals to the typical Emmons sequence are likely to be explained in terms of either disequilibrium, or precipitation of metals from different classes.

The predicted precipitation sequence for metals in specifically defined zonation classes is illustrated in Figure 3.19. The precipitation sequence for metals in solution from the same class can be read on this diagram in terms of decreasing Gibbs free energy values for a specific temperature. Thus, the precipitation sequence for metals in the MS (q = 2) zoning class is Mn–Zn–Cd–Pb–Hg for any temperature, but this sequence would not necessarily prevail under conditions where a different stoichiometry and valence state prevails.

Replacement processes

In the previous section the precipitation of minerals and metals was discussed in the context of aqueous solutions passing through open spaces in a rock, especially vugs and veins at shallow crustal levels. Different conditions apply to metals that are precipitated during the *replacement* of minerals deeper in the Earth's crust. Replacement occurs when the original minerals in a rock are dissolved and near simultaneous precipitation of secondary minerals occurs (Seward and Barnes, 1997). In contrast to the more permeable near-surface environment where ore deposition takes place by open space filling, metal precipitation deeper in the crust occurs as fluids percolate along poorly interconnected microfractures and pore spaces (see section 3.3.4). Thus, the process of replacement will only persist if porosity is maintained and if the accompanying fluid–rock reactions are characterized by a reduction in the molar volume of the mineral being replaced. An increase in molar volume would effectively block the through-flow of fluid as microfractures and pores are filled by secondary mineral precipitates whose volumes are greater than the material being replaced.

Comparison of molar volumes shows that calcite, for example, can be replaced by most calc–silicate and sulfide minerals, a feature that is commonly observed in skarn deposits. By contrast, oxide minerals such as magnetite and ilmenite are less likely to be completely sulfidized since the relevant reactions will involve an increase in molar volume. At best, only partial replacement of oxide by sulfide would occur since the volume increase, together with the accompanying decrease in microporosity that accompanies the reaction, would limit fluid flow. The sequence of precipitation of secondary or ore minerals during replacement processes can best be predicted in terms of decreasing molar volumes of the respective solids involved, as discussed by Seward and Barnes (1997). The mineral sequence shown below, with relevant molar volumes, is useful for the understanding of replacement processes and the prediction of replacement sequences. Replacement will only be effective when minerals of smaller volume replace those with larger volume. In the sequence presented below minerals will only comprehensively replace those occurring to their left. In addition, mineral replacement will presumably occur more readily the greater the volume deficit between original and secondary mineral.

microcline ← scheelite ← anhydrite ← calcite
[54]   [47]   [46]   [37]
← kaolinite ← galena ← molybdenite ← siderite
[33]   [31]   [30]   [29]
← cinnabar ← muscovite ← arsenopyrite
[28]   [28]   [26]
← bornite ← pyrite ← sphalerite ← chalcopyrite
[25]   [24]   [24]   [22]
← pyrrhotite ← ilmenite ← hematite
[18]   [16]   [15]
← magnetite ← chalcocite
[15]   [14]

(This sequence is from Seward and Barnes (1979); [molar volumes] in $cm^3 \, mol^{-1}$.)

3.8 MODERN ANALOGUES OF ORE-FORMING PROCESSES – THE VMS–SEDEX CONTINUUM

The term "volcanogenic massive sulfide," or VMS, refers to a large family of mainly Cu–Zn (occasionally with minor Pb and Au) deposit types that formed during episodes of major orogenesis throughout Earth history (see Chapter 6). They are also referred to as VHMS deposits, where the acronym stands for "volcanic hosted massive sulfide." VMS deposits occur in a variety of tectonic settings, but are typically related to precipitation of metals from hydrothermal solutions circulating in volcanically active submarine environments. Sedimentary exhalative (SEDEX) deposits, by contrast, are dominated by a Zn–Pb (with lesser Cu, but commonly Ba and Ag) metal association and are also related to hydrothermal fluids venting onto the sea floor, but without an obvious or direct link to volcanism. Many of the large SEDEX deposits of the world are Proterozoic in age, although several examples, such as Red Dog (see Box 3.4) also formed in Phanerozoic times. Although there is generally no spatial or temporal link between SEDEX and VMS deposits, it is widely held that they represent a continuum and are conceptually linked by the fact that they formed by the same basic processes (Gilmour, 1976; Plimer, 1978; Guilbert and Park, 1986; Kirkham and Roscoe, 1993; Misra, 2000). These processes are active and can be studied in modern day environments, as discussed below.

The notion of a continuum between VMS and SEDEX deposit types is, however, contentious and readers should be wary of over-interpreting the genetic link between the two deposit types. The principal VMS and SEDEX deposits apparently formed at different times of Earth history and in different tectonic settings. In addition, studies have shown that some of the stratiform base metal deposits, previously thought to be syngenetic and related to exhalative venting of hydrothermal solutions onto the sea floor, are more likely to be the product of replacement processes and, therefore, epigenetic in origin. A reinterpretation of this type has, for example, recently been made with respect to the Mount Isa deposits in Australia (Perkins, 1997). With this cautionary proviso in mind, it is nevertheless convenient to discuss VMS and SEDEX deposits as a conceptual continuum, at least insofar as the principal ore-forming processes are concerned. Both deposit types can be discussed in terms of modern analogues, which is advantageous in that the ore-forming processes can be studied directly. VMS deposits are discussed in the light of the spectacular discoveries on the ocean floors of "black smokers," whereas SEDEX deposits are considered in terms of the rift-related hydrothermal activity in the Red Sea and also around the Salton Sea in California.

3.8.1 "Black smokers" – a modern analogue for VMS deposit formation

Even though it had been known since the 1960s that warm brines vented onto the ocean floor, it was the discovery in 1979 of "black smokers" at 21° N on the East Pacific Rise (Francheteau et al., 1979) that provided spectacular insights into the nature of submarine hydrothermal activity and its potential impact on the understanding of ore deposition in such environments. Black smokers are described as hot (up to 400 °C), metal charged, reduced, and slightly acidic hydrothermal fluids that vent onto the sea floor, usually in zones of extension and active volcanism along mid-ocean ridges (Figure 3.20). The fluids originate essentially from cold (2 °C), alkaline, oxidizing, and metal-deficient sea water. They circulate through the basaltic ocean crust and, in so doing, scavenge metals to form the hydrothermal fluids now observed at more than 100 black smoker sites in the Pacific, Atlantic, and Indian Oceans as well as the Mediterranean Sea (Scott, 1997). Black smoker fluids usually vent through tube-like structures, called chimneys (Figure 3.20), that are built out of a mixture of anhydrite, barite, and sulfide minerals such as pyrite, pyrrhotite, chalcopyrite, and sphalerite, as well as gangue opaline silica.

Metal-charged fluids venting on the ocean floor point to the hydrothermal exhalative processes by which most, if not all, VMS and SEDEX can be explained. Black smokers venting along mid-ocean ridges represent a direct analogy for one specific type of the VMS family of deposits, namely the ophiolite-hosted Cu–Zn deposits such as those of the Troodos Massif, Cyprus (Box 3.3). An ophiolite represents a section of a mid-ocean ridge spreading center that is preserved by obduction onto continental material, and is characterized by a sheeted dyke complex, pillowed basalt, and pelagic sediment. A lens of massive sulfide ore, comprising mainly pyrite, chalcopyrite, and sphalerite is located at the ocean floor interface and this is underlain by a pipe-like zone of disseminated sulfides and intense chloritic alteration representing the conduit along which fluids passed on their way to the ocean floor (Figure 3.21a). The geometry of this ore deposit type is fairly typical of most other VMS deposits (Figure 3.21b) even though they may form in other tectonic settings such as island arcs, back-arc basins, and fore-arc troughs. Other well known Cyprus-type VMS deposits include Lokken in Norway and Outokumpu in Finland. Famous examples of VMS deposits formed in other tectonic settings include the greenstone belt hosted Kidd Creek and Mattabi deposits in the Archean Superior Province of Canada, Besshi and the numerous Kuroko-type deposits of the Japanese island arc, Rio Tinto and Neves Corvo in the Iberian Pyrite Belt of Spain and Portugal, the Buchans and Bathurst deposits of Newfoundland, Jerome in Arizona, and the Mount Lyell and Hellyer deposits in Tasmania.

Figure 3.20 Conceptual diagram illustrating the fluid characteristics and circulation pattern in mid-ocean ridge environments that give rise to the formation of "black smokers" on the sea floor. Inset is a cross section of an exhalative vent site showing the construction of anhydrite–sulfide chimneys on top of a mound of massive sulfide mineralization (after Lydon 1988; Scott, 1997).

There is now general consensus that submarine venting represents a very good analogue for the processes that applied during the formation of most of the actual VMS deposits preserved or fossilized in the Earth's crust. Excellent reviews of the characteristics of actual VMS deposits and the nature of their ore-forming processes are provided by Franklin *et al.* (1981), Hekinian and Fouquet (1985), Lydon (1988), Large (1992), and Scott (1997). Studies of many actual deposits confirm that the fluids involved are derived dominantly from sea water, although fluid inclusion and stable isotope studies suggest that in certain cases a minor magmatic fluid component may have been incorporated into the circulating fluid system. The main source of metals is believed

(a)

Pelagic sediments

Oxidized zone

Massive sulfide ore zone

Mafic pillow lavas

Stockwork ore zone (disseminated sulfides and chloritic alteration)

Sheeted dyke complex

(b)

Sulfide-bearing epiclastic

Massive sulfide

Quartz-hematite ± magnetite exhalite

Pyritic siltstone

Stringer sulfide

Bedded carbonate-sulfide lens

0   20
m

Figure 3.21 (a) Section through a typical ophiolite-hosted, Cyprus-type VMS deposit. Footwall rocks may consist of a sheeted dyke complex and the associated volcanics are often pillowed and have a tholeiitic composition. After Hutchinson and Searle (1971). (b) Section showing the characteristics of VMS deposits other than the ophiolite-hosted type. Associated volcanics may be intermediate or felsic in composition and a closer lateral link to chemical and epiclastic sediments is often apparent. The lens of massive sulfide ore formed on the ocean floor, underlain by a stockwork zone of disseminated sulfides and intensely altered volcanic rock, is typical of VMS deposits in general (after Large, 1992).

to have been the volcanic rocks through which the sea water was percolating, and evidence in support of this comes from mass balance considerations and the fact that metal assemblages in different VMS deposits are consistent with the expected metal contents and ratios in the associated primary igneous rock. For example, Cyprus-type VMS deposits, which reflect leaching of a dominantly mafic volcanic source rock, are typified by a Cu + Zn metal association (Franklin, 1993) and this is explained by the fact that mafic volcanics are characterized by much higher Cu and Zn contents than their felsic equivalents. However, the reverse is true of Pb (see Table 1.2, Chapter 1) and this helps to explain why the

Kuroko deposits of Japan, for example, described as a Zn–Pb–Cu variant of the VMS family (Pirajno, 1992; Franklin, 1993; Misra, 2000) and associated with arc-related bimodal (i.e. felsic and mafic) volcanism, have a different metal association. By contrast, the source of sulfur is essentially from the sulfate component of the sea water itself with reduction of sulfate to sulfide occurring during fluid–rock interaction prior to venting (Ohmoto *et al.*, 1983). This is demonstrated in the compilation by Large (1992), which shows similar trends in sulfur isotope variations of VMS sulfide ores and sea water derived sulfate minerals over time (at least for Phanerozoic deposits).

BOX 3.3 Exhalative venting and "black smokers" on the sea floor: the VMS deposits of the Troodos ophiolite, Cyprus

The 91 Myr old Troodos ophiolite complex in Cyprus represents an obducted and exposed fragment of oceanic crust that has been extremely well studied. It is also famous as a site of copper mining since the Bronze Age and contains some 90 small to intermediate sized Cu–Zn

VMS deposits hosted in pillowed basalts, mainly along the northern edge of the complex (Figure 1). The ophiolite is well exposed and comprises a cross section of the ocean crust, from lower mafic and ultramafic cumulates (gabbro and harzburgite that contain podiform chromitite

Figure 1 Generalized geology of the Troodos ophiolite complex in Cyprus and the distribution of VMS style Cu–Zn mineralization.

Figure 2 The nature and geometry of VMS mineralization in typical Cyprus deposits. Mineralization can be concentrated at the interface between successive basaltic lava flows, as shown, or it can occur between the upper pillow lavas and the umber sediments (after Constantinou and Govett, 1973).

deposits; see Chapter 1), overlain by a sheeted dyke complex and pillowed basalts. The largest deposits are Mavrovouni (15 million tons) and Skouriotissa (6 million tons), although several others have been mined in the recent past (Herzig and Hannington, 1995).

Mineralization in the Cyprus deposits comprises massive pyrite and chalcopyrite, with lesser sphalerite, hosted in pillow lavas and associated with zones of intense silicification and chlorite alteration (Figure 2; Constantinou and Govett, 1973). The lavas are overlain by shales and cherts that are Fe- and Mn-rich (referred to as umber), and may also contain concentrations of Au. The hydrothermal fluid responsible for mineralization in the Troodos VMS ores was modified sea water that discharged through black smoker vents located along ridge axis parallel faults at temperatures of 300–350 °C (Spooner, 1980). The characteristics of the Cyprus deposits have been compared directly with the TAG site, an active exhalative vent system on the mid-Atlantic ridge (Eddy *et al.*, 1998). It is also evident, however, that VMS mineralization can be associated with magmatic activity that is removed from that occurring along the ridge axis. The intrusion of discrete gabbroic plutons, and the formation of seamounts and sea floor calderas, for example, are features that pro-

Figure 3 Pillow lavas exposed adjacent to a small VMS-type Cu–Zn deposit in the Troodos ophiolite, Cyprus (photograph by Carl Anhaeusser).

mote fluid circulation and VMS styles of mineralization in areas that can be well away from the ridge axis. This observation has obvious exploration significance, and the Alestos and Memi deposits in Cyprus are two examples of classic VMS type mineralization associated with off-axis mineralization (Eddy *et al.*, 1998).

VMS deposits are characterized by well developed metal zonation patterns defined by a typical sequence from Fe to Fe–Cu to Cu–Pb–Zn to Pb–Zn–Ba in an upward and lateral sense. At a first approximation this sequence reflects the variable solubilities of these metals at progressively lower temperatures and could be seen as a paragenetic sequence. In detail, however, the development of this zonation is more complex and reflects the evolution of fluids and the growth mechanism of the massive sulfide mound with time, as described in Figure 3.22a. In this model it is envisaged that the temperature of the ore fluid increases with time as the deposit grows. Low temperatures would not be able to dissolve much in the way of base metals, although such fluids could transport sulfate complexes and precipitate anhydrite or barite on mixing with sea water (the so-called "white smokers" seen associated with low temperature vents). At temperatures approaching 250 °C, however, the solubilities of Pb and Zn as chloride complexes would be high, reaching 100 ppm under the conditions applicable to Figure 3.22b. Copper would be poorly soluble,

but some Au could be transported as a bisulfide complex. Discharge of such fluids would result in precipitation of barite/anhydrite together with sphalerite and galena, as well as minor gold (Stage 1, Figure 3.22a). As fluids evolve to higher temperatures (250–300 °C) they are capable of containing significant Cu as a chloride complex and chalcopyrite will be precipitated in the footwall stockwork zone and at the base of the massive sulfide mound (Stage 2, Figure 3.22a). In the latter area it has been observed that chalcopyrite replaces sphalerite. Since the solvent capacity of a 250 °C fluid with respect to both Zn and Pb is high, it is feasible for the earlier formed sulfide minerals to be dissolved and reprecipitated further up in the mound, or distal to it. This zone-refining type of process accounts for the development of high grade massive sulfide cappings seen in certain VMS deposits. At still higher temperatures (300–350 °C) both Cu and Au are in solution as chloride complexes, ultimately giving rise to further chalcopyrite precipitation, together with Au and pyrite. In this model the sequence Fe–Cu–Pb–Zn–Ba is in fact the reverse of the

Figure 3.22 (a) Secular model explaining the evolution of fluids, growth of massive sulfide mounds, zoning, and paragenetic sequence for VMS deposits. (b) Plot of temperature versus Cu, Pb, Zn, and Au solubilities appropriate to fluid conditions during VMS ore deposition (pH = 4; 1 M NaCl; $aH_2S = 0.001$; $SO_4/H_2S = 0.01$). Both diagrams after Large (1992).

paragenetic sequence predicted simply in terms of solubility variations with declining temperature. This scheme also predicts that VMS deposits could grow by input of metals from below and not necessarily by sulfide particles sedimenting out

from the sea water, or aggregation of collapsed chimneys. Finally, it should be emphasized that biologically mediated precipitation mechanisms, such as the involvement of sulfate-reducing bacteria in exhalative vent processes, are likely to be important contributing factors during the formation of both VMS and SEDEX deposits. Large-scale precipitation of sulfides by bacterial reduction of sea water sulfate has, for example, been suggested for the Irish Zn–Pb–Ba deposits (see section 3.5.3 above; Fallick *et al.*, 2001).

Not all VMS deposits are characterized by a classic lens shaped sulfide mound and a well defined footwall alteration zone. Some have flat or tabular morphologies and appear to be distal from a vent, showing little or no evidence of footwall alteration/mineralization. Others exhibit indications of massive sulfide lenses stacked one on top of the other or significant metal deposition below the sea water–rock interface (Large, 1992). The morphology of atypical VMS deposits may largely be a function of the physical properties of the ore fluids themselves as they infiltrate up through the footwall volcanics and then vent onto the sea floor. Sato (1972) has suggested that submarine fluids would be either more or less dense than sea water as a function of their temperature, salinity, and degree of mixing with cold sea water. Figure 3.23a (Type I) shows a situation where an ore solution is more dense than sea water, giving rise to concentrated metal precipitation that remains proximal to the site of venting. This mechanism could explain the formation of high grade tabular VMS deposits. If the ore solution and sea water have similar densities venting will occur but metals will be precipitated close to the site or in nearby topographic depressions (Type II, Figure 3.23a). A different product would result if the black smoker fluids were much less dense than sea water (Type III, Figure 3.23a), giving rise to buoyant metal-rich plumes that disperse metals into more distal marine sediments. Although this is not likely to be a particularly efficient process it remains a possible mechanism for explaining distal, low grade deposits associated with a higher proportion of ocean floor sediment.

Another factor that may be important in considerations of exactly where in the system metals accumulate relates to whether or not the hydrothermal solutions undergo boiling. The phase change from liquid to vapor is strongly pressure-dependent and even though many black smoker fluids have been observed venting at temperatures as high as 400 °C, they appear on the sea floor as fluids because of the high confining pressures that exist deep in the oceans. This is confirmed in Figure 3.23b, where the boiling point curve for sea water is plotted relative to deep (represented by 21° N East Pacific Rise) and shallow (represented by the Juan de Fuca ridge) ocean floor settings. Any 350 °C hydrothermal solution rising adiabatically through the crust would intersect the deep ocean floor as a liquid since it would not yet have intersected the boiling point curve. Metal precipitation on the sea floor from the black smoker would, in this case, occur by rapid quenching of the ore solution as it mixed with a virtually limitless volume of cold sea water. By contrast, the same fluid moving up toward a shallower sea floor is likely to intersect the boiling point curve before it vents to surface (Figure 3.23b). Boiling below the ocean floor is likely to promote brecciation of the footwall and local metal precipitation, possibly resulting in extensive stockwork mineralization. Classic VMS deposition is unlikely to occur and ore bodies may appear stacked one on top of the other. Although there are many variants in the family of VMS ores the processes applicable to the submarine exhalative model appear capable of explaining many of the features of this very important class of deposits.

3.8.2 The Salton Sea and Red Sea geothermal systems – modern analogues for SEDEX mineralization processes

SEDEX deposits contain more than half of the world's known resources of Pb and Zn and are generally represented by bigger and richer deposits than the VMS category, although there may be fewer of them. They are typically formed within intracratonic rift basins and are hosted by marine clastic or chemical sediments with little or no direct association with volcanic rocks. Most of the world's giant SEDEX deposits are Paleo- to Mesoproterozoic in age and well known examples include HYC (McArthur River), Mount Isa and Broken Hill in eastern Australia, Sullivan in British Columbia, Aggeneys and Gamsberg in South Africa, and Rajpura-Dariba in India. A

(a)

(b)

Figure 3.23 (a) Plot of temperature versus density for a variety of possible hydrothermal solutions (where 1 M, 3 M, etc. refer to the NaCl molality or the salinity of the solution) relative to sea water at 10°C. Different solutions may be either less or more dense than sea water. At one extreme they would form buoyant plumes capable of distributing metals some distance away from the site of venting (Type III), whereas at the other they would precipitate metals proximally to the vent (Type I). After Sato (1972). (b) Pressure (or depth) versus temperature plot showing the sea water (with 3.5 wt% NaCl) boiling curve relative to deep (21° N East Pacific Rise) and shallow (Juan de Fuca ridge) sea floor. Because of the strong pressure dependency on boiling, a 350 °C hydrothermal fluid rising adiabatically in the crust would intersect a deep ocean floor as a liquid and would vent as a black smoker precipitating metals into the sea. The same fluid relative to a shallower ocean would boil before intersecting the floor such that only a vapor phase would reach the surface. Metal precipitation in such a case will likely occur beneath the ocean floor. After Delaney and Cosens (1982).

significant group of deposits is Paleozoic in age and these include Meggen and Rammelsberg in Germany, Navan in Ireland, Red Dog in Alaska, and Howard's Pass in eastern Canada.

Modern analogues for the genesis of SEDEX deposits have been described from the Salton Sea and Gulf of California (Figure 3.24) and also the Red Sea. The study of these hydrothermal systems reveals both syn-sedimentary exhalative and replacement processes and can, to a certain extent, be used to discount the often controversial views that prevail regarding the origin of sediment-hosted stratiform deposits.

Salton Sea geothermal system

The East Pacific Rise intersects the North American plate at the head of the Gulf of California (Figure 3.24a). At this point the prevailing stresses along this mid-ocean ridge are transferred onto the continent to form the essentially dextral San Andreas fault system. The fault cuts through a dry intermontane region called Imperial Valley, which is characterized by active, rift-related sedimentation. Early settlers discovered a huge salt pan in this valley, named the Salton Sink, that was mined for a few years in the late 1800s. In 1905, however, a canal, designed to bring irrigation water from the Colorado River to settler farmers in Imperial Valley, was breached by spring floods and the entire volume of this large river was channeled into the Salton Sink, at that time close to 100 meters below sea level. It was two years before the breach was plugged and the Colorado River reverted to its natural course. By that time the salt pan had become the Salton Sea, a huge inland lake that covered an area of several hundred square kilometers. The Salton Sea soon became brackish as the lake waters dissolved the salt on its floor. Evaporation also increased the salinity of Salton Sea waters to the Na–Cl–SO$_4$ dominated composition that is observed today (McKibben and Hardie, 1997).

Over the past century water from the Salton Sea has been percolating downwards along fault-related pathways and through earlier formed lacustrine sediments to form an extensive hydrothermal system from which geothermal power is now derived. In addition, hot metalliferous brines, also derived directly from Salton Sea waters and heated by a combination of the high prevailing

Figure 3.24 (*left*) The Salton Sea Geothermal System (SSGS) and its location (inset) relative to the Gulf of California transform fault region and the dextral San Andreas fault system (after McKibben and Hardie, 1997).

geothermal gradient and active volcanism in the region, vent from numerous sites, and it is these that are of particular interest to the study of ore-forming processes (White, 1963; Skinner et al., 1969). The combination of well understood fluid compositional and circulation pathways, set in an active seismic and volcanic, intracontinental rift environment, has made the Salton Sea geothermal system a classic example of an ore-forming environment whose evolution can be observed, and from which many inferences about ancient sediment-hosted ore-forming processes can be made. In addition to its obvious applicability to the understanding of SEDEX ore-forming processes, the processes observed in this environment might also be relevant to the formation of stratiform red-bed hosted Cu deposits such as the Kupferschiefer ores of central Europe and the Central African Copperbelt (McKibben et al., 1988; McKibben and Hardie, 1997).

Although the Salton Sea geothermal system does not exist in a submarine environment, the geometry of the system and the processes involved are considered to be useful for the understanding of sediment-hosted hydrothermal base metal deposits in which fluids circulated during and soon after deposition. A variety of conditions need to prevail in order to make SEDEX ore-forming processes viable. These include an abundant fluid source, a rich source of metals and complexing agents, active rifting, and deformation induced fluid flow. Detailed study of geothermal wells around the Salton Sea has shown that at depths of 1000–3000 meters a hot (350 °C), dense (up to 26 wt% dissolved solids), Na–Ca–K–Cl brine exists (McKibben et al., 1988). This fluid also contains significant concentrations of metals, in particular Fe, Mn, Pb, Zn, and Cu, derived from local lacustrine sediments. Precipitation of these metals has been induced by mixing of the hot metal charged brine with cooler, dilute surface waters about 1000 meters below the surface, to form sediment-hosted base metal sulfide veins and associated chloritic alteration. This is clearly not an exhalative system and the ores that form will appear epigenetic in character. Ores that form in this environment could also have a stratiform geometry, with metals being deposited by replacement

of pre-existing phases such as diagenetic cements or easily dissolvable detrital minerals. In the Salton Sea setting it is also conceivable, especially in the event of very energetic fluid circulation, that the metal-charged brine could intersect the lake floor and vent ore-bearing solutions in much the same way that black smokers are exhaled along the mid-ocean ridges. It seems feasible, therefore, for SEDEX ore bodies to appear syngenetic and exhalative in sediments that were deposited at the time of fluid venting, but also distinctly epigenetic relative to the footwall sedimentary sequence. A model illustrating the main features of SEDEX deposits and incorporating the concept that syngenetic exhalative and epigenetic replacement type ores could be coeval and form part of the same system is presented in Figure 3.25.

The Red Sea and the VMS–SEDEX continuum

The extension of the East Pacific Rise (mid-ocean ridge) onto continental North America to form the San Andreas fault system (Figure 3.24) provides support for the view that a conceptual continuum exists between VMS and SEDEX styles of mineralization. Present day ocean floor black smokers at 21° N on the East Pacific Rise and the active, metal-charged geothermal systems of the Salton Sea perhaps represent extremes in the range of VMS and SEDEX ore-forming systems. The Guaymas Basin in the Gulf of California is also known to contain terrigenous sediment-hosted styles of VMS mineralization, also known as Besshi-type ores, from the type location in Japan. These intermediate styles of mineralization also provide support for the view that VMS and SEDEX styles of base/precious metal mineralization can be linked in terms of both tectonic setting and hydrothermal systems. Perhaps the best example of the conceptual link between VMS and SEDEX deposit types, however, is provided by the Red Sea rift, separating Africa and Arabia. The Red Sea is an ocean basin in the early stages of its development, containing active geothermal venting and deposition of base metal deposits in clayey muds accumulating in depressions on the sea floor (Bischoff, 1969). Mineralization is particularly well developed at a site known as the

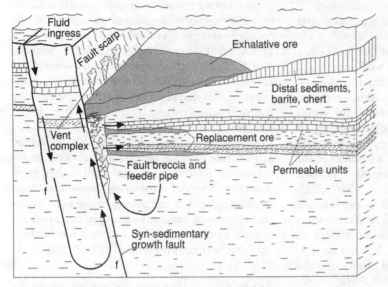

Figure 3.25 Diagram illustrating the setting for the formation of SEDEX-type Pb–Zn ores and a scenario which incorporates both exhalative and replacement concepts for the formation of these ores (after compilations by Goodfellow *et al.*, 1993; Misra, 2000).

BOX 3.4 Sedimentary exhalative (SEDEX) processes: the Red Dog Zn–Pb–Ag deposit, Alaska

The Red Dog mine in northwest Alaska is presently the world's largest producer of zinc concentrate, contributing about 6% of annual global supply. It is a very rich deposit and in 2002 had reserves of close to 100 million tons of ore grading 18% zinc, 5% lead, and 85 g ton^{-1} silver (www.teckcominco.com). It was discovered in 1968 by an astute bush pilot who noticed a color anomaly in the rocks caused by oxidation of the sulfide ores.

The Red Dog ores are hosted in Carboniferous black shales and limestone of the Kuna Formation in the De Long mountains of the Brooks Range, northern Alaska. The host succession has been deformed into a sequence of thrust allochthons during a Jurassic orogeny. Figure 1 shows an interpretive section through a Devonian–Carboniferous sequence of sediments in the Brooks Range prior to thrusting. The sequence of sediments, including

Figure 1 Interpretive, pre-thrusting, cross section through Devonian–Carboniferous sediments in the Brooks Range, illustrating the depositional setting of host rocks at the Red Dog mine. Syn-sedimentary growth faults and abrupt lateral facies variations are also a feature of the regional setting (after Moore *et al.*, 1986).

Figure 2 Simplified block diagram showing the environment of ore formation in the Carboniferous for the Red Dog deposit (after Moore et al., 1986).

limestones and turbiditic assemblages, is consistent with deposition in a restricted ocean basin, with no indication of volcanism in the immediate environs. Abrupt lateral facies changes in the succession point to the presence of syn-sedimentary growth faults that would have facilitated fluid circulation through the basin.

Mineralization is stratabound and, despite the thrusting, is relatively flat-lying (Moore et al., 1986). It is, marked by laterally extensive zones of silicification (chert and chalcedony) within which poorly bedded sulfide minerals (sphalerite, pyrite–marcasite, and galena) occur. Barite is closely associated with the ore and tends to cap the mineralized zones. An interesting feature of the ore zones is the occurrence of sinuous cylindrical structures interpreted to be worm tubes, similar to biotic structures observed in present day exhalative vent environments. This evidence supports the notion that silica and sulfide precipitation took place at the rock–water interface on the ocean floor and was, therefore, coeval with the deposi-

tion of the sediments. There is also, however, evidence for sulfide replacement of sediments at Red Dog, indicating that the dual processes of exhalation and replacement were taking place (see section 3.8.2 of this chapter).

Figure 2 presents a simplified model of the ore-forming environment at Red Dog. Fluids circulating through Carboniferous organic-rich marine sediments scavenged metals from these host rocks and were vented onto the ocean floor at sights created by syn-sedimentary growth faults. Mineralization at Red Dog is massive, brecciated, and poorly bedded, suggesting that sulfides were precipitated fairly close to the vent sites (Moore et al., 1986). Variable sulfur isotope signatures in sulfide minerals suggest that precipitation was a product of mixing a buoyant hydrothermal plume with sea water that was becoming progressively more oxic over time. It is suggested that mineralization ceased when the sea water became sufficiently oxidizing to favor barite precipitation over sulfides (Moore et al., 1986).

Atlantis II Deep where muds are estimated to contain around 50 million tons of rich Zn–Cu–Pb–Ag–Au mineralization. Although the geological and tectonic setting of the Red Sea mineralization is analogous to a mid-ocean ridge VMS setting, the absence of black smokers and the presence of both clastic and carbonate sediment hosts to the mineralization are features perhaps more akin to SEDEX ores (Pirajno, 1992).

3.9 MINERAL DEPOSITS ASSOCIATED WITH AQUEO-CARBONIC METAMORPHIC FLUIDS

A significant proportion of the world's gold deposits are genetically linked to the formation of metamorphic fluids that are typically characterized by low salinity, near neutral pH, and mixed H_2O–CO_2 compositions. These gold deposits, of which there are many different types that formed

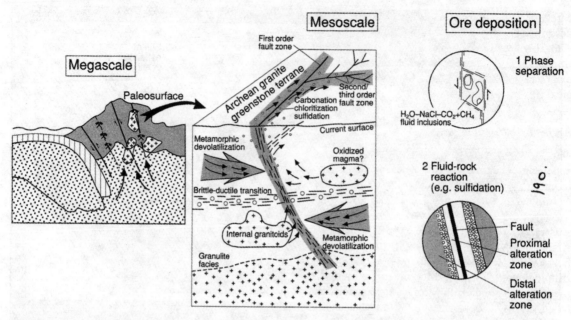

Figure 3.26 Schematic illustrations showing the principal features of Archean orogenic gold deposits – many of which also apply to Proterozoic and Phanerozoic examples. The main features at a megascale are that the deposits are associated with a convergent plate margin where metamorphism results in the production of fluids that are focused along major structural discontinuities. At a mesoscale major shear zones within or along the margins of greenstone belts represent district-scale hosts to mineralization that are accompanied by broad zones of intense alteration. Individual deposits occur along second- and third-order structures. Ore deposition is a function of fluid rock reaction and/or H_2O–CO_2 phase separation (after Hagemann and Cassidy, 2000).

over the entire span of Earth history, are associated with regionally metamorphosed terranes resulting from compression at convergent plate margins, and have been termed *orogenic gold deposits* (Groves *et al.*, 1998). They are also widely referred to, especially in the older literature, as "mesothermal" or "lode-gold" deposits, as they commonly precipitated at around 300 °C, forming quartz-vein or fracture dominated ore systems. Although orogenic gold deposits are commonly associated with Archean granite–greenstone terranes (see Chapter 6), important examples of orogenic gold ores are also found hosted in a variety of Proterozoic and Phanerozoic settings. The dominant and characteristic genetic features that link all orogenic gold deposits are a synchroneity with major accretionary or collisional orogenic episodes and the production of metamorphic – and in some cases magmatic – fluids that precipitate metals at various crustal levels along

deep-seated shear and fracture zones (Figure 3.26; mega- and mesoscale models). It is widely recognized that these deposits were formed over a range of P–T conditions, occurring in granulite to greenschist facies host environments and ductile through to brittle structural regimes (Colvine, 1989; Groves, 1993).

In the sections that follow, a variety of orogenic gold deposits from throughout geological time are described. In addition, Carlin-type deposits, as well as the hydrothermal component of mineralization in quartz pebble conglomerate hosted gold ores such as the Witwatersrand and Tarkwaian deposits, are described, as they share several common features with orogenic gold deposits.

3.9.1 Orogenic gold deposits

There are many different types of orogenic gold deposits and their classification into a single category is bound to be controversial. From a descriptive and organizational point of view, however, the classification is appropriate and recognition of the different subtypes that undoubtedly do exist can perhaps best be made in terms of geological time and crustal evolution.

Archean

The Archean was a major gold metallogenic epoch and many important gold deposits occur in the granite–greenstone terranes of the world, examples of which include the Superior Province of Canada, the Yilgarn Craton of Western Australia, and the Zimbabwe Craton. A feature of Archean orogenic gold deposits is that they can be hosted in a variety of greenstone belt associated lithologies, including mafic volcanics, metasediments, and banded iron-formations, as well as in felsic plutonic rocks. Despite the range of host rock lithologies, they are invariably found associated with zones of high strain that are manifest as brittle, brittle–ductile or ductile deformation, depending on the crustal depth at which fluids were circulating. Reviews of the nature and characteristics of Archean deposits can be found in McCuaig and Kerrich (1998) and Hagemann and Cassidy (2000). Figure 3.26 illustrates the main features of Archean orogenic gold deposits. At a megascale the energy required to form huge zones of fluid flow, alteration, and mineralization, such as those preserved in the Abitibi (Superior) and Norseman–Wiluna (Yilgarn) greenstone belts, is ultimately derived from plate subduction and collision. Crustal thickening, deformation, metamorphism, and synorogenic magmatism all play important roles in the ultimate origin of fluids and their focused flow upwards into the crust. A major part of the fluids implicated in mineralization appears to have been derived from the dehydration that accompanies regional prograde metamorphism. These fluids are fairly reduced (fO_2 around the quartz–fayalite–magnetite or QFM buffer) and gold is preferentially transported as the $Au(HS)_2^-$ complex (Hagemann and Cassidy, 2000; Ridley and Diamond, 2000). Derivation of mineralizing fluids from oxidized granitic magma is also considered likely, although such fluids are probably restricted to environments where a spatial link between mineralization and granite intrusion is evident, or an association between Au and metals such as Mo, W, or Cu occurs (Burrows and Spooner, 1987). Gold mineralization is broadly synchronous with the regional peak of metamorphism, although this peak may be in the lower crust rather than at the site of deposition in the upper crust. Fluids tend to be focused along major structural discontinuities that have strike lengths of tens to hundreds of kilometers and extend to considerable depths in the crust. Examples of well mineralized structural systems include the Larder Lake–Cadillac fault zone in the Abitibi belt and the Boulder–Lefroy fault zone in the Yilgarn craton. Individual deposits and mines are typically found along second- and third-order structures within these major discontinuities. Movement of fluid along these structures is explained by the fault-valve model, as discussed in section 3.3.3 above. The sites of mineralization are marked, at a regional scale, by zones of intense carbonation and chloritization that can extend for hundreds of meters around the conduit (see Box 3.2). Alteration plays a major role in metal precipitation, and this is particularly the case for intense wall-rock alteration and sulfidization. $H_2O–CO_2$ phase separation is also considered to be an important process in gold deposition and may explain the siting of rich accumulations of gold in quartz veins (i.e. the bonanza lodes). The latter mechanism may also explain the common association of gold mineralization with the brittle–ductile transition, as this zone coincides broadly with the relevant P–T conditions along parts of the $H_2O–CO_2$ solvus (see Figure 3.5c). Mixing of metamorphic with meteoric fluids may explain gold precipitation at high levels in the crust.

Proterozoic

The Proterozoic Eon is not as important as either its Archean or Phanerozoic counterparts in terms of gold mineralization (see Chapter 6). There are, nevertheless, several important examples of orogenic gold deposits from this period of time and these include Ashanti–Obuasi and several other deposits associated with the Birimian orogeny of West Africa, Telfer in Western Australia, Homestake in South Dakota, USA, Omai on the Guayanian craton of South America, and the Sabie–Pilgrim's Rest goldfield in South Africa. All these examples are associated with periods of major orogenesis and largely involve metamorphic fluids very similar in character to those applicable to the formation of Archean orogenic gold deposits. Gold deposition is generally late orogenic and is hosted in major, high-angle thrust faults (Partington and Williams, 2000). Granite intrusions, and possibly a magmatic fluid component, are associated with many of the Proterozoic deposits and, in cases such as Telfer (Rowins *et al.*, 1997) and Sabie–Pilgrim's Rest (Boer *et al.*, 1995), a polymetallic association of Cu, Co, and Bi, in addition to Au, is evident. In general, however, the characteristics of Proterozoic orogenic gold deposits are very similar to those of the Archean.

Phanerozoic

Orogenic gold deposits of the Phanerozoic Eon were formed during two mineralization episodes, one in the Silurian–Devonian at around 450–350 Ma and the other in the Cretaceous–Paleogene at around 150–50 Ma (Bierlein and Crowe, 2000). These gold deposits are again associated with convergent plate margins and hosted in compressional to transpressional shear zones that typically cut through thick marine shale sequences that have been metamorphosed to greenschist facies grades. They are often referred to in the older literature as "slate-belt hosted" gold deposits. There are many important examples of Phanerozoic orogenic gold deposits and these include, as Paleozoic examples, Bendigo, Stawell, and Ballarat in the Lachlan orogen of southeastern Australia, Haile in the Carolina slate belt, USA, Muruntau in Uzbekistan, the Urals of central Russia, and the Meguma terrane of Nova Scotia, Canada. Younger, Mesozoic examples include the Juneau gold belt of southern Alaska and other portions of the Cordilleran orogen of Canada and the western USA, including the Mother Lode of California (Bierlein and Crowe, 2000).

3.9.2 Carlin-type gold deposits

Although several of the features of Carlin-type ores mirror those of orogenic gold deposits, they are generally classified separately because of one very notable difference. While linked to orogenic activity and hosted along major, deep-crustal structures, they are not related to compression but formed after the onset of *extensional* forces that followed earlier, subduction-related processes (Hofstra and Cline, 2000). Carlin-type ores are located in Nevada, USA, and formed over a short period of time in the Paleogene Period, between 42 and 30 Ma. In this sense they are regarded as an essentially unique deposit type, although it is likely that similar ores will be located elsewhere, such as in China. In Nevada they are hosted in Paleozoic carbonate rocks that have been subjected to severe crustal shortening and west to east directed thrusting (Figure 3.27a and Box 3.5). The carbonate sequences are structurally overlain by less permeable siliciclastic rocks and have acted as aquifers along which metamorphically derived fluids have flowed. During mid-Miocene times host rocks were subjected to uplift and extension, which thinned the crust and gave rise to the Basin and Range faulting and associated fluid circulation along the newly formed dilatant structures.

Fluids associated with Carlin deposits are very similar to the metamorphic fluids implicated in orogenic gold deposits, comprising low salinity, moderately acidic, reduced H_2O–CO_2 solutions in which gold is transported as either $Au(HS)_2^-$ or $Au(HS)$. Fluid temperatures are cooler than those associated with orogenic ores and fall in the range 150–250 °C, which has led to the suggestion that they may, however, be meteoric rather than metamorphic in origin. Gold deposition occurs where normal faults intersect a less permeable cap rock, usually at a shale/limestone contact and in the crests of fault-propagated anticlines (Figure 3.27b). The precipitation mechanism is believed to be related to neutralization of the ore fluid during carbonate dissolution, although argillic alteration, silicification, and sulfidization also played a role in the ore-forming process. In Carlin-type deposits the gold occurs as micrometer-sized particles or

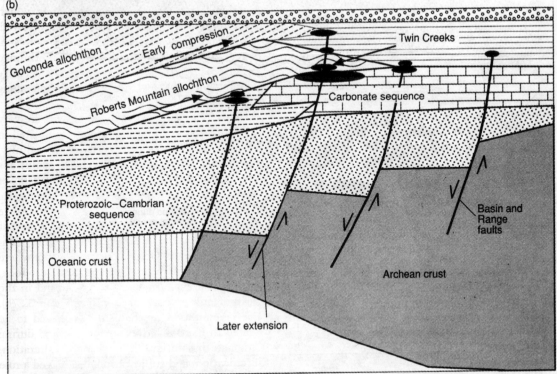

Figure 3.27 (a) Map showing the distribution of Carlin-type gold deposits in Nevada and the geological framework. (b) Cross section illustrating the fundamental controls behind the location of Carlin-type gold deposits (after Hofstra and Cline, 2000).

BOX 3.5 Circulation of orogeny-driven aqueo-carbonic fluids: Twin Creeks – a Carlin-type gold deposit, Nevada

Twin Creeks mine, formed in 1993 after the merger of the Chimney Creek and Rabbit Creek mines, is one of the largest Carlin-type deposits in Nevada, with reserves in 1999 of some 90 million tons of ore at an average gold grade of 2.5 g ton^{-1}. Most of the gold at the mine is extracted from the huge Mega Pit which produces some 280 000 tons of ore per day. Although gold at the Mega Pit is hosted essentially in limestones of the Ordovician Comus Formation, mineralization elsewhere on the mine (i.e. the Vista Pit) also occurs in overlying sequences that form a package of thrusted allochthons (see Figure 3.27a and b) emplaced in Carboniferous times. Gold mineralization occurs mainly in the arsenic-rich rims to pyrite grains formed during hydrothermal alteration (i.e. decalcification, dolomitization,

silicification, and sulfidization) of the Comus Formation limestones (Thoreson et al., 2000).

In the Mega Pit the mineralized limestones are capped by the Roberts Mountain thrust which folded the underlying limestones and also possibly acted as a cap that limited further egress of hydrothermal fluids and concentrated mineralization within the Comus Formation. Figure 1 shows a cross section through the Mega Pit, illustrating the relationships between the early thrusting and folding of Comus limestones, and the later extensional faults along which mineralizing fluids are thought to have been focused. In this section line gold mineralization is concentrated largely within the core of a prominent eastward verging recumbent antiform.

Figure 1 Cross section looking north of the Mega Pit at the Twin Creeks mine (after Thoreson et al., 2000).

Mineralization at Twin Creeks, as elsewhere in the Carlin district of Nevada, is considered to have been a result of fluid circulation between 42 and 30 Ma (Eocene–Oligocene) during the onset of extensional (Basin and Range) tectonism and mantle plume activity (Hofstra and Cline, 2000). Gold deposition, therefore, took place long after deposition of the host rocks (in the Ordovician) and their subsequent deformation (thrusting and folding) in Carboniferous times. Although subduction-related magmatism took place in the region between 43 and 34 Ma, no intrusives are directly implicated in the formation of any Carlin-type deposit and most workers refer to a metamorphic fluid as the mineralizing agent. This fluid was a moderately acidic, reduced, $H_2O–CO_2$ solution at around 150–250 °C in which gold was transported as bisulfide complexes (Hofstra and Cline, 2000). Gold precipitation is believed to have accompanied cooling and neutralization of the fluid as it interacted with reactive country rocks such as the Comus Formation limestones. Circulation of mineralizing fluids was focused essentially along major extensional faults, which is the main reason why major deposits are located along well defined structural trend lines. Individual deposits tend to occur beneath a less permeable, often siliciclastic, cap rock (such as the Roberts Mountain allochthon at Twin Creeks) causing the fluids ascending along the faults to flow laterally into more reactive sequences such as the Comus Formation. Carlin-type deposits are unique in the broader family of orogenic gold deposits and are perhaps intermediate in character between more typical compression-related orogenic gold ores and low-sulfidation epithermal gold deposits (see Chapter 2). There is, however, no reason why similar styles of epigenetic, sediment-hosted deposits, containing "invisible" or micrometer-sized gold in sulfides, should not be located in other parts of the world besides Nevada.

in solid solution in arsenic rich pyrite, marcasite, or arsenopyrite.

3.9.3 Quartz pebble conglomerate hosted gold deposits

Quartz pebble conglomerates of Archean and Paleoproterozoic ages represent a very important source of gold, although production over the past century has been dominated by the Witwatersrand Basin in South Africa. The seven major goldfields associated with the Witwatersrand sequences have produced a staggering 48 000 tons of gold metal – some 35% of all the gold produced in the history of mankind – since 1886 (Phillips and Law, 2000). Other conglomerate-hosted gold deposits such as those of the Tarkwa (Ghana) and Jacobina (Brazil) basins are relatively unimportant by comparison. Irrespective of their production statistics, quartz pebble conglomerate hosted gold deposits are characterized by considerable controversy regarding the origin of their gold mineralization. Arguments revolve essentially around whether gold was introduced as detrital particles during sedimentation (a placer process; see Chapter 5) or precipitated from hydrothermal solutions circulating through the sediments at some stage after sediment deposition. There is little doubt, however, that in all three cases (i.e. the Witwatersrand,

Tarkwa, and Jacobina) the host sediments underwent burial and regional metamorphism and that the associated circulation of metamorphic fluids resulted in a clearly epigenetic component of mineralization. Fluid inclusion studies indicate that certain of these fluids have a mixed $H_2O–CO_2$ composition and have some similarities to those involved with orogenic gold deposits.

One view of the origin of gold mineralization in the Witwatersrand sediments is that it occurs along major unconformities, represented by conglomerate deposition, which represent zones of intense fluid flow and alteration (Figure 3.28a). Alteration is the product of fluid–rock reactions involving progressive neutralization of an acid fluid (see section 3.5 above), with the most intense alteration being characterized by the assemblage pyrophyllite–chloritoid–muscovite–chlorite (Barnicoat et al., 1997; Philips and Law, 2000). In the Witwatersrand Basin, however, gold mineralization is characterized by a long-lived paragenetic sequence (Robb et al., 1997; Frimmel and Minter, 2002) and is likely to be related to more than just one-pass fluid–rock interaction. The existence of a prominent alteration halo around zones of pervasive fluid flow is nevertheless one of the reasons why the Witwatersrand gold deposits are so large. At the scale of a single deposit similar effects can be seen, as exemplified

(a)

Witwatersrand basin

S

N

Central Rand Group

Elsburg sequence

Kimberley sequence

Bird sequence

Main sequence

West Rand Group

Gold-bearing conglomerate packages

Elsburg

Kimberley

Bird

Main

Alteration assemblages (+Qtz)

- Pyrophyllite, chloritoid, muscovite, chlorite
- Muscovite, chlorite
- Albite, epidote, calcite, muscovite, chlorite, paragonite
- Stratigraphic boundaries
- Principal zones of fluid flow

500 m

20 km

(b)

João Belo Reef, Jacobina Basin

W

E

Gold-bearing conglomerate

Barren conglomerate

Shear zones

Shear zones

0   2
metres

- Cr mica, tourmaline, rutile, muscovite alteration
- Zone of sulfidation (pyrite)

by the João Belo reef in the Jacobina Basin of Brazil (Figure 3.28b). Here gold mineralization coincides with a section of the conglomerate horizon that is cut by a number of bedding-parallel shear zones along which fluids have flowed resulting in fuchsite (Cr–mica)–tourmaline–rutile–muscovite –pyrite alteration (Milési *et al.*, 2002). Outside this alteration zone the conglomerate is reported to be barren.

The nature of the ore-forming fluid associated with the Witwatersrand, Jacobina, and Tarkwa auriferous conglomerates has been described as mixed H_2O–CO_2, fairly reducing, near-neutral, and with low salinity (Philips and Law, 2000). Barnicoat *et al.* (1997) preferred a more oxidized, acidic fluid for the Witwatersrand Basin whereas Klemd *et al.* (1993) suggested that the ore fluids associated with the Tarkwaian conglomerates were dominantly high density carbonic with significant contained methane and nitrogen. Detailed fluid inclusion studies (Drennan *et al.*, 1999; Frimmel *et al.*, 1999) have indicated that in the Witwatersrand Basin different fluids are implicated in at least two distinct episodes of mineralization, and these include mixed H_2O–CO_2 compositions as well as aqueous, high-salinity fluids. The origin of these fluids is also contentious and options range from devolatilization of greenschist to amphibolite facies mafic rocks beneath the sedimentary basins, to derivation by prograde metamorphic reactions within the basin itself (Stevens *et al.*, 1997 and Figure 3.4). The hydrothermal ore-forming processes of the Witwatersrand Basin in particular are long-lived and complex and this is the reason why there has been, and still is, so much debate on the genesis of these ores. It is, for example, now reasonably well established

Figure 3.28 (*Opposite*) (a) Simplified north–south section showing the pattern of alteration at a regional scale associated with gold-bearing conglomerate packages in the Central Rand Group of the Witwatersrand Basin (after Barnicoat *et al.*, 1997); (b) Cross section through the João Belo reef in the Jacobina Basin showing the relationship between shear zone related fluid conduits, alteration, and gold mineralization at a deposit scale (after Milési *et al.*, 2002).

that the basin was struck by a large meteorite at 2025 Ma and that the catastrophic exhumation of the gold-bearing sedimentary host rocks, as well as the likely circulation of related meteoric fluids, must also have played an important role in the ore formation process (Gibson and Reimold, 1999).

3.10 ORE DEPOSITS ASSOCIATED WITH CONNATE FLUIDS

A number of sediment-hosted base metal deposits are genetically linked to the circulation of connate fluids during diagenesis. In these deposit types metal transport and deposition is generally restricted to the sedimentary sequence through which the connate fluids circulate. Ores included in this category are the important stratiform, sediment-hosted copper deposits (abbreviated to SSC, but also called red-bed copper deposits) and the family of Pb–Zn ores, usually associated with carbonate sediments (although some are sandstone-hosted), known as Mississippi Valley type (or MVT) deposits. Although the two deposit types are different in several respects, they both owe their origins to circulating basinal brines.

Sverjensky (1989) has suggested that the major differences between SSC and MVT deposits relate mainly to the type of sediment through which the fluids have traveled prior to ore deposition and also to the contrasting properties of Cu, Pb, and Zn in hydrothermal solutions. It is suggested that a basinal brine channeled into an *oxidized* (red-bed) aquifer would scavenge all three base metals from fertile detritus in the basin, but that the resulting ore fluid would be saturated only with respect to Cu and undersaturated relative to Pb and Zn. The tendency in such an environment would be for fluids to preferentially deposit copper sulfide minerals while the higher solubility metals remain in solution. Accordingly, SSC deposits tend to be characterized by a Cu > (Pb + Zn) metal association (Figure 3.29). By contrast, the same original fluid channeled into a relatively reduced carbonate aquifer would evolve to Zn and Pb saturated conditions in the presence of dissolved sulfur species and ore deposition would yield sphalerite > galena >> chalcopyrite, as is typical of most

Figure 3.29 Diagrammatic representation showing the relationship between a single basinal brine and the conditions under which it might form SSC, as well as carbonate- and sandstone-hosted, MVT deposits (after Sverjensky, 1989; Metcalfe *et al.*, 1994).

MVT deposits. In the situation where the original basinal brine passed through a quartzose sandstone aquifer, the fluid would not evolve significantly from its original metal carrying capacity, with saturated levels of Cu and Pb but undersaturated relative to Zn. Maintenance of the oxidation state of the fluid at levels appropriate to hematite–magnetite coexistence would nevertheless limit the mobility of copper and resulting ores would be galena-rich, consistent with the fact that sandstone-hosted MVT deposits tend to have Pb > Zn >> Cu metal ratios. It is interesting to note that in the Central African Copperbelt, for example, Cu(–Co) mineralization is typically hosted in clastic sediments such as arkose and shale, whereas Zn–Pb mineralization is found associated with carbonate rocks.

Some of the processes relevant to the formation of SSC and MVT deposits are discussed in more detail below.

3.10.1 Stratiform sediment-hosted copper (SSC) deposits

SSC deposits worldwide rank second only to porphyry copper deposits in terms of copper production and they represent the most important global source of cobalt, as well as containing resources of many other metals such as Pb, Zn, Ag, U, Au, PGE, and Re. There are several deposits of varying ages around the world, but these are overshadowed by the huge resources of only two regions, the Neoproterozoic Central African Copperbelt (Box 3.6) and the Permo-Triassic Kupferschiefer (or "copper shale") of central Europe. Other important deposits include White Pine in Michigan, Udokan and Dzhezhkazgan in Kazakhstan, Corocoro in Bolivia, and the Dongchuan district of China (Misra, 2000). The formation of major SSC deposits seems to coincide with periods of supercontinent amalgamation such as Rodinia in the Neoproterozoic and Pangea in the Permo-Triassic (see Chapter 6).

SSC deposits are typically hosted within an intracontinental, rift-related sedimentary sequence. The early part of the sequence was either deposited originally as an oxidized (red-bed), aeolian to evaporitic assemblage, or was rapidly oxidized during burial and diagenesis. This sequence is overlain by a shallow marine transgression that deposited a more reduced assemblage of shales, carbonates, and evaporites. Basin-derived fluid circulation was promoted by the high heat flow conditions accompanying rapid rifting and subsidence, and the very permeable environment created by porous clastic sediments and active growth faults. The connate fluids circulating at this stage of basin evolution were saline, relatively oxidized, and pH neutral. Metals, in particular copper, are believed to have been leached from detrital minerals such as magnetite, biotite, hornblende, and pyroxene which themselves may have been derived from erosion of a fertile basement assemblage (a Paleoproterozoic magmatic arc in the case, for example, of the Central African Copperbelt; Rainault *et al.*, 1999; and Box 3.6). The aqueous transport of copper under these conditions was as a cuprous–chloride complex, probably $CuCl_3^{2-}$ (Rose, 1976). Metal deposition occurred at a redox interface where the oxidized, metal-charged connate fluids intersected overlying or laterally equivalent reduced sediments or fluids. The ore deposits are generally zoned, usually at a district scale, and typical zonation is characterized by the sequence barren/hematite – native copper – chalcocite – bornite – chalcopyrite – Pb/Zn/Co sulfides – pyrite.

SSC deposits can be subdivided into two sub-types (Kirkham, 1989). The first, less important, subtype is hosted in continental red-beds that were probably originally oxidized, with ores precipitated around locally developed zones of reduction (for example, Dzhezhkazgan in Kazakhstan and Corocoro in Bolivia). The second subtype, represented by the much larger Kupferschiefer and Copperbelt deposits, is characterized by metal deposition in more reduced shallow marine sequences that were partially oxidized subsequent to deposition, and where oxidized (red-bed) sediments occur stratigraphically beneath the ore zone. In both cases, however, ore fluids are considered to have interacted with the dominantly clastic, oxidized sedimentary sequence and it is this feature that determines the nature and properties of the hydrothermal solutions. Such fluids are likely to have been characterized by low temperatures ($<150 \, ^{\circ}C$ and possibly even $<100 \, ^{\circ}C$), a neutral range of pH (5–9) constrained by carbonate or silicate equilibria (K-feldspar/illite), oxidized conditions (hematite and other ferric-oxyhydroxides stable), and moderate salinities (typically up to 20 wt% NaCl equivalent), reflecting interac-

tion of the fluids with evaporitic rocks. Rose (1976) showed that under these conditions the $CuCl_3^{2-}$ complex would have been particularly stable (Figure 3.30), although other aqueous species, such as $CuSO_4$ or $Cu(OH)_2^{2+}$ could also have existed. Solubility of copper as a chloride complex under such conditions has been estimated to be as high as 35–100 ppm (Haynes, 1986a). In Figure 3.30 it is evident that the stability field of the $CuCl_3^{2-}$ complex largely coincides with that of hematite stability, and that the aqueous sulfur species would be SO_4^{2-} rather than H_2S or HS^-. Rose (1976) points out that the conditions described above are particularly well suited to copper mobilization. By comparison, copper is relatively insoluble in normal meteoric waters and it is also unlikely to be easily leached from more reduced sediments where copper sulfides are stable. An extensive red-bed sedimentary environment where fertile detrital minerals readily break down to form a source of copper metal, and where stable $CuCl_3^{2-}$ complexes result in high copper solubilities, is, therefore, ideal for the formation of Cu > (Pb + Zn) SSC deposits.

The formation of SSC deposits has, in the past, been a controversial topic and models supporting syngenetic as opposed to diagenetic origins have been much debated (Garlick, 1982; Fleischer, 1984; Jowett *et al.*, 1987; Annels, 1989; Sweeney *et al.*, 1991). The syngenetic view, in which sulfides were believed to have precipitated directly out of anoxic sea water in processes akin perhaps to those giving rise to Mn deposition in the present day Black Sea (see Chapter 5), have now largely been superseded by models that view ore genesis in terms of either early or late diagenesis. A diagenetic origin is substantiated by many of the prominent features of SSC deposits, especially the broadly transgressive nature of ore zones relative to lithologies, the clear relationship of metal deposition to a redox front, and replacement textures in the sulfide mineral paragenetic sequence. There are, nevertheless, several processes that can be called upon to explain ore deposition and metal zonation in SSC deposits.

It is evident in the Kupferschiefer deposits, for example, that metal deposition is spatially associated with a reddish oxidized zone (termed

Figure 3.30 Eh–pH plot for the system Cu–O–H–S–Cl at 25 °C (with $\Sigma S = 10^{-4}$ m and Cl$^-$ = 0.5 m). Also shown are the stability fields for hematite, various sulfur species, and the cuprous-chloride complex for conditions compatible with the formation of SSC deposits (after Rose, 1976).

the "Rote Fäule") that transgresses different lithologies and comprises hematite-replacing early diagenetic sulfides. The oxidized zone represents a chemical front in the footwall of the ore zone and against which a zoned sequence of base metal sulfides (chalcocite–bornite–chalcopyrite–galena–sphalerite–pyrite) is arranged. Much of the metal concentration is nevertheless concentrated within the organic-rich shale (i.e. the Kupferschiefer itself) since it is this unit that contained concentrations of early diagenetic framboidal iron sulfides (such as marcasite or pyrite) formed by bacterial reduction of sulfate to sulfide. Sawlowicz (1992) has documented evid-

ence of copper sulfide replacement of framboids in the Kupferschiefer, and the applicability of early chalcocite replacement of biogenic sulfide material to SSC deposits in general has been discussed by Haynes (1986b). These features suggest low temperature processes and point to metal deposition during the early stages of diagenesis of the sedimentary succession. A schematic representation of the zonal distribution of metals against the Rote Fäule in the Kupferscheifer ores is shown in Figure 3.31a, together with a model by Metcalfe et al. (1994) that demonstrates the effect of changing the redox state of the ore fluid on sequential metal precipitation (Figure 3.31b). In

(a)

(b)

Figure 3.31 (a) Section showing metal zonation in typical Kupferschiefer ores in relation to the transgressive, oxidized "Rote Fäule" zone (after Jowett *et al.*, 1987). (b) Model showing the effects of mixing a typical SSC-type ore fluid with a reduced fluid on metal precipitation. The sequence of deposition is the same as the zonal pattern observed in the Kupferschiefer (after Metcalfe *et al.*, 1994).

the latter metal precipitation is achieved by mixing the oxidized ore-bearing fluid with a reduced fluid, rather than reacting the fluid with a reduced sediment. The effect is nevertheless the same and metals are precipitated in the sequence Cu–Pb–Zn as a function of increased mixing of the two fluids. This is exactly the sequence observed in the Kupferschiefer ores and confirms that this type of zoning could be a result of sequential metal precipitation from mixed connate fluids.

There are other ways of explaining the patterns of metal zoning and paragenetic sequence in SSC-type deposits. Alternative proposals prefer a late

diagenetic origin for metal precipitation in SSC deposits where sulfate reduction to sulfide occurs at higher temperatures and is not bacterially induced. This could be achieved by fluid mixing (as suggested in Figure 3.31b) or simply by interaction between oxidized fluid and reduced country rock. Ripley *et al.* (1985) have proposed a scheme in which the pattern of zoning in SSC type ores is explained in terms of either fluid mixing or fluid-rock reaction. In a plot of Fe^{2+} versus Cu^+ activities (Figure 3.32) it is evident that a fluid with a high initial Cu content will become progressively more dilute as copper sulfides precipitate. This

Figure 3.32 Plot of Cu⁺/H⁺ versus Fe⁺/H⁺ activity ratios to explain the zoning and paragenetic sequence that is often observed in SSC deposits when a Cu-bearing fluid reacts with a pyritic shale. In this situation the original copper content of the fluid is high and then decreases as a function of Cu-sulfide precipitation to form the paragenetic sequence chalcocite–bornite–chalcopyrite–pyrite (after Ripley *et al.*, 1985).

would produce a paragenetic sequence and zonation pattern that reflects a decreasing Cu content in the sulfide ores, such as chalcocite – bornite – chalcopyrite – pyrite.

Another feature of SSC deposits is that they contain appreciable amounts of other metals, such as Ag, Pb, and Zn (Kupferschiefer) and Co (Copperbelt), all of which form part of a broadly zonal arrangement of ores. Such patterns may be difficult to explain in terms of solubility contrasts when metal concentrations are well below their saturation levels, and in such cases a mechanism such as adsorption may be relevant (see section 3.5 above). Figure 3.15b, for example, shows the variations in adsorption efficiency as a function of pH. It is feasible that variable adsorption efficiencies could control the uptake of different metals

from red-beds into connate fluids as well as their subsequent deposition into nearby reducing sediments. This could explain regional zonation patterns in SSC ores, although the details of how this might relate ultimately to paragenetic sequences are likely to be complex (Rose and Bianchi-Mosquera, 1993).

3.10.2 Mississippi Valley type (MVT) Pb–Zn deposits

MVT deposits, like SEDEX and SSC ores, owe their origin to fluid circulation and metal transport/deposition within sedimentary basins. Unlike the syngenetic to diagenetic time frame of SEDEX and SSC deposit formation, however, MVT ores are distinctly epigenetic and metals can be deposited tens of millions of years after sediment deposition. The deposits form from relatively low temperature fluids (<150 °C) and are broadly stratabound, mainly carbonate-hosted, and dominated by sphalerite and galena with associated fluorite and barite. Most MVT deposits contain significantly more sphalerite than galena, with the notable exception of the Viburnum Trend in southeast Missouri, where the reverse applies. The sandstone-hosted MVT deposits (such as Laisvall and some deposits in southeast Missouri) represent a conceptually intermediate category between SSC and carbonate-hosted MVT ores (Figure 3.29) and are characterized by Pb > Zn >> Cu. MVT deposits contain a significant proportion of the world's Zn and Pb reserves and there are many other deposits around the world in addition to the numerous mines in the MVT "type area" of the southeastern USA. In the latter region the main metal-producing districts include the Viburnum Trend of southeast Missouri (which is mainly a Pb-producing region), the Tri-State (i.e. Oklahoma, Kansas, Missouri) region, the Illinois-Wisconsin region and the Mascot–Jefferson City area of east Tennessee. Other well known MVT districts or deposits elsewhere in the world include the Pine Point and Polaris deposits of northern Canada, the Silesian district of Poland, Mechernich in Austria, the Lennard Shelf district, Sorby Hills and Coxco in Australia, and Pering in South Africa (Misra, 2000).

BOX 3.6 Circulation of sediment-hosted connate fluids: 1 The Central African Copperbelt

The stratiform, sediment-hosted Cu–Co deposits hosted within the Neoproterozoic Katangan sequence of Zambia and the Democratic Republic of the Congo (DRC) form the Central African Copperbelt, undoubtedly one of the great metallogenic provinces of the world. Several world class deposits (such as Nchanga, Konkola, and Tenke Fungurume), together with dozens of smaller mines, combine to make this region one of the foremost copper-producing areas of the world, as well as its most important Co supplier. Although figures for the entire Central African Copperbelt are unreliable, it has been estimated that the region still contains resources in excess of 150 million tons of Cu metal and 8 million tons of Co metal (Misra, 2000).

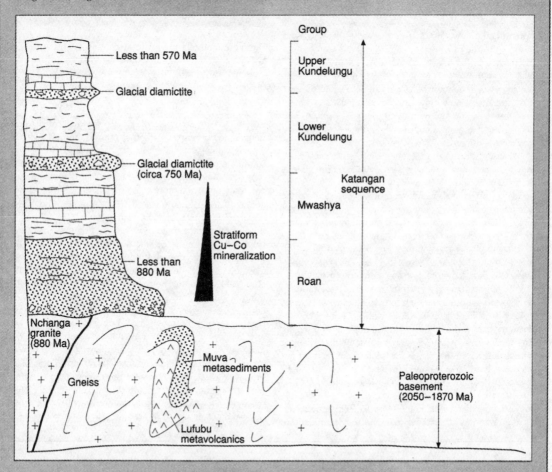

Figure 1 Simplified stratigraphic profile through the rocks of the Central African Copperbelt showing the relationship between the Paleoproterozoic granite–gneiss and volcano-sedimentary basement and the overlying Katangan sequence. Stratiform Cu–Co mineralization is largely hosted in a variety of sedimentary lithotypes in the lower part of the Roan Group, but does also occur higher up in the succession and up into the Mwashya Group. The age constraints used in this compilation are after Rainaud *et al.* (2002a), Master *et al.* (2002), and Key *et al.* (2001).

The Katangan sediments were deposited in an intra-cratonic rift formed on a Paleoproterozoic basement comprising 2050–1870 Myr old granite–gneiss, and meta-volcanosedimentary sequences (Figure 1; Unrug, 1988). The basement is thought to represent a deformed but fertile magmatic arc that contained the ultimate source of Cu (in porphyry type intrusions; Rainaud et al., 1999), and possibly Co too. Initiation of rifting and sediment deposition followed soon after intrusion of the Nchanga granite at 880 Ma. Initially sedimentation was dominated by siliciclastic deposition, but this was followed by playa lake and restricted marine incursions to form evaporites, shales, and carbonate rocks. A major glacial diamictite (the "grand conglomerat") occurs at the top of the Mwashya Group, the age of which (circa 750 Ma) makes it a likely correlative of the mid-Neoproterozoic "Snowball Earth" glaciation (Robb et al., 2002). The uppermost parts of the Katangan sequence (i.e. the Upper Kundelungu Group and its correlatives) now appear to be substantially younger (i.e. less than 565 Ma) than the underlying portions and are regarded as a separate basin that formed as a foreland to the Pan-African orogeny (Wendorff, 2001).

Mineralization in the Central African Copperbelt is a much debated and contentious issue. Ideas on ore genesis in the 1960s and 1970s were dominated by syngenetic models, where metals were accumulated essentially at the same time as the sediments were being deposited (Fleisher et al., 1976). More recent work has shown that mineralization is more likely to be related to later fluids circulating through the sediments, either during diagenesis and compaction of the sequence (Sweeney et al., 1991) or significantly later during deformation and metamorphism (Unrug, 1988). Although much work is still required, it seems likely that metals were sequentially precipitated by processes related to reduction–oxidation reactions between sedimentary host rocks and a fertile connate fluid. A highly oxidized, saline, and sulfate-rich connate fluid, derived by interaction with evaporites in the Roan Group, is regarded as the agent that scavenged Cu and Co from the sediments themselves. The Cu may have been introduced into the basin in Cu-rich magnetite or mafic mineral detritus eroded from the fertile Paleoproterozoic magmatic arc in the hinterland (S. Master, personal communication).

Figure 2 Folded metasediments hosting stratiform Cu–Co sulfide ore at the Chambishi Mine, Zambia. The bedding parallel ore is cut by an axial planar cleavage (photograph by Lynnette Greyling).

Co, on the other hand, may have been derived from penecontemporaneous sills that intrude the upper Roan Group (Annels, 1984). Cu and Co would be highly soluble as chloride complexes in a connate fluid of this type (see section 3.10.1 of this chapter) and it is likely that very efficient leaching of these metals during diagenesis and oxidative alteration of the host rocks would have occurred. Precipitation of these metals would occur as the fluid reacted, either with more reduced strata (containing organic carbon or diagenetic framboidal pyrite), or with a second, more reduced, fluid. Metal zonation, which is a feature of mineralization throughout the Copperbelt, could, at least in part, be a product of the variable reduction potentials of metals such as Cu, Co, Pb, and Zn. An early or late diagenetic model for the origin and timing of stratiform mineralization in the Central African Copperbelt is consistent with the fact that it pre-dates the major period of compressive deformation that affected the entire region during the Lufilian orogeny (590–510 Ma; Rainaud et al., 2002b). Figure 2 shows the folded nature of the host rock strata at the Chambishi Mine in Zambia; the stratiform Cu–sulfide ore here is folded and cut by an axial planar cleavage.

The majority of MVT deposits worldwide formed in the Phanerozoic Eon, but more specifically, in Devonian to Permian times; some deposits, such as Pine Point and the Silesian district, also formed during the Cretaceous–Paleogene period (Leach et al., 2001). The former, far more important, metallogenic epoch coincides with the assembly of Pangea when major compressional orogenies were active over many parts of the Earth (see Chapter 6). The later period is more specifically related to the Alpine and Laramide orogenies and, likewise, associated with compressional tectonic regimes. The timing of MVT deposits in relation to associated orogenic activity

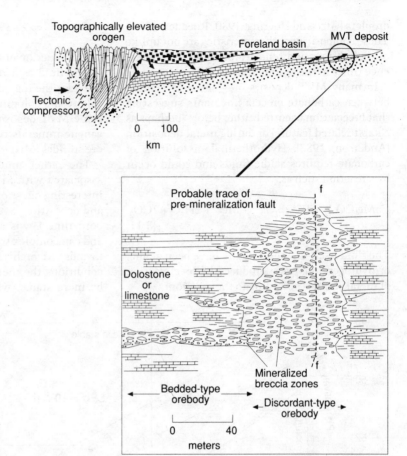

Figure 3.33 Diagram illustrating the concept of hydrological continuity between a compressional orogenic belt and a foreland sedimentary basin through which orogenically and topographically driven fluids flow, and within which MVT Zn–Pb deposits form. Inset shows characteristics of bedded and discordant mineralization at a deposit scale. Mineralization may be bedded and associated with dolostone/limestone sequences, or in discordant carbonate breccia zones (after Garven et al., 1993).

provides an important clue as to the causes of fluid flow and hydrothermal activity involved in their formation. It is generally accepted that topographically driven fluid pathways were critical to the development of large MVT ore districts, and that the carbonate host rocks maintained a hydrological connection to orogenic belts active during the period of ore deposition (Rickard et al., 1979; Oliver, 1986; Duane and De Wit, 1988). Other features believed to conceptually link most MVT deposits include a low-latitudinal setting, where high rainfall ensured an adequate fluid reservoir, and the presence, somewhere in the fluid flow system, of a high-evaporation sabkha environment that resulted in the high fluid salinities necessary for viable levels of metal solubility and transport (Leach et al., 2001).

Figure 3.33 illustrates the main characteristics

of MVT deposits. Regional fluid flow is stimulated by compressional orogeny that results in thrust faulting and uplift and this, in turn, creates a topographic head and fluid flow down a hydrological gradient. Fluid flow in these tectonic settings occurs over distances of hundreds of kilometers and such fluids are implicated in the migration of hydrocarbons as well as metals (Rickard, 1976; Oliver, 1986). At the site of metal deposition MVT ores are sometimes bedded and focused along conformable dolostone/limestone interfaces, but are more commonly associated with discordant, dissolution-related zones of brecciation. The hydrothermal fluids that are linked to MVT deposit formation are typically low-temperature (100–150 °C), high-salinity (>15 wt% NaCl equivalent) brines, with appreciable SO_4^{2-}, CO_2 and CH_4 and associated organic compounds and oil-like droplets (Gize and Hoering, 1980; Roedder, 1984). These compositional characteristics are not unlike oil-field brines and reflect protracted fluid residence times in the sedimentary basin.

In many MVT deposits ores occur as cement between carbonate breccia fragments suggesting that brecciation occurred either before (perhaps as a karst related feature) or during metal deposition (Anderson, 1983). Hydrothermal dissolution of carbonate requires acidic fluids and could occur by a reaction such as:

$$CaMg(CO_3)_2 + 4H^+ \Leftrightarrow Ca^{2+} + Mg^{2+} + 2H_2O + 2CO_2 \tag{3.11}$$

The fluid itself might originally have been acidic, or hydrogen ions were produced by precipitation of metal sulfides according to the reaction:

$$H_2S + Zn^{2+} \Leftrightarrow ZnS + 2H^+ \tag{3.12}$$

The production of additional Ca^{2+}, Mg^{2+}, and CO_2 in the fluid as a result of carbonate dissolution provides the ingredients for later precipitation of calcite and dolomite, a feature that is observed in some MVT deposits where secondary carbonate gangue minerals cement previously precipitated ore sulfides (Misra, 2000).

The rather unusual nature of the ore fluid associated with MVT ore formation raises some interesting questions concerning metal transport and deposition (Sverjensky, 1986). Zn and Pb are borderline Lewis acids (see section 3.4.1 above) and can complex with both chloride and bisulfide ligands. At high temperatures and under acidic conditions the metal–chloride complex tends to be more stable, whereas at lower temperatures

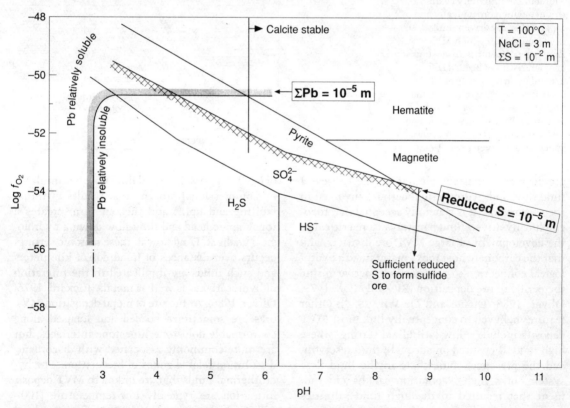

Figure 3.34 fO_2–pH plot showing key mineral and aqueous species stabilities under the conditions shown. Solubility contours of $\Sigma Pb = 10^{-5}$ m and reduced sulfur $= 10^{-5}$ m are also shown. Higher solubilities lie to the left of and above the Pb contour, and below the sulfur contour (after Anderson, 1975).

and neutral to alkaline pH the metal–bisulfide complexes dominate. There seems little doubt, given the prevailing conditions, that metal–chloride complexes predominate during MVT ore formation (Sverjensky, 1986). Anderson (1975) pointed out that viable Zn and Pb solubilities are, however, only achieved when fluids are either relatively oxidized (i.e. the sulfur in the fluid is transported as SO_4^{2-} and not as H_2S or HS^-), or at low pH. Figure 3.34 shows that if a fluid was sufficiently oxidized for SO_4^{2-} to have been stable then high Pb solubilities could have occurred over a range of pH. That the sites of MVT ore deposition are characterized by sulfide minerals, however, implies that metal precipitation must have been accompanied by the reduction of sulfate to sulfide. In some MVT deposits, such as the Pine Point district, such a process is feasible and ore deposition has been attributed to the mixing of a sulfur-deficient ore fluid with another carrying significant reduced sulfur (i.e. H_2S or HS^-) at the site of ore deposition (Beales and Jackson, 1966). Alternatively, the ore fluid might itself originally contain significant SO_4^{2-}, with reduction and metal precipitation occurring, again either

by mixing with a reduced fluid, or simply by reaction of the fluid with organic matter. In many MVT deposits, however, textures and geochemistry are incompatible with a fluid mixing model and ores appear to have precipitated over a protracted period of time. If fluid mixing and/or sulfate reduction did not occur then the ore fluid itself would have needed sufficient reduced sulfur to form sulfide minerals (i.e. in excess of 10^{-5} m; see Figure 3.34). In a reduced fluid metal–chloride complexes will only be stable under acidic conditions (low pH) and it has been suggested that this could not apply to MVT fluids that have equilibrated with carbonate host rocks. It appears, however, that the CO_2 contents of fluids associated with some MVT deposits are sufficiently high to form low pH solutions (Sverjensky, 1981; Jones and Kesler, 1992). Such acidic fluids will promote the stability of metal–chloride complexes resulting in high metal solubilities. Such fluids also promote ground preparation by creating dissolution breccias at the site of ore deposition. This in turn results in metal precipitation as the ore fluid is neutralized (equation [3.11] above) by reaction with the carbonate host rock.

BOX 3.7 Circulation of sediment-hosted connate fluids: 2 The Viburnum Trend, Missouri

The Viburnum Trend, also known as the "New Lead Belt," in southeast Missouri is the world's largest lead-producing metallogenic province. In the mid-1980s production plus total reserves from this remarkable, 65 km long, belt of mineralization amounted to some 540 million tons of ore at an average grade of 6% Pb and 1% Zn (Misra, 2000). The Viburnum Trend occurs to the west of the St Francois Mountains, a Precambrian basement outlier that is unconformably overlain by a Cambro–Ordovician sequence of siliciclastic and carbonate sediments. The host rocks to Pb–Zn ore are mainly Cambrian dolostones of the Bonneterre Formation, although mineralization took place more than 200 million years later during Carboniferous times. The Pb–Zn ores of the Viburnum Trend are regarded as a classic example of Mississippi Valley type (MVT) deposits.

The galena–sphalerite dominated mineralization of the Viburnum Trend is hosted within a sequence of carbonate rocks that formed during a shallow marine incursion over a continental shelf (Larsen, 1977). A stromatolitic reef developed around the northern and western margins of a positive feature (the St Francois Mountains) on this shelf, resulting in the formation of biostomal dolomites that are underlain by the porous Lamotte sandstone and overlain by the relatively impervious Davis shale (Figure 2). Accurate age dating of the actual mineralization in the Viburnum Trend, and indeed for much of the related Pb–Zn MVT styles of mineralization throughout the southeastern USA, indicates that it formed during a relatively brief interval of time in the late Carboniferous (i.e. between about 330 and 300 Ma; Leach et al., 2001). This interval coincides with a period of Earth history characterized

Figure 1 Geological setting of the Viburnum Trend Pb–Zn mineralization and the major mines in this belt (after Kisvarsanyi, 1977).

Figure 2 West–east section through the Fletcher Mine, Viburnum Trend, showing the close association between mineralization, basement topographic highs, and stratal pinch-outs (after Paarlberg and Evans, 1977).

by major compressional orogeny, during which time the amalgamation of the supercontinent Pangea was taking place (see Chapter 6). In the southeastern USA this event is recorded by the Ouachita collisional orogen and it is suggested that it was this event that stimulated fluid flow throughout the region. Orogeny- or topography-driven fluid flow (see sections 3.3.1 and 3.10.2 of this chapter) focused hydrothermal solutions into connected paleo-aquifers such as the Lamotte sandstone, with subsequent metal precipitation occurring in response to features such as fluid interaction and dissolution of carbonate rocks. An interesting feature of many of the Viburnum Trend deposits

is the close association between basement topography, overlying sedimentary strata pinch-outs, and mineralization. Figure 2 shows a west–east section through the Fletcher Mine where mineralization is constrained to a zone in the Bonneterre dolostones that is directly above a basement topographic high. Stratal pinch-outs against this buttress suggest that fluids, perhaps originally flowing through underlying successions such as the Lamotte sandstone (where some mineralization does occur) or the lower stromatolitic reefs, might have been forced upwards into the clastic carbonates, and that this was an important factor influencing metal precipitation.

3.11 ORE DEPOSITS ASSOCIATED WITH NEAR SURFACE METEORIC FLUIDS (GROUNDWATER)

Few hydrothermal ore deposits are linked to the circulation of ambient meteoric fluids, or groundwaters, in the near surface environment since metals are generally not transported in these types of fluids. A notable exception is the family of sediment-hosted uranium deposit types associated with low temperature meteoric fluid flow (Nash *et al.*, 1981). One category of these deposit types is the calcrete-hosted, uranium–vanadium ores that form in arid regions. These deposits are related to high rates of evaporation in surficial environments and, consequently, are discussed in Chapter 4. The other category, the sandstone-hosted uranium ores, is related to groundwater flow and redox precipitation mechanisms, and is discussed below.

3.11.1 A brief note on the aqueous transport and deposition of uranium

In nature uranium occurs in two valence states, as the uranous (U^{4+}) ion and the uranyl (U^{6+}) ion. In the magmatic environment uranium occurs essentially as U^{4+} and in this form is a highly incompatible trace element that occurs in only a few accessory minerals (zircon, monazite, apatite, sphene, etc.) and is concentrated into residual melts. The uranous ion is, however, readily oxidized to U^{6+} in meteoric waters. In most natural aqueous solutions uranous complexes are insoluble, but U^{6+} forms stable complexes with fluoride (under acidic conditions at pH < 4), phosphate (under near neutral conditions at 5 < pH < 7.5) and carbonate (under alkaline conditions at pH > 8) ligands. The oxidized form of uranium is, therefore, easily transported over a wide range of

Figure 3.35 Eh–pH diagram showing relevant aqueous uranium species for the conditions specified. For most meteoric waters in the near neutral pH range, the dominant aqueous species are likely to be U^{6+}-oxide or -carbonate complexes. These will be precipitated from solution by a reduction of Eh to form U^{4+}-oxide, or uraninite (after Langmuir, 1978).

pH conditions, whereas the reduced form of the metal is generally insoluble. Figure 3.35, an Eh–pH diagram for the system $U-O_2-CO_2-H_2O$ at 25°C, shows that for most meteoric waters in the near neutral pH range, the dominant aqueous species are likely to be U^{6+}-oxide or -carbonate complexes. Uranium can be precipitated by lowering Eh of the fluid to form a uranous oxide, in the form of either uraninite or pitchblende.

Consequently, many low temperature uranium deposit types are a product of oxidation–reduction processes where the metal is transported as U^{6+} and precipitated by reduction. In the presence of high concentrations of other ligands, uranium can be transported as a variety of different complexes, and at higher temperatures (>100 °C) and under acidic conditions a molecule such as UO_2Cl^+ may be stable (Kojima et al., 1994). In addition to redox

controls, uranium precipitation may also be promoted by fluid mixing, changes in fluid pH, and adsorption. A more complete overview of uranium ore-forming processes is presented in Nash et al. (1981).

3.11.2 Sandstone-hosted uranium deposits

Most of the world's productive sandstone-hosted uranium deposits occur in the USA. These deposits occur mainly in three regions, the Colorado Plateau region (around the mutual corners of Utah, Colorado, New Mexico, and Arizona states), south Texas, and the Wyoming–South Dakota region. Smaller, generally non-viable, deposits are known from elsewhere, such as the Permian Beaufort Group sandstones of the Karoo sequence in South Africa and the Lodève deposits in France. The deposits are generally associated with Paleozoic to Mesozoic fluvio-lacustrine sandstones and arkoses and are stratabound, although different geometrical variants exist. Most of the deposits in the Colorado Plateau region are tabular and associated with either organic material or vanadium (Northrop and Goldhaber, 1990). Deposits in Wyoming and south Texas, by contrast, are sinuous in plan and have a crescent shape in cross section. Although still stratabound these ores are discordant to bedding and are typically formed at the interface between oxidized and reduced portions of the same sandstone aquifer (Reynolds and Goldhaber, 1983; Goldhaber et al., 1983). It is the latter type that is commonly referred to as roll-front uranium deposits. The genesis of the two subtypes is quite different and they are discussed separately.

Colorado Plateau (tabular) uranium–vanadium type

Important features of tabular sandstone-hosted deposits are that they can occur stacked one on top of the other, and that the ore zones are bounded above and below by sandstones containing a dolomitic cement. The generally accepted model for the formation of these deposit types is based on work done in the Henry Basin of Utah, where stacked U–V ore bodies are considered typical of the Colorado Plateau region as a whole

(Northrop and Goldhaber, 1990). The ore bodies of this area occur predominantly within the Jurassic, sandstone-dominated Salt Wash Member of the Morrison Formation, although on a regional scale they are slightly discordant with respect to bedding (Figure 3.36a). The ores are believed to have formed at the interface between two discrete, low temperature meteoric fluids. One of these fluids, a relatively stagnant but saline basinal brine containing Na^+, Mg^{2+}, and Ca^{2+} cations and Cl^- and SO_4^{2-} anions, underlies a low salinity, meteoric fluid that flows readily along aquifer horizons bringing with it highly soluble metal species such as $UO_2(CO_3)_2^{2-}$ and VO^+. Mixing of these two fluids results in precipitation of metals in subhorizontal tabular zones reflecting the fluid interface (Figure 3.36b). The main uranium ore mineral in these deposits is a uranous silicate, coffinite $(U(SiO_4)_{1-x}(OH)_{4x})$, which is associated either with syn-sedimentary organic (plant) debris, or together with a vanadium-rich chlorite in the intergranular sandstone pore spaces.

Fluid mixing and metal precipitation occurred within a few hundred meters of the surface such that fluid temperatures were unlikely to have exceeded 30–40 °C. The stagnant basinal brine is considered to have been locally derived, but interacted with evaporitic sequences, which explains its high Mg/Ca ratios. The overlying meteoric fluid was essentially groundwater that scavenged U^{6+} and V^{4+}, as well as other oxide-soluble metals such as Cu, Co, As, Se, and Mo, from overlying, uranium-enriched tuffaceous rocks, or from breakdown of detrital Fe–Ti oxide minerals in the aquifer sediments through which it flowed. Mixing of the two fluids and associated diagenetic reactions ultimately gave rise to ore formation, the details of which are presented in Northrop and Goldhaber (1990). One of the products of fluid mixing in this environment was a dolomite cement that precipitated from pH-related $(Ca,Mg)CO_3$ oversaturation within the basinal brine. The pH changes in the mixing zone appear to have been a product of the formation of vanadium-rich clays (smectite–chlorite) during compaction and sediment diagenesis. Vanadium is incorporated into the dioctahedral interlayer hydroxide sites (as $V(OH)_3$) of the clay minerals, which reduces the $[OH^-]$ activity of the fluid and

decreases its pH. The same chemical controls are also implicated in the formation of coffinite ore, although the actual processes are more complex and involved two stages. The uranyl–dicarbonate complex most likely relevant to this meteoric fluid is stable over only a limited pH range (around 7–8 in the conditions applicable to Figure 3.35). A decrease in fluid pH caused by fluid mixing and V-clay formation causes a lowering of $UO_2(CO_3)_2^{2-}$ solubility which promotes the adsorption of UO_2^+ molecules onto the surface of quartz grains. Once the fluid is reduced (probably by bacterially induced SO_4 reduction and production of H_2S) to stabilize U^{4+} complexes, bonding between the uranous ion and silica leads to the formation of coffinite (Northrop and Goldhaber, 1990). It should be noted that organic matter played an important role during the ore-forming process, as is evident from the very close association between coffinite and plant debris. In addition to the fact that organic matter is itself a reductant, it supplies a source of nutrient for sulfate-reducing bacteria that in turn supply biogenic H_2S for reduction of U^{6+} and V^{4+} to their insoluble lower valency forms. In the Grants mineral belt of the Colorado Plateau region uranium mineralization is associated with organic matter in the form of humate that was introduced epigenetically into the sediments by organic acid rich fluids.

The model illustrated in Figure 3.36b is particularly applicable to the tabular, stacked ores of the Colorado Plateau region in which there is a uranium–vanadium association. It suggests that the stacked nature of the tabular ore bodies could be the product of a two-fluid interface that episodically migrates upwards with time. The dominant control on ore formation is pH, although adsorption, bacterial mediation, and redox reactions are also important processes. Evidence for the migration of the low pH zone is provided by the fact that the footwall zones to each ore horizon retain evidence of ore-related dolomite crystals partly dissolved by the acidic fluids as they move upwards through the sequence.

Roll-front type

Although somewhat similar to tabular deposits, roll-front ores form as a consequence of very

Figure 3.36 (a) The orebody geometry and nature of host rocks for the tabular uranium–vanadium deposits of the Henry Basin area of Utah, considered typical of the Colorado Plateau region as a whole. (b) Secular genetic model for the tabular, stacked orebody geometries of Colorado Plateau type deposits, involving an upward-migrating mixing zone between a lower stagnant brine and an overlying, ore-bearing, aquifer-focused meteoric fluid (after Northrop and Goldhaber, 1990).

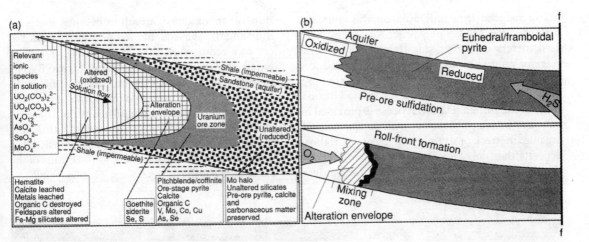

Figure 3.37 (a) Cross section through a typical roll front type sandstone-hosted uranium deposit, such as those in Wyoming, South Dakota, and south Texas. Uranium mineralization occurs at the interface (or redox front) between the altered/oxidized and unaltered/reduced portions of the same aquifer (after De Voto, 1978; Misra, 2000). (b) A two-fluid mixing model for roll front deposits. Initially a reduced fluid migrates up a syn-depositional fault (f) and sulfidizes the sandstone (top box). This is followed by down-dip migration of an oxygenated, uranium-bearing meteoric fluid and the precipitation of uranium ore at the redox front formed in the mixing zone (bottom box). This model is after Goldhaber *et al.* (1978).

different chemical processes. In its simplest form the ore genesis model for roll-front deposits that best accommodates their geometry, in both plan and section, is one where an oxidized, meteoric fluid transporting soluble uranyl–carbonate complexes flows along a sandstone aquifer and precipitates uranium ore at a redox front (Figure 3.37a). Up-dip of the roll-front the sandstones are altered (detrital silicate minerals are altered to clays, Fe–Ti oxide phases are leached) and oxidized (secondary hematite has formed, organic carbon is biodegraded). The redox front itself is characterized by an inner alteration envelope (marked by goethite, siderite, pyrite, or marcasite) and an outer ore zone (comprising pitchblende and/or coffinite with pyrite and some organic carbon). Down-dip of the redox front the sandstone is relatively unaltered and contains a more reduced assemblage of pre-ore pyrite, calcite, and organic matter, with detrital mineral phases relatively intact (Figure 3.37a). In this model the redox front can be regarded as the position in space and time where the meteoric fluid has lost its capacity to oxidize the sandstone through which it is per-

colating. Eh of the fluid changes dramatically at the redox front and soluble uranyl–carbonate complexes are destabilized with precipitation of uranous oxide or silicate minerals. Other soluble metal–oxide complexes also present in the fluid (such as V, As, Se, Mo, Cu, Co) are likewise reduced and precipitate as various minerals, either before or after uranium depending on their relative solubilities as a function of Eh. The roll-front does not remain static and it will migrate down the paleoslope as the meteoric fluid is recharged and the process of progressive, down-dip oxidation of the sandstone evolves with time. The down-dip migration of the redox front can be equated to the process of zone-refining and the ore body is "frozen in" only once the paleohydrological regime changes and fluid flow ceases.

A modification of this scheme has been proposed by Goldhaber *et al.* (1978, 1983), who noted that some roll-front deposits are spatially associated with syn-depositional faults, and that the uranium ores are superseded by paragenetically later sulfide minerals. A fluid mixing model was proposed to accommodate these features and it is envisaged that a reduced fluid migrated up the fault and sulfidized the sandstone aquifer for several hundred meters on either side (Figure 3.37b). This stage of ground preparation created the reduced environment responsible for locating the ore-related redox front. Evidence for this additional stage in the mineralization process is provided by euhedral pyrite (in deposits that do not contain organic matter) or framboidal pyrite (in those deposits that do). This stage was followed by, or was largely coincidental with, down-dip migra-

tion of an oxidized, uranium-bearing meteoric fluid and the subsequent precipitation of uranium ore at a redox front that, in this case, is represented by a zone of fluid mixing (Figure 3.37b). In certain cases, such as the deposits of south Texas, continued emanation up the fault of sulfide-bearing solutions from deep within the basin resulted in post-mineralization sulfidization and the growth of late-stage pyrite and marcasite that overprinted even the altered up-dip sections of the sandstone aquifer.

SUMMARY

There are many different types of fluids circulating through the Earth's crust and these have given rise to a wide variety of hydrothermal ore deposit types that exist in virtually every tectonic setting and have formed over most of Earth history. Juvenile fluids exsolve from magmas, in particular those with felsic compositions, and give rise to granite (*sensu lato*) related ore deposits that include porphyry Cu–Mo, skarn and greisen related Sn–W, intrusion linked Fe oxide–Cu–Au, and high sulphidation Au–Ag ores (discussed in Chapter 2). Metamorphic fluids, derived from volatiles liberated during prograde mineral reactions, are typically aqueo-carbonic in composition and are associated worldwide with orogenic gold deposits that are particularly well developed in Archean and Phanerozoic rocks. Connate fluids formed during diagenesis interact with either reduced (forming Pb–Zn dominant ores) or oxidized (forming Cu dominant ores) sedimentary environments. These fluids are implicated in the formation of Mississippi Valley type (Pb–Zn) and stratiform sediment-hosted copper ores. Circulation of near surface meteoric waters can dissolve labile constituents such as the uranyl ion, giving rise to a variety of different sediment-hosted uranium deposits. Finally, sea water circulating through the oceanic crust in the vicinity of (ridge-related) fracturing and volcanic activity is vented onto the sea floor as black smokers, providing a modern analogue for the formation of Cu–Zn-dominated VMS deposits. Similar exhalative processes also

occur in different tectonic settings and with different metal assemblages, giving rise to sediment-hosted, Zn–Pb-dominated SEDEX type deposits.

The various hydrothermal deposits described in Chapters 2 and 3 and their relationship to the different fluid types discussed in these sections are summarized in Figure 3.38.

Formation of hydrothermal ore deposits is linked not only to the generation of significant volumes of fluid in the Earth's crust, but also to its ability to circulate through rock and be focused into structural conduits (shear zones, faults, breccias, etc.) created during deformation. The ability of hydrothermal fluids to dissolve metals provides the means whereby ore-forming constituents are concentrated in this medium. Temperature and composition of hydrothermal fluids (in particular the presence and abundance of dissolved ligands able to complex with different metals), together with pH and fO_2, control the metal-carrying capability of any given fluid. Precipitation of metals is governed by a reduction in solubility which can be caused by either compositional changes (interaction between fluid and rock, or mixing with another fluid), or changes in the physical parameters (P and T) of the fluid itself. Economically viable hydrothermal ore deposits occur when a large volume of fluid with a high metal-carrying capacity is focused into a geological location that is both localized and accessible, and where efficient precipitation mechanisms can be sustained for a substantial period of time.

Figure 3.38 Diagram illustrating the relationship between different fluid types and various hydrothermal ore deposit types. The diagram is relevant to both Chapters 2 and 3, and is modified after Skinner (1997).

FURTHER READING

For those readers wishing to delve further into hydrothermal ore-forming processes, the following is a selection of references to books and journal special issues.

Geochemistry of Hydrothermal Ore Deposits, ed. H.L. Barnes. 1st edn 1967. Holt, Rinehart and Winston Inc., pp. 34–76. 2nd edn 1979. John Wiley and Sons, pp. 71–136. 3rd edn 1997. John Wiley and Sons, pp. 63–124 and 737–96.

Gill, R. (1996) *Chemical Fundamentals of Geology*. London: Chapman & Hall, 290 pp.

Guilbert, J.M. and Park, C.F. (1986) *The Geology of Ore Deposits*. London: W.H. Freeman and Co., 985 pp.

Pirajno, F. (1992) *Hydrothermal Mineral Deposits*. New York: Springer-Verlag, 709 pp.

Misra, K.C. (2000) *Understanding Mineral Deposits*. Dordrecht: Kluwer Academic Publishers, 845 pp.

Reviews in Economic Geology: Volume 8: Barrie, C.T. and Hannington, M.D. (eds) (1999) *Volcanic-associated Massive Sulfide Deposits: Processes and Examples in Modern and Ancient Settings*. El Paso, TX: Society of Economic Geologists, 408 pp.

Reviews in Economic Geology: Volume 10: Richards, J.P. and Larson, P.B. (eds) (1999) *Techniques in Hydrothermal Ore Deposits Geology*. El Paso, TX: Society of Economic Geologists, 256 pp.

Reviews in Economic Geology: Volume 13: Hagemann, S.P. and Brown, P.E. (eds) (2000) *Gold in 2000*. El Paso, TX: Society of Economic Geologists, 559 pp.

Wolf, K.H. (ed.) (1976) *Handbook of Strata-bound and Stratiform Ore Deposits*, volumes 1–14. New York: Elsevier.

Figure 5.22 (a) Map showing the distribution of phosphate-rich sediments along the continental margins of South Africa and Namibia. (b) Model showing contrasting modes of phosphate deposition in the outer shelf (where diagenetic accumulation of apatite is taking place) and in restricted near-shore environments characterized by high biological productivity and seasonal mass mortality (where precipitation of apatite directly from sea water is occurring). Diagrams after Birch (1980).

CHAPTER FOUR

Surficial and supergene ore-forming processes

4.1 INTRODUCTION

Once metals have been concentrated in the Earth's crust and then exposed at its surface, they are commonly subjected to further concentration by chemical weathering. The relationship between weathering and ore formation is often a key ingredient that leads to the creation of a viable deposit and many ores would not be mineable were it not for the fact that grade enhancement commonly occurs in the surficial environment. There are several deposit types where the final enrichment stage is related to surficial weathering processes. Some of these deposit types are economically very important and contain ores, such as bauxite, that do not occur in any other form. Ore-forming processes in the surficial environment are intimately asso-

ciated with pedogenesis, or soil formation, which is a complex, multifaceted process reflecting local climate and the dominantly chemical interactions between rock and atmosphere. Soil itself is an extremely valuable resource since the world's food production is largely dependent on its existence and preservation. This chapter examines the concentration of metals in soil, as well as in the associated regolith (i.e. all the unconsolidated material that rests on top of solid, unaltered rock). Many different metals are enriched in the surficial environment, the most important of which, from a metallogenic viewpoint, include Al, Ni, Mn, Fe, Cu, Au, Pt, and U. Emphasis is placed here on laterites, with their associated enrichments of Al, Ni, Au, and platinum group elements (PGE). In addition, clay deposits, calcretes, and associated uranium mineralization, as well as the supergene enrichment of Cu in porphyry-type deposits, are discussed. Surficial enrichment of metals takes place in many other settings too, and is a key process, for example, in the formation of viable iron ores associated with banded iron-formations. The latter are described in more detail in Chapter 5 (Box 5.2).

Wt%	
Mn	25
Fe	7
Ni	1.1
Cu	1.1
Co	0.2
Zn	0.1

Figure 5.24 Map showing sub-equatorial zones of base metal enriched manganese nodule concentration in the Pacific Ocean, contoured with respect to the copper content (in wt%) of nodules. Nodule-free areas occur close to the continents, where sedimentation rates are high, as well as along the equator and East Pacific Rise, where biological productivity is high. The Clarion–Clipperton region, a particularly enriched zone, is boxed (after Heath, 1981).

normal metal contents, with up to 2 wt% combined Cu + Ni and substantial Co and Zn (Figure 5.24). One such area is the Clarion–Clipperton region, to the west of Mexico.

Manganese nodules are typically ovoid, a few centimeters in diameter, and have the appearance on the sea floor of a burnt potato. In cross section they are complexly layered, often partly concentric, and represent concretions that have apparently nucleated around a clastic or biogenic fragment. They often exhibit internal radiating shrinkage cracks reflecting a change in mineralogy from hydrated Fe and Mn oxyhydroxides to a variety of more compact, but chemically complex, Fe and Mn oxides such as vernadite, birnessite, todorokite, goethite, and hematite (Heath, 1981). The formation of manganese nodules is a complex process and still not fully understood. Metals are undoubtedly derived from the sea water itself, but ultimately come from various sources including submarine exhalative vents, clastic and volcanic input, and diagenesis of

pelagic sediments. The formation of the nodules and the concentration of metals within them have been attributed to one or more of the following mechanisms:

• Settling of clay and biogenic (fecal) debris that contained either absorbed or ingested metals obtained from the sea water, with subsequent release of metals during dissolution and decomposition.

• Direct precipitation of metals from sea water onto a suitable substrate which forms the nucleus around which concretionary growth takes place.

• Upward diffusion of metals in ocean bottom sediment pore waters.

• Authigenic reactions in ocean bottom sediments during alteration and compaction.

• Bacterial activity and the oxidation of transition metals. In this regard, certain types of bacteria (such as *Metallogenium*) are known to be particularly prevalent in the oxidation and subsequent precipitation of labile Mn^{2+} and have been detected in manganese nodules from the Atlantic Ocean (Trudinger, 1976).

• Preferential uptake of dissolved transition metals into specific Fe and Mn oxyhydroxide minerals, such as the affinity of Cu and Ni for todorokite (a multi-element Mn–oxyhydroxide).

The current level of uncertainty about the processes involved in the formation of deep ocean manganese nodules is reflected in the variety of suggested mechanisms listed above. Many of these suggestions are not mutually exclusive and it is likely that nodule formation is a long-lived and complex process. The biggest problem with the exploitation of manganese nodules at present is not so much technical as it is political and economic. The technologies required for exploiting manganese nodules at depth in several kilometers of ocean water could be overcome, but the formulation of an internationally acceptable Law of the Sea is a much bigger and more contentious issue. Manganese nodules, nevertheless, represent an enormous metal resource for the future.

5.3.6 Evaporites

The bulk of the world's production of rock salt (halite), as well as of potash, borates, and nitrates for agricultural fertilizers, comes from rocks known as evaporites. These are chemical precipitates that form as a result of evaporation of a brine, usually derived from sea water. There are two main environments in which evaporites form. The major one, in which the so-called "saline giants" of the world formed, is marginal marine in setting and represented by large lagoons or restricted embayments into which periodic or continual sea water recharge occurs. This type of deposit may be both laterally extensive and thick, but is characterized by a relatively limited range of mineral precipitants derived from sea water, which itself has remained fairly constant in terms of bulk composition over much of geological time. The second setting is intracontinental and lacustrine and results in much smaller, thinner deposits which are characterized by a more diverse range of mineral precipitants since continental fluvial input introduces a broader range of dissolved ingredients to the lake waters. Examples of deposits representing the former include the Permian Zechstein Formation, which formed in a shallow sea covering large areas of the United Kingdom, The Netherlands, Germany, and Poland, and also the Silurian Salina Formation of New York and Michigan states in the USA. Typical products mined from these deposits include halite, potash, and sulfates. Probably the largest known evaporite sequence occurs in late Miocene strata beneath the floor of the Mediterranean Sea, where deposits extend laterally for over 2000 km and may be up to 2 km thick. Much of this resource is obviously unexploitable, but is so large that its formation must have caused a significant reduction in oceanic salinity at the time (Kendall and Harwood, 1996). Examples of intracontinental lacustrine deposits include the dry lakes of Chile, Death Valley in California, and the Great Salt Lake of Utah. In addition to the products mentioned above, these deposits are also important producers of borates (from California) and nitrates (from Chile), as well as Mg, Br, and Li (from Utah).

The principles behind the formation of evaporite deposits are relatively simple in theory, although actual deposits can be complex and exhibit a large variety of different mineral salts and paragenetic sequences. As sea water or brine evaporates and water vapor is removed into the atmosphere, the salinity (i.e. the total content of dissolved salts in solution) of the residual solution increases and individual salts precipitate as their respective solubility limits are reached. The order or sequence of precipitation reflects the scale of increasing solubility at a given temperature, such that the salts with the lower solubilities precipitate first, followed consecutively by salts with progressively higher solubilities. The relative quantities of precipitated products in an evaporite deposit are also constrained by the solubility limits of the various salts dissolved in the brine solution. These considerations seem to suggest a relatively straightforward precipitation process and uniform paragenetic sequence. In fact the chemistry of brine solutions is very complex and factors such as convection dynamics, post-precipitation diagenesis, and equilibrium as opposed to fractional crystallization combine to ensure considerable diversity in the nature of these deposits.

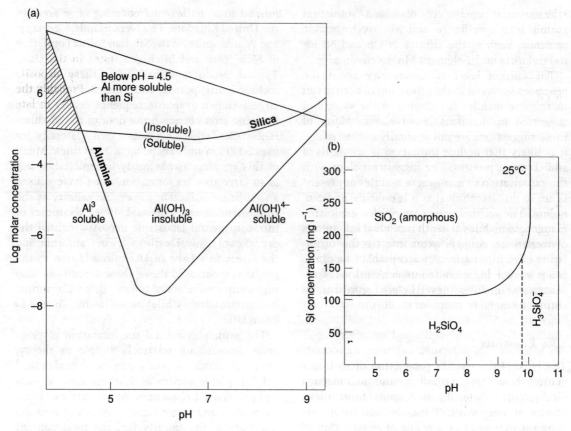

Figure 4.2 (a) The solubility of Si and Al as a function of pH (after Raiswell *et al.*, 1980). (b) The solubility of amorphous silica at 25 °C (after Bland and Rolls, 1998).

of the role of oxidation in chemical weathering is provided by the relative instability of biotite compared to muscovite. Biotite has the formula $K^+[(Mg^{2+}, Fe^{2+})_3(Si_3Al)O_{10}(OH)_2]^-$ and is much more easily weathered than muscovite $K^+[(Al_2)(Si_3Al)O_{10}(OH)_2]^-$ because of the ease with which the ferrous iron can be oxidized to ferric iron. Weathering and the resulting oxidation of Fe in biotite leads to a charge inbalance that destabilizes the mineral, a process that is less likely to happen in muscovite since it contains no iron in its lattice. The presence of iron in minerals such as olivine and the orthopyroxenes is one of the main reasons why they are so unstable in the weathering zone.

4.2.4 Cation exchange

Clay particles are often colloidal in nature (i.e. they have diameters < 2 μm) and are characterized by a net negative surface charge brought about by the replacement of Si^{4+} by Al^{3+} in the clay lattice. The negative charge is neutralized by adsorption of cations onto the surface of the colloids (see Figure 3.16, Chapter 3). The adsorbed cations may be exchanged for others when water passes through weathered material containing clay colloids and this has an effect on mineral stabilities as well as the nature of leaching and precipitation in regolith profiles. A simplified scheme (after Bland and Rolls, 1998) illustrating the effect of cation exchange at the surface of a colloidal particle is shown in reaction [4.3] below. In this example cation exchange promotes the solution of Ca in groundwaters:

$$\boxed{COLLOID} - Ca^{2+} + 2H^+(aq) \rightarrow$$

$$\boxed{COLLOID} - H^+ + Ca^{2+}(aq) \qquad [4.3]$$
$$\mid$$
$$H^+$$

4.3 LATERITIC DEPOSITS

4.3.1 Laterite formation

Laterite is defined as the product of intense weathering in humid, warm, intertropical regions of the world, and is typically rich in kaolinitic clay as well as Fe- and Al-oxides/oxyhydroxides. Laterites are generally well layered, due to alternating downward percolation of rainwater and upward movement of moisture in the regolith during seasonal dry spells, and are often capped by some form of duricrust. Laterites are economically important as they represent the principal environment within which aluminum ores (bauxite) occur. They can also contain significant concentrations of other metals such as Ni, Mn, and Au, as well as Cu and PGE. Laterites form on

stable continental land masses, over long periods of time. In parts of Africa, South America, and Australia laterization has been ongoing for over 100 million years (Butt *et al.*, 2000), and, consequently, they are characterized by thick regolith profiles (up to 150 m) in which intense leaching of most elements has occurred such that they no longer reflect the rock compositions from which they were derived. As with most soil/regolith profiles the main processes involved in lateritization can be subdivided into those of *eluviation*, where clays and solutes are removed from a particular horizon, and *illuviation*, where material is accumulated, usually at a lower level. A generalized lateritic regolith profile is shown in Figure 4.3, together with an indication of the pattern of horizontally orientated leaching and retention of a variety of different elements in the regolith zones (Butt *et al.*, 2000).

The base of a lateritic regolith profile is characterized by the saprolith zone, which is highly weathered rock where the primary texture and fabric is still preserved. Given that the fluids involved in this type of weathering are typically oxidizing and slightly acidic, the lowermost saprock zone (Figure 4.3) is characterized by the destabilization of sulfides and carbonates and the associated leaching of most chalcophile metals

(a) Generalized lateritic regolith profile

(b) Element mobility in typical lateritic profiles

Host minerals	Leached	Partly retained (in secondary minerals)
Released in the mottled and ferruginous zones		
Aluminosilicates (muscovite, kaolinite)	K, Rb, Cs	Si, Al (kaolinite)
iron oxides; gold	Trace elements; Au	
Released in upper saprolite		
Aluminosilicates (muscovite)	Cs, K, Rb	Si, Al (kaolinite)
Ferromagnesians (chlorite, talc, amphibole)	Mg, Li	Fe, Ni, Co, Cr, Ga, Mn, Ti, V (Fe and Mn oxides)
Smectite clays	Ca, Mg, Na	Si, Al (kaolinite)
Released in the lower saprolite		
Aluminosilicates	Ca, Cs, K, Na, Rb	Si, Al (kaolinite); Ba (barite)
Ferromagnesians (pyroxene, olivine amphiboles, chlorite, biotite)	Ca, Mg	Fe, Ni, Co, Cr, Ga, Mn, Ti, V (Fe and Mn oxides)
Released at weathering front		
Sulfides	As, Au, Cd, Co, Cu, Mo, Ni, Zn, S	As, Cu, Ni, Pb, Sb, Zn, (Fe oxides; sulfates, arsenates, carbonates, alunite-jarosite)
Carbonates	Ca, Mg, Fe, Mn, Sr	

Profile column labels: Lag, Soil, Fe laterite | Lateritic gravel, Residuum | Lateritic duricrust, Mottled zone (kaolinite matrix), Plasmic zone, mainly kaolinite and goethite (Primary fabric destroyed), Saprolite >20% weatherable minerals altered (Primary fabric preserved), Saprock <20% weatherable minerals altered, Unaltered bedrock. Side labels: Regolith, Pedolith, Saprolith, Cementation front, Weathering front.

Figure 4.3 (a) A generalized lateritic regolith profile showing the different horizons and the terminology used in their description. (b) Generalized pattern of element mobility in lateritic regoliths (after Butt *et al.*, 2000).

Figure 5.26 Simplified scheme illustrating the formation of oil, gas, and coal by the progressive burial of different types of mainly vegetative matter (after Hunt, 1979).

settings, from accumulation of vegetation in either humid, tropical swamp environments or, as in the case of younger coal seams, more temperate to polar regions. Oil and gas deposits, by contrast, develop mainly from the accumulation of phyto- and zooplankton in marine settings.

When organisms die they decompose by bacterial decay and/or oxidation, and rapidly break down to relatively simple molecular constituents such as CO_2 and CH_4. Such a process would not be conducive to the formation of fossil fuels, which requires preservation of much of the complex organic hydrocarbon material. Suitable source rocks from which fossil fuels accumulate must, therefore, have formed in reducing environments where sedimentation rates are neither too slow (in which case oxidation and molecular breakdown might occur) nor too rapid (in which case dilution of the total organic matter content of the rock would occur).

The prevailing theory for the origin of both petroleum and coal is based on the notion that organisms are buried during the sedimentary process and then subjected to a series of alteration stages as pressure and temperature increase. As shown in Figure 5.26, progressive burial of phytoplankton results in the early liberation of CO_2 and

H_2O and formation of kerogen (a collective name for sedimentary organic matter that is not soluble in organic solvents and has a polymer like structure; Bjørlykke, 1989). As the kerogen "matures" the long-chain covalent bonds that typify organic molecules are progressively broken to form lower molecular weight compounds. At around 100–120 °C and burial depths of 3–4 km (depending on the geothermal gradient), a liquid hydrocarbon fraction develops which can then migrate from the source rock. This interval is known as the "oil window." With further burial and cracking of molecular bonds, significant volumes of gas (mainly methane, CH_4) develop, which are also amenable to migration. The solid residue remaining in the sediment is referred to as kerogen, but with progressive burial it devolatilizes further and has a composition approaching pure carbon (graphite). By contrast, when humic, land-derived vegetation is buried, little or no liquid oil is formed, although significant volumes of gas will, again, be generated. The solid residue that remains in this case is more voluminous and compacts to form coal seams. The nature of the solid coal residue changes with depth, from peat and lignite at shallow burial depths (less than about 500 m), to bituminous coal and subsequently

Table 5.1 Average chemical compositions (in wt%) of the main organic building blocks compared to those of petroleum and a typical coal

	C	H	O	N	S
Carbohydrates	44	6	50	–	–
Lignin	63	5	31.6	0.3	0.1
Proteins	53	7	22	17	1
Lipids	76	12	12	–	–
Petroleum	85	13	0.5	0.5	1
Coal	70	5	23	1	1

Source: after Hunt (1979).

anthracitic coal (at depths of around 5000 m). The calorific value (i.e. the amount of energy produced on combustion) of the coal increases with maturity or burial depth.

5.4.2 Oil and gas formation

All living organisms are made up of relatively few molecular building blocks that have apparently changed little over geologic time. The main molecular building blocks involved in petroleum formation include:
• Carbohydrates and related substances – these are mono- and polysaccharide polymers and include the sugars, chitin and lignin, the latter being a major precursor to coal.
• Proteins – these are high molecular weight amino acid polymers and represent one of the most important constituents of life processes.
• Lipids, which are represented in animal fats and vegetable oils and are abundant in crude oils.
• Other substances such as resins and pigments are of lesser importance but also occur variably in both plant and animal matter.
Plants comprise mainly carbohydrates (40–70%), although the higher, woody forms also contain substantial lignin for strength. Phytoplankton contains around 20% protein. Animals, by contrast, are made up mainly of proteins (55–70%) with lesser carbohydrates and lipids but no lignin (Hunt, 1979). The average chemical composition of these various organic building blocks is shown in Table 5.1.

As the original organic constituents are buried, they are subjected to increases in pressure and

temperature, resulting in systematic changes which are divided into three stages, termed diagenesis, catagenesis, and metamorphism. This progression, and its application to the burial of organic matter in sediments, together with the organic processes and changes that occur in each, are summarized in Figure 5.27. Diagenesis refers to the early biological and chemical changes that occur in organic-rich sediments prior to the pronounced temperature-dependent effects of later reactions (i.e. less than about 50 °C). During this stage the biopolymers of living organisms undergo a wide variety of complex low-temperature reactions. Put simply, they are either oxidized or attacked by microbes and converted into less complex molecules which may, in turn, react and condense to form more complex, high molecular weight geopolymers that are the precursors to kerogen. Biogenic reactions during diagenesis also produce significant amounts of gas, termed biogenic gas, which typically escapes into the atmosphere or water column and is not retained in the sediment. Catagenesis occurs between about 50 and 150 °C and is the most important stage as far as petroleum generation is concerned. During this stage temperature plays an important role in catalyzing reactions, the majority of which result in the formation of light hydrocarbons from high molecular weight kerogen by the breaking of carbon–carbon bonds. In this process, known as *thermal cracking*, a complex organic molecule such as a paraffin or alkane will split and form two smaller molecules (a different paraffin and an alkene or olefin). Each of the products contains a carbon atom, with an outer orbital electron from the original covalent pairing that is now shared. The shared electron means that the resultant alkane and alkene each contain a "free radical" that makes them reactive and amenable to further breakdown. Alternatively, reactions may occur by *catalytic cracking*, where a carbon atom in one of the resultant molecules takes both electrons, thereby becoming a "Lewis acid" or double electron acceptor. The molecule that loses the electron pair is called a carbonium ion and with its net positive charge is also amenable to further decomposition. For example, alkanes subjected to catalytic cracking could

BOX 4.1 Lateritization: Bauxite: the Los Pijiguaos deposit, Venezuela

Approximately 90% of the world's bauxite, the principal source of alumina, is obtained from laterites formed by deep weathering of continental planation surfaces exposed to hot humid climates. Global production of bauxite has risen significantly in recent years and is presently at around 125 million tons per annum (Meyer *et al.*, 2002). One of the largest bauxite deposits in the world is at Los Pijiguaos in Venezuela, where annual production is about 5 million tons from a total resource that could be as much as 6 billion tons.

The Los Pijiguaos bauxite deposit formed from a Mesoproterozoic, metaluminous Rapakivi-type granite (the Parguaza granite) that was deeply eroded and weathered during Cretaceous–Paleogene times to form the Nuria planation surface (Figure 1). This profound weathering event gave rise to the development of thick lateritic soil cover in which economic concentrations of bauxite (around 50 wt% Al_2O_3) form a mineable zone that averages 8 m thick. The complete laterite profile comprises an upper concretionary zone (bauxite), underlain by a mottled or saprolitic layer and then the granitic bedrock. The bauxite layer itself can be subdivided into four zones comprising various concretionary and pisolitic textures.

The deposit as a whole is subdivided into blocks that are defined by fluvial channels that cut through the deposit subsequent to its formation (Figure 1).

The bauxite at Los Pijiguaos is made up principally of gibbsite with lesser quartz and rare kaolinite. The original granite textures in the bauxite layer have been almost entirely destroyed, with feldspars, and to a lesser extent quartz, being largely replaced by gibbsite (Figure 3). An increasing degree of lateritization is marked by systematic compositional changes in the rock. This is demonstrated in the Al_2O_3–SiO_2–Fe_2O_3 ternary plot in Figure 2 where the process of lateritization is characterized by an increase in the alumina content. Quartz and gibbsite are inversely correlated in the bauxite ore and iron contents remain relatively constant, with an increase in Fe_2O_3 in the most highly lateritized samples. The bauxite at Los Pijiguaos is a product of desilication, hydration and residual Al_2O_3 concentration of the Parguaza granite, and involves a mass loss of some 60% (Meyer *et al.*, 2002). These processes produce a high grade and high purity gibbsitic ore from which alumina can be extracted by low temperature digestion, making Los Pijiguaos one of the most commercially profitable bauxite deposits in the world.

Figure 1 Schematic profile through the Los Pijiguaos bauxite deposit showing the concentration of laterite on a dissected late Cretaceous planation surface (after Meyer *et al.*, 2002).

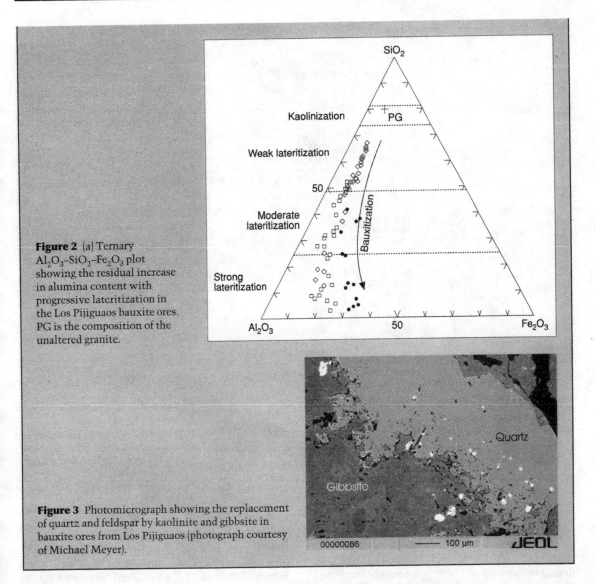

Figure 2 (a) Ternary Al_2O_3–SiO_2–Fe_2O_3 plot showing the residual increase in alumina content with progressive lateritization in the Los Pijiguaos bauxite ores. PG is the composition of the unaltered granite.

Figure 3 Photomicrograph showing the replacement of quartz and feldspar by kaolinite and gibbsite in bauxite ores from Los Pijiguaos (photograph courtesy of Michael Meyer).

4.3.3 Nickel laterites

Laterites that are developed on ultramafic rocks containing abundant olivine and orthopyroxene and, hence, with high Ni contents (i.e. 0.1 to 0.3%; see Chapter 2), commonly develop concentrations of Ni silicate or oxide that are up to 10 times the original concentration. Given the relative ease of mining of this type of ore compared to hard-rock magmatic sulfide ores, as well as recent developments in extractive metallurgical processes, Ni laterites are a much sought after commodity. The principles by which these ores form are relatively straightforward and basically involve eluviation of Ni from the uppermost lateritic residuum and concentration in underlying saprolitic illuvium as nickeliferous talc, serpentine, or smectite, or less commonly together with goethite.

The primary olivine and orthopyroxene minerals that are the source of the Ni form the main ingredients of an ultramafic rock that may originally

Figure 5.29 Classification scheme for kerogen types based on the hydrogen index and oxygen index (after Cornford, 1998). Inset diagram shows the original classification of kerogen on the basis of H/C and O/C atomic ratios (after Tissot and Welte, 1984).

oil-prone Type I and II kerogens will yield not only oil, but also both "wet" (i.e. with a high condensable fraction) and "dry" gas (mainly methane). Gas-prone kerogen (usually Type III) will produce mainly dry gas.

Modern analytical and modeling techniques allow the quantitative estimation of gas and oil yields to be calculated from a source rock undergoing progressive burial. A summary of hydrocarbon yields from two different source rocks is shown in Figure 5.30. Figure 5.30a shows the quantities of petroleum products derived from a source rock comprising Type II kerogen and differentiates between the condensate, comprising

high (C15+) and low (C2–C8) molecular weight oils, and a dominantly methane gas component. Figure 5.30b is the equivalent scenario for a source rock sediment comprising kerogen that is only gas-prone, which on maturation initially yields only a minor amount of wet gas (ethane, propane, butane, etc.) but mainly dry gas (methane), leaving a coal residue. The latter process is relevant to the generation of coal-bed methane resources.

Source rock considerations are important during petroleum exploration. The origin of organic matter is obviously a pointer to the depositional environment of the sedimentary rock and, there-

Figure 5.30 Maturity curves showing (a) the cumulative generation of oil types and methane gas from sediment source rock originally containing a 1% total organic carbon (TOC) content of Type II oil-prone kerogen; and (b) the generation of wet and dry gas only from a 1 km³ sediment volume of gas-prone kerogen which ultimately yields a coal deposit (after Cornford, 1998).

fore, also useful in placing constraints on the nature of oil/gas migration and entrapment.

Petroleum migration and reservoir considerations

One of the features of oil and gas formation is the fact that petroleum originates in a fine grained source rock and then migrates into more permeable, coarser grained, reservoir sediments. Knowledge of petroleum migration and entrapment processes is obviously important to both the exploration and exploitation stages of the industry. Although the processes are complex, they can now be accurately evaluated in terms of fluid hydraulic principles and sophisticated computer modeling techniques.

Petroleum engineers differentiate between *primary migration*, which accounts for the movement of oil and gas out of the source rock during compaction, and *secondary migration*, which describes flow within the permeable reservoir, as well as the segregation of oil and gas. As the organic source rock is lithified during diagenesis, water (usually a low to moderate salinity brine) is expelled from the sediment to form a connate fluid (see Chapter 3). In the early catagenic stages of hydrocarbon maturation, therefore, oil and gas

Figure 4.6 The nature and characteristics of gold and silver redistribution in a typical lateritic profile. The inset diagram shows two mechanisms whereby a primary Au–Ag alloy particle could be broken down during lateritization and silver preferentially removed (modified after Mann, 1984; Nahon et al., 1992).

when Fe^{2+} is completely oxidized in the presence of free oxygen. By contrast, silver will go into solution more readily, and under more reducing conditions, as several complexes, including AgCl (the most stable) and $AgCl_2^-$ or $AgCl_3^{2-}$ (Figure 4.7). Accordingly, particles of Au–Ag alloy in the surficial environment will be more likely to

be leached of their Ag over a broader range of conditions.

A model for gold concentration in laterites is shown in Figure 4.6 and is discussed below in terms of gold– and silver–chloride speciation, as well as the likely Eh–pH conditions of a typical lateritic profile, shown in Figure 4.7. Using these

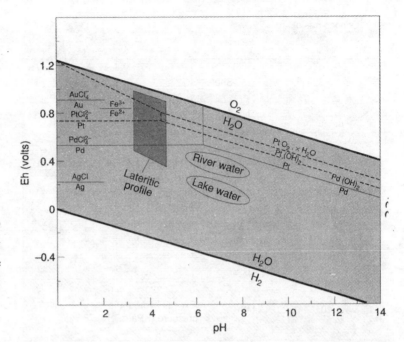

Figure 4.7 Eh–pH diagram showing the characteristics of a lateritic profile in relation to lacustrine and riverine waters. Also shown are the redox potentials and stabilities of Au, Ag, Pt, and Pd as chloride complexes, illustrating the range of Eh that controls solubility of the various metals (information compiled from data in Fuchs and Rose, 1974; Mann, 1984; Bowles, 1986).

constraints it is apparent that primary Au–Ag alloy particles in the near surface regolith above the water table will be readily dissolved in the acidic, oxygenated, and moderately saline groundwaters prevailing in this environment. Mann (1984) has shown that the breakdown of the particle and dissolution of Au and Ag actually takes place by replacement of the alloy by an iron oxyhydroxide phase (such as goethite). The goethite itself, however, can be seen to contain tiny particles of high purity gold (Figure 4.6 inset b) suggesting that the latter metal is rapidly reprecipitated as goethite forms, whereas silver remains in solution and is transported away. This is explained by the fact that high gold solubilities are only maintained at high Eh and that the metal will precipitate with only a slight decrease in Eh under mildly reducing conditions, as described by the following reaction:

$$AuCl_4^- + 3Fe^{2+} + 6H_2O \Leftrightarrow$$
$$Au + 3FeOOH + 4Cl^- + 9H^+ \qquad [4.9]$$

A decrease in $AuCl_4^-$ solubility and precipitation of gold is, therefore, promoted by interaction of

the fluid with a more reducing regolith in which Fe^{2+} and Mn^{2+} contents are higher with increasing depth in the profile and below the water table. Redox reactions, therefore, control the precipitation of gold in this environment and explain its association with minerals such as goethite and manganite. It is clear in Figure 4.6 that under the same conditions in which gold precipitates, silver as AgCl remains in solution and will be transported away from the site of gold deposition.

Primary Au–Ag alloy particles that are not closely associated with an iron or manganese oxyhydroxide tend to show a preferential depletion in silver around their edges and the formation of higher purity gold halos (Figure 4.6 inset a). Such features are a product either of silver diffusion from the outer margins of the particle, or of complete dissolution of the entire alloy and *in situ* reprecipitation of the gold. It should also be noted that the efficacy of chloride ion ligands in promoting gold and silver dissolution is particularly appropriate to laterites that presently occur in arid climates, such as Western Australia. In humid, tropical regions chloride ion activity is reduced by high rainfall dilution and other compounds, such

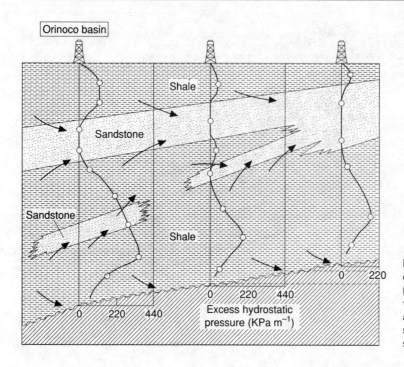

Figure 5.32 Actual measurements of excess hydrostatic pressures (i.e. overpressure) in three drill wells in the Orinoco basin and the anticipated fluid flow lines in the sequence of alternating shale and sandstone (after Hunt, 1979).

If the removal of pore water is impeded by low permeability in, for example a fine grained shale, then compaction will be retarded and fluid pressures increased to values above normal hydrostatic pressures. Fine and coarse sediment will expel pore waters at different rates during burial and will, therefore, compact along different pressure gradients. Overpressured fluids will tend to exist in the finer grained sediments. Figure 5.32 shows actual measurements of fluid pressures in a series of drill wells from the Orinoco Basin and the hydrostatic overpressures that occur in the poorly drained shale units relative to the well drained sandstone. This information allows the migration pathways to be identified and shows that the main sandstone aquifer can be fed by fluids from both above and below. Several factors actually control the stresses that cause hydrostatic fluid overpressures in rocks and these include rapid sediment deposition, thermal expansion of fluids, tectonic compression, and the actual generation of low density oil and gas in the source rock.

Many of the factors discussed above also apply to secondary petroleum migration. In the advanced stages of catagenesis, however, temperatures and pressures are such that many hydrocarbons exist close to their critical points such that density contrasts between liquid and vapor are minimized. The segregation of oil from gas, therefore, mainly reflects the decline in temperatures that accompanies migration of petroleum products into reservoirs that are well away from the sites of oil/gas generation. The progressive separation of liquid and vapor, into a low density, buoyant gas phase and a more dense, viscous oil, is a process that generally accompanies secondary migration.

Entrapment of oil and gas

Primary migration of hydrocarbons typically occurs over short distances (hundreds of meters or less) and is constrained by the proximity of the first available aquifer to the source rock. Secondary migration, by contrast, occurs over tens, and possibly even hundreds, of kilometers and is only constrained by the presence of a trap which prevents the petroleum from further flow and allows it to accumulate. Hydrocarbon traps are critical to the formation of viable oil and

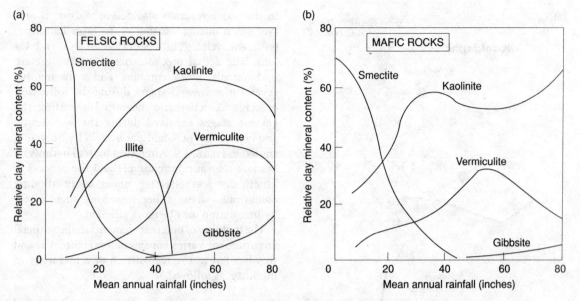

Figure 4.8 The effect of rainfall on clay mineral formation in (a) felsic and (b) mafic rocks (after Barshad, 1966).

Most of the ore constituents have been extensively remobilized during lateritization, with base metals occurring in Mn oxides and Au–Pt–Pd occurring together with amorphous carbon and Fe–Mn oxides/oxyhydroxides. Some of the ore also occurs as nuggets of Au and PGE alloy, some of which are reported to weigh as much as 60 kg (Grainger et al., 2002).

4.4 Clay deposits

Clay minerals are volumetrically the most abundant product of weathering and either occur *in situ* or have been transported to a site of deposition. They are also economically important and used for a variety of industrial applications including paper, ceramics, filtration, and lubricants. Clay formed during weathering reflects both the nature of the source material and the weathering conditions. Nevertheless, very similar clay mineral assemblages ultimately form from both felsic and mafic rocks (Figure 4.8). Temperature and rainfall in particular, as well as local Eh–pH conditions, determine the nature and rates of clay-forming processes. Some of the more important clay minerals considered here include kaolinite, illite and the smectite group (including montmorillonite). Kaolinite is formed under humid conditions by acid hydrolysis of feldspar-bearing rocks (e.g. in laterites), whereas illite forms under more alkaline conditions by weathering of feldspars and micas. The smectite clays commonly weather from intermediate to basic rocks under alkaline conditions and are highly expandable, containing intracrystalline layers of water and exchangeable cations. It should be noted that clay minerals are not only the result of weathering processes but can also form as the products of low temperature hydrothermal alteration (see Chapter 3).

Clay formation is initiated during chemical weathering by acid hydrolysis (see section 4.2.2 above and Figure 4.9). A typical reaction that describes the process is shown below:

$$(Ca,Na)Al_2Si_2O_8 + 2H^+ + H_2O \Leftrightarrow$$
plagioclase
$$Al_2Si_2O_5(OH)_4 + Na^+ + Ca^{2+} \qquad [4.10]$$
kaolinite

(a)

(b)

(c)

In the above reaction plagioclase feldspar is broken down during weathering to form kaolinite, with the release into solution of Na and Ca ions. The actual mechanisms of weathering are undoubtedly more complex and may involve several incremental stages during the formation of clays. A schematic diagram illustrating the various stages involved during the weathering and breakdown of K-feldspar by acid hydrolysis is shown in Figure 4.9. Alteration by acid hydrolysis is most relevant at acidic pH and the process is kinetically less effective under more alkaline conditions, where other processes such as Si-hydroxylation may be more efficient.

The mobility of different elements in the surficial environment varies considerably (Figure 4.1) and this has led to the recognition of a hierarchy of mobility, as follows:

$$Ca > Na > Mg > Si > K > Al = Fe \qquad [4.11]$$

The alkaline and alkali earth elements are typically the most soluble in groundwaters, with Al and ferric Fe being relatively immobile. The combination of kinetic and thermodynamic constraints on clay mineral formation during weathering results in a well defined sequence of reaction pathways that can be related, for example, to climatic conditions. The effects of rainfall on the formation of clay mineral assemblages is shown in Figure 4.8, for both felsic and mafic parental rock compositions. The general pattern is that smectitic clays tend to form under relatively arid to semi-arid conditions, whereas kaolinite tends to dominate in wetter climates. This pattern may also reflect a paragenetic sequence of clay formation, with smectites forming relatively early on and being superseded, or replaced, by kaolinite or vermiculite.

Figure 4.9 (*left*) Representation of the stages during the progressive weathering and breakdown of K-feldspar by acid hydrolysis, leading to the formation of clay minerals (modified after Leeder, 1999).

Figure 4.10 Strongly kaolinized granite in Cornwall, being mined for "china clay."

4.4.1 The kaolinite (china clay) deposits of Cornwall

The Cornubian batholith of southwest England, so well known for its polymetallic magmatic-hydrothermal mineralization (Box 2.2 in Chapter 2), also hosts some of the largest and best quality kaolinite (or china clay) deposits in the world. Of considerable demand in the paper and ceramic industries, the kaolinite resource of Cornwall surpasses the base metal resource in value, and considerable reserves of high quality china clay still exist.

The formation of the Cornish kaolinite deposits is complex and controversial. Some workers have argued in favor of a weathering-related origin (Sheppard, 1977), but this has been countered by proponents of a hydrothermal process who maintain that clay formation represents the end stage of a very long-lived paragenetic sequence initiated soon after granite emplacement and terminated with circulation of low temperature meteoric fluids during clay formation (Alderton, 1993). The actual processes of kaolinite formation are essentially the same irrespective of the actual fluid origin and on balance it seems likely that both a late hydrothermal process and a tertiary weathering event contributed to clay formation.

Zones of intense kaolinization are best developed in areas where greisen altered Sn–W ore veins and major NW–SE trending faulting have occurred. This suggests a genetic link to previous, higher temperature, hydrothermal processes, but could also point to groundwater circulation focused into sites previously accessed by high temperature fluids. Kaolinite itself is preferentially developed from the plagioclase feldspar component of the granite, while K–feldspar remains relatively stable except in zones of extreme alteration/weathering. This is consistent with the mobility hierarchy described in [4.11] above, where Ca and Na are more easily leached than K during acid hydrolysis. The process is also demonstrated in reaction [4.10] although, as mentioned previously, the actual mechanism is likely to be more complex. Many workers have described an intermediate stage of either muscovite or smectite formation prior to the ultimate formation of kaolinite (Exley, 1976; Durrance and Bristow, 1986). This, too, is consistent with the pattern of progressive clay mineral formation illustrated as a function of rainfall in Figure 4.8. It seems likely, therefore, that acid hydrolysis type reactions gave rise to early alteration of plagioclase feldspars to form sericite (fine grained muscovite), as well as incipient argillic alteration. Exhumation of the batholith during Mesozoic times, together with further meteoric fluid circulation and deep weathering, continued the alteration process to form zones of intense kaolinization, particularly in areas where previous alteration had taken place. It appears likely that kaolinization was also accompanied by leaching of Fe from the altered granite, a process that contributed to the very high purity and "whiteness" of the Cornish china clay.

4.5 CALCRETE-HOSTED DEPOSITS

Most of the laterally extensive surface or near-surface calcrete (or caliche) layers that typify arid environments around the world are referred to as "pedogenic calcrete" because they represent calcified soils (Klappa, 1983). Calcrete is defined simply as an accumulation of fine grained calcite ($CaCO_3$) in the vadose zone (i.e. above the water table) during a combination of pedogenic (soil forming) and diagenetic (lithification) processes. The solution and precipitation of calcite in the

Figure 4.11 Simplified classification scheme for calcretes and a summary of the processes by which they form. An indication of the suitability of calcretes for hosting surficial uranium deposits is also provided (after Carlisle, 1983).

surficial environment is represented by the following general equation (after Klappa, 1983):

$$Ca^{2+} + 2HCO_3^- \Leftrightarrow CaCO_3 + CO_2 + H_2O \qquad [4.12]$$

The solubility of $CaCO_3$ increases with decreasing temperature, with lower pH, and with increasing partial pressure of CO_2. Thus, extraction of CO_2 from an aqueous solution will precipitate $CaCO_3$. Precipitation of calcite may also result when water is removed from a soil profile during evaporation and evapotranspiration, resulting in an increase in the concentration of aqueous ions in the solution. A simplified classification of calcrete types is shown in Figure 4.11 where it is evident that, in addition to the very extensive pedogenic calcretes, a more locally distributed non-pedogenic variant, termed valley or channel calcrete, also occurs. It is the latter variety that is particularly important as the host rock for surficial uranium deposits.

4.5.1 Calcrete-hosted or surficial uranium deposits

Important uranium resources have been discovered in channelized calcretes from arid regions in Australia and Namibia. The Yeelirrie (Western Australia) and Langer Heinrich (Namibia) deposits represent well known examples of surficial uranium ores formed by accumulations of a bright yellow potassium–uranium vanadate mineral, carnotite $(K_2(UO_2)_2(V_2O_8).3H_2O)$, within calcretized fluvial drainage channels (Carlisle, 1983). Since carnotite is a uranyl (U^{6+})–vanadate, reduction of hexavalent uranium is not the main process involved in the precipitation and concentration of uranium ores (see Chapter 3). Rather, the formation of this type of uranium deposit is related to high rates of groundwater evaporation and the resultant decrease of aqueous carbonate, vanadium, and uranium solubilities within a few meters of the surface. Calcretized fluvial channels represent the remnants of rivers from a previous higher rainfall interval. Such channels occasionally drained a uranium-fertile source region and, where preserved, represent zones of focused groundwater flow within which mineral precipitation resulted in concentration of uranium ore. In this process uranium and other components are required to remain in solution until they reach a zone where carnotite can be precipitated by evaporation of the groundwater.

At Yeelirrie in Western Australia, fluvial

(a)

(b)

Figure 4.12 (a) Geological setting of the Yeelirrie carnotite deposit hosted in channelized calcrete, Western Australia (after Mann and Deutscher, 1978; Carlisle, 1983). (b) Model depicting the setting and processes involved in the formation of carnotite deposits in calcretized channels (after Carlisle, 1983).

channels started to incise the bedrock during Paleogene times, although the period of aridity commenced only in the late Pliocene. Active calcrete deposition and carnotite ore formation are thought to have occurred in only the past 500 000 years (Carlisle, 1983). Calcrete crops out along the axis of a paleochannel that can be traced for over 100 km and within which a carnotite bearing orebody, some 6 km long, 0.5 km wide, and up to 8 m thick with a resource of about 46 000 tons of U_3O_8, is defined (Figure 4.12a). The Langer

Heinrich deposit in Namibia is remarkably similar in most respects to Yeelirrie.

The main ingredients of carnotite, U, K, and V, are derived locally from weathered granites (for the uranium and potassium) and possibly more mafic rocks for the vanadium. In relatively carbonated groundwaters under near neutral conditions, U^{6+} would be transported as a carbonate complex (see Figure 3.36), whereas vanadium was probably in solution as V^{4+}, although the exact species and complexing agent is not known

(Mann and Deutscher, 1978). Focused groundwater flow introduced the ore-forming ingredients into the channel, with the combination of high evaporation rates and calcite precipitation ensuring that the solution evolved toward higher salinities and pH along the flow path (Figure 4.12b). In detail, however, the actual precipitation of carnotite is a complex process and appears to be related either to evaporation and decomplexation of uranyl–carbonate complexes, or to oxidation of V^{4+} to V^{5+}, or both (Mann and Deutscher, 1978). A general equation for the precipitation of carnotite can be written as follows (after Carlisle, 1983):

$$2UO_2^{2+} + 2H_2VO_4^- + 2K^+ + 3H_2O \Leftrightarrow$$
$$K_2(UO_2)_2(V_2O_8).3H_2O + 4H^+ \qquad [4.13]$$
$$\text{carnotite}$$

Evaporation on its own removes CO_2 from solution and drives equilibrium equations such as [4.12] and [4.13] above to the right, promoting precipitation of calcite and carnotite. Precipitation of carnotite, however, produces hydrogen ions (see equation [4.13]), which lowers pH and increases the solubility of calcite. Dissolution of calcite provides additional CO_3^{2-} to the solution, which in turn increases uranium solubility and favors dissolution of carnotite. The processes described in terms of equations [4.12] and [4.13] appear, therefore, to be counter-productive and this is evident because the orebodies themselves provide textural evidence for repeated dissolution and reprecipitation of ore and gangue minerals. In reality, however, the very high rates of evaporation increase the Ca^{2+} and Mg^{2+} concentrations of the groundwater to such an extent that calcite (as well as dolomite) is forced to precipitate and carbonate activities are decreased. Formation of carbonate minerals, under conditions in which they would not otherwise have precipitated, also promotes the destabilization of uranyl–carbonate complexes and eventually results in carnotite formation coeval with calcretization. Mann and Deutscher (1978) have suggested that oxidation of vanadium may also play a role in carnotite formation, since V^{4+} is soluble in mildly reducing waters at near neutral pH, but is precipitated as V^{5+} with increasing Eh. They envisage that vanadium might have been transported separately in deeper groundwaters flowing below the calcretized channel and that this fluid mixed with the surficial, oxidized, U- and K-bearing fluid to form carnotite in a mixing zone. The migration of the lower V-bearing fluid to the near surface environment is caused by high points in the basement topography (Figure 4.12b) which force groundwaters upwards into the evaporative zone to mix with oxidized fluids, or be directly oxidized by interaction with the atmosphere. This notion is consistent with the common observation that carnotite mineralization is spatially related to pinch-outs and constrictions in the fluid flow path.

4.6 SUPERGENE ENRICHMENT OF CU AND OTHER METALS IN NEAR SURFACE DEPOSITS

The processes of weathering can be responsible for the *in situ* enrichment of Cu, as well as other metals such as Zn, Ag, and Au, in many deposits that occur at or near the surface. The process is generally referred to as *supergene enrichment* and is a product of oxidation and hydrolysis of sulfide minerals in the upper portions of weathering profiles. It is an extremely important process in the formation of low-grade porphyry copper deposits because the presence of an enriched, easily extractable supergene blanket of secondary copper ore minerals above the primary or *hypogene* ore is often the one factor that makes them economically viable. The processes involved in the formation of supergene mineralization are similar to those already discussed in section 4.3.4 above and applicable to the concentration of gold nuggets or platinum group elements in lateritic weathering zones. This section focuses specifically on copper and the formation of supergene enrichments in porphyry-type deposits, although the principles also apply to other deposit types, in particular VMS and SEDEX base metal ores.

4.6.1 Supergene oxidation of copper deposits

Unlike the processes applicable to gold and nickel, copper enrichments are not specific to lateritic environments and supergene copper deposits occur in any surficial environment where oxidized,

WEATHERING ZONES | **MINERALS**

Mineralized vein · Water seepage · Weathered surface

Eluvial / Illuvial — Supergene enrichment

Leached capping (gossan)

Leached zone

Cu^{2+}

Cu^{2+}

Oxidized ores

Water table (redox barrier)

Secondary sulfide enrichment

Primary, unaltered hypogene ore

Reducing ← oxidizing

Hydrated iron oxides

Copper carbonates, oxides, silicates, etc.

Chalcocite, covellite, bornite

Chalcopyrite, pyrite

Figure 4.13 Schematic section through a copper deposit showing the typical pattern of an upper, oxidized horizon (the leached or eluvial zone) overlying a more reduced zone of metal accumulation (the supergene blanket or illuvial zone). The uppermost zone of ferruginous material, often containing the skeletal outlines of original sulfide minerals, is known as gossan. The redox barrier may be the water table or simply a rock buffer (after Webb, 1995).

acidic groundwaters are able to destabilize sulfide minerals and leach copper. The principles involved in this process are illustrated in Figure 4.13 and also summarized in terms of the reaction below:

$$4CuFeS_2 + 17O_2 + 10H_2O \Rightarrow$$
chalcopyrite
$$4Fe(OH)_3 + 4Cu^{2+} + 8SO_4^{2-} + 8H^+ \qquad [4.14]$$
    goethite

In most porphyry copper environments pyrite is the dominant sulfide mineral and its hydrolysis and oxidation dictates the production of hydrogen ions (i.e. the decrease in pH) in the weathering zone (see equations [4.7] and [4.8] above). Pyrite breakdown is also accompanied by the formation of goethite in the regolith and the liberation of SO_4^{2-}. Chalcopyrite is the major copper–iron sulfide mineral and its breakdown, described in reaction [4.14], produces soluble cuprous ions that are dissolved in groundwater solutions. In the regolith profile, therefore, oxidizing, acidic groundwaters leach the primary, hypogene ore-body of its metals, leaving behind an eluviated zone that may, if the intensity of leaching is not too severe, be residually enriched in iron,

as hematite or goethite/limonite. The upper clay- and Fe–oxyhydroxide-rich capping, which also contains the skeletal outlines of the original sulfide minerals, is referred to as a *gossan*. Gossans are very useful indicators of the previous existence of sulfidic ore, not only in porphyry systems, but in many other ore-forming environments too. The soluble copper ions percolate downwards in the regolith profile and encounter progressively more reducing conditions, either as a function of the neutralization of acid solutions by the host rock, or at the water table. Copper is then precipitated as various secondary minerals, the compositions of which reflect the ground-water composition as well as local pH and Eh in the supergene zone. The so-called "copper-oxide" minerals that precipitate here are actually compositionally and mineralogically very complex and can include a variety of copper –carbonate, –silicate, –phosphate, –sulfate, –arsenate, as well as –oxyhydroxide phases (Chávez, 2000). In addition, Cu also replaces pre-existing sulfide minerals (i.e. pyrite and chalcopyrite) in more reduced zones where the latter minerals are still stable. Cu typically replaces the Fe in hypogene minerals such as pyrite and chalcopyrite, to form a suite of

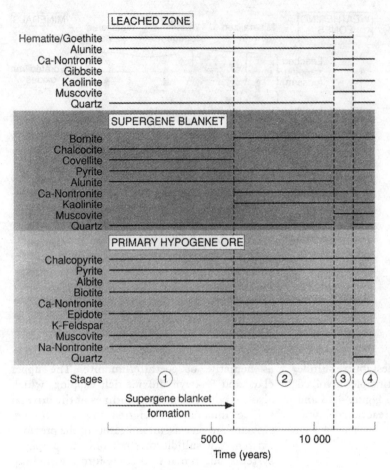

Figure 4.14 Illustration of the stable mineral assemblages modeled as a function of time in the weathering zones above a porphyry copper deposit. The primary, hypogene ore (least altered) is compared to the overlying supergene blanket and the oxidized, leached zone. Note that with time (from stages 1 to 4) the mineral assemblages evolve as certain phases are consumed and others precipitated (after Ague and Brimhall, 1989).

Cu-enriched sulfide phases including chalcocite (Cu_2S), covellite (CuS), and bornite (Cu_5FeS_4).

A more detailed illustration of the distribution of stable mineral assemblages in a typical supergene weathering profile over a porphyry copper deposit is shown in Figure 4.14. This simulation integrates the effects of time (or more accurately the evolution of the chemical system in terms of fluid/rock ratio) in much the same way that alteration processes were described in dynamic terms as a function of evolving fluid/rock ratios in section 3.6 of Chapter 3. The primary, hypogene ore is considered to be hosted in a granite and comprises pyrite + chalcopyrite that is weathered by a flux of slightly acidic rainfall. Within about 6000 years (period 1 in Figure 4.14) the primary sulfides are totally dissolved from the leached zone and copper is reprecipitated as chalcocite and covel-

lite by replacement of primary sulfides in the supergene blanket, as shown in reaction [4.15]:

$$CuFeS_2 + 3Cu^{2+} \Rightarrow 2Cu_2S + Fe^{2+} \qquad [4.15]$$
chalcopyrite   chalcocite

The stable assemblage in the leached (gossanous) zone during stage 1, and also into stage 2, is hematite/goethite, alunite, and quartz. The dissolution and/or replacement of primary sulfides is differential and chalcopyrite tends to disappear from both leached and supergene zones before pyrite, which is only removed completely from the upper zone by stage 2. With time, and as the fluid/rock ratio increases, the leached zone develops gibbsite, muscovite/sericite, and minor clay minerals (stage 3), eventually evolving into a unit dominated by sericite and kaolinite (stage 4).

Alunite disappears and SO_4^{2-} is removed from the weathering zone. The pH of groundwaters in the leached zone starts off low (acidic) during the sulfide dissolution stage and then evolves to slightly more alkaline conditions with time. The supergene blanket initially develops an assemblage comprising covellite and chalcocite, as the primary sulfides are replaced, together with quartz and alunite. Once chalcopyrite is consumed from the leached zone, the downward migrating flux of Cu ions in solution is reduced and bornite develops later in the paragenetic sequence (i.e. from stage 2 onwards). Again in this zone, the clay minerals and muscovite/sericite are stabilized by progressive hydrolysis of primary feldspars and micas and, ultimately, the stable mineral assemblage is not unlike that of the overlying leached zone except that copper sulfide (bornite) is still stable. In the primary host rock weathering has only limited effects, although over time relatively unstable minerals such as plagioclase, biotite, and magnetite will tend to disappear. It is interesting to note that sulfate (SO_4^{2-}), produced in abundance during the oxidation of primary sulfides (see reaction [4.14] above), is generally transported away from the *in situ* weathering zone, and very little sulfate reduction (either organic or inorganic) tends to occur in the supergene blanket, or below the water table. This is another reason why low-S copper sulfides such as covellite and chalcocite form in this environment.

In addition to the formation of high metal/sulfur copper sulfide minerals at a redox barrier in the supergene blanket, it is apparent that a diverse suite of secondary copper minerals can form at the base of the oxidized zone (Figure 4.13). This suite includes oxides such as cuprite and tenorite (the former usually associated with native Cu), carbonates such as malachite and azurite, sulfates such as brochantite, antlerite, and chalcanthite, chlorides such as atacamite, silicates such as chrysocolla, and phosphates such as libethinite. The precipitation of these oxidized secondary minerals is generally due to direct precipitation from groundwaters that are saturated with respect to one or more of the various components that make up this suite of minerals. Figure 4.15 shows an Eh–pH diagram that identifies

the stability fields of several of the copper minerals encountered in supergene enrichment zones above porphyry copper deposits. Under relatively low Eh conditions, below the water table, the high metal/sulfur copper sulfides are stable, whereas at or close to the water table, cuprite and native Cu form. Above the water table the stability fields of a range of secondary copper minerals (note only a few are shown) occur and these are controlled essentially by pH. This is because it is essentially the pH that controls the solubilities of complexing ligands (i.e. CO_3^{2-}, OH^-, SO_4^{2-}, PO_4^{2-}, etc.) and determines which of the relevant copper complexes are likely to be saturated in any given environment. The extent to which leached and supergene zones develop, and the nature of the secondary minerals that form, depends to a certain extent on the amount of primary, hypogene sulfides in the host rock and the acidity generated in the groundwaters as a consequence of their oxidation/weathering. Weathering of a host rock with a low sulfide content will typically result in minimal acidity, limited mobility of Fe and other metals, and formation of secondary copper minerals that are stable in the near neutral to slightly acidic pH range (Chávez, 2000). Conversely, weathering of protores with a high sulfide mineral content will result in more extreme acidity and the formation of secondary copper minerals stable only at lower pH. Local conditions also play an important role, however, and supergene enrichment in the proximity of a limestone, for example, will result in local groundwaters with a high CO_3^{2-} content, resulting in the stabilization of minerals such as malachite or azurite under neutral to alkaline conditions (Figure 4.15 and equation [4.16] below).

$$2Cu^{2+} + CO_3^{2-} + 2OH^- \Leftrightarrow Cu_2(OH)_2CO_3 \qquad [4.16]$$
$$\text{malachite}$$

Probably the most spectacular examples of supergene enrichment are associated with the giant porphyry copper deposits of northern Chile, such as Chuquicamata, El Salvador, and El Abra. In addition to world-class hypogene orebodies at depth, these deposits have been subjected to a complex Paleogene to Neogene geomorphological evolution that resulted in very significant supergene

Figure 4.15 Eh–pH diagram showing the stability fields of selected copper minerals at 25 °C and 1 atmosphere (after Guilbert and Park, 1986).

enrichment (Sillitoe and McKee, 1996). The supergene and "exotic" ores at Chuquicamata and El Salvador are described in more detail in Box 4.2.

A note on supergene enrichment of other metals

Zones of supergene enrichment are also found in the surficial environment above any exposed metal orebody. In porphyry systems, molybdenum is normally comprehensively removed from regolith profiles, although it can accumulate under very oxidizing conditions as ferrimolybdite, and under alkaline conditions as powellite (Ca–molybdate). Relative to Cu, the other base metals do not form as commonly as secondary mineral enrichments. Zn is often dispersed in

groundwaters, whereas Pb tends to be relatively immobile. These two metals do, however, form a range of sulfate and carbonate supergene minerals, such as anglesite ($PbSO_4$), cerrusite ($PbCO_3$), and smithsonite ($ZnCO_3$), under certain conditions With new technologies available in extractive metallurgy, non-sulfide zinc ores, especially those comprising willemite (Zn_2SiO_4), now represent an important category of mineralization associated with oxidation of stratiform, sediment-hosted base metal deposits. Examples include the Skorpion Zn mine in Namibia and Vazante in Brazil. Silver tends to behave in much the same way as copper, and acanthite (Ag_2S) is readily oxidized in acidic groundwaters, with Ag being reprecipitated as the native metal, or as Ag–halides

BOX 4.2   Supergene processes: supergene and "exotic" mineralization in the porphyry copper giants of northern Chile

Porphyry coppers are high tonnage–low grade deposits. The average grade of primary sulfide, or hypogene, mineralization is typically so low that they are only marginally economic. Fortunately, many porphyry copper deposits are capped by a blanket of enriched ore formed by supergene processes. The supergene blanket, usually accessible during the early stages of mining, contributes significantly to the overall viability of the mining operation. At Chuquicamata, for example, which is the largest copper deposit in the world, with a total reserve of some 11.4 billion tons of ore at 0.76 wt% copper, the supergene blanket comprised a major proportion of the ore body that has now largely been mined out. The supergene blanket is made up of a barren leached zone, an upper copper "oxide" zone of antlerite, brochantite, atacamite, and chrysocolla, and an underlying copper sulfide zone made up mainly of chalcocite (Ossandón et al., 2001). In addition to the in situ supergene ores, some of the giant porphyry copper deposits of northern Chile, such as Chuquicamata, El Salvador, and El Abra, also contain "exotic" copper oxide mineralization. This is secondary ore that has been transported laterally from the leached portion of the supergene blanket and precipitated in the drainage network surrounding the deposits. Again at Chuquicamata, exotic copper oxide mineralization is located in a gravel filled paleochannel, extending from the main pit to the South or Mina Sur deposit, a distance of about 7 km. Some 300 million tons of exotic ore was deposited in these gravels as chrysocolla and copper wad, a Cu-rich, K-bearing Mn oxyhydrate (Mote et al., 2001). Similar exotic copper mineralization occurs at El Salvador (the Damiana and Quebrada Turquesa deposits) and also at El Abra.

Supergene and exotic mineralization is related to the formation of acidic groundwaters that take up Cu into solution and reprecipitate it elsewhere. Secondary copper is either reprecipitated in the chalcocite rich supergene blanket beneath the leached zone (Figure 1a), or transported laterally by groundwaters moving through paleodrainage channels to form the distal exotic ore bodies of chrysocolla and copper wad (Figure 1b). The high degree of preservation of secondary copper ores in northern Chile is related to episodic tectonic uplift in combination with the pattern of global climatic rainfall and watertable fluctuations (Mote et al., 2001). Accurate dating of copper wad and alteration assemblages in supergene

Figure 1 (a) Cross section through the Chuquicamata mine showing the distribution of the supergene blanket (represented by the leached cap, the copper "oxide" zone, and supergene chalcocite ore) in relation to the primary hypogene ore (after Ossandón et al., 2001).

(b)

Figure 1 (*cont'd*) (b) Simplified map of the El Salvador district showing the distribution of gravel-filled paleochannels and exotic deposits extending radially away from the main pit (after Mote *et al.*, 2001).

Figure 2 Exotic Cu-Mn oxide mineralization (wad) in gravels exposed in a bench cut through the Damiana ore body, El Salvador (photo courtesy of George Brimhall).

mineralized zones of northern Chile indicates that surficial processes were long-lived and episodic. Some supergene mineralization is preserved from just a few million years after the hypogene ores formed at the Eocene–Oligocene boundary (around 35 Ma). The main pulses of supergene ore formation, however, occurred toward the end of the Oligocene (20–25 Ma) and in the mid-Miocene (12–15 Ma). These pulses coincided broadly with periods of relatively high rainfall which promoted weathering, leaching of copper, and groundwater flow, as well as the deposition of gravels in proximal drainage channels. The subsequent preservation of both supergene and exotic styles of mineralization is due to the drop in erosion rates (i.e. reduction in uplift) and, more importantly, the onset of hyperaridity and limited groundwater flow, as the Atacama desert formed from the mid-Miocene onwards (Alpers and Brimhall, 1989).

(AgCl, AgBr, AgI) in regions characterized by arid climates. In the Atacama desert of Chile there have been spectacular concentrations of supergene silver ores discovered, including a 20 ton aggregate of embolite (Ag(Cl,Br)) and native silver (Guilbert and Park, 1986). The concentration of gold, with specific reference to lateritic regolith profiles, is discussed in section 4.3.4 above.

SUMMARY

The chemical processes that contribute to weathering include hydration and dissolution, hydrolysis and acid hydrolysis, oxidation and cation exchange. Surficial and supergene ore-forming processes are related essentially to pedogenesis, which can be simplified into an upper zone of eluviation (leaching of labile constituents and residual concentration of immobile elements) and an underlying zone of illuviation (precipitation of labile constituents from above). Laterites are the product of intense weathering in humid, warm intertropical regions and are important hosts to bauxite ores, as well as concentrations of metals such as Ni, Au, and the PGE. Residual concentrations of alumina, and the formation of bauxitic ores, occur in high rainfall areas where Eh and pH are such that both Si and Fe in laterites are more soluble than Al. Ni enrichments occur above ultramafic intrusions in the illuviated laterite zone where the metal is concentrated in phyllosilicate minerals by cation exchange. Au and Pt enrichments also occur in laterites above previously mineralized terranes, forming in the presence of highly oxidized, acidic, and saline groundwaters. Fixation of the precious metals occurs by reduction or adsorption, in the presence of carbonaceous matter or Fe and Mn oxyhydroxides. Oxidized, acidic groundwaters are capable of leaching metals, not only during laterite formation, but in any environment where such fluids are present. Supergene enrichment of Cu can be very important in the surficial environment above hypogene porphyry styles of mineralization. Enrichment of copper again occurs in the illuviated zone, although in this case both Cu–sulfide minerals (in the relatively reduced zone beneath the water table) and Cu–oxide minerals (above the water table) form.

The formation of viable clay deposits, such as kaolinite, is a product of progressive acid hydrolysis, essentially of plagioclase feldspar. Calcrete is a pedogenic product of high evaporation environments, but can also form in paleo-drainage channels in now arid climatic regions. In uranium-fertile drainage systems calcrete channels represent zones where concentrations of secondary uranium minerals precipitate together with calcite by evaporation-induced processes.

FURTHER READING

Bland, W. and Rolls, D. (1998) *Weathering: An Introduction to the Scientific Principles*. London: Arnold, 271 pp.

Guilbert, J.M. and Park, C.F. (1986) *The Geology of Ore Deposits*. New York: W.H. Freeman and Co., 985 pp. (Chapter 17).

Leeder, M. (1999) *Sedimentology and Sedimentary Basins: From Turbulence to Tectonics*. Oxford: Blackwell Science, 592 pp. (Chapter 2).

Martini, I.P. and Chesworth, W. (1992) *Weathering, Soils and Paleosols*. Developments in Earth Surface Processes 2. New York: Elsevier, 618 pp.

Williams, P.A. (1990) *Oxide Zone Geochemistry*. New York: Ellis Horwood, 286 pp.

Wilson, R.C.L. (1983) *Residual Deposits: Surface Related Weathering Processes and Materials*. London: The Geological Society of London and Blackwell Scientific Publications, 258 pp.

CHAPTER FIVE

Sedimentary ore-forming processes

5.1 INTRODUCTION

Sedimentary rocks host a significant proportion of the global inventory of mineral deposits and also contain the world's fossil fuel resources. Previous chapters have considered a variety of ore-forming processes that have resulted in the epigenetic concentration of metals and minerals in sedimentary rocks. This chapter will concentrate on processes that are syngenetic with respect to the host sediments and where the ores are themselves sediments or part of the sedimentary sequence. Processes to be discussed include the accumulation of heavy, detrital minerals and the formation of placer deposits, the deposition of organic-rich black shales, and the precipitation mechanisms that give rise to Fe, Mn, and P concentrations in chemical sediments. In addition, there is a brief overview of the origins of oil and gas deposits, as well as of coalification processes, because the organic source material for these deposits reflects the local depositional environment and ore formation was broadly coeval with sediment accumulation. Although it might be argued that the migration of oil through sediments involves later fluid flow through the depository, such processes are generally early diagenetic in character and therefore warrant inclusion in the present chapter. By contrast, syngenetic, clastic sediment-hosted SEDEX Pb–Zn–Ag, sandstone-hosted U ores, and late diagenetic red-bed Cu–(Ag–Co) type deposits are discussed in Chapter 3, since they involve processes that are more hydrothermal in character, or have their metals originating from outside the sedimentary host rocks. These subdivisions are somewhat arbitrary and reflect more the organizational structure of this book than a rigorous genetic classification.

Modern trends in the application of basin analysis techniques to exploration have undoubtedly been set in the oil industry, where, in recent decades, major advances have been made in understanding the relationships between sedimentology, tectonics, and the maturation of organic material. The evolution of oil and gas within this cycle can be effectively assessed in terms of organic chemistry and fluid flow patterns in the rock (Eidel, 1991). This level of understanding requires a high degree of integration of numerous earth science disciplines (including paleontology, stratigraphy, sedimentology, structural geology, plate tectonics, geohydrology, organic geochemistry, and others), an approach that is increasingly being applied to all types of exploration in sedimentary basins (Force *et al.*, 1991).

As with the fossil fuels, ore-forming processes that give rise to placer deposits and metal enrichments associated with chemical sediments and diagenetic fluid flow are intimately related to the origin, tectonic setting, and evolution of the sedimentary host rocks. Most major syn-sedimentary ore deposits tend to occur in a limited range of basin types (Eidel, 1991). Passive continental margin chemical sedimentary ores (banded iron-formations and ironstones, bedded Mn deposits, and phosphate ores), as well as shoreline and fluvial placer deposits (gold, cassiterite, diamonds, and zircon–ilmenite–rutile black sands), reflect ore-forming processes that prevail in cratonic settings, where features such as protracted stability and high depositional energies for reworking of sediment load apply. Sediment-hosted ores in which late diagenetic or epigenetic processes are responsible for metal accumulation (such as red-bed Cu–(Ag–Co) deposits and some SEDEX Pb–Zn–Ag ores; see Chapter 3) tend to be associated with rift basins where rates of deposition are high and active faulting promotes the circulation of connate and meteoric fluids. It is also noteworthy that many oil and gas fields are also associated with rift-related cratonic basins.

The relationships between sedimentation and ore formation are multifaceted and only selected topics are discussed in this chapter. Additional information is available from the works listed at the end of this chapter.

5.2 CLASTIC SEDIMENTATION AND HEAVY MINERAL CONCENTRATION – PLACER DEPOSITS

A placer deposit is one in which dense (or "heavy") detrital minerals are concentrated during sediment deposition. They are an important class of deposit type and can contain a wide variety of minerals and metals, including gold, uraninite, diamond, cassiterite, ilmenite, rutile, and zircon. Well known examples of placer deposits include the late Archean Witwatersrand and Huronian basins (Au and U) in South Africa and Canada respectively, although the origin of these ores is controversial. Geologically more recent occurrences include the diamond placers of the Orange River system (see Box 5.1) and the western coastline of southern Africa, the cassiterite (Sn) placers of the west coast of peninsula Malaysia, and the beach-related "black sand" placers (Ti, Zr, Th) of Western Australia and New South Wales, South Africa, Florida, and India.

The fluid dynamic processes involved in placer formation are invariably very complex. It is exceedingly difficult to predict, for either exploration or mining purposes, where heavy mineral concentrations occur. This section will only touch briefly on what has become a highly mathematical subject that has applicability to geomorphology and flood control engineering, in addition to ore deposit geology. More detailed reviews of the principles involved in clastic sedimentation and placer formation can be found in Miall (1978), Slingerland (1984), Slingerland and Smith (1986), Force (1991), and Pye (1994).

5.2.1 Basic principles

The formation of placer deposits is essentially a process of sorting light from heavy minerals during sedimentation. In nature heavy mineral concentration occurs at a variety of scales, ranging from regional systems (alluvial fans, beaches, etc.), through intermediate features (the inner

Figure 5.1 Results of a flume experiment simulating (a) fluid flow at the confluence of a tributary with its trunk river and (b) the resulting distribution of heavy minerals (after Best and Brayshaw, 1985).

bank of a river bend or a point bar), to small-scale features (bedding laminae or cross-bed foresets). An experimental simulation of placer processes is illustrated in Figure 5.1, where a heavy mineral is fed via a "tributary" into the "trunk river." The confluence of two orthogonal flow streams results in the creation of a vortex or eddy downstream of the junction, with the accompanying erosion of the bed removing light particles and heavy minerals concentrated in the scoured zone.

The transportation and deposition of sediment in fluvial and related systems is a complex topic (see overviews in Selley, 1988; Friedman *et al.*, 1992; Pye, 1994; Allen, 1997; Leeder, 1999), the basic principles of which are essential to the understanding of placer processes. To complicate matters, sediments can also be sorted by the action of wind, and this process has applicability to the formation of placers in, for example, beach environments (Kocurek, 1996).

One of the parameters used to quantify the conditions of fluid motion is the Reynolds number, which is a dimensionless ratio identifying fluid flow as either laminar and stable, or turbulent and unstable. The Reynolds equation is expressed as:

$$Re = UL\delta_f/\eta \qquad [5.1]$$

where Re is the dimensionless Reynolds number; U is the fluid velocity; L is the length over which the fluid is flowing; δ_f is the fluid density; and η is the fluid (molecular) viscosity.

For low Reynolds numbers flow is laminar and vice versa for turbulent flow (Figure 5.2a). The behavior of a particle in a river channel will obviously depend to a large extent on the type of flow it is being subjected to. Flow in natural stream channels is predominantly turbulent, the detailed anatomy of which is shown schematically in Figure 5.2b. Three layers of flow can be identified. The bottom zone is the non-turbulent *viscous sublayer*, which is very thin and and may break down altogether in cases where the channel floor is very rough and turbulence is generated by the upward protrusion of clasts from the bed load. Above it is the *turbulence generation sublayer*, where shear stresses are high and eddies are generated. The remainder of the stream profile is the *outer or core layer*, which has the highest flow velocities. A shear stress (τ_o in Figure 5.2b) is imposed on the bed load by the moving fluid and is a function of fluid density, the slope of the stream bed, and flow depth. The curved velocity profile of the channel section is caused by frictional drag of the fluid against the bed.

The types of fluid flow in water (or air) define the character and efficiency of mass (sediment) transport. A particle or grain will move through a fluid as a function of its size, shape, and density, as well as the velocity and viscosity of the fluid itself. In water, a particle at any instant will move in one of three ways: the heaviest particles (boulders, gravel) roll or slide along the channel floor to form the bedload (or traction carpet); intermediate sized particles (sand) effectively bounce along with the current (a process known as saltation); while the finest or lightest material (silt and clay) will be carried in suspension by the current (Figure 5.3a). In air the types of movement are similar, but the lower density and viscosity of air relative to water dictate that moving particles are smaller, but their motion is more vigorous (Figure 5.3b).

The type of particles moving in a fluvial channel by saltation and suspension is partly a

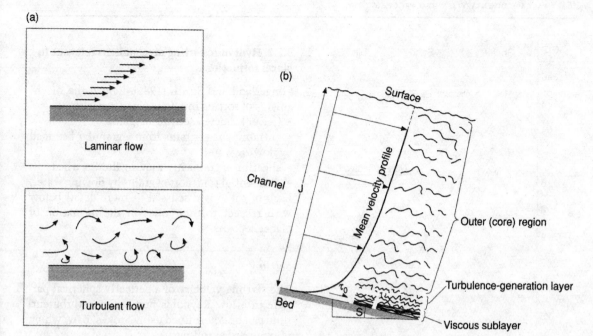

Figure 5.2 (a) Schematic illustration, using streamlines, of the nature of laminar and turbulent fluid flow. (b) Internal structure of turbulent fluid flow in a natural channel. τ_o is the boundary shear stress imposed by the fluid on its bed and is a function of J (the flow depth) and S (the bed slope), as well as fluid density (after Slingerland and Smith, 1986).

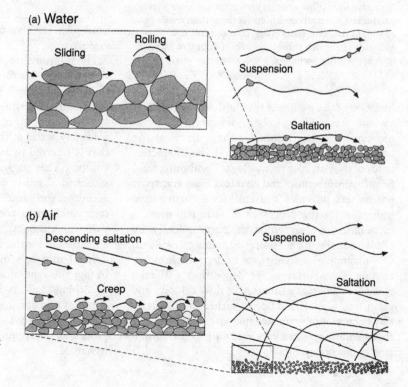

Figure 5.3 Illustration of the different mechanisms of sediment transport in water (a) and air (b) (after Allen, 1994).

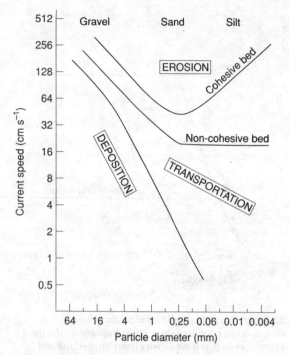

Figure 5.4 A Hjulström diagram showing how sedimentary processes can be assessed in terms of hydrodynamic (flow velocity) and physical (grain size) parameters. Critical conditions for deposition are shown, as well as those for erosion and transportation for two situations in which cohesive and non-cohesive channel beds apply (after Sundborg, 1956; Friedman *et al.*, 1992).

function of the nature of the fluid flow (as defined by the Reynolds number), whereas bed load movement is determined by shear stress at the boundary layer (Figure 5.2b) and the characteristics of the particles themselves. Combining fluid flow (hydrodynamic) and physical mass transport parameters provides a useful semi-quantitative indication of the processes of sedimentation, a technique first presented diagrammatically by Hjulström (Figure 5.4; after Sundborg, 1956). In this diagram the conditions under which either erosion, transportation, or deposition will take place are shown as a function of flow velocity and grain size. Deposition occurs either as flow velocity decreases or grain size increases (or both), and these parameters are very relevant to the formation of placer deposits.

5.2.2 Hydraulic sorting mechanisms relevant to placer formation

Slingerland and Smith (1986) divided the mechanisms of sorting into four types, namely:
- free or hindered settling of grains;
- entrainment of grains from a granular bed load by flowing water;
- shearing of grains in a moving fluidized bed;
- differential transport of grains by flowing water.
Each of these is discussed in more detail below with respect to their roles in the formation of placer deposits.

Settling

The settling velocity of a perfectly spherical particle in a low Reynolds number (non-turbulent) fluid can be determined using Stokes' Law, which is expressed as follows:

$$V = gd^2(\delta_p - \delta_f)/18\eta \qquad [5.2]$$

where V is the particle settling velocity; g is the acceleration due to gravity; d is the particle diameter; δ_p and δ_f are the densities of particle and fluid respectively; and η is the fluid (molecular) viscosity.

The relationship indicates that particle settling velocities in the same fluid medium are proportional to particle diameters (squared) and densities. Figure 5.5 shows that, in terms of Stokes' Law, different sized grains of quartz, pyrite, and gold may settle at the same velocity, a condition that is referred to as *hydraulic (or settling) equivalence*. This suggests that particles of differing size and density could conceivably reside together in the same sedimentary layer, to form a rock such as a conglomerate. Hydraulic equivalence is sometimes mistakenly taken as an explanation for the concentration of small, heavy detrital minerals in a coarse sedimentary rock. In fact the type of settling equivalence predicted by Stokes' Law is a poor approximation of the complex and dynamic sorting mechanisms taking place during actual placer formation and other processes are required to explain the situation in nature.

Figure 5.5 Illustration showing the principle of hydraulic equivalence for particles settling according to Stokes' Law. The settling velocities of quartz, pyrite, and gold, with radii and densities as shown, are the same, indicating that they would settle out of a non-turbulent column of water into the same sedimentary layer.

There are several reasons why a simple Stokesian settling is inadequate as an explanation for placer forming process. These include the fact that stream flow is generally turbulent (it has a high Reynolds number), particles are not spherical, and particle sizes may be either too big or too small for the relationship in equation [5.2] to be upheld. In addition, if the concentrations of grains in the fluid is high (>5%) then settling is no longer unhindered and settling velocities are retarded by grain–grain collisions and current counterflow.

The random instability of turbulent flow makes it virtually impossible to predict particle settling velocities and there is no completely satisfactory model for simulating this condition (Slingerland and Smith, 1986). Likewise, particle shape has an important effect on settling velocity. A tabular biotite grain, for example, will settle between 4 and 12 times slower than a quartz grain of equivalent diameter. Big grains have large coefficients of drag in a fluid and accordingly their settling velocities vary as a function, not of the square of the diameter (equation [5.2]), but of the square root (Figure 5.5). Smaller grains are, therefore, much more effectively sorted by settling than are big grains. Although the ratios of particle diameters (quartz:pyrite:gold approximately 32:2:1) reflecting hydraulic equivalence in Figure 5.5 appear to

be reasonably consistent with what one might expect in a gold-bearing conglomerate such as in the Witwatersrand Basin, the diameter of gold itself in these deposits is typically much too small to be explainable by Stokesian-type settling. For that component of Witwatersrand gold that is detrital, it is, therefore, likely that some other concentration mechanisms, such as entrainment (see below) might have applied (Frimmel and Minter, 2002).

Particle settling in nature is a difficult parameter to quantify because of the wide range of variables likely to affect it. A more realistic expression of particle settling velocity, which takes into account the frictional drag that arises from different shapes, is provided by the following expression (after Slingerland and Smith, 1986):

$$V = [4(\delta_p - \delta_f)gd/3\delta_f C_d]^{1/2} \qquad [5.3]$$

where V is the particle settling velocity; g is the acceleration due to gravity; d is the particle diameter; δ_p and δ_f are the densities of particle and fluid respectively; and C_d is the coefficient of drag and is defined as 24/Reynolds number.

Settling does play a role in the formation of placer deposits, but on its own is of little use in understanding the processes by which they form. The existence of a state of hydraulic equivalence will not explain how heavy detrital minerals are sorted or concentrated in dynamic river or beach systems. Hydraulic equivalence describes a condition of equal settling velocities and accounts for unsorted accumulation of heavy minerals in coarser grained sediment (conglomerate). By contrast, if settling velocities are not equal and settling occurs in a system that is flowing (i.e. a river), then heavy minerals will be segregated laterally downstream as a function of size and density (see section on transport sorting below). In any event it is the movement or flow of the fluid medium that has the dominant role to play in placer formation.

Entrainment

Entrainment sorting refers to the ability of a fluid in contact with bed load particles to dislocate certain grains from that bed and move them further downstream. As with settling, a considerable amount of effort has been spent by fluid dynamicists to quantify the criteria for entrainment in terms of variables such as the hydraulic/flow conditions, particle size, shape and density. In the channel cross section shown in Figure 5.2b, the concept of a fluid force (referred to as τ_o, the boundary shear stress) acting on the bed load is demonstrated. It is clear that τ_o must exceed the forces that keep any given particle in place (i.e. size, mass, shape, friction) before the particle can start to move. The critical shear stress required to initiate movement of any given particle is known as the Shields entrainment function, or simply the Shields parameter (θ), a detailed description and derivation of which is provided in Slingerland and Smith (1986). The Shields parameter is expressed as:

$$\theta = \tau_c / [(\delta_p - \delta_f)gd] \qquad [5.4]$$

where θ is the dimensionless Shields parameter; g is the acceleration due to gravity; d is the particle diameter; δ_p and δ_f are the densities of particle and fluid respectively; and τ_c is the critical boundary shear stress.

In relatively simple situations the Shields criterion can be shown to simulate the movement of

bed load particles in a channel reasonably well, and Figure 5.6a illustrates the critical conditions that differentiate between entrainment of a particle into the channel and non-movement of the grain. For a uniform bed load, particle size is the dominant control and sand, for example, will have a lower entrainment threshold than gravel. Again, however, a uniform bed load seldom applies and there are many factors which complicate entrainment sorting. The bed load roughness, or, put another way, the extent to which a particle sits proud of the bed, will clearly have an effect on the entrainment threshold. In Figure 5.6a this variable is illustrated and quantified by the ratio p/D. An increase in this value equates with grains which jut out and this can be seen to have the logical effect of decreasing the entrainment threshold. Other factors which complicate entrainment sorting include the clast shape (sphericity tends to make entrainment easier), bed consolidation, and the range of grain sizes in any given bed load. The latter point is particularly important in the situation where sediment is made up of a bimodal assemblage of large and small grains. In this case small grains, even if they are relatively light, will not be entrained because they rapidly become entrapped within the much larger particles and are no longer available for entrainment.

The effects of entrainment on sorting and placer accumulation are shown in Figure 5.6b. In this diagram (similar to the Shields diagram but where θ is replaced by τ_c and Re* is replaced by grain diameter) the critical boundary shear stress for entrainment increases as a function of grain density. This indicates that, for a uniformly sized bed and with all other factors being equal, lighter particles will be effectively entrained at lower shear stresses and, therefore, winnowed away, leaving a residual concentration of heavier particles. It is, therefore, quite feasible to entrain quartz from the bed load of a stream and leave behind a residual accumulation of heavy minerals that could be preserved as a placer deposit. Thin laminae of heavy minerals in a fluvial setting, or along cross-bed foresets, are likely to be the result of this type of sorting process. Entrainment processes also apply to wind-blown sedimentation and sorting, but the magnitude of the critical

(a)

(b)

Figure 5.6 (a) Shields diagram showing the threshold conditions between entrainment and non-movement of a grain for a bed load of uniform size in terms of the Shields parameter (defined in equation [5.6]) and the grain Reynolds number (Re* or the Reynolds number as it pertains to a single particle). The effects of increasing the protrusion of a particle above the bed floor (i.e. increasing the ratio p/D) will have the effect of shifting the entrainment threshold: the higher a particle protrudes above the bed, the easier it will be to entrain. (b) Diagram showing the effects of grain density (δ) on the critical boundary shear stress (τ_c). Greater shear stresses are required to entrain denser particles. Details after Slingerland and Smith (1986) and Reid and Frostick (1994).

thresholds will be quite different because of the quite different mechanical conditions that pertain to the aeolian environment.

Shear sorting

Shear sorting of grains is a process that only applies to the concentrated flow of suspended particles in a fluidized bed. During the movement of suspended particles in a dense granular dispersion, grain collisions create a net force that is perpendicular to the plane of shearing and

disperses the granules toward the free surface (i.e. upwards). Counter-intuitively, the dispersive pressure is greater on large and dense grains within the same horizon of flow so that these grains migrate upwards relative to smaller and lighter particles. The same effect can be rationalized in terms of a concept known as kinetic sieving, where smaller grains simply fall between larger ones (Slingerland, 1984).

The effects of shear sorting have been quantified for sediment populations of mixed sizes and densities by Sallenger (1979), who showed that

Figure 5.7 Quartz grain size and magnetite concentrations in a shear sorted granular dispersion comprising quartz and magnetite in the proportion 90:10. The relative depth of the granular bed is on the ordinate; original magnetite concentration (10%) is shown as the vertical dashed line (after Slingerland, 1984).

two grains of different densities (δ) coming to rest in the same horizon would have relative sizes (d) given by:

$$d_h = d_l(\delta_l/\delta_h)^{1/2} \qquad [5.5]$$

where d_h and d_l are the diameters of heavy and light fractions and δ_h and δ_l are the densities of heavy and light particles respectively.

An illustration of shear sorting in a concentrated granular dispersion comprising quartz and magnetite, in the proportion 90:10, is shown in Figure 5.7. The horizon at a relative height of between 0.75 and 0.5 units from the surface is seen to contain magnetite concentrations up to double the initial concentration. The mechanism is, therefore, one of the few processes that will explain heavy mineral concentrations in an elevated horizon of the sediment strata and could also explain inversely graded particle concentrations. Shear sorting can apply only to concentrated suspended particle loads such as beach swash zones and wind-related dune formation. The process could be applicable to the concentration of Ti–Zr–Th black sand placers in these environments.

Transport sorting

Transport sorting is by far the most important sorting process and the one most applicable to the broadest range of environments in which placer deposits form. The quantification of transport sorting is a complex process, but conceptually it refers simply to the differential transport rates that exist during movement of particles in a flowing fluid medium. It is complex because it incorporates two distinct components, namely the varying rates of movement of grains both in the bed load (determined by entrainment), and in suspension (determined by settling).

The previous discussion of settling considered the concept only in terms of unhindered, non-turbulent flow and it was emphasized that it had limited use in understanding the dynamics of placer-forming processes. The concept of suspension sorting, however, is an extension to the rather simplistic considerations of the previous section and refers to the fractionation of grains with different settling velocities into different levels above the bed in a turbulent channel flow system. Subsequent to its deposition downstream, sediment sorted in this fashion can result in substantial heavy mineral enrichments. It is discussed here, rather than earlier, because it is one of the two components that contribute to the determination of transport sorting.

The concentrations of heavy (h) and light (l) particles that coexist at any point in the channel flow system can be quantified in terms of an equation derived in Slingerland (1984):

$$(C/C_a)_h = (C/C_a)_l^{V_h/V_l} \qquad [5.6]$$

where C is the concentration at a given level in the channel flow; C_a is a reference concentration; and V_h and V_l are the settling velocities of heavy and light particles respectively.

The above equation predicts that particles in a turbulent flowing channel will be sorted vertically according to their settling velocities which, in turn according to Stokes' Law, are determined by their relative sizes and densities. The concept is pertinent to transport sorting because the effects of suspension sorting are only relevant downstream once deposition of a particular sediment horizon, with its possible enrichment of a hydraulically equivalent mineral, has taken place. Note that the results of suspension sorting are contrary to those obtained by shear sorting in a concentrated fluidized bed.

The other component of transport sorting applies to the movement of bed load and is discussed previously in the section on entrainment. The entrainment threshold of a particle sitting on the bed is determined by the Shields parameter (equation [5.4]) but is also strongly influenced by bed roughness. Consequently sediment transport rates would be expected to decrease as bed roughness increases. Slingerland (1984) has computer modeled transport sorting processes using an initial sediment comprising quartz and magnetite, in the proportion 90:10, and mean grain diameters of about 0.4 and 0.2 mm respectively. The results confirm that for a given shear velocity (another measure of the boundary shear stress, as shown in Figure 5.2b) all sizes of quartz and magnetite exhibit a decrease in transport rate as bed roughness increases. In addition, and as shown in Figure 5.8a, the proportion of magnetite in the moving sediment load increases as a direct function of shear velocity for a given bed roughness (trend a–a′) but decreases as a function of roughness for a given shear velocity (trend b–b′).

The effects of transport sorting have also been demonstrated experimentally in a flume, where sediment transport is simulated using simplified, scaled down parameters. Figure 5.8b shows that a positive relationship exists between transport velocity and shear velocity for any particle size and bed roughness. However, for any measure of bed roughness (K) larger grains move faster than smaller ones, a feature that is explained by the fact that smaller grains progress less easily over a rough bed because of trapping and shielding. Thus, for any given shear velocity and bed rough-

ness, the largest grains have the fastest transport rates (trend c–c′–c″ in Figure 5.8b). Conversely, the slowest transport rates for a given shear velocity are a feature of the smallest particles (i.e. 0.21 mm in this particular experiment) moving over the roughest bed (K = 0.78 in Figure 5.8b). Clearly, transport sorting is a complex process which can have quite different outcomes from one part of a channel flow system to another. A bed of sediment that is being deposited at any given moment may undergo enrichment in heavy minerals if the combination of shear velocity and the sizes of heavy and light particles relative to bed roughness mitigate against entrainment, thereby resulting in the formation of a lag deposit. If, on the other hand, the same particles are subsequently entrained into the sediment load under a different flow regime, they might then be subjected to suspension sorting which would result in heavy mineral enrichment at a completely different downstream location.

5.2.3 Application of sorting principles to placer deposits

Enrichment of heavy minerals by grain-sorting mechanisms occurs on all scales in nature, from single grain laminae on cross-bed foresets, to large regional scale concentrations that have accumulated in a particular sedimentary environment such as an alluvial fan or beach system. It is tempting to suggest that small scale systems might be more easily explained in terms of only one of the mechanisms discussed above, and that regional systems were more complex, involving several mechanisms acting in concert. This rationale does not hold, however, and even small scale systems can be a product of complex interactions; the following examples demonstrate the application of sorting mechanisms to different scales of deposition.

Small scale

As an example of heavy mineral concentration at a small scale, the mechanisms of grain sorting in and around a dune or ripple migrating along the bed of a stream are shown in Figure 5.9a. The dune

(a)

(b)

Figure 5.8 (a) Computer simulation showing the effects of transport sorting in terms of bed roughness (measured by the height of clasts protruding from the bed in millimeters) and shear velocity U^*. The plot shows the approximate limit for transport of magnetite and the magnetite concentrations (%) in the sediment load. Maximum enrichment of magnetite on the bed (i.e. the formation of a lag deposit) would occur above this limit under conditions of low shear velocity and high bed roughness (after Slingerland, 1984). (b) Results of a flume experiment showing the effects on grain transport velocities (V_g) of shear velocity (U^*), bed roughness, and grain diameter (after Meland and Norman, 1966).

crest is characterized by high shear velocities and non-turbulent flow which increases the Shields factor and promotes entrainment of larger, lighter grains and residual concentration of the heavier particles. The dune foreset, on the other hand, is likely to receive heavy mineral concentrations by shear sorting of high concentration grain avalanches down the slope of the advancing dune. The trough or scour forming ahead of the dune is likely to receive heavy grain concentrations by settling sorting in a locally turbulent microenvironment. It is, therefore, evident that several

(a) Small scale

0   20
cm

Stream flow

c | Settling sorting
(settling sorting of
suspended particles
in turbulent zone)

a

Bed

a | Entrainment sorting
(high shear velocity
and laminar flow)

b

c | b | Shear sorting (concentrated
granular avalanches down
slope)

(b) Intermediate scale

A

Channel   meander

Divergent
flow

Point   bar

0   30
meters

A'

Convergent
flow

A   A'

Older
alluvium

(c) Large scale

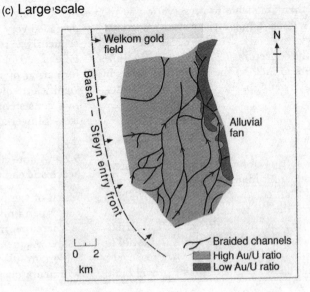

Welkom gold
field

N

Basal – Steyn entry front

Alluvial
fan

0   2
km

Braided channels
High Au/U ratio
Low Au/U ratio

Figure 5.9 Heavy mineral sorting processes at various scales and in different sedimentary environments: (a) at a small scale along laminae associated with dunes and ripples forming along a stream bed (after Slingerland, 1984); (b) at an intermediate scale in an aggrading point bar forming along the convex bank of a meander channel (after Smith and Beukes, 1983); and (c) at a large scale on a large braided, alluvial fan complex such as the Welkom goldfield, Witwatersrand Basin (after Minter, 1978).

sorting mechanisms apply even to the small scale heavy mineral concentrations that one often sees in and around dune and ripple features in river- or beach-related sediments.

Intermediate scale

An example of heavy mineral concentration at an intermediate scale is provided by the development of point bars along the convex bank of a meandering river channel. Such sites are well known to miners dredging river channels for accumulations of minerals such as cassiterite or gold. Meandering river channels are also prime targets during the exploitation of placer diamonds along the Orange River in southern Africa (see Box 5.1). Figure 5.9b shows the geometry and flow patterns associated with the aggradation of a point bar in a meander channel and its migration toward the opposite concave bank, which is being subjected to erosion. Heavy mineral concentrations actually form in degraded scours along the bottom of the channel itself. Both components of transport sorting seem to contribute to the enrichment process, namely settling of grains in the highly turbulent environment formed by convergence of disparate flow orientations, and entrainment, since shear stresses are above the thresholds for most of the bed load. Transport sorting, therefore, results in placer accumulations which are then amenable to preservation as the point bar sediment migrates over the accumulated heavy minerals. This process has been applied to the concentration of gold and uraninite in point bars formed on the fluvial fan deltas of the Witwatersrand basin (Smith and Minter, 1980).

Large scale

Large scale sorting of heavy minerals over areas of tens of square kilometers has been described from deltaic fan conglomerates of the Welkom goldfield in the Witwatersrand basin, South Africa. Figure 5.9c shows the relative distributions of gold and uraninite (as the Au/U ratio) in the composite Basal–Steyn placer with respect to the sediment entry point and major fluvial braid

channels on the fan delta complex. Close to the entry point channel fill and longitudinal bars comprise coarse pebble conglomerate, with maximum clast sizes in the range 20–40 mm in diameter. By contrast, the contained gold particles are much finer and range between about 0.5 and 0.005 mm in size, although accurate size distribution patterns are not known. Several kilometers downstream the fan delta is built of less deeply channeled quartz–arenite. The Au/U ratio decreases downstream and this is a function of both a decrease in gold and an increase in uraninite down the paleoslope (Minter, 1978). This has been interpreted to reflect transport sorting which results in net deposition of gold in more proximal locations of the fan, with the less dense uraninite being more effectively concentrated in distal parts. Transport sorting ensures that clast sizes (and also, therefore, bed roughness), as well as shear velocity, decrease exponentially down slope. Uraninite is significantly larger, and also lighter, than gold and will exhibit higher grain transport velocities, and, therefore, be carried a greater distance down slope. In addition, gold will be transported less easily over the proximal, high bed roughness portions of the fan delta complex and will, therefore, be trapped more effectively in these areas compared to uraninite. Many of the laterally extensive Witwatersrand placers represent regional, low dip angle, unconformity surfaces where the fan delta complexes are being degraded very slowly and the fluid regime is consequently very consistent over large areas. This type of setting represents an excellent site for the formation of very large placer deposits because significant volumes of sediment can be subjected to a consistent set of transport sorting mechanisms (Slingerland and Smith, 1986).

5.2.4 A note concerning sediment sorting in beach and eolian environments

Much of the previous discussion applies to processes pertaining to unidirectional water flow and is, therefore, mainly relevant to fluvial environments. As mentioned previously, however, many important placer deposits are associated with sediments deposited in shoreline environments

BOX 5.1 Placer processes: the alluvial diamond deposits of the Orange River, southern Africa

Diamond is the hardest known natural substance. High quality (i.e. based on clarity, colour and a lack of flaws) diamonds are used for jewelry, whereas flawed and poorly crystalline stones are used as abrasives in a wide range of cutting tools. The specific gravity (3.5) and hardness of diamond ensure that it is concentrated together with other heavy minerals in both fluvial and marine placer deposits. Over much of recorded history India was the only country to produce diamonds from alluvial sources, but in the 1860s diamonds were discovered in South Africa, specifically in gravels of the Orange River and its tributaries.

This led to the discovery of the primary kimberlitic source of diamonds around the town of Kimberley, and then in 1908 of the huge beach placers along the west coast of southern Africa.

The alluvial and beach diamond placers of South Africa and Namibia are the product of deep erosion of kimberlites on the Kalahari Craton in Cenozoic times. The erosion of diamondiferous kimberlite liberated the diamonds onto the land surface for subsequent redistribution into the very sizable catchment of the Orange River drainage system and its precursors. This drainage

Figure 1 Map showing the Orange River drainage system in relation to the distribution of deeply eroded kimberlites on the Kalahari Craton. The distribution of alluvial diamond deposits along major river channels and paleo-channels, as well as the beach placers along the west coast of southern Africa, are also shown (after Lynn *et al.*, 1998).

Figure 2 Map showing the distribution of gravel terraces in the vicinity of the Bloeddrift diamond mine along the lower reaches of the Orange River (after Van Wyk and Pienaar, 1986).

flows westwards and exits into the southern Atlantic at Alexander Bay–Oranjemund at the South Africa–Namibia border. Diamonds are trapped in gravel terraces that represent preserved sections of river sediment, abandoned by the present river as it migrates laterally or incises downwards (Lynn *et al.*, 1998). Diamonds are also washed out into the ocean and redistributed by long-shore currents to be concentrated in gravels either beneath the wave base, or in remnant beaches reflecting previous fluctuations of sea level.

In the upper reaches of the Orange River system (which includes the Vaal River) diamonds are preferentially concentrated in areas where the rivers flow over resistant bedrock, such as the Ventersdorp lavas, where good gully and pothole trap sites can form. Diamonds are concentrated as residual lag deposits in such traps. Concentration is enhanced by the extreme hardness of diamond as other less resistant minerals undergo attrition and are more easily washed out of irregularities in the bedrock (Lynn *et al.*, 1998). In the lower, more mature reaches of the Orange River, a number of gravel terraces occur. These contain large, low grade accumulations of diamonds and were deposited in lower Miocene to upper Pleistocene times, occuring at different elevations relative to the present day channel (Van Wyk and Pienaar, 1986). As many as five terraces can be identified, each characterized by diagnostic fossil faunal and floral assemblages.

Diamonds derived from gravels of the lower reaches of the Orange River are 97% gem quality since it is the unflawed diamonds that typically resist the rigors of mechanical transport and abrasion. Most of the diamonds are between 0.85 and 1.30 carats in size, but occasionally very large stones (60–100 carats) are also recovered.

The single most important feature in the concentration of diamonds in the terrace gravels is bedrock irregularity. The development of large potholes, plunge pools, and bedrock ribbing are all features that impinge on grade distribution in the gravels. The lowermost sections of the gravel profile are typically the highest grade. Bedrock

depressions can be extremely productive, with grades of over 40 carats per 100 tons of ore being reported (Van Wyk and Pienaar, 1986). Large terraces are generally higher grade and contain bigger stones in their upstream portions, attesting to efficient trapping and sorting mechanisms prior to preservation.

Figure 3 Diamondiferous gravels related to the paleo-Orange River system, deposited unconformably on irregular, potholed bedrock (foreground).

where sediment sorting is largely controlled by the dynamics of waves and by tidal fluctuations. It is also possible in such environments that sorting processes could be influenced by wind action and that the latter might interact with water-borne sediment dispersal patterns. In fact, heavy mineral concentrations in some of the enormous beach-related "black sand" (Ti–Zr) placer deposits of the world, such as Richard's Bay in South Africa, are a likely product of both beach- and wind-related sorting processes. This section briefly considers the physical processes involved in such environments and emphasizes some of the differences that exist compared to the fluvial system.

Beaches

The sorting of sediment in beach environments occurs at a number of scales, ranging from long-shore and orthogonal processes (related to mass transport parallel and at right angles to the shore line) to swash zone-related features attributed to

the "to and fro" motion of waves breaking on the shore. A detailed overview of these various processes is presented in Hardisty (1994) and Allen (1997). Beach-related placer deposits appear to be mainly related to processes occurring in the swash zone and it is on this environment that the present discussion will focus.

The origin and nature of ocean waves is a quantifiable topic of study and the effects of wave action on sediment bed forms are well understood. Beaches represent the interplay between sediment supply, wave energy, and shoreline gradient. Sediment transfer on beaches is influenced largely by tides and currents, whereas sediment sorting is dominated by waves and swash processes. Figure 5.10a illustrates the spectrum of wave-dominated shoreline types, emphasizing the differences between a low energy, shallow gradient beach comprising mud and silt, and a steep, highly energetic environment in which gravel beaches are deposited. An intermediate situation reflects the setting in which sand-dominated beaches are likely to form.

(a)

(b)

Figure 5.10 (a) Factors controlling the nature of wave dominated beaches and shorelines (after Reading and Collinson, 1996). (b) Mathematical model illustrating the dynamics of the swash zone created for a 0.5 m high breaker at the shoreline (after Hughes *et al.*, 2000).

Although the type of beach forming is important to whether a placer deposit is likely to develop, environmental considerations alone are unlikely to explain the dominant processes in beach placer formation. It is apparent from the limited amount of research that has been carried out in this field that factors such as source fertility and swash processes are a more important consideration (Komar and Wang, 1984; Komar, 1989; Hughes *et al.*, 2000). Source fertility is self-evident and dictates whether a placer deposit is likely to contain ilmenite–zircon or diamond concentrations, or none at all. By contrast, the flow dynamics of a swash zone are more difficult to evaluate. The application of these processes to the concentration of heavy minerals on a beach has been studied by Hughes *et al.* (2000). An illustration of modeled swash dynamics is presented in Figure 5.10b and shows that motion of the swash front is symmetric about the surge and backwash, but the water velocity is asymmetric because local flow reversal occurs before the front has reached its final landward advance. The dynamics of the swash zone have been used to evaluate mineral-sorting mechanisms in the beach placers of southeast Australia and show that neither settling nor entrainment is likely to be important in the concentration of heavy minerals. Settling is discounted because swash zones are typically not deep enough to allow effective settling of heavy minerals to occur. Entrainment, likewise, was ineffective as a sorting mechanism because the large bed shear stresses prevailing imply that most, if not all, the minerals would be in motion with little or no prospect of selective entrainment (Hughes *et al.*, 2000). The dominant process appears rather to have been shear sorting, where the dispersive (upward) pressures acting on large, dense grains moving in a concentrated sheet flow were larger than those applicable to smaller, less dense grains. In a study of the heavy mineral placers of the Oregon, USA, coastline, Komar and Wang (1984) were also able to discount grain settling as a sorting mechanism because the settling velocities of light and heavy mineral fractions were found to be similar. In contrast to the Australian situation, this study found that selective grain entrainment was likely to have been the

Figure 5.11 (a) Plot showing the changes in heavy mineral contents along a profile of beach sediment in Oregon as a function of distance offshore. (b) Plot of concentration factors of the principal minerals in an Oregon beach placer deposit as a function of calculated threshold stress, illustrating the likelihood of selective entrainment processes during the formation of the deposit (after Komar and Wang, 1984).

most efficient concentration process and the one that also accounted for lateral variations observed in the distribution of heavy minerals. Figure 5.11a shows the variable distribution of heavy minerals as a function of distance offshore, a local characteristic that demands a sorting process capable of laterally sorting the mineral components. Figure 5.11b illustrates the calculated threshold stresses for the various minerals examined in the Oregon beach placers as a function of the measured concentration factors and shows that the densest and smallest grains were the most effectively concentrated. This may be due largely to the fact that these grains were the most difficult to entrain and, consequently, were residually concentrated in the near shore environment. The fact that entrainment sorting seems to apply to the Oregon placers, but not those formed along the Australian coastline, is possibly a function of the higher wave energy in the latter area and the development of conditions favoring shear sorting over entrainment (Hughes *et al.*, 2000). Although the mechanics of the sorting processes are similar, the detailed patterns of heavy mineral distribution on beaches may be quite different to those in fluvial systems where transport sorting is the dominant process.

Wind-borne sediment transport

As illustrated in Figure 5.3, the transport of sediment by wind, although similar in principle to that by water, differs in detail because of the much lower viscosity and density of air and the generally higher kinetic energies of eolian transport. Grains transported by wind are subjected to different entrainment criteria than those moved subaqueously, and are also subjected to more dramatic ballistic effects due to their energetic motion. In equation [5.4], the critical shear stress required to initiate entrainment of a given particle is seen to vary linearly as a function of its density and size. Bagnold (1941) showed that for eolian sediment transport the critical shear stress required to initiate entrainment varied as a function of the square root of density and size. This implies that it is easier to move small particles by wind than it is to move them by water, which explains the abundance of widespread, coarse grained lag deposits in desert and beach environments. Such deposits form by the deflation of a surface initially comprising multiple sized particles, by winnowing away the fine grained material and leaving behind the gravel residue. Wind-related sediment transport characteristics

Figure 5.12 Wind blown (eolian) sediment transport characteristics as a function of shear velocity and grain size (after Tsoar and Pye, 1987).

are shown in Figure 5.12 and can be compared with the Hjulström diagram of Figure 5.4 which pertains to subaqueous sediment transport.

The extent to which beach-related placer deposits are modified by wind-blown sediment dispersal is a question that has not received much attention, despite the fact that such interactions are almost certain to have taken place (Chan and Kocurek, 1988). At the Richard's Bay deposits, for example, a substantial proportion of the Ti–Zr heavy minerals are extracted from eolian dunes even though much of the original concentration took place in the swash zone of the adjacent beaches.

5.2.5 Numerical simulation of placer processes

Sophisticated computer simulations of complex natural placer processes have now been developed with a view to improving the prediction of heavy mineral distribution patterns in placer deposits. An example is the MIDAS (Model Investigating Density And Size sorting) program that predicts the transport and sorting of heterogeneous size–density graded sediment under natural conditions (Van Niekerk *et al.*, 1992; Vogel *et al.*, 1992). It has been applied to the problem of grade control in the Witwatersrand basin and can predict gold distribution patterns in the host conglomerates with remarkable accuracy (Nami and James, 1987).

The conglomerates that host concentrations of detrital gold in the Witwatersrand basin were deposited in braided alluvial fan systems, the

main elements of which comprise channel and overbank flow deposits. The geometry of this environment is shown in Figure 5.13a, which illustrates that fluid flow can be resolved into two components, a higher velocity flow contained within the channel, and a lower velocity flow in the overbank plain that is transverse to that in the channel. Hydrodynamic considerations suggest that the fine grained detrital gold particles in the Witwatersrand deposits were transported in suspension as the prevailing hydraulic conditions exceeded those required to entrain and suspend gold in the channel. The model considers the distribution of gold, therefore, in terms of an interaction between flow in the channel where gold is being entrained, and flow on the overbank plain where suspended particles will tend to settle because of reduced transport capacity. The MIDAS program integrates the effects of flow velocity, sediment concentration, and the various parameters of transport sorting for both the longitudinal flow in the channel and the transverse flow in the overbank plain. The results of computer simulations are compared to actual gold grade distributions in two examples from the Carbon Leader Reef (Figure 5.13b) and exhibit a remarkable degree of correlation, even when the bed morphology is complex. The fact that the highest gold grades are often found along the edges of channels has long been known, but has lacked a feasible explanation. The simulation suggests that the highest gold grades coincide with zones of flow interaction and that gold

(a)

(b)

Figure 5.13 (a) Geometry and flow characteristics of a braided fan delta complex used to simulate gold distribution patterns in Witwatersrand placer deposits. (b) Comparisons of computer simulations and actual gold distribution patterns in two different profiles across the Carbon leader reef. Channel edge gold concentrations are reasonably well modeled in terms of transport sorting (after Nami and James, 1987).

distribution patterns in the Witwatersrand deposits are a function, at least in part, of transport sorting. It should be emphasized, however, that this relationship exists despite the fact that it is well known that most of the presently observed gold in the basin has been remobilized and is secondary in nature. This is one of the reasons why the origin of Witwatersrand ores is still so controversial.

5.3 CHEMICAL SEDIMENTATION – BANDED IRON-FORMATIONS, PHOSPHORITES, AND EVAPORITES

In contrast to the mechanical processes of sedimentation discussed above, where clastic sediment is sorted and deposited by water and wind, chemical sedimentation refers to the precipitation of dissolved components from solution, essentially out of sea water or brine. A wide variety of rocks are formed by the compaction and lithification of chemical precipitates and these include carbonate sediments (limestone and dolomite), siliceous sediments (chert) and iron-rich sediments (ironstones and banded iron-formations), as well as less voluminous accumulations of manganese oxides, phosphates, and barite. The majority of the world's Fe, Mn, and phosphate resources, all extremely important and strategic commodities, are the products of chemical sedimentation and are hosted in chemical sediments. In addition, rocks such as limestone, comprising essentially $CaCO_3$, have great value as the primary raw material for the manufacture of cement. Furthermore, sediments known as evaporites, in which chemical precipitation is promoted by evaporation, contain the main economically viable concentrations of elements such as K, Na, Ca, Mg, Li, I, Br, and Cl, as well as compounds such as borates, nitrates, and sulfates, all of which are widely used in the chemical and agricultural industries.

Most chemical sediments form in marine or marginal marine environments. The continental shelves, together with intratidal and lagoonal settings, represent the geological settings where chemical sediments and associated deposits are generally located. The chemical processes by which ore concentrations form are complex and controlled by parameters such as oxidation–reduction and pH, as well as climate, paleolatitude, and biological–atmospheric evolution. This section will first consider the processes associated with the formation of ironstones, banded iron-formations, and bedded manganese oxide ores. This is followed by a discussion of phosphorites and also the formation of evaporites, carbonaceous "black shales," and manganese nodules.

5.3.1 Ironstones and banded iron-formations

In terms of morphology, texture and mineralogy, there are three main types of iron ores and it is instructive to consider each of these individually since they illustrate different ore-forming process. The three types, in order of increasing importance, are bog iron deposits, ironstone deposits, and banded iron-formations, the latter generally referred to by the acronym BIF.

Bog iron ores

Bog ores form principally in lakes and swamps of the glaciated tundra regions of the northern hemisphere, such as northern Canada and Scandanavia. The deposits are typically small and thin, and comprise concentrations of goethite and limonite (Fe–oxyhydroxides) associated with organic-rich shale. They formed in the recent geological past, and in some places are still doing so at present (Stanton, 1972). The principal concentration mechanism for iron in bog ores, as well as other iron ore deposits, is related to the fact that the metal occurs in two valence states, namely Fe^{2+} (the ferrous ion) which is generally soluble in surface waters, and Fe^{3+} (the ferric ion) which is insoluble and precipitates out of surface solutions. Concentration of iron occurs when aqueous solutions containing labile Fe^{2+}, in a relatively reduced environment, are oxidized, with the subsequent formation and precipitation of Fe^{3+}. Figure 5.14 illustrates the principle with respect to bog iron ores accumulating at the interface between oxygenated surface waters flowing along an aquifer and the reduced iron-rich solutions percolating downwards through a swamp.

Figure 5.14 The development of limonitic concentrations in the formation of a bog iron ore where a reduced solution transporting ferrous iron interacts with oxidized groundwater flowing along an aquifer (after Stanton, 1972).

At this interface ferrous iron in solution is oxidized to ferric iron which precipitates as limonite or goethite.

Ironstone deposits

Ironstones are typically Phanerozoic in age and are widespread in occurrence, representing an important source of iron in the eastern USA and western Europe, particularly in the early part of the twentieth century. Ironstone deposits are commonly referred to as minette or Lorraine-type iron ores, well known occurrences of which were found in the Jurassic sediments of England and the Alsace-Lorraine region of France and Germany. In North America the Silurian Clinton type iron ores of Kentucky and Alabama are analogues of the younger European deposits. Ironstones form in shallow marine and deltaic environments and typically consist of goethite and hematite that has been rolled into oolites or pellets, suggesting the action of mechanical abrasion. The deposits contain little or no chert, but are commonly associated with Fe-rich silicate minerals such as glauconite and chamosite. The environment of deposition suggests that the iron was introduced from a continental source via a fluvial system in which the metal was either in solution as Fe^{2+} or transported as a colloid (see Chapter 3). Ironstones are often linked stratigraphically to organic-rich black shales and, in

certain cases, seem to develop in strata representing periods of major marine transgression and continental margin flooding. They do not occur randomly in time and show distinct peaks in the Ordovician–Silurian and again in the Jurassic periods. Their formation appears, therefore, to be related to a pattern of global tectonic cyclicity and specifically to times of continental dispersal and sea-level highstand (see Chapter 6), as well as periods of warmer climate and increased rates of chemical sedimentation (Van Houten and Authur, 1989).

The origin of ironstones is complex and controversial and needs to account for both the Fe concentration processes and the formation of the ubiquitous oolites that typify these ores (Young and Taylor, 1989). A model for the formation of minette-type ironstones, after Siehl and Thein (1989), is presented in Figure 5.15. Iron is thought to have been concentrated initially on continents that were being subjected to deep weathering and erosion in a warm, humid climatic regime. Highly oxidized lateritic soils forming in such an environment would have been the sites of iron enrichment as insoluble Fe^{3+} remained *in situ* while other components of the regolith were leached away (see Chapter 4). In addition, laterites were also the sites where iron ooids formed in response to low temperature chemical and biogenically mediated processes. The lateritic soils and ooids were then transferred into a shallow marine

Figure 5.15 Simplified environmental model for the formation of oolitic ironstone ores. The model invokes initial Fe enrichment and pedogenic ooid formation in lateritic soils on the continental edge and transfer of this "protore" to a marginal marine setting with subsequent mechanical abrasion and reworking/concentration of ooids (after Siehl and Thein, 1989).

environment, either by flooding during transgression or by erosion during regression, to be reworked and concentrated in fluvio-deltaic or littoral settings. Note that the chemically or biogenically formed pedogenic ooids are different to those that arise from the mechanical abrasion of particles in the swash zones of shallow marine environments. Subsequent diagenesis of the ironstone accumulations resulted in further post-depositional modifications to the texture and mineralogy of the ores. Unlike the relatively simple processes invoked to explain the formation of bog ores, ironstones appear to require a combination of specific environmental conditions, as well as a variety of processes (including oxidation–reduction, diagenesis, mechanical sedimentation, and microbial activity), to form substantial deposits.

Banded iron-formations (BIFs)

The term banded iron-formation is somewhat controversial because of the connotation it has with respect to stratigraphic terminology. For this reason the term is hyphenated, and applies strictly to a bedded chemical sediment comprising alternating layers rich in iron and chert (Klein and Beukes, 1993). BIFs represent the most important global source of iron ore and far outweigh the

ironstone and bog iron ores in terms of reserves and total production. Whereas the latter occur predominantly in Phanerozoic rock sequences, BIFs are much older and formed in essentially three periods of Archean and Proterozoic Earth history, namely 3500–3000 Ma, 2500–2000 Ma, and 1000–500 Ma (Figure 5.16). These three classes equate broadly with different tectonic settings and are referred to as, respectively, Algoma, Lake Superior, and Rapitan types. Algoma type BIFs are associated with volcanic arcs and are typically found in Archean greenstone belts. These deposits tend to be fairly small but they are mined in places such as the Abitibi greenstone belt of Ontario, Canada. The majority of Lake Superior, or simply Superior, type BIFs are located on stable continental platforms and were mainly deposited in Paleoproterozoic times. They represent by far the most important category of iron ore deposits (Figure 5.16) and most of the major currently producing iron ore districts of the world fall into this category. Examples include the Hamersley Basin of Western Australia (see Box 5.2), the Transvaal Basin of South Africa, the "Quadrilatero Ferrifero" of Brazil, the Labrador trough of Canada, the Krivoy Rog–Kursk deposits of the Ukraine, the Singhbhum region of India, and the type area in the Lake Superior region of the USA. Finally, the Rapitan type iron ores represent a rather unusual

Figure 5.16 Tectonic and environmental model showing the depositional settings for Algoma, Superior, and Rapitan type BIFs (after Clemmey, 1985; Maynard, 1991). The inset histogram illustrates the approximate tonnages of BIF resource for each of the three major types as a function of time (after Holland, 1984).

occurrence of iron ores associated with glaciogenic sediments formed during the major Neoproterozoic ice ages. The type occurrence is the Rapitan Group in the McKenzie Mountains of northwest Canada.

In addition to the above tectonic classification, BIFs have also been categorized in terms of the mineralogy of the associated iron phases. Although in most BIFs the iron mineral is an oxide phase (hematite or magnetite), carbonate (siderite), silicate (greenalite and minnesotaite), and sulfide (pyrite) iron minerals also occur, together with chert or carbonaceous shale. This observation led James (1954) to suggest a facies concept for BIF formation whereby the progression from oxide through carbonate to sulfide

phases was considered to reflect precipitation of the relevant iron minerals in successively more reducing environments (iron silicate phases are stable over a wide range of Eh and do not, therefore, conform to this simple progression). A consideration of the stability of the main iron phases as a function of Eh and pH confirms that the redox state of the depositional environment plays an important role in determining the mineralogy of BIFs, although the situation is undoubtedly more complex than the facies concept would suggest. Figure 5.17a shows that ferrous iron is stable in solutions that are acidic and reducing, but that for a given pH, oxidation (or an increase in the Eh) will stabilize hematite (Fe_2O_3 or ferric oxide), which is the principal iron phase over a wide

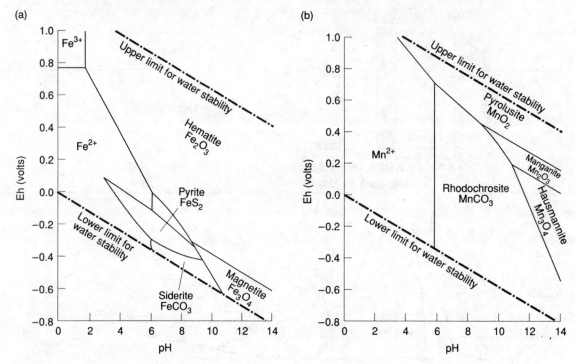

Figure 5.17 (a) Eh–pH diagram showing the stabilities of common iron minerals. The conditions that apply to this particular phase diagram are: T = 25 °C, P_{total} = 1 bar, molarities of Fe, S, and CO_3 are, respectively, 10^{-6}, 10^{-6}, and 1. (b) Eh–pH diagram showing the stabilities of common manganese minerals. Identical conditions apply, but with the molarity of Mn = 10^{-6} (diagrams modified after Garrels and Christ, 1965; Krauskopf and Bird, 1995). Note that the manganese oxides (MnO_2 and Mn_2O_3) are stable at higher Eh than the equivalent ferric oxide (hematite), and would only form, therefore, under more oxidizing conditions.

range of geologically pertinent conditions. Siderite and pyrite are only stable under reducing conditions although these fields would obviously expand if the activities of total carbonate or sulphur in solution were increased. Similarly, the phase diagram indicates that magnetite is only stable under reducing and alkaline conditions, but this field expands well into the range of neutral pH if the activities of carbonate and sulphur are lower than the prevailing conditions for this diagram.

Banded iron-formations are chemical sediments in which the major components, Fe and Si, appear to have been derived from the ocean itself, rather than from a continental source, as in the case for ironstones. This is evident from the lack of aluminous and silicate mineral particulate matter in

BIFs. Models for the formation of these rocks are controversial and hampered by a lack of modern analogues. Features which need to be explained include the origin of the Fe and Si, their transport and precipitation mechanisms, the cause of the delicate silica- and iron-rich banding at various scales, and their formation during certain time periods, in particular between around 2500 and 2000 Ma.

The source of iron is dominantly from the ocean itself, through either direct introduction of Fe^{2+} from hydrothermal exhalations (black smokers; see Chapter 3) on the sea floor or dissolution of oceanic crust. Rare earth element patterns of BIFs suggest that hydrothermal venting and volcanic activity are likely to have contributed significantly to the source of Fe^{2+} in Algoma

Figure 5.18 Model invoking upwelling and oxidation of ferrous iron from an oceanic source to explain the depositional environment for BIFs. Oxidation of ferrous iron and precipitation of ferric iron compounds occurs at a diffuse redox interface formed by the production of oxygen in the upper water levels, either by photosynthesizing organisms or by ultraviolet radiation induced photo-oxidation, or both. The lateral zonation of BIF facies (i.e. siderite–magnetite–hematite) shown here differs from the simple scheme envisaged by James (1954). Diagram modified after Klein and Beukes (1993).

type BIFs, but that this influence diminished with time such that Rapitan ores reflect a direct ocean water character (Misra, 2000). However, the enormous volumes of iron required to form the Lake Superior type BIFs, given that they appear to be spatially unrelated to volcanic or exhalative sea-floor activity, remains something of a problem. The oceans themselves are likely to represent an adequate source of Si since the solubility of amorphous silica (as $Si(OH)_4$) is relatively high (about 120 mg l^{-1}). It seems likely that the Archean–Paleoproterozoic oceans would have been saturated with respect to silica, ensuring a steady precipitation and accumulation of siliceous matter on the ocean floor during this early stage of Earth history. This pattern is likely to have changed in later geological times when the organisms that use silica to build an exoskeleton (i.e. siliceous protozoans such as radiolaria) evolved and the element was extracted from the water column. The modern oceans, for example, typically contain <10 mg l^{-1} dissolved silica and are markedly undersaturated (MacKenzie, 1975). The decrease of available Si in the oceans as a function of biological evolution contributes to an explana-

tion for the changing character of iron ores, from BIFs to ironstones, with time.

The transport and precipitation mechanisms involved in BIF genesis have traditionally been explained in terms of the Fe^{2+} upwelling model, analogous to the observations of phosphorus upwelling onto the continental shelves (see section 5.3.3 below). Figure 5.18 illustrates the main elements of the model, after Klein and Beukes (1993). Ferrous iron from deep, reduced ocean levels is introduced to shallower shelf environments by upwelling currents similiar to those seen along the western coastlines of continents such as Africa and the Americas today. These currents interact with the shallower waters and Fe^{2+} is oxidized, with subsequent hydrolysis and precipitation of ferric hydroxide ($Fe(OH)_3$). In marine environments where CO_3 activities are sufficiently high, $FeCO_3$ would precipitate. Oxidation takes place at shallow water levels where sunlight can penetrate and is due either to production of oxygen by photosynthesizing organisms living in the photic zone, or to photons of ultraviolet and blue light, which induce photo-oxidation of ferrous to ferric ions (Cairns-Smith,

1978). Precipitation of silica is problematical, but it has been suggested that evaporation from the ocean surface could promote local silica oversaturation and thereby promote precipitation as a gel which, on compaction, is transformed to chert. The explanation of banding in BIFs remains a problem and suggestions range from diurnal cycles (where photosynthesis and photo-oxidation shut down at night) for very thin lamellae, to seasonal cycles (where summer seasons promote biological activity and enhance iron precipitation) for mesobands. Other mechanisms that may have contributed to the formation of banding in BIFs include differential flocculation of Fe and Si colloids as a function of water chemistry, and some form of biological mediation. Studies of biomineralization processes (see Chapter 3) in modern day environments have shown that the filamentous bacterium *Chloroflexus* is capable of binding either silica or iron, and occasionally both silica and iron, to the cell walls (Konhauser and Ferris, 1996). This form of induced biomineralization is considered to apply to the formation of some Precambrian BIFs, a notion supported by the presence of spheroidal structures in BIFs interpreted as microfossils (LaBerge, 1973). During the late Archean and Paleoproterozoic, early marine planktonic bacteria that photosynthetically produced oxygen may have been responsible for the oxidation of ferrous iron in the ocean waters and precipitation of ferric hydroxides. At the same time oversaturation of the oceans with respect to silica would have led to continuous biologically mediated precipitation of chert, where cell walls acted as the templates for nucleation of silica (Konhauser and Ferris, 1996). In this model, the banding in iron-formations is attributed either to episodic depletion of ferrous iron or to periodic (seasonal) diminished activity of the oxygen producing planktonic bacteria.

The formation of BIFs in discrete time periods (Figure 5.16) is another feature that lacks detailed explanation, but is almost certainly related to atmospheric and biological evolution, as well as to the pattern of global tectonic cycles (see Chapter 6). The enormous Superior type BIFs formed on stable continental shelves during periods of marine transgression and sea-level highstand,

conditions which reflect tectonic cycles of continental dispersion and active, elevated mid-ocean ridges. These conditions, coupled with the relevant states of biological and ocean–atmosphere evolution, were unique to the Paleoproterozoic and help to explain the predominance of BIFs at this time. Subsequent to oxyatmoinversion (i.e. the period in the Paleoproterozoic when oxygen levels in the atmosphere increased substantially; see Chapter 6) the atmosphere and oceans became more oxidized and iron existed largely as insoluble Fe^{3+}, such that the likelihood of Lake Superior type BIFs forming diminished. Rapitan type ores, on the other hand, appear to be intimately associated with widely distributed Neoproterozoic glaciogenic sediments and the near-global glaciations that characterized this time period (i.e. the so-called "Snowball Earth" period). The large-scale covering of the oceans with an ice-cap would have isolated them from the atmosphere and reintroduced the sort of reducing conditions in much of the ocean water column that only existed prior to oxyatmoinversion. It is widely held that the development of the Rapitan type iron ores is related to this near global oceanic anoxia, which, in turn, led to enrichment of the oceans in ferrous iron. Inter- and postglacial melting of the ice-cap resulted in glaciogenic sedimentation, reoxidation of the oceans and associated precipitation of ferric iron. Such a scenario has been used, for example, to explain the formation of the Braemar BIFs and diamictic ironstones associated with Sturtian aged (circa 750 Ma) glaciogenic sediments in the Adelaide geosyncline of South Australia (Lottermoser and Ashley, 2000).

5.3.2 Bedded manganese deposits

Most of the world's sedimentary manganese deposits formed in environments similar to those in which BIF and ironstone ores also formed. Superior type BIFs are sometimes closely associated with manganese ores, the prime example being the world's largest exploited Mn deposits in the Kalahari manganese field of South Africa. In this case, enormous reserves of bedded manganese oxide ores were formed within the

BOX 5.2 Chemical sedimentation: banded iron-formations: the Mount Whaleback iron ore deposit, Hamersley Province, Western Australia

The Archean to Paleoproterozoic Hamersley Province of Western Australia contains huge volumes of Superior-type banded iron-formations (BIF) that host some of the world's largest iron deposits. Western Australia is the world's largest exporter of iron ore, the bulk of which comes from enriched BIF in the Hamersley Province. Several large mines, including Mesa J, Tom Price, Paraburdoo, and Mount Whaleback, together with smaller operations, combine to produce over 170 million tons of export quality iron ore annually, much of which goes to Japan, South Korea, and China (Kneeshaw, 2002).

The Mount Whaleback deposit is the largest single iron ore deposit in Australia, with an original ore resource of some 1.8 billion tons. The deposit is located in the southeastern portion of the Hamersley Province in an area that was episodically deformed, with the most intense folding attributed to the Ophthalmian orogeny between 2400 and 2200 Ma (Figure 1). The ore is hosted in BIF and ferruginous shales of the Dales Gorge Member of the Brockman Iron Formation. The latter unit is the middle of three major iron-formation sequences in the Hamersley Province, forming between 2540 and 2450 Ma (Barley et al., 1997). This period of Paleoproterozoic Earth history was a time when similar chemical sediments were being deposited in continental margin or platformal settings elsewhere in the world, such as South Africa, Brazil, and the USA (see section 5.3.1 of this chapter). These countries also contain large BIF-hosted iron ore deposits that are very similar to those of the Hamersley Province. The BIF host rock in all these deposits was originally a bedded chert–magnetite/hematite chemical sediment that typically contains around 25–30% Fe. In order to make an economically viable ore deposit the BIF needs to be upgraded so that the Fe content is at least double this value, a process that is achieved by either selectively leaching or replacing the silica in the rock. The processes whereby BIF is enriched to form iron ore are complex and episodic. There is considerable controversy in the literature regarding the nature of the enrichment process and both supergene and hypogene processes have been advocated.

The conventional model of ore formation at Mount Whaleback, and indeed most other deposits of the Hamersley Province, is that BIF was exposed and subjected to supergene alteration after the main period of deformation and folding of the host rock. This process involved in situ replacement of chert by goethite and oxidation of magnetite to hematite (a process called martitization). The actual processes involved are some-

what akin to those taking place during the formation of laterites (see section 4.3 in Chapter 4), although rather than simple leaching of silica and residual enrichment of iron, the chert is largely replaced by Fe-oxyhydroxides. After supergene alteration the resulting goethite–martite rock was then buried and metamorphosed to form microcrystalline hematite–martite ore. This model, envisaging a combination of supergene and metamorphic processes, was initially attributed to Morris (1985) and is believed to be consistent with the characteristics of most of the enriched BIF deposits of the region. These characteristics include the high Fe grades (65% Fe) of the enriched BIF, the lumpy character of the ore, and low phosphorous contents (around 0.05%), all features that are highly desirable in the marketing of the ore (Kneeshaw, 2002).

Exposure of the BIF and supergene alteration apparently took place prior to 2200 Ma (Martin et al., 1998a), which is the maximum age of deposition of conglomerates adjacent to the Hamersley Province (i.e. the Wyloo Group; Figure 1) within which detrital fragments of hematite ore are found. Fluid inclusion and stable isotope data have also suggested that the fluids involved with the early phases of hematite–martite ore formation were hot (up to 400 °C), saline hydrothermal solutions with characteristics inconsistent with a supergene or near-surface setting. These and other observations, such as the mineralogy of the ore assemblage at the Tom Price mine, have resulted in a number of workers suggesting a hypogene origin for the enriched BIF-hosted hematite–martite ores (Barley et al., 1999; Powell et al., 1999). One suggestion is that hot, oxidizing basinal fluids were focused into low angle thrust faults during the main stage of deformation and folding (i.e. "orogenic fluids"; see Chapter 3) and that it was these fluids that were initially responsible for silica dissolution and hematite recrystallization in the BIF.

One of the features that appears to favor a hypogene origin for the Hamersley iron ores is that they can extend to considerable depths (over 500 m) below the surface. This feature on its own does not, however, militate against supergene processes. The Morris et al. (1980) model for Mount Whaleback envisages supergene alteration by electrochemical processes (Figure 2). The high electrical conductivity of magnetite-rich layers in BIF enables oxidation potentials to extend to significant depths, with an electrical circuit being completed by ionic conduction through groundwaters circulating along suitably positioned fault systems. A cathode is set up at surface where electrons are consumed in oxygenated groundwaters. The anode

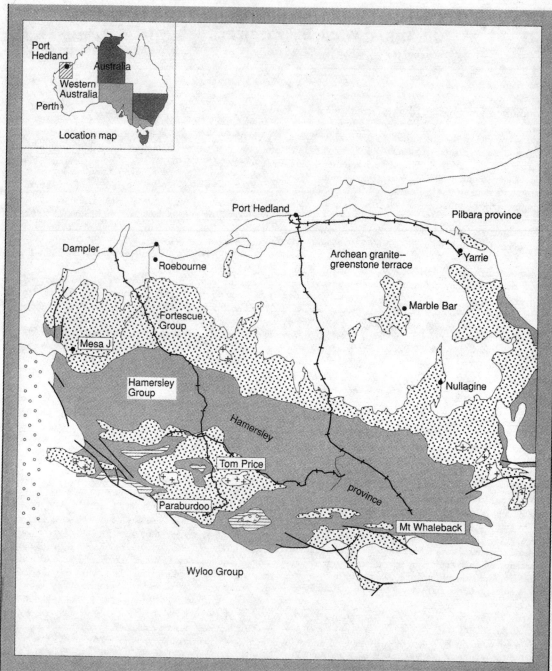

Figure 1 Simplified geology and location of some of the major iron ore deposits in the Hamersley Province, Western Australia (after Kneeshaw, 2002).

exists at depth where ferrous ions are oxidized to ferric ions and then precipitated as an iron-oxyhydroxide such as goethite. This electrochemical process explains alteration processes at significant depths, but does not preclude the existence of normal supergene processes, or lateritization, in the near surface environment (Morris et al., 1980).

Finally, it should be noted that the Hamersley Province is characterized by a significant component (about 35%) of much younger mineralization that clearly is related to supergene processes active during a cycle of Paleogene erosion and weathering. These iron deposits are referred to as channel and detrital ores and are located in mature river courses and colluvial fans, both of which are spatially linked to bedded ores (Kneeshaw, 2002). Although the origin of the enriched BIF ores remains controversial, the region has been subjected to a long and involved geological history and the ore-forming processes are expected to be complex and episodic.

Figure 2 Simplified cross section through the Mount Whaleback iron ore deposit showing the extent of enriched BIF-hosted ore and the postulated nature of iron enrichment by an electrolytically mediated process (after Morris et al., 1980).

Transvaal basin at stratigraphic levels just above those where the equally substantial BIF-hosted iron ores occur. This is not unexpected given the remarkably similar chemical properties of Fe and Mn. The geochemical behavior of manganese, like iron, is controlled by oxidation potential and it exists as Mn^{2+}, which is soluble under reducing and acidic conditions, as well as Mn^{3+} and Mn^{4+}, which are less soluble and stabilize as manganese oxides under relatively oxidizing and alkaline conditions (Figure 5.17b). Pyrolusite, or MnO_2, is the dominant oxide phase at high Eh and over a range of pH. Comparison of the manganese with the iron phase diagram (Figure 5.17a and b) shows that higher oxidation potentials are required to stabilize pyrolusite than hematite. The fact that

Figure 5.19 (a) Depth concentration profile for Fe and Mn in the Black Sea. Fe is depleted in the water column by pyrite accumulation on the sea floor, whereas Mn occurs to moderately high levels in solution in the dominantly reduced water column. Maximum enrichment of Mn occurs just below the redox interface where Mn^{2+} is oxidized to Mn^{3+} and precipitates. (b) The distribution of Mn in sea floor sediments of the Black Sea. Accumulation of Mn occurs at the intersection of the zone of Mn precipitation with the sea floor (diagrams modified after Force and Maynard, 1991).

Fe^{2+} oxidizes more readily than Mn^{2+} means that iron can precipitate while Mn remains in solution, and provides a possible explanation for the observation that iron ores may be spatially (or stratigraphically) separated from manganese ores, as in the case of the Transvaal basin. In the latter case, early precipitation of ferric iron out of solution to form huge volumes of BIF (within which the Sishen and Thabazimbi deposits occur) would have depleted the water column of iron so that later precipitation, at a higher stratigraphic level and under more oxidizing conditions, resulted in the formation of Fe-depleted manganese oxide ores.

Manganese deposits are located in sediments of variable age, from the Paleoproterozoic to recent. Some of the biggest deposits are Phanerozoic in age, such as the Cretaceous Groote Eylandt manganese oxide ores in northern Australia, and the Molango district of Mexico where the ores are made up dominantly of rhodochrosite ($MnCO_3$). An interesting modern day analogue for the formation of sedimentary manganese ores is provided by the Black Sea, where active sedimentation results in ongoing accumulation of MnO_2. The

Black Sea is markedly stratified in terms of water density and composition and the waters below about 200 m depth are euxinic (i.e. highly reduced, with H_2S stable). Pyritic muds accumulate on the sea floor and this effectively depletes the entire water column of iron. Mn by contrast is concentrated in the deeper waters, since it exists in solution as Mn^{2+}, but is depleted in the upper oxidized 200 m where it precipitates and settles out. The depth–concentration profiles for Mn and Fe in the Black Sea are illustrated in Figure 5.19a, which shows the zone of manganese enrichment that forms just below the redox interface where mixing between high-Mn euxinic and oxidized surface waters occurs. At the interface Mn^{2+} is oxidized to Mn^{3+} and particulate Mn forms and then settles at deeper levels where it can redissolve. However, where the enriched mixing zone intersects shallow sea floor, accumulation of either MnO_2 or $MnCO_3$ (depending on the local oxidation potential; see Figure 5.17b) takes place on the substrate. Mineralization is further enhanced if the sites of accumulation are protected from dilution by clastic sediment input, as shown for the north-central portion of the Black Sea (Figure 5.19b).

5.3.3 Phosphorites

Phosphorus is a very important element that is essential for the growth and development of most living organisms. It is a basic ingredient of some proteins but, more importantly, it is a building block for the bones and teeth of vertebrates, as well as the shells and chitinous exoskeletons of many invertebrates. Plants also require it for growth and it is for this reason that phosphate is such an important ingredient of fertilizer. In order to sustain global food requirements the manufacture of artificial fertilizers has become an enormous industry that requires approximately 150 million tons of phosphate per year, the raw material for which comes predominantly from phosphorus-rich sediments or phosphorites (i.e. a sediment containing more than 15–20% P_2O_5).

Phosphorites generally form in much the same environmental niches as do banded iron-formations, ironstones, and bedded manganese ores, namely along continental shelves and in shallow marginal marine settings such as lagoons and deltas. The processes of formation are, therefore, very similar to those for Fe and Mn deposits and essentially involve the upwelling of cold ocean water containing above-normal concentrations of metals, and their subsequent precipitation onto the continental shelves. In fact one of the earliest published accounts of the upwelling hypothesis, attributed to the Russian scientist A.V. Kazakov in the 1930s, applied to the formation of phosphate-rich sediments in a continental shelf ·setting, and the concept was only later applied to iron and manganese deposits. Deep sea drilling and ocean floor exploration have shown that phosphate concentrations are presently forming off-shore along the coastlines of Namibia and Chile–Peru, and are related to upwelling of deep, cold currents carrying small amounts of phosphate in solution. The same environments are also well known as prolific fishing grounds, a feature which substantiates the relationship between the supply of phosphatic nutrients and biological productivity.

When the idea of oceanic upwelling was first introduced, it was suggested that precipitation of phosphorus onto the sea floor in areas of upwelling was inorganic and related to decreasing solubility in the near shore environment. This notion is over-simplified and it is now known that the phosphorus cycle in the oceans is largely controlled by organic processes. A role for micro-organisms in the deposition of phosphate is also considered likely (Trudinger, 1976). Phosphorus dissolves in sea water as either PO_4^{3-} (stable under very alkaline conditions), HPO_4^{2-} (the dominant anionic complex), or $H_2PO_4^-$ (stable under acidic conditions) complexes. These anionic complexes are absorbed by the organisms living in shallow marine environments to form their shells, bones, and teeth. The subsequent accumulation of phosphorus on the sea floor, therefore, is not related to a chemical redox reaction, as in the cases of Fe and Mn, but occurs after the host organism dies and settles to the ocean floor. Phosphorus is released from the decaying organism to form a calcium phosphate compound, which then converts to an impure, cryptocrystalline form of apatite $(Ca_5(PO_4)_3[F,OH])$ or collophane (a carbonate–apatite). The concentration of calcium phosphate on the sea floor is described in terms of the reaction:

$$3Ca^{2+} + H_2PO_4 \Leftrightarrow Ca_3(PO_4)_2 + 2H^+ \qquad [5.7]$$

which suggests that its precipitation is dependent, among other things, on pH. Figure 5.20 shows apatite solubility in sea water as a function of pH and oxalate content of the solution (oxalic acid is $H_2C_2O_4$). It is apparent that apatite solubility is significantly higher under more acidic conditions and, on this basis, that apatite formation is more likely to occur under the relatively alkaline, warm-water conditions that apply to continental shelves. Deeper, colder and more acidic waters will promote phosphate solubility.

The formation of apatite/collophane in phosphatic sediments is, however, not a straight-forward process and there has been considerable debate as to whether it develops as a primary precipitate at the sea water–sediment interface (i.e. where the organic material is decaying) or as a

Figure 5.20 Estimates of apatite solubility in sea water (expressed in terms of phosphate concentration) as a function of solution pH and oxalate concentration (after Schwartz, 1971).

product of diagenesis during later compaction and dewatering of the sediment. This debate has considerable bearing on the origin and formation of phosphorite ores and evidence seems to exist for both processes. Typical concentrations of dissolved phosphate in the deep portions of the present day oceans are low (about 50–100 ppb; Bentor, 1980) and the shallow marine environment is even more strongly depleted because of biological uptake. Given the low present day concentrations of phosphate in solution, even in the deep ocean, it seems very unlikely that sea water is saturated with respect to apatite. This, in turn, suggests that the primary precipitation of apatite at the sea water–sediment interface is also unlikely. Although this situation applies generally to the present day oceans, it may not, however, have prevailed in previous geological eras when factors such as ocean chemistry and biological evolutionary development were different. It may also not apply to restricted, but biologically productive, environments (such as a lagoon) where high rates of organic decay can produce localized saturation of phosphate in sea water, as in the case of the southern African example described below.

Sheldon (1980) has suggested that phosphate concentrations in the Precambrian oceans might

have been higher than at present because the lower-O_2, higher-CO_2 atmospheric conditions prevailing at that time would have meant a more acidic sea-water composition and higher phosphate solubility. It is also apparent that oceans that existed before the development of phosphate-dependent organisms did not witness biological phosphorus depletion. By the same token, oceans at this time could not produce the environments in which biologically mediated deposition and concentration of apatite or collophane might occur. Substantial Precambrian phosphorite deposits, therefore, do not exist, and the few that do occur are likely to have formed from the direct precipitation of phosphate from sea water. As the atmosphere evolved, however, any event that coincided with a substantial proliferation of life, such as the Cambrian explosion, could have had the effect of removing CO_2 from the oceans and atmosphere, increasing pH in the shallow water environment and further promoting the direct precipitation of apatite from a saturated sea water column. A more efficient form of concentration, however, would have been through the decay of phosphate-dependent life forms and the formation of phosphorites in association with organic-rich sediments. This is probably the reason why all large phosphorite deposits are Phanerozoic in age. It is pertinent to note that the Precambrian–Cambrian boundary, for example, coincides with a period in Earth history when substantial deposition of phosphoritic sediments took place (Cook and Shergold, 1984), good examples of which include the deposits of Mongolia, southeast Asia and Australia. By contrast, formation of Mesozoic and Cenozoic phosphorite deposits must have taken place essentially during the diagenetic stage of sediment evolution, since the phosphate concentration levels in the water column were too low to allow for direct apatite or collophane precipitation. In this scenario, the concentration of phosphate in the organic-rich host sediments builds up progressively with time such that the interstitial waters would eventually become highly enriched in phosphate (measurements of up to several thousands ppb HPO_4^{2-} in solution have been recorded; Bentor, 1980). This represents an ideal environment for the formation of diagenetic apatite as the sediments are compacted and lithified. Such processes would appear to pertain to deposits such as the Cretaceous–Paleogene deposits of Morocco and possibly also the oolitic phosphorites of Florida. In the latter case, however, subsequent mechanical abrasion and sedimentary transport of diagenetic aggregations resulted in deposits that are reworked and allochthonous (Riggs, 1979).

Other factors, such as global climatic patterns and eustatic sea-level changes, are also known to have played a role in the formation of phosphorites (Cook and McElhinny, 1979; Sheldon, 1980). Figure 5.21a shows that there is a broad correlation between the number of phosphate deposits that have formed and periods of sea-level highstand. The explanation offered is that elevated sea levels and flooding of the continental shelves enhanced circulation and upwelling. If enhanced upwelling occurred in an equatorially aligned sea way (Figure 5.21b) then phosphorite formation would have been promoted by the biogenic concentration and/or solubility decrease that accompanied the existence of such a biologically productive environment. The late Mesozoic to Cenozoic phosphorite deposits of North Africa, deposited in the Tethyan sea way, may well represent examples of this control mechanism. Figure 5.21a shows that there is also a correlation between glacial events and phosphogenesis. In this case the lack of vertical mixing in the oceans during stable periods results in a phosphate build-up in the deep water sink. The development of strong trade wind systems between glacial and non-glacial events in mature, longitudinally orientated oceans would promote the establishment of major oceanic gyrals which would, in turn, result in strong upwelling along the western edges of continental land masses (Figure 5.21c). This mechanism could explain the development of the Permian Phosphoria Formation, probably the world's largest accumulation of phosphate ores, along the western margin of continental USA in Pangean times. This scenario also obviously applies to the present day Atlantic ocean and accounts for the pattern of upwelling and phosphate deposition along the western margin of Africa (see below).

A model for phosphogenesis based on present day deposition

Birch (1980) studied the nature and origin of phosphorites forming off the western and southern continental margins of South Africa and Namibia. Exploration of the continental shelf in this region reveals two types of phosphorite (Figure 5.22a). One variety developed mainly along the Namibian coastline and comprises oolitic apatite/collophane ores derived by accretionary growth arising from the direct precipitation of phosphate from sea water. The other type, formed mainly along the South African coastline, consists of phosphatic replacement of fossiliferous limestone and is diagenetic in origin. Both types of phosphorite are geologically recent (Eocene to Miocene) in age and are believed to have formed at the same time. A model for this type of penecontemporaneous ore formation is shown in Figure 5.22b. Diffuse upwelling along the outer reaches of the shelf results in reduced nutrient supply and biological productivity, and consequently the rate of phosphate release during decay of organisms on the sea floor is also low. Apatite is undersaturated and cannot precipitate directly from the sea water, but subsequent diagenesis can lead to replacement of limestone by calcium phosphate. By contrast, in the near shore environment very high biological productivity in restricted shallow embayments and lagoons is maintained by wind-induced nutrient upwelling. Mass mortality of life forms in these restricted environments (especially during summer low tides) leads to the accumulation of abundant organic matter on the substrate with local increases in dissolved phosphate content to saturation levels. Varve-like layers of pure apatite as well as accretionary oolitic growth provide the textural support for a mode of formation by direct precipitation of phosphate at the sea water–sediment interface.

5.3.4 Black shales

Shales that are rich in organic matter are economically important because they are often enriched in a large variety of metals, including V, Cr, Co, Ni, Ti, Cu, Pb, Zn, Mo, U, Ag, Sb, Tl, Se, and Cd.

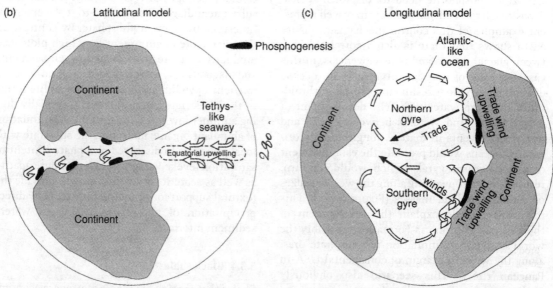

Figure 5.21 (a) Generalized correlations between the development of phosphate deposits, glacial events and eustatic sea level changes in the Phanerozoic Eon. (b) Model for phosphate deposition related to equatorial upwelling in a latitudinally orientated seaway such as Mesozoic Tethys. (c) Model for phosphate deposition related to trade wind induced circulation patterns in a mature longitudinally orientated ocean (after Sheldon, 1980).

Figure 5.22 (a) Map showing the distribution of phosphate-rich sediments along the continental margins of South Africa and Namibia. (b) Model showing contrasting modes of phosphate deposition in the outer shelf (where diagenetic accumulation of apatite is taking place) and in restricted near-shore environments characterized by high biological productivity and seasonal mass mortality (where precipitation of apatite directly from sea water is occurring). Diagrams after Birch (1980).

Although few metalliferous black shales are presently mined (with the exception of China where several small deposits are exploited) they represent a significant metal resource and probably also a source of ore components for younger hydrothermal deposits. As mentioned previously, many black shales are spatially associated with ironstones (Figure 5.15) and form in the same environments. At a global scale, they formed penecontemporaneously with ironstones, and their major periods of development can be linked to the first order eustatic sea-level highstands in the Ordovician–Devonian and Jurassic–Paleogene intervals (see Chapter 6). In this respect they are also linked to the Ocean Anoxic Events (OAEs) that are now well documented in the Phanerozoic Eon. Sea-level highstand resulted in continental margin flooding and transgression of muddy sediment across the shelf. The deeper water conditions that generally applied resulted in poorer circulation, a reduction in oxygen levels, and widespread oceanic stagnation (Van Houten and Authur, 1989), providing the kind of depositional environment favorable for metalliferous black shale formation.

Well known examples of metalliferous black shales include the Cambro–Ordovician Alum shale of Scandanavia, which is particularly enriched in uranium, and the Devonian New Albany shale of Indiana, USA, which has significant concentrations of Pb as well as V, Cu, Mo, and Ni. The euxinic shaley sediments forming on the floor of the Black Sea represent an example of manganese, as well as Co, Cu, Ni, and V, enrichment, in a present day sedimentary basin (Holland, 1984).

Black shales are characterized by significant quantities of organic carbon which is preserved from degradation/oxidation by the almost total lack of free oxygen in the immediate environment of deposition. This environment is not only anoxic but also euxinic (where reduced sulfur species are stable) and it is this combination, together with a lack of clastic dilution, that provides the optimal conditions for development of metalliferous black shales (Leventhal, 1993). A sediment organic content of even 1% will bacterially and chemically deplete the oxygen content of the immediate environment to virtually zero. This microenvir-

onment promotes the growth of sulfate-reducing bacteria which in turn produce HS^- or H_2S (depending on the local pH) and the development of euxinic conditions. The biologically mediated development of euxinic waters can be described in terms of the following reaction:

$$R(CH_2O)_2 + SO_4^{2-} \Rightarrow R + 2HCO_3^- + H_2S \qquad [5.8]$$

where $R(CH_2O)_2$ is an abbreviated representation of a complex (organic) carbohydrate molecule. The subsequent concentration of metals in this environment is brought about by the affinity of positively charged metals in solution in the sea water for the thio complex, as demonstrated in the following simplified reaction:

$$HS^- + Me^{2+} \Rightarrow MeS + H^+ \qquad [5.9]$$

where Me is a metal. The above reactions imply a correlation between organic carbon, sulfur, and metal contents in black shales since the higher the content of sulfate-reducing bacteria, the more sulfide is produced and the greater the degree of extraction of metal from the sea water column would be. Such a correlation is well demonstrated in Figure 5.23a, for Devonian black shales in the eastern USA, and lends support to the processes outlined above.

The source and metal content of black shales will obviously vary from place to place and this accounts for the observation that different horizons have characteristic metal signatures. In oceanic settings submarine exhalative vents, or black smokers, represent likely metal sources, whereas in continental margin settings (such as the Black Sea) metals are derived from terrigenous clastic input. Figure 5.23b summarizes the geological and environmental conditions necessary for the optimal development of a metalliferous black shale. This type of sedimentary rock represents a potentially important source of exploitable metals in the future.

5.3.5 A note on ocean floor manganese nodules

Since their discovery during the 1872–6 oceanographic expedition by *HMS Challenger*, it has

Figure 5.23 (a) Plots of carbon content versus sulfur, molybdenum, and uranium for Devonian black shales from the eastern USA (after compilations by Holland, 1984). (b) Schematic outline of the geological and environmental conditions required for the optimal formation of metalliferous black shales (after Leventhal, 1993).

become apparent that a vast resource of Mn, Fe, Cu, and Ni (as well as lesser amounts of Co, Zn, and other metals) is contained within the (ferro)-manganese nodules that occur in the deep, pelagic portions of all the major oceans. Manganese nodules typically occur in parts of the ocean basins where sediment accumulation rates are very low (less than 7 meters per million years; Heath, 1981)

and are absent from areas of rapid sedimentation, as well as from equatorial and high-latitude regions of high biological productivity and chemical sedimentation. They appear to be best developed in the Pacific Ocean, where exploration has identified large areas of prolific nodule formation (up to 100 nodules per square meter). These areas also contain nodules that have higher than

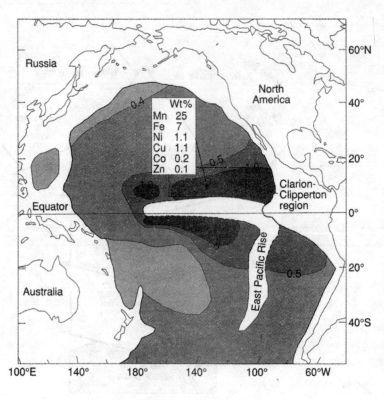

Figure 5.24 Map showing sub-equatorial zones of base metal enriched manganese nodule concentration in the Pacific Ocean, contoured with respect to the copper content (in wt%) of nodules. Nodule-free areas occur close to the continents, where sedimentation rates are high, as well as along the equator and East Pacific Rise, where biological productivity is high. The Clarion–Clipperton region, a particularly enriched zone, is boxed (after Heath, 1981).

normal metal contents, with up to 2 wt% combined Cu + Ni and substantial Co and Zn (Figure 5.24). One such area is the Clarion–Clipperton region, to the west of Mexico.

Manganese nodules are typically ovoid, a few centimeters in diameter, and have the appearance on the sea floor of a burnt potato. In cross section they are complexly layered, often partly concentric, and represent concretions that have apparently nucleated around a clastic or biogenic fragment. They often exhibit internal radiating shrinkage cracks reflecting a change in mineralogy from hydrated Fe and Mn oxyhydroxides to a variety of more compact, but chemically complex, Fe and Mn oxides such as vernadite, birnessite, todorokite, goethite, and hematite (Heath, 1981). The formation of manganese nodules is a complex process and still not fully understood. Metals are undoubtedly derived from the sea water itself, but ultimately come from various sources including submarine exhalative vents, clastic and volcanic input, and diagenesis of

pelagic sediments. The formation of the nodules and the concentration of metals within them have been attributed to one or more of the following mechanisms:

• Settling of clay and biogenic (fecal) debris that contained either absorbed or ingested metals obtained from the sea water, with subsequent release of metals during dissolution and decomposition.

• Direct precipitation of metals from sea water onto a suitable substrate which forms the nucleus around which concretionary growth takes place.

• Upward diffusion of metals in ocean bottom sediment pore waters.

• Authigenic reactions in ocean bottom sediments during alteration and compaction.

• Bacterial activity and the oxidation of transition metals. In this regard, certain types of bacteria (such as *Metallogenium*) are known to be particularly prevalent in the oxidation and subsequent precipitation of labile Mn^{2+} and have been detected in manganese nodules from the Atlantic Ocean (Trudinger, 1976).

• Preferential uptake of dissolved transition metals into specific Fe and Mn oxyhydroxide minerals, such as the affinity of Cu and Ni for todorokite (a multi-element Mn–oxyhydroxide).

The current level of uncertainty about the processes involved in the formation of deep ocean manganese nodules is reflected in the variety of suggested mechanisms listed above. Many of these suggestions are not mutually exclusive and it is likely that nodule formation is a long-lived and complex process. The biggest problem with the exploitation of manganese nodules at present is not so much technical as it is political and economic. The technologies required for exploiting manganese nodules at depth in several kilometers of ocean water could be overcome, but the formulation of an internationally acceptable Law of the Sea is a much bigger and more contentious issue. Manganese nodules, nevertheless, represent an enormous metal resource for the future.

5.3.6 Evaporites

The bulk of the world's production of rock salt (halite), as well as of potash, borates, and nitrates for agricultural fertilizers, comes from rocks known as evaporites. These are chemical precipitates that form as a result of evaporation of a brine, usually derived from sea water. There are two main environments in which evaporites form. The major one, in which the so-called "saline giants" of the world formed, is marginal marine in setting and represented by large lagoons or restricted embayments into which periodic or continual sea water recharge occurs. This type of deposit may be both laterally extensive and thick, but is characterized by a relatively limited range of mineral precipitants derived from sea water, which itself has remained fairly constant in terms of bulk composition over much of geological time. The second setting is intracontinental and lacustrine and results in much smaller, thinner deposits which are characterized by a more diverse range of mineral precipitants since continental fluvial input introduces a broader range of dissolved ingredients to the lake waters. Examples of deposits representing the former include the Permian Zechstein Formation, which formed in a shallow sea covering large areas of the United Kingdom, The Netherlands, Germany, and Poland, and also the Silurian Salina Formation of New York and Michigan states in the USA. Typical products mined from these deposits include halite, potash, and sulfates. Probably the largest known evaporite sequence occurs in late Miocene strata beneath the floor of the Mediterranean Sea, where deposits extend laterally for over 2000 km and may be up to 2 km thick. Much of this resource is obviously unexploitable, but is so large that its formation must have caused a significant reduction in oceanic salinity at the time (Kendall and Harwood, 1996). Examples of intracontinental lacustrine deposits include the dry lakes of Chile, Death Valley in California, and the Great Salt Lake of Utah. In addition to the products mentioned above, these deposits are also important producers of borates (from California) and nitrates (from Chile), as well as Mg, Br, and Li (from Utah).

The principles behind the formation of evaporite deposits are relatively simple in theory, although actual deposits can be complex and exhibit a large variety of different mineral salts and paragenetic sequences. As sea water or brine evaporates and water vapor is removed into the atmosphere, the salinity (i.e. the total content of dissolved salts in solution) of the residual solution increases and individual salts precipitate as their respective solubility limits are reached. The order or sequence of precipitation reflects the scale of increasing solubility at a given temperature, such that the salts with the lower solubilities precipitate first, followed consecutively by salts with progressively higher solubilities. The relative quantities of precipitated products in an evaporite deposit are also constrained by the solubility limits of the various salts dissolved in the brine solution. These considerations seem to suggest a relatively straightforward precipitation process and uniform paragenetic sequence. In fact the chemistry of brine solutions is very complex and factors such as convection dynamics, post-precipitation diagenesis, and equilibrium as opposed to fractional crystallization combine to ensure considerable diversity in the nature of these deposits.

Figure 5.25 (a) Schematic cross section showing the important features necessary for the formation of large marine evaporite sequences. (b) Paragenetic sequence for an evaporite assemblage from typical sea water containing the ingredients shown in the left hand column. The amount of sea water (per 1000 liter volume) that has to evaporate in order to consecutively precipitate the observed sequence of mineral salts is shown by the curve adjacent to the paragenetic sequence (diagrams modified after Guilbert and Park, 1986).

Marine evaporites that formed from sea water that was well mixed and had a constant composition over much of geological time tend to be dominated by the same assemblage of major mineral precipitates, namely halite (NaCl), gypsum/anhydrite (CaSO$_4$/CaSO$_4$.2H$_2$O), and sylvite (KCl). Evaporite deposits can, however, also contain minor accumulations of other salts, especially

those representing the late stage precipitation of high solubility compounds. The latter typically comprise hydrated, multi-element, Mg, Br, Sr, K chlorides and borates, and are called bitterns. The preservation of bitterns in evaporite deposits appears to be controlled largely by geological factors. Figure 5.25a shows a schematic cross section through a shallow, marginal marine setting in which an evaporite sequence is being deposited. Sea water recharge ensures replenishment of the solution and sustained mineral precipitation from the brine. Intense evaporation results in marked density stratification and accumulation of highly saline, dense brines in the bottom waters. In environments where there is a constriction at the entrance of the basin, there is little opportunity for this dense brine to discharge back into the deep parts of the open ocean and, hence, the high solubility components of the solution remain within the basin to eventually precipitate out as bitterns once the solubility limits are exceeded. Bitterns do not accumulate if reflux of the dense bottom water brines to the open ocean occurs because the high solubility components of the solution are then flushed out of the basin. In the latter case, if the bitterns do not precipitate, the evaporite mineral assemblage may be truncated or incomplete and the deposit less diverse in terms of the commodities it could exploit. Figure 5.25b illustrates the typical mineral paragenetic sequence for evaporite deposits as a function of precipitation from sea water, the composition of which is shown on the left hand side of the figure. The proportion of sea water remaining after evaporation (as a function of a 1000 liter volume) and its increasing density are also shown in relation to the precipitation sequence.

The formation of the giant Phanerozoic saline deposits is a contentious issue, mainly because modern analogues do not exist and ancient evaporite sequences are generally altered and tectonically modified. The evaporite deposits on the floor of the Mediterranean Sea are now believed to have formed in a sabkha environment, implying that much of the Mediterranean basin was subaerial and desiccated during late Miocene times (Kendall and Harwood, 1996). Evaporitic minerals which form in a sabkha environment precipitate from groundwater brines that evaporate in the capillary zone immediately above the water table. Recharge of the brine occurs either by periodic flooding or by sea water seepage into the sabkha basin. A good example of a complete evaporate deposit formed as part of a Phanerozoic saline giant is the Boulby Mine in the Zechstein of northeast England.

5.4 FOSSIL FUELS – OIL/GAS FORMATION AND COALIFICATION

A fossil fuel is formed from the altered remains of organic matter (plant and animal) trapped in sedimentary rock. The hydrocarbon compounds that form during the burial and degradation of organic material retain a significant proportion of the chemical energy imparted into the original living organism by the sun. This energy is harnessed in many different ways by burning or combusting the fuel. The main fossil fuels are coal and petroleum, the latter being a general term that encompasses crude oil and natural gas (mainly methane), as well as solid hydrocarbons.

Although most ore deposit books do not include descriptions of fossil fuel occurrences, it is felt that any text dealing with ore-forming *processes* would be incomplete without a brief discussion on the accumulation of hydrocarbons in the Earth's crust. There is an enormous volume of published literature on the origin and nature of fossil fuel deposits and, consequently, the following section presents only brief overviews relevant to oil/gas formation and coalification processes. Mention is also made of tar sands, oil shales, and gas-hydrates, all of which represent potential fuel resources in the future.

5.4.1 Basic principles

The global carbon cycle is complex, involving both circulation, mainly in the form of gaseous CO_2 and CH_4, and storage, as reduced carbon or carbonate minerals, in different reservoirs such as the deep ocean and sedimentary rocks. Organic processes (mainly photosynthesis) ensure that a small proportion of the carbon in the global cycle is combined with hydrogen and oxygen to form the molecular building blocks of the various biota that inhabit the Earth's surface. The areas of greatest organic productivity on Earth are represented on the continents by tropical vegetative zones, and in the oceans by areas of cold current upwelling. As a first approximation, therefore, it is logical to expect that fossil fuels are most likely to have formed in these two environments. Indeed, coals develop mainly in continental

Figure 5.26 Simplified scheme illustrating the formation of oil, gas, and coal by the progressive burial of different types of mainly vegetative matter (after Hunt, 1979).

settings, from accumulation of vegetation in either humid, tropical swamp environments or, as in the case of younger coal seams, more temperate to polar regions. Oil and gas deposits, by contrast, develop mainly from the accumulation of phyto- and zooplankton in marine settings.

When organisms die they decompose by bacterial decay and/or oxidation, and rapidly break down to relatively simple molecular constituents such as CO_2 and CH_4. Such a process would not be conducive to the formation of fossil fuels, which requires preservation of much of the complex organic hydrocarbon material. Suitable source rocks from which fossil fuels accumulate must, therefore, have formed in reducing environments where sedimentation rates are neither too slow (in which case oxidation and molecular breakdown might occur) nor too rapid (in which case dilution of the total organic matter content of the rock would occur).

The prevailing theory for the origin of both petroleum and coal is based on the notion that organisms are buried during the sedimentary process and then subjected to a series of alteration stages as pressure and temperature increase. As shown in Figure 5.26, progressive burial of phytoplankton results in the early liberation of CO_2 and

H_2O and formation of kerogen (a collective name for sedimentary organic matter that is not soluble in organic solvents and has a polymer like structure; Bjørlykke, 1989). As the kerogen "matures" the long-chain covalent bonds that typify organic molecules are progressively broken to form lower molecular weight compounds. At around 100–120 °C and burial depths of 3–4 km (depending on the geothermal gradient), a liquid hydrocarbon fraction develops which can then migrate from the source rock. This interval is known as the "oil window." With further burial and cracking of molecular bonds, significant volumes of gas (mainly methane, CH_4) develop, which are also amenable to migration. The solid residue remaining in the sediment is referred to as kerogen, but with progressive burial it devolatilizes further and has a composition approaching pure carbon (graphite). By contrast, when humic, land-derived vegetation is buried, little or no liquid oil is formed, although significant volumes of gas will, again, be generated. The solid residue that remains in this case is more voluminous and compacts to form coal seams. The nature of the solid coal residue changes with depth, from peat and lignite at shallow burial depths (less than about 500 m), to bituminous coal and subsequently

Table 5.1 Average chemical compositions (in wt%) of the main organic building blocks compared to those of petroleum and a typical coal

	C	H	O	N	S
Carbohydrates	44	6	50	–	–
Lignin	63	5	31.6	0.3	0.1
Proteins	53	7	22	17	1
Lipids	76	12	12	–	–
Petroleum	85	13	0.5	0.5	1
Coal	70	5	23	1	1

Source: after Hunt (1979).

anthracitic coal (at depths of around 5000 m). The calorific value (i.e. the amount of energy produced on combustion) of the coal increases with maturity or burial depth.

5.4.2 Oil and gas formation

All living organisms are made up of relatively few molecular building blocks that have apparently changed little over geologic time. The main molecular building blocks involved in petroleum formation include:
- Carbohydrates and related substances – these are mono- and polysaccharide polymers and include the sugars, chitin and lignin, the latter being a major precursor to coal.
- Proteins – these are high molecular weight amino acid polymers and represent one of the most important constituents of life processes.
- Lipids, which are represented in animal fats and vegetable oils and are abundant in crude oils.
- Other substances such as resins and pigments are of lesser importance but also occur variably in both plant and animal matter.

Plants comprise mainly carbohydrates (40–70%), although the higher, woody forms also contain substantial lignin for strength. Phytoplankton contains around 20% protein. Animals, by contrast, are made up mainly of proteins (55–70%) with lesser carbohydrates and lipids but no lignin (Hunt, 1979). The average chemical composition of these various organic building blocks is shown in Table 5.1.

As the original organic constituents are buried, they are subjected to increases in pressure and temperature, resulting in systematic changes which are divided into three stages, termed diagenesis, catagenesis, and metamorphism. This progression, and its application to the burial of organic matter in sediments, together with the organic processes and changes that occur in each, are summarized in Figure 5.27. Diagenesis refers to the early biological and chemical changes that occur in organic-rich sediments prior to the pronounced temperature-dependent effects of later reactions (i.e. less than about 50 °C). During this stage the biopolymers of living organisms undergo a wide variety of complex low-temperature reactions. Put simply, they are either oxidized or attacked by microbes and converted into less complex molecules which may, in turn, react and condense to form more complex, high molecular weight geopolymers that are the precursors to kerogen. Biogenic reactions during diagenesis also produce significant amounts of gas, termed biogenic gas, which typically escapes into the atmosphere or water column and is not retained in the sediment. Catagenesis occurs between about 50 and 150 °C and is the most important stage as far as petroleum generation is concerned. During this stage temperature plays an important role in catalyzing reactions, the majority of which result in the formation of light hydrocarbons from high molecular weight kerogen by the breaking of carbon–carbon bonds. In this process, known as *thermal cracking*, a complex organic molecule such as a paraffin or alkane will split and form two smaller molecules (a different paraffin and an alkene or olefin). Each of the products contains a carbon atom, with an outer orbital electron from the original covalent pairing that is now shared. The shared electron means that the resultant alkane and alkene each contain a "free radical" that makes them reactive and amenable to further breakdown. Alternatively, reactions may occur by *catalytic cracking*, where a carbon atom in one of the resultant molecules takes both electrons, thereby becoming a "Lewis acid" or double electron acceptor. The molecule that loses the electron pair is called a carbonium ion and with its net positive charge is also amenable to further decomposition. For example, alkanes subjected to catalytic cracking could

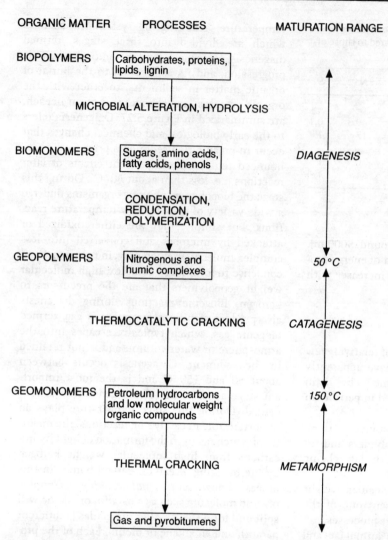

Figure 5.27 Summary of the stages and processes involved in the transformation of organic matter during burial to form oil and gas (after Hunt, 1979).

yield gaseous products such as ethane or butane (Hunt, 1979). Catalytic cracking tends to be the dominant process in petroleum generation up to about 120 °C, but at higher temperatures thermal cracking becomes increasingly important.

The integrated effects of time and temperature have important implications for petroleum generation. Temperature and time are inversely related in terms of petroleum productivity so that, for example, a given quantity of oil formed at 110 °C over 25 million years would require 100 million years to form at 90 °C (Hunt, 1979). This relationship is quantified on a plot of time versus temper-

ature in Figure 5.28, where data for selected petroleum-bearing basins are also shown. The graph can be very useful in petroleum exploration as it predicts, for example, that oil would not be formed in a young basin with low geothermal gradient because the threshold for efficient hydrocarbon generation might not yet have been reached. Likewise, little oil could be preserved in an old, hot basin as it would all have been destroyed during metamorphism. The time–temperature evolution of sedimentary basins is, therefore, a critical factor in petroleum exploration. As a general rule, oil resources are sought either in young, hot

Figure 5.28 Graph showing the relationships between temperature and time with respect to the generation of oil and gas in sedimentary basins. The shaded area refers to the optimum range of conditions for petroleum generation and the points are actual examples of petroleum-bearing basins from several locations around the world (after Connan, 1974).

basins or in old, cold ones, as identified by the relevant field in Figure 5.28.

Source considerations

Most of the organic matter on Earth can be classified into two major types, namely *sapropelic*, which refers to the decomposition products of microscopic plants such as phytoplankton, and *humic*, which refers essentially to the maturation products of macroscopic land plants. Sapropelic organic matter has H/C ratios in the range 1.3–1.7, whereas humic matter has a lower H/C ratio around 0.9. These compositional differences have led to a more rigorous classification of kerogen types that has relevance to the generation of fossil fuels. The classification was originally devised by Tissot *et al.* (1974) in terms of the so-called Van Krevelen diagram, a plot of H/C against O/C (see inset in Figure 5.29). A more recent version of the Tissot classification is described in Cornford (1998) using a plot of hydrogen index versus oxygen index (Figure 5.29), two parameters which are analogous to H/C and O/C,

respectively, but can be obtained directly by spectrometric analysis.

The classification scheme recognizes three main kerogen types, with a fourth type having little or no relevance to petroleum generation. Type I kerogen is derived from algal material and, on maturation, yields mainly oil. Type II kerogen is obtained from the breakdown of plant spores, pollens, exines, and resins, but it may also comprise bacterially degraded algal (Type I) organic matter. The Jurassic source rocks of the North Sea oil deposits represent an example of hydrocarbon derivation from the Type II kerogen. Type III kerogen is derived from humic land plants rich in lignin and cellulosic tissue and on maturation yields only gas. As mentioned previously, this is the material from which coals are formed. Type IV kerogen is obtained from oxidized woody material and has no hydrocarbon potential. The arrows in Figure 5.29 indicate the compositional trends of different kerogens with progressive burial and maturation, and all coalesce toward the origin, represented by pure carbon (graphite). In considerations of source it should be noted that

Figure 5.29 Classification scheme for kerogen types based on the hydrogen index and oxygen index (after Cornford, 1998). Inset diagram shows the original classification of kerogen on the basis of H/C and O/C atomic ratios (after Tissot and Welte, 1984).

oil-prone Type I and II kerogens will yield not only oil, but also both "wet" (i.e. with a high condensable fraction) and "dry" gas (mainly methane). Gas-prone kerogen (usually Type III) will produce mainly dry gas.

Modern analytical and modeling techniques allow the quantitative estimation of gas and oil yields to be calculated from a source rock undergoing progressive burial. A summary of hydrocarbon yields from two different source rocks is shown in Figure 5.30. Figure 5.30a shows the quantities of petroleum products derived from a source rock comprising Type II kerogen and differentiates between the condensate, comprising

high (C15+) and low (C2–C8) molecular weight oils, and a dominantly methane gas component. Figure 5.30b is the equivalent scenario for a source rock sediment comprising kerogen that is only gas-prone, which on maturation initially yields only a minor amount of wet gas (ethane, propane, butane, etc.) but mainly dry gas (methane), leaving a coal residue. The latter process is relevant to the generation of coal-bed methane resources.

Source rock considerations are important during petroleum exploration. The origin of organic matter is obviously a pointer to the depositional environment of the sedimentary rock and, there-

Figure 5.30 Maturity curves showing (a) the cumulative generation of oil types and methane gas from sediment source rock originally containing a 1% total organic carbon (TOC) content of Type II oil-prone kerogen; and (b) the generation of wet and dry gas only from a 1 km^3 sediment volume of gas-prone kerogen which ultimately yields a coal deposit (after Cornford, 1998).

fore, also useful in placing constraints on the nature of oil/gas migration and entrapment.

Petroleum migration and reservoir considerations

One of the features of oil and gas formation is the fact that petroleum originates in a fine grained source rock and then migrates into more permeable, coarser grained, reservoir sediments. Knowledge of petroleum migration and entrapment processes is obviously important to both the exploration and exploitation stages of the industry. Although the processes are complex, they can now be accurately evaluated in terms of fluid hydraulic principles and sophisticated computer modeling techniques.

Petroleum engineers differentiate between *primary migration*, which accounts for the movement of oil and gas out of the source rock during compaction, and *secondary migration*, which describes flow within the permeable reservoir, as well as the segregation of oil and gas. As the organic source rock is lithified during diagenesis, water (usually a low to moderate salinity brine) is expelled from the sediment to form a connate fluid (see Chapter 3). In the early catagenic stages of hydrocarbon maturation, therefore, oil and gas migrate in the presence of water. The actual mechanisms of hydrocarbon migration and the role of water in this process are not completely understood. Oil is unlikely to migrate in aqueous solution since hydrocarbons generally have low solubilities in water (e.g. 3 ppm for pentane, 24 ppm for methane, 1800 ppm for benzene, all at room temperature; Bjørlykke, 1989). However, small hydrocarbon molecules dissolve more readily than large ones and methane (CH_4), for example, does become fairly soluble in water as pressure increases (about 7500 ppm at 6000 m depth; Hunt, 1979). Methane and other low molecular weight compounds can, therefore, be dissolved at depth and then released as the aqueous solution rises to the surface. Major amounts of hydrocarbon liquids and high molecular weight compounds, however, are unlikely to flow by this mechanism. At catagenic pressures and temperatures, hydrocarbon gases themselves will increasingly dissolve oils and in some source rocks there is evidence that primary migration is achieved by gas phase dissolution.

Although dissolution mechanisms are likely to play a role in petroleum flow, they cannot account for the huge oil accumulations observed in the major oil producing regions of the world. Two other mechanisms are considered to be more important during the primary flow of hydrocarbons and these are oil phase migration and diffusion. The movement of crude oil out of the source rock is initiated once compaction has driven off much of the bulk pore water in the sediment. Initially a source rock will usually contain a relatively high proportion of pore water relative to oil and in such a case the hydrocarbon will be unable to move. This is mainly because the flow of oil is impeded by the presence of water which, because of its lower surface tension, tends to "water-wet" the sediment pore spaces. In such a situation, oil globules floating in the water-dominated pore spaces cannot generate the capillary forces required to initiate migration (Figure 5.31a). As compaction progresses, however, the bulk of the pore water is driven off and the little remaining water is structurally bound on clay particles. Oil now occupies enough of the pore volume to be subjected to capillary forces and start flowing through the rock (Figure 5.31b). Once "oil-saturated" pathways are established in the rock, oil migration becomes feasible because permeability is not impeded by the presence of water. In the less common situation when pore spaces are initially "oil-wet" because of very high initial organic/hydrocarbon contents, then porosity reduction is not necessary to invoke the unimpeded flow of oil through the source rock.

Another way in which hydrocarbon molecules could migrate in the primary environment is by diffusion along an activity or free energy gradient (Hunt, 1979). Figure 5.31c illustrates, at a nanometer scale, the arrangement of structured water tetrahedra along the edge of a clay particle. Hydrocarbon molecules or aggregates in the sediment pore space will typically be encased by a jacket of water molecules to form hydrate or clathrate compounds. Interaction of the hydrocarbon clathrate with structured water would, from a thermodynamic viewpoint, require energy to facilitate the breakdown of one or both molecules. A diffusional energy gradient is, therefore, set up that promotes migration of the hydrocarbon clathrate towards lower free energy and, therefore, away from the structured water clay mineral edge. This type of diffusion translates, at a geological scale, to movement of hydrocarbons from finer grained shales towards coarser sands, which accords with natural observations. Although not directly involved as the transporting agent in primary migration, it is evident that water is implicated in all the mechanisms involved. In the case of low organic content source rocks generating mainly gas, hydrocarbon migration would occur by diffusion, in aqueous solution, or directly as the gas phase. In high organic content, oil-prone, source rocks, however, hydrocarbons will migrate predominantly as the oil phase. Intermediate situations might well exhibit the entire range of migration processes (Hunt, 1979).

At a geological scale, where oil and gas are migrating over tens to hundreds of kilometers, the main factor that controls hydrocarbon migration pathways is the existence of a pressure differential in the host rock. Particularly relevant to petroleum migration is the concept of fluid overpressure, described in more detail in section 3.3.2 of Chapter 3.

Figure 5.31 Explanation of oil-phase primary migration.
(a) "Water saturated" pore spaces in a sedimentary source rock in which little or no oil migration takes place because oil capillarity is impeded by the presence of water-wet pores which block the pore throats.
(b) "Oil saturated" pore spaces formed after compaction of the sediment has driven off much of the bulk pore water, which facilitates capillary-related oil migration by removing pore throat blocking free water (after Bjørlykke, 1989).
(c) Simplified arrangement, at a nanometer scale, of a hypothetical pore space and the setting in which diffusional migration of hydrocarbons takes place away from structural water-bound mineral grains (after Hunt, 1979).

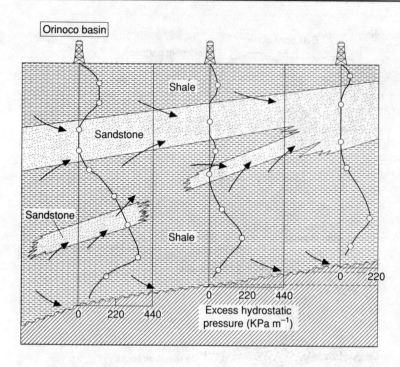

Figure 5.32 Actual measurements of excess hydrostatic pressures (i.e. overpressure) in three drill wells in the Orinoco basin and the anticipated fluid flow lines in the sequence of alternating shale and sandstone (after Hunt, 1979).

If the removal of pore water is impeded by low permeability in, for example a fine grained shale, then compaction will be retarded and fluid pressures increased to values above normal hydrostatic pressures. Fine and coarse sediment will expel pore waters at different rates during burial and will, therefore, compact along different pressure gradients. Overpressured fluids will tend to exist in the finer grained sediments. Figure 5.32 shows actual measurements of fluid pressures in a series of drill wells from the Orinoco Basin and the hydrostatic overpressures that occur in the poorly drained shale units relative to the well drained sandstone. This information allows the migration pathways to be identified and shows that the main sandstone aquifer can be fed by fluids from both above and below. Several factors actually control the stresses that cause hydrostatic fluid overpressures in rocks and these include rapid sediment deposition, thermal expansion of fluids, tectonic compression, and the actual generation of low density oil and gas in the source rock.

Many of the factors discussed above also apply to secondary petroleum migration. In the advanced stages of catagenesis, however, temperatures and pressures are such that many hydrocarbons exist close to their critical points such that density contrasts between liquid and vapor are minimized. The segregation of oil from gas, therefore, mainly reflects the decline in temperatures that accompanies migration of petroleum products into reservoirs that are well away from the sites of oil/gas generation. The progressive separation of liquid and vapor, into a low density, buoyant gas phase and a more dense, viscous oil, is a process that generally accompanies secondary migration.

Entrapment of oil and gas

Primary migration of hydrocarbons typically occurs over short distances (hundreds of meters or less) and is constrained by the proximity of the first available aquifer to the source rock. Secondary migration, by contrast, occurs over tens, and possibly even hundreds, of kilometers and is only constrained by the presence of a trap which prevents the petroleum from further flow and allows it to accumulate. Hydrocarbon traps are critical to the formation of viable oil and gas deposits and take the form of any geological feature that either reduces permeability of the reservoir or provides a physical barrier that impedes the further migration of fluid. Evaporite layers, for example, may be good hydrocarbon traps as they are laterally extensive and have virtually zero permeability because of the ability of halite to flow plastically at elevated temperatures. Many of the giant oil fields of the Arabian (Persian) Gulf are capped by evaporite sequences (Box 5.3), as are some of the North Sea gas deposits. In general, however, structural features such as faults and anticlines tend to be the dominant hydrocarbon traps. This section briefly outlines some of the geological scenarios that represent potential traps for hydrocarbon deposits in various parts of the world.

Figure 5.33 shows that there are basically three categories of trap site, namely stratigraphic, structural, and a less common miscellaneous class that includes hydrodynamic and asphalt traps. Stratigraphic traps arise entirely from sedimentological features and can be represented by features such as sediment pinch-out zones, where permeability is reduced as one sediment facies grades into another, or unconformities where the reservoir rock sub-outcrops against a unit of reduced flow capability (Figure 5.33a). The Athabasca tar sands (see section 5.4.4 below) are believed to have resulted from migration and entrapment of hydrocarbons along a major unconformity in the early Paleogene period. In addition to sandstones, carbonate rocks represent important reservoirs because the high solubility of minerals such as calcite promotes secondary porosity and migration of hydrocarbons. Sedimentary features such as limestone "pinnacle" reefs (Figure 5.33a), are important trap sites in carbonate sequences, especially in the giant Middle East deposits.

Structural traps result from some form of sediment deformation and generally provide physical barriers which prevent the continuation of fluid flow along an aquifer. A fault, for example, might juxtapose a reservoir sediment against a shaley unit and, as long as the fault itself remains impervious, will act as a barrage behind which hydrocarbons will accumulate. Since most hydro-carbons flow up-dip, the folding of a reservoir rock into an anticline or dome-like feature also provides a very efficient trap site. The huge oilfield at Prudhoe Bay in Alaska represents an example where petroleum is trapped by a combination of both folding and faulting of the reservoir sediments. The scale of hydrocarbon accumulation in this setting can be estimated by considering the closure volume of the structure and also the spill point, beyond which oil will continue its migration into another aquifer system (Figure 5.33b). Other important structurally related trap sites are linked to the deformation that accompanies salt diapirism. When salt beds underlie more dense rock strata the resultant gravitational instability causes the diapir to pierce the overlying beds and terminate reservoir sediments creating ideal trap sites for hydrocarbons (Figure 5.33b). Such trap sites are of great importance in many parts of the Arabian Gulf. Other trap sites of lesser importance include sites where oil migration is diverted by a strong flow of groundwater which, as explained previously, will water-wet the sediment pore spaces and impede the flow of hydrocarbons. These are known as hydrodynamic traps and result from the shear stresses set up at the oil–water contact in aquifers where strong water flow is occurring. Groundwater will also interact chemically with reservoir oil, resulting in oxidation, biodegradation, and the formation of a bituminous asphalt layer at the interface. This layer, known as an asphalt trap, will itself act as a barrier beneath which hydrocarbons may accumulate (Figure 5.33c).

5.4.3 Coalification processes

The majority of the world's energy requirements is still obtained from the burning of coal and lignite. The two largest producers of coal in the world are China and the USA, although Australia ranks top as an exporter of high quality coal.

As mentioned previously, most coal is derived from Type III kerogen and generally represents the *in situ* accumulation of land-derived vegetation subjected to alteration and compaction. Figure 5.26 shows that coal is derived from a peat precursor and, with burial or coalification, is progressively

Figure 5.33 Geological scenarios for hydrocarbon trap sites. (a) Stratigraphic traps represented by unconformities, pinch-outs, and carbonate "pinnacle" reefs. (b) Structural traps represented by faults, diapiric features, and anticlinal or dome like structures. (c) Other features, such as hydrodynamic and asphalt traps (after Hunt, 1979; Bjørlykke, 1989).

BOX 5.3 Fossil fuels: oil and gas – the Arabian (Persian) Gulf, Middle East

The Arabian (or Persian) Gulf Basin contains well over half of the conventionally recoverable oil reserves of the world, and also huge reserves of natural gas. This extraordinarily rich basin extends over a length of more than 2000 km from Oman in the south to Syria and southeast Turkey in the north (Figure 1). Production has been derived from some 250 reservoirs in the region, of which more than 80% are in Jurassic–Cretaceous sediments. The Middle East is unique for the size of its individual deposits, with 14 fields having recoverable reserves in excess of 10 billion barrels (Shannon and Naylor, 1989). These include such giants as the Ghawar field in Saudi Arabia and Burgan field in Kuwait (both with more than 70 billion barrels of oil) and the Rumaila and Kirkuk fields in Iraq, each with around 15–20 billion barrels of oil (Tiratsoo, 1984). Many of the oil fields in the Persian Gulf are also associated with huge gas resources. In addition, however, some very large unassociated gas fields also occur in the region, such as the North Dome field off Qatar. These gas deposits occur in the Permian Khuff limestone and are, therefore, older and underlie the main oil deposits. Unassociated gas deposits in many other parts of the world appear to be related to coal measures of Carboniferous age. There are several reasons why the Middle East is so well endowed in hydrocarbon resources and these are briefly discussed below.

The oil fields of the Arabian Gulf are located in late Mesozoic to early Paleogene reservoir sediments that were deposited on a continental shelf forming off the northeastern margin of the Arabian portion of Gondwana. A significant proportion of these sediments are limestones, indicating deposition at equatorial paleolatitudes in the Tethyan seaway (North, 1985). As Pangea fragmented the Arabian land mass became part of a downgoing slab involved in subduction to the north and east. Fortunately, subduction ceased in Pliocene times with the formation of the Zagros mountains in present day Iran, and this hydrocarbon-rich basin was preserved largely intact. It is likely that other parts of the Tethyan seaway, probably equally well endowed, were consumed by subduction in Cenozoic times, perhaps accounting for the fact that the western and eastern extremities of the seaway contain lesser oil and gas deposits.

The tectonic and sedimentological regimes active in this environment produced at least three major source rock sediments in the Arabian foreland, along the axis of the present day basin and in the orogenic belt of Iran. Source rocks are all marine in origin and developed over the entire extent of the Arabian platform. Oil and gas is hosted in a variety of different lithologies and the principal reservoirs become progressively younger from southwest to northeast. The thick carbonate and sandstone reservoirs that

Figure 1 Location and distribution of some of the major oil and gas fields in the Arabian Gulf (after Shannon and Naylor, 1989).

formed in the Persian Gulf Basin are also characterized by a remarkable lack of intergranular cements and a high degree of primary porosity, making them very effective for the migration and ultimate concentration of hydrocarbons. This also contributes to very good recovery rates and the fact that very few wells need to be be drilled in order to exploit a given field. Periodic uplift and subaerial exposure also resulted in the deposition of numerous evaporitic horizons that make good seals for oil and gas entrapment. Sedimentation in the Jurassic and Cretaceous periods was characterized in general by a marine transgression over the Arabian platform. Initially widespread carbonate sedimentation occurred and this was followed by increasing aridity and evaporate formation. In detail, sea level fluctuations and climate changes gave rise to complex interfingering of lithologies (Shannon and Naylor, 1989), as illustrated in the environmental interpretations for the region during mid-Jurassic and mid-Cretaceous times (Figure 2).

The structural development of the region was also conducive to the formation of very large and effective trap sites. Three types of structural traps are recognized in the Arabian Gulf Basin. These include large, but gently dipping, anticlinal warps which caused oil entrapment mainly in Jurassic limestones (e.g. Ghawar in Saudi Arabia); diapiric salt dome structures arising from basement evaporitic sequences which deform Cretaceous and Jurassic limestones (e.g. Burgan in Kuwait); and steeply dipping anticlines in the foothills of the Pliocene mountain building episode in Iraq and Iran (e.g. Kirkuk in Iraq). The presence of thick evaporitic sequences is considered to be one of the most important features of the region because the salt horizons are believed to have absorbed much of the shortening that accompanied subduction to the north and east of the basin. This had the effect of preserving the large gently anticlinal structural traps that characterize the southwestern portions of the region and accounts for the huge sizes (up to 100 km long) of many of the oil fields (Shannon and Naylor, 1989). In addition to the presence of salt, some of the other geological features of the Middle East that have made it so productive for oil and gas include a long history of marine sedimentation at relatively low paleolatitudes, numerous transgressive and regressive sedimentary cycles resulting in a close association between source and reservoir rocks, and the occurrence of widespread seals, in the form of evaporitic sequences, that prevent leakage of the oil and gas.

Figure 2 Interpretations of the evolving sedimentary environment in the region of the Arabian Gulf during (a) mid-Jurassic and (b) mid-Cretaceous times (after Shannon and Naylor, 1989).

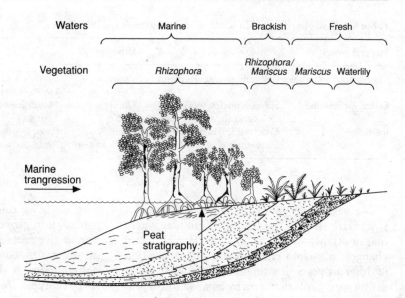

Waters   Marine   Brackish   Fresh

Vegetation   *Rhizophora*   *Rhizophora/ Mariscus*   *Mariscus*   Waterlily

Marine trangression

Peat stratigraphy

Figure 5.34 Generalized scheme illustrating the nature of peat stratigraphy in terms of vegetation type and transgressive/regressive effects in a swamp environment (after Spackman *et al.*, 1976).

transformed to a series of products ranging from lignite and sub-bituminous coal (known as "brown coals"), to bituminous coal and finally anthracite (the "hard coals"). The formation of peat is an essential initial step in the process and involves restrained biochemical degradation of plant matter without rampant oxidative and bacterial decay. Coalification follows once peat is covered by overburden and subjected to an increase in temperature with progressive burial.

Coal is a sedimentary rock that contains more than 50% by weight of carbonaceous material and can readily be burnt (McCabe, 1984). It forms by the compaction of peat in an environment represented by a well vegetated land surface that is saturated with water. This environment is loosely termed a "swamp", but should not necessarily imply a tropical or equatorial climate as it is now well known that many coals have accumulated in cold climates at mid- to high latitudes. The greatest concentrations of peat are in fact accumulating in Russia (with about 60% of the world's resources; McCabe, 1984) at latitudes of around 50–70° N. High rainfall is not an environmental prerequisite, although abundant free-standing water promotes plant growth and also submerges dead vegetation, retarding the rate of decomposition. Furthermore, swampy environments often

contain waters that are both anaerobic and acidic, which promotes the preservation of organic material by minimizing oxidation and destroying bacteria. Tropical rain forests seldom form peat accumulations because the high temperatures promote rapid oxidation and decay of organic material. The best conditions for peat accumulation reflect a balance between organic productivity and decay, with the added prerequisite of low sediment input necessary to keep dilution of the peat by clastic material to a minimum.

Coal characteristics

Coal is a heterogeneous sedimentary rock that reflects both the different sedimentological regimes within which peat forms and the varied vegetation types from which it is derived. Peat deposits are known to have formed in many settings including lacustrine, fluvial, deltaic, and beach-related (Galloway and Hobday, 1983; McCabe, 1984; Selley, 1988). Peat and coal deposits, therefore, exhibit a wide range of shapes, and are also characterized by the facies variations expected of any sedimentary rock. Figure 5.34 illustrates the stratigraphic variations one might expect to see in peat, as a function of vegetation type and fluctuating water levels.

Table 5.2 Coal classification in terms of maceral groups and lithotypes

Maceral group		Lithotype		
Vitrinite (or huminite)	Cell walls of vascular plants	Vitrain	Vitrinite + <20% exinite	
		Clarain	Layers of all three maceral groups	} Humic coals
Exinite (or liptinite)	Spores, cuticles, waxes, resins and algae	Durain	Mainly inertinite and exinite	
		Fusain	Fusinite	
Inertinite	Oxidized and burnt (fusinite) plant material	Cannel coal	Spore-dominated exinite	} Sapropelic coals
		Boghead coal	Algae-dominated exinite	

The vegetation shown in Figure 5.34 applies specifically to the Everglades in Florida, where marine transgression results in lateral facies changes in swamp environment and deposition of different peats that originate from a variety of plant types. Coals that form by compaction of peat will also, therefore, exhibit marked variations in composition and vegetative make-up. This characteristic has led to a rigorous classification of coals, the main elements of which are shown in Table 5.2. In the same way that a rock is made up of minerals, a coal is made up of "macerals," which are components of plant tissue, or their degraded products, altered during compaction and diagenesis. The main maceral groups are *vitrinite* (also called huminite in brown coals), made up of woody material (branches, roots, leaves, etc.), and *exinite* (also called liptinite), which comprises spores, cuticles, waxes, resins, and algae. A third grouping is also recognized, termed *inertinite*, which comprises mainly the remains of oxidized plant material and fungal remains. Each maceral group is further subdivided into individual macerals, but listing of these is beyond the scope of this book and can be obtained in more detailed texts, such as Stach *et al.* (1982). Different combinations of maceral groups identify the coal lithotypes (i.e. analogous to a rock type) and these are also listed in Table 5.2.

The majority of coals are humic (i.e. made up of macroscopic plant parts), are peat derived, and can be subdivided into four lithotypes. These are vitrain, clarain, durain, and fusain, whose maceral compositions are shown in Table 5.2. The coal lithotypes are important in determining its properties, in particular factors of economic import-

ance such as calorific value and liquefaction potential. In general, the highly reflective, more combustive coals are made up of vitrain, whereas the duller, less combustive coals comprise essentially durains. It should be noted, however, that coal lithotypes should not be confused with coal rank, which separates low calorific value brown coals from high heat capacity hard coals essentially on the basis of degree of compaction or burial depth.

A small proportion of coals are sapropelic and formed largely from microscopic plant remains such as spores and algae (exinite). The sapropelic lithotypes, also referred to as cannel and boghead coals (Table 5.2), did not form from peat. They can be found overlying humic coals, forming in muddy environments as the swamp was flooded and buried, and occasionally are linked to the formation of oil shales (see section 5.4.4 below).

In addition to the maceral-based classification, coals can also be subdivided in terms of their chemical composition, specifically their carbon, hydrogen, and oxygen contents. Figure 5.35 is a ternary plot of normalized C, H, and O in which the compositional fields of peat and the coals are shown in relation to those for oil and oil shales. As peat is progressively compacted and coalification commences, the carbon content increases noticeably, whereas hydrogen remains fairly constant and oxygen decreases. Hydrogen only starts to diminish noticeably once the hard coals start to develop. The chemical changes that accompany coalification are accompanied by the production of CO_2 and CH_4 gas. The source rocks for some of the gas fields in the North Sea are believed to be underlying Westphalian coal beds.

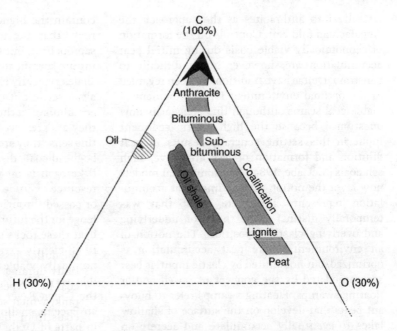

Figure 5.35 Ternary C–H–O plot showing the compositional trend accompanying coalification and the comparison between coals and oil and oil shale compositions (after Forsman and Hunt, 1958).

Another important property of coal, but one which is unrelated to its organic or maceral characteristics, is ash content. As peat forms it inevitably incorporates inorganic, clastic detritus from a variety of sources. During coalification this detritus is diagenetically altered to form a variety of authigenic mineral components such as quartz, carbonate, sulfide, and clay minerals. These components remain behind to make up its ash content once the coal is combusted or processed. Low ash content coals are obviously economically advantageous as this parameter translates favorably into higher calorific values, better grindability, and less deleterious environmental effects such as sulfur emissions.

A note concerning formation of economically viable coals

The formation of economically viable coals is determined by processes active during both initial peat accumulation and later coalification. In the latter case bituminous coals and anthracite are the high rank products of thermal maturation and burial, and are characterized by the best calorific values and lowest volatile contents. Progressive

Figure 5.36 Bituminous coal seam from the Witbank area, South Africa, hosted in carbonaceous shales and deltaic sandstones of the Permian Ecca Group (photo is courtesy of Bruce Cairncross).

compaction will transform most humic coals to these products, which, if extensive and thick enough, will likely be economically viable. In addition simply to burial, some anthracites are also known to be products of tectonic deformation or devolatilization by nearby igneous intrusions, a good example of the former being the Pennsylvanian coals of the USA, which grade laterally into anthracites as they approach the Appalachian fold belt. Controls on the formation of economically viable coals during initial peat accumulation are, however, more difficult to constrain. Deltas have traditionally been regarded as the optimal environment for development of viable coal seams, although this concept is now questioned because the high clastic sediment input in this setting generally results in peat dilution and formation of less attractive, high ash coals (McCabe, 1984). Environmental models now favor the notion that optimal peat accumulation represents a discrete event that was temporally distinct from those of underlying and overlying clastic deposition. The notion of an environment where peat accumulation is optimized, but not diluted by clastic input, is best accommodated by the concept of raised and/or floating swamps. Floating swamps refer to buoyant peats that develop on the surface of shallow lakes to eventually accumulate and accrete on the lake margins (Figure 5.37). Raised swamps are seen as the final product in a continuum of processes which extend from initial development of shallow lakes with floating peat, followed by formation of well vegetated, low-lying swamps, and eventually to raised swamps as accretion of organic material eventually sculpts a landscape that is elevated with respect to the sediment substrate. The latter environment is obviously one in which clastic sediment input is minimized. This evolutionary sequence, illustrated in Figure 5.37, serves as a model for the depositional environment in which optimal formation of thick peat, and subsequently economic coal horizons, might form. Raised swamps can form in deltaic environments, but the above model applies specifically to those settings in which sediment input is minimized and the resultant coals are low-ash in character. Examples of raised swamps include the Klang-Langat delta in Malaysia and areas of Sarawak where peat accumulation of more than 2 mm yr^{-1} is occurring (McCabe, 1984).

5.4.4 Oil shales and tar sands

Although organic matter accumulates in most sediments, it is the shales or mud rocks which contain the highest hydrocarbon contents. Mud rocks that are rich in organic matter are called sapropelites, but those that yield free oil on heating are specifically referred to as "oil shales." Oil shales typically form in lacustrine settings where algae settle out of the aerated upper layers and accumulate in the anaerobic bottom muds where they are preserved from rapid oxidative decay. In this sense they are akin to the sapropelic cannel or boghead coals discussed above. Since algal (Type I) kerogen is oil prone, these shales represent a resource of crude oil that has not as yet matured, or passed through the oil window. A major challenge for the future is to develop the technology to heat these rocks up to the temperatures required to efficiently extract oil, and to do so in an economically viable and environmentally responsible way. The best known oil shale is perhaps the Green River Formation which developed in an Eocene, shallow-lacustrine or sabkha setting, in parts of Utah, Colorado, and Wyoming, USA. Despite an enormous potential capacity to produce oil (grades of up to 240 liters of oil per ton of rock are reported), production from the Green River shale resource has, thus far, proven non-viable. Successful processing of oil shale has nevertheless been achieved in countries such as Estonia, Russia, and China. Present day oil shale formation is taking place in Australian saline lakes where the alga *Botryococcus braunii* is accumulating to form a type of sapropelic peat known as coorongite. Likewise, the torbanites of Scotland formed in lacustrine settings from accumulation of a Carboniferous variety of *Botryococcus*, as did the Permian oil shales of Tasmania (tasmanites).

Tar sands are often confused with oil shales, although they are in fact quite different. Tar sands are sandstones within which bitumen or asphalt occurs. Bitumen is a solid or semi-solid hydrocarbon either derived by normal degradation of crude oils, or formed directly as a high molecular weight hydrocarbon without ever having been a light oil. In certain instances, tar sands that are near the surface can be extracted and processed to produce oil and a range of other useful hydrocarbon by-products. The best known of these is the Athabasca tar sand of northern Alberta, Canada. As with oil shales, though, technological and environmental

(I) Floating swamp on lake margins

(II) Low-lying swamp,
diverse and luxuriant flora

(III) Slightly raised swamp,
restricted flora

(IV) Extensive raised swamp,
restricted and stunted flora

Lakes

Vertically zoned peat

Figure 5.37 Environmental model for optimal peat accumulation, in terms of an evolutionary development of swamp types which leads ultimately to the formation of raised swamps in which extensive, thick peats, devoid of major sediment input, form (after Romanov, 1968; McCabe, 1984).

difficulties provide major obstacles to more wide-spread production from this resource at present. Both tar sands and oil shales, however, clearly represent significant petroleum resources for the future.

5.4.5 Gas hydrates

A fairly recent discovery in the permafrost regions of the world, as well as in ocean sediments sampled during the Deep Sea Drilling Program, is the presence of vast resources of hydrocarbon locked up as frozen gas hydrates. Gas hydrates are crystalline aqueous compounds that form at low temperatures when the ice lattice expands to accommodate a variety of gaseous molecules, the most important of which, for the purposes of this discussion, is methane (CH_4). A methane hydrate forms when sufficient CH_4 is present in water, at the appropriate pressure and temperature, to form a solid compound with the ideal composition $CH_4.5^{3/4}H_2O$ (i.e. the unit cell comprises 46 water molecules with up to 8 methane molecules). Other gases, including CO_2, H_2S, and C_2H_6, also form gas hydrates with a similar structure. On a global scale the volumes of natural gas present in gas hydrate reservoirs are estimated to be a factor of two times greater than the total fossil fuel reserve to present (Kennicutt et al., 1993). Methane hydrates clearly, therefore, represent an enormous energy resource for the future. They are also, however, an object of concern in that global warming might accelerate the natural release of CH_4 by melting gas hydrates and further accentuate the influences of greenhouse gas accumulation on climate change.

It is of interest to consider the conditions under which methane hydrates form in the ocean basins of the world. Figure 5.38a shows a simplified phase diagram with the H_2O ice–water and CH_4 hydrate–gas boundaries marked. If sufficient methane and pore water are available methane hydrates will stabilize in ocean floor sediment where temperatures are around 3–4 °C at pressures of about 50 atmospheres (equivalent to about 500 meters water depth). Gas hydrates will melt if either the temperature increases or the pressure decreases. The thickness of the methane hydrate stability zone in oceanic sediments will depend on the pressure (an increase in which has the effect of stabilizing hydrates to lower temperatures) and the geothermal gradient, the latter dictating the rate at which sediment is heated with progressive burial. For a constant geothermal gradient the thickness of the methane hydrate layer will increase directly as a function of water depth. Figure 5.38b shows this graphically for a typical ocean-sediment profile on the continental shelf. It illustrates the initiation of gas hydrate formation

in sediment under about 500 m of water and the progressive increase in thickness of the hydrate stability zone with depth. Under 3 km of water a methane hydrate zone almost 1000 m thick could form if the ingredients were available. This particular profile was calculated for a geothermal gradient of 27 °C km^{-1} but would be thinner if the sediment profile was subjected to higher geothermal gradients. These considerations, even if viewed conservatively, point to the enormous volumes of gaseous hydrocarbons that potentially could be locked up in the ocean sediments.

Figure 5.38 (a) Phase diagram illustrating the regions of gas hydrate stability under most natural conditions in the near-surface (after Kvenvolden and McMenamin, 1980). (b) Profile across a typical ocean–sediment interface in a continental margin setting, showing the progressive increase in the width of the gas hydrate stability zone in the ocean sediment with increasing depth of sea water (after Kvenvolden, 1988).

(b)

Figure 5.38 (cont'd)

SUMMARY

Sedimentation is a fundamental geological process that takes place over much of the Earth's surface, in response to the pattern of global tectonic cycles. A number of very important mineral and fossil fuel commodities are concentrated during the formation of sedimentary rocks. Placer processes are important during clastic sedimentation and form by the sorting of light from heavy particles. A number of hydrodynamic mechanisms, such as settling, entrainment, shear sorting, and transport sorting, are responsible for the concentration of different commodities in a variety of sedimentary micro- and meso-environments. At a larger scale, placer deposits form mainly in fluvial and beach-related environments and include concentrations of gold, diamonds, tin, zirconium, and titanium. Chemical sedimentation, where dissolved components precipitate out of solution from brines, also gives rise to a wide range of important natural resources. Precipitation of ferric iron from sea water is one of the principal mechanisms for the formation of iron ore deposits. Banded iron-formations formed in a variety of oceanic settings mainly in the Paleoproterozoic and prior to the onset of significant levels of oxygen in the atmosphere. Ironstone deposits tend to form mainly in Phanerozoic times. Other types of metal concentration linked to syn-sedimentary and early diagenetic chemical processes occur in carbonaceous black shales (Ni, Co, Cr, Cu, Mn, Zn, Ag, etc.) and in Mn nodules on the ocean floor. Accumulation of phosphorus and the development of phosphorites in ocean settings is a process that is linked both to direct chemical precipitation from sea water and to biological mediation. The upwelling of cold currents onto the continental shelf and biological productivity are processes implicated in the formation of most of the world's important phosphate deposits, so important for fertilizer production and global food production. Chemical sediments formed by high rates of evaporation of sea water and lacustrine brines host most of the world's Na, K, borate, nitrate, and sulfate resources, also important to the agricultural industry.

Fossil fuels, in the form of oil, natural gas, and coal, are the most important and valuable of all natural resources as they provide the world with most of its combustion-derived energy. Oil and natural gas are derived in the initial stages by biodegradation of largely planktonic organisms in marine environments to form oil-prone kerogen and biogenic gas. Further burial results in subsequent chemical and thermal modification of kerogen to produce wet gas, and a liquid condensate in the "oil window," typically at burial depths of 3000–4000 m and temperatures of 100–150 °C. Further burial results only in the production of more dry gas. Burial of vascular land plants gives rise initially to the formation of peat and the production of mainly dry gas. Further compaction of peat gives rise to coals, the rank of which is a function of progressive burial. Other forms of fossil fuel, important for the future but largely unexploited at present for technological and economic reasons, include oil shales and tar sands, as well as methane hydrates in permafrost regions and ocean floor sediments.

FURTHER READING

A huge volume of literature is available in the fields of sedimentology and fossil fuels, but less with respect to chemical sedimentation and metallogeny. The following books and reviews are subdivided in accordance with the main topics covered in this chapter.

Sedimentological and placer processes

Allen, P.A. (1997) *Earth Surface Processes*. Oxford: Blackwell Science, 404 pp.

Leeder, M. (1999) *Sedimentology and Sedimentary Basins: From Turbulence to Tectonics*. Oxford: Blackwell Science, 592 pp.

Slingerland, R. and Smith, N.D. (1986) Occurrence and formation of water-laid placers. *Annual Reviews of Earth and Planetary Sciences*, 14, 113–47.

Chemical sedimentation and ore formation

Mel'nik, Y.P. (1982) *Precambrian Banded Iron Formations*. New York: Elsevier, 282 pp.

Melvin, J.L. (1991) *Evaporites, Petroleum and Mineral Resources*. Developments in Sedimentology, 50. New York: Elsevier, Chapter 4.

Parnell, J., Ye, L. and Chen, C. (1990) *Sediment-hosted Mineral Deposits*. Special Publication, 11, International Association of Sedimentologists. Oxford: Blackwell Scientific Publications, 227 pp.

Young, T.P. and Gordon Taylor, W.E. (1989) *Phanerozoic Ironstones*. Special Publication 46. London: The Geological Society of London, 257 pp.

Fossil fuels

Engel, M.H. and Mack, S.A. (1993) *Organic Geochemistry: Principles and Applications*. New York: Plenum Press, 861 pp.

Glennie, K.W. (1998) *Petroleum Geology of the North Sea: Basic Concepts and Recent Advances*. Oxford: Blackwell Science, 636 pp.

North, F.K. (1985) *Petroleum Geology*. London: Allen & Unwin, 607 pp.

Selley, R.C. (1998) *Elements of Petroleum Geology*, 2nd edn. New York: Academic Press, 470 pp.

Thomas, L. (1992) *Handbook of Practical Coal Geology*. New York: John Wiley.

Ward, C.R. (1984) *Coal Geology and Coal Technology*. Oxford: Blackwell Science, 345 pp.

PART FOUR

Global Tectonics and Metallogeny

CHAPTER SIX

Ore deposits in a global tectonic context

6.1 INTRODUCTION

Most of the world's great mineral deposits are the products of a fortuitous superposition of geological processes that resulted in anomalous concentration of ores, often over an extended period of time. The preceding chapters have shown that the formation of ore deposits is, nevertheless, related to much the same sort of processes that gave rise to the formation of normal igneous, sedimentary, and metamorphic rocks in the Earth's crust. The fact that a close relationship exists between rock-forming and ore-forming processes means that metallogeny must be relevant to understanding the nature of crustal evolution through geological time (Barley and Groves, 1992; Windley, 1995). Conversely, crust-forming processes and the global plate tectonic paradigm have become indispensable to the broader understanding of how ore deposits form and no modern economic geologist can practice successfully without an appreciation of the history and evolution of the continents and oceans. Consequently, this chapter summarizes some of the recent thinking that relates the formation of ore deposits to global tectonics and the evolution of the continents. There are essentially two ways of doing this. One is to chart continental evolution and place ore deposits into a secular and tectonic framework (e.g. Meyer, 1981, 1988; Veizer *et al.*, 1989; Barley and Groves, 1992). The other is to empirically describe ore deposits in the context of the tectonic environment and host rocks in which they occur (e.g. Mitchell and Garson, 1981; Hutchison, 1983; Sawkins, 1990). The latter approach has been covered in considerable detail in Sawkins's (1990) *Metal Deposits in Relation to Plate Tectonics*, and there is little point in summarizing this extensive compilation here. The former approach is a more difficult undertaking and requires a thorough knowledge of the evolution of continents with time, a topic that becomes progressively less well constrained – and more controversial – the further back in Earth history one goes. There are, however, significant benefits to be gained by understanding the intricate processes of ore formation in terms of the secular evolution of the Earth's crust and atmosphere. This is the approach that has been adopted below, even though it is necessarily cursory and in places speculative.

6.2 PATTERNS IN THE DISTRIBUTION OF MINERAL DEPOSITS

It has long been known that the different styles of mineralization are not randomly distributed, either in time or in space, and that broad patterns exist when relating deposit types to crustal evolution and global tectonic setting. The original compilations of ore deposit type as a function of geological time by Meyer (1981, 1988) have been re-examined by Veizer *et al.* (1989) and Barley and Groves (1992) and reveal consistent patterns. Figure 6.1 distinguishes between the secular distribution of metal deposits formed in *orogenic* settings and those formed in *anorogenic* environments and in continental basins. Although this compilation is a "first-order" generalization, it is nevertheless clear that deposit types classified as orogenic (including lode-gold or orogenic gold ores, volcanogenic massive base metal sulfides, and the porphyry-epithermal family of base and precious metal deposits) occur either in the late stages of the Archean Eon (between 3000 and 2500 Ma) or in the Phanerozoic Eon (between 540 Ma and present). The Proterozoic Eon, between 2500 and 540 Ma, contains fewer of these types of deposits. By contrast, the majority of metal deposits that are associated with so-called "anorogenic" magmatism (such as the anorthosite-hosted Ti deposits and the Olympic Dam and Kiruna type Fe oxide–Cu–Au ores), as well as sediment hosted ores (such as the SEDEX type Pb–Zn deposits and the stratiform "red-bed" type Cu deposits), are dominantly hosted in Proterozoic rocks (Figure 6.1). An explanation for this pattern, as discussed below (see sections 6.4.3 and 6.5 in particular), is that ore formation might be closely linked to the so-called "supercontinent cycle," which describes the broad scale amalgamation and dispersal of the major continental fragments with time. It is, for example, evident that peaks in the production of anorogenic and continental sediment-hosted metal deposits (Figure 6.1, lower histogram) coincide with the periods of crustal stability and the existence of large, stable continental amalgamations such as Nena in the Mesoproterozoic, Rodinia in the Neoproterozoic and Pangea in the early Mesozoic. Periods of large-scale continental fragmentation, by contrast,

appear to be orogenically more active and give rise to a different suite of ore deposit types.

In a study designed to examine the rates at which ore deposits are recycled or dispersed (either by erosive or tectonic dismembering) in the Earth's crust, Veizer *et al.* (1989) have produced a very similar pattern of ore deposit distribution with time. In this compilation hydrothermal and volcano-sedimentary base–precious metal deposits formed mainly in late Archean and Phanerozoic times, whereas chemical–sedimentary and ultramafic deposits reflect concentration mechanisms that took place in the mid-Proterozoic. The reasons behind this pattern are likely to be complex and multifaceted and are discussed in more detail below. It should be emphasized at this stage, however, that the relationships observed in Figure 6.1 could also be due, at least in part, to a preservation factor. The existence of numerous arc-related orogenic deposits in the late Archean, for example, reflects the preservation of greenstone belts in stable shield areas of the world. In Proterozoic times, by contrast, the preponderance of collisional orogenies might have uplifted and eroded similar mineralized arcs so that many of the related near-surface ores were destroyed. The products of young Cenozoic orogenies are also preserved because many of them have not yet suffered collision and uplift and are, therefore, still preserved.

6.3 CONTINENTAL GROWTH RATES

The relationships illustrated in Figure 6.1 indicate that estimates of the rates of continental growth with time are important to any consideration of the patterns of continental assembly and dispersal and, therefore, metallogeny. Such estimates are problematic because of the difficulties in calculating the rates of recycling (or destruction) of continental material relative to new crust formation. Growth rate estimates vary enormously, and range from one scenario, where the majority of continental crust formed rapidly in the early Archean (curve A in Figure 6.2a), to another where continents grew exponentially with time, with the most substantial contributions coming after

Orogenic

Anorogenic and continental sediment-hosted

Figure 6.1 Distribution of ore deposit styles, classified according to orogenic (upper set of histograms) and anorogenic/continental sediment-hosted metal deposits (lower set of histograms) as a function of time. The length of each histogram bar is an estimate of the proportion of ore formed over a 50 million year interval relative to the global resource for that deposit type. Periods of supercontinent amalgamation are shown as Pangea, Rodinia, and Nena, with decreasing levels of confidence further back in time. The diagram is originally after Meyer (1988) and modified after Barley and Groves (1992).

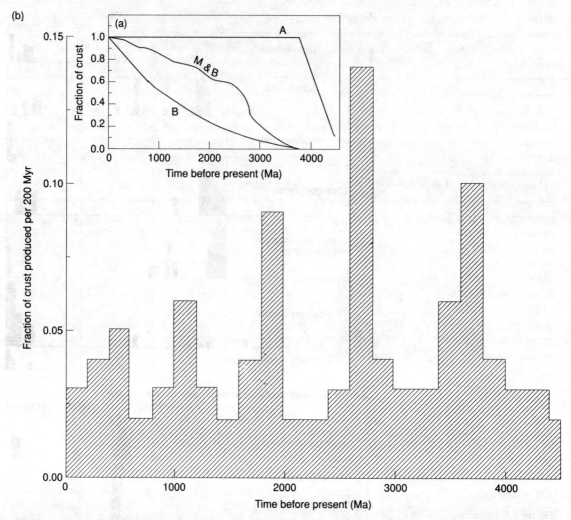

Figure 6.2 (a) Different models for the rates of continental growth. Curves A and B contrast considerations of early Archean continental growth with an exponential growth rate model in which the bulk of the continents grew subsequent to about 1500 Ma. The curve M&B illustrates the broadly linear but episodic continental growth rate curve suggested by McCulloch and Bennett (1994). (b) Histogram showing the estimated rates of continental growth averaged over 200 million year intervals based on a global compilation of Sm–Nd model ages (after McCulloch and Bennett, 1994).

1.5 Ga (curve B in Figure 6.2a). The most likely situation probably reflects an intermediate case where approximately linear, but episodic, crustal growth took place. McCulloch and Bennett (1994) supported this scenario on the basis of Sm–Nd model and U–Pb zircon age distribution data for the continental crust, showing that the propor-

tion of crustal recycling relative to growth is approximately constant. The model, illustrated in Figure 6.2b, suggests discrete episodes of enhanced crustal growth. It envisages that 50–60% of the Earth's continental crust had been produced by the end of the Archean, but that this occurred in two major episodes at 3600–3500 Ma and at

2800–2600 Ma, with the latter being the most important period of crustal growth in Earth history. Two important episodes of crust formation were also considered to have taken place in the Proterozoic, one at 2000–1800 Ma and the other at around 1100–1000 Ma.

It is interesting to note that the McCulloch and Bennett model suggests that only a relatively small proportion of new crust was added to the Earth's surface in the Phanerozoic Eon. This appears to be somewhat at odds with the observation that this period of Earth history was particularly productive in terms of ore deposit formation. This supports the notion of preferential preservation of younger ore-forming environments compared to older sequences which become either progressively more eroded, or buried and metamorphosed, with time. The episodic continental growth model described in Figure 6.2 is reasonably consistent with the pattern of metallogenic evolution described here and is used as the basis for a closer examination of the relationships between crustal evolution and ore deposit formation.

6.4 Crustal evolution and metallogenesis

The review by Barley and Groves (1992) suggested that there were three principal factors which affected the pattern of global metallogeny. These are the evolution of the hydrosphere–atmosphere, the secular decrease in global heat production, and long-term global tectonic trends. These major factors, together with a number of related parameters, are discussed in more detail below, with an indication of how and why they influence the temporal and geographic distribution of ore deposit types.

6.4.1 Evolution of the hydrosphere and atmosphere

The changing budget of O_2, and to a lesser degree CO_2, in the Earth's atmosphere with time had a significant role to play in the formation of ore deposits, especially those related to redox processes and to the weathering and erosion of continental crust. During the Archean it is generally held that the atmosphere contained very little free molecular oxygen (although the actual amounts are still strongly debated) and what little did exist was the result of inorganic photodissociation of water vapor. A reduced atmosphere in the Archean helps to explain many of the features of ore formation at that time, including the widespread mobility of Fe^{2+} and development of Algoma and Superior type banded iron-formations, and the preservation of detrital grains of uraninite and pyrite in sedimentary sequences such as those of the Witwatersrand and Huronian basins. The transition from the Archean to the Proterozoic Eons, at 2500 Ma, broadly coincides with the first major increase in atmospheric oxygen (Figure 6.3). This event is possibly related to the evolution of primitive life and the development of cyanobacteria capable of photosynthetically producing oxygen. The partial pressures of O_2 in the atmosphere can be estimated from the mobility of Fe^{2+} in paleosols (the remnants of weathering horizons or soils preserved in the rock record) and suggest that a sharp increase in the partial pressure of oxygen (pO_2) occurred at around 2200 Ma (Rye and Holland, 1998). The interval between about 2500 and 2000 Ma is known as the period of "oxyatmoinversion" and is generally believed to coincide with a significant rise in atmospheric oxygen levels. It is also the period *after* which development of Superior type banded iron-formations and related bedded manganese deposits ceased. Another significant increase in atmospheric oxygen levels coincided with the end of the Proterozoic Eon, when macroscopic, multicellular life forms (the Metazoan fauna which required oxygenated respiration) proliferated. In addition, the early Phanerozoic is also the time when vascular plants evolved and this, too, would have contributed to the increase in atmospheric oxygen levels (Figure 6.3). In contrast with the net addition of O_2 in the atmosphere, CO_2 has progressively decreased with time. The initially high levels of CO_2 in the atmosphere were a product of extensive volcanism and outgassing during the Archean, but levels have dropped steadily, but episodically, as a result of carbon and carbonate deposition in sediments. The evolution of the Earth's atmosphere and, in particular, the global O_2 and CO_2 trends are essentially non-recurrent

Figure 6.3 Estimates of the episodic rise of pO_2 over the past 3 Gyr, constrained by data derived from the mobility of Fe in paleosols (fossilized soil horizons). Bars and arrows show actual estimates of the ages and pO_2 for a number of paleosol horizons worldwide, whereas the solid curve is the best estimate of the atmospheric pO_2 trajectory with time (after Rye and Holland, 1998).

and irreversible and contribute to the time-specific occurrence of ore deposit types such as banded iron-formations and Witwatersrand type placers.

6.4.2 Secular decrease in global heat production

The production of heat from the Earth, mainly from the decay of long-lived isotopes such as U, Th, and K, was significantly greater (by a factor of two to three times) in the Archean than it is today. This pattern, like that for atmospheric evolution, is also non-recurrent and irreversible. Figure 6.4 shows the decline in global heat production with time and a corresponding crustal growth curve similar to that discussed above. There are several consequences for crust formation related to the secular decrease in heat production. One of the most obvious is that the Archean mantle was hotter (by about 200–300 °C; Windley, 1995) than at present and this could have led to an increase in the volume of melting at this time. A higher degree of partial melting could account for

production of the high-Mg komatiites that typify many Archean greenstone belts and which are relatively rare in younger oceanic settings (see Figure 6.4), although other explanations are also feasible. Higher heat production thus provides an explanation for the preferential occurrence, in the Archean, of komatiite-related magmatic Ni–Cu sulfide deposits, such as those at Kambalda, Western Australia and in Zimbabwe. Another consequence of higher heat flow in the Archean is the suggestion that convective overturn in the mantle would have been more rapid, leading to shorter ocean crust residence times and more rapid plate motion (Windley, 1995). Archean oceanic crust is also considered to have been thicker than in later periods, which is supported by suggestions that ophiolites greater than 1000 years old are more than double the thickness of their younger equivalents (Moores, 1993). As another consequence, Archean oceans may have been more shallow than those at present, resulting in a reduced continental freeboard.

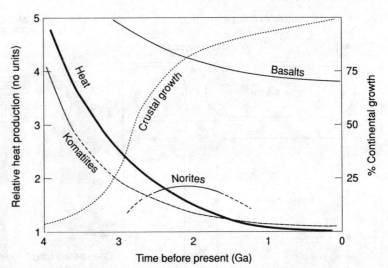

Figure 6.4 Schematic diagram showing the exponential decline in global heat production with time and the matching decline in production of komatiite volcanism. Also shown is a crustal growth curve and the period of enhanced mafic or "norite" magmatism in the late Archean and early Proterozoic (after Hall and Hughes, 1993).

6.4.3 Long-term global tectonic trends

The broad-scale amalgamation and dispersal of continental fragments with time, also referred to as the "supercontinent cycle," is an all-encompassing feature of Earth history that has implications for virtually every aspect of global evolution, including metallogeny. As seen in Figure 6.1, broad temporal trends in ore formation reflect the contrast between episodes of orogeny and periods of stability. In detail, however, it is the supercontinent cycle that controls the many other factors more directly related to secular metallogenic trends. Unlike the patterns imposed by atmospheric evolution and heat production, the supercontinent cycle is recurrent and cyclical in that continental fragments have amalgamated and dispersed several times through Earth history. This cyclicity helps explain why some ore deposit types, or at least the processes that give rise to them, are recognizably repetitive despite the preservation bias of ore deposits in younger rocks. A detailed understanding of how the supercontinent cycle can be used in the study of ore deposits is a complex issue and likely to remain a profitable area of future research. Some of the concepts that are relevant to both global tectonics and the pattern of crustal/metallogenic evolution are briefly mentioned below.

Rates of continental growth

The growth of continental crust, whether it be episodic or linear, early or late, will affect global metallogeny simply because the majority of viable ore deposits are located in or on continental crust. Periods of rapid continental growth reflect episodes of more intense magmatic activity and tectonism, and this, in turn, promotes the formation of magmatic, magmatic-hydrothermal, and hydrothermal ores. The majority of the world's gold deposits, for example, are related to events in either the late Archean or Mesozoic–Cenozoic (Figure 6.1), both periods of major orogenesis and crust formation (Figure 6.2b).

The nature of mantle convection

Models for mantle convection suggest two modes of occurrence (Figure 6.5), which may not be mutually exclusive and could operate at the same time. One model suggests overturn of material in two discrete layers with little or no mass transfer between them, and the other envisages that the entire mantle overturns due to the major downwelling of cold lithospheric slab material with concomitant up-rise of large magmatic plumes (Stein and Hofmann, 1994). The first scheme (Figure 6.5a) is considered to represent the situation

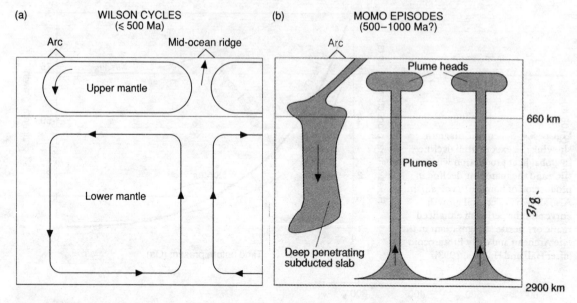

Figure 6.5 Two contrasting models for mantle circulation (after Stein and Hofmann, 1994). (a) Mantle convection in two discrete layers with little or no mass transfer from one to the other, corresponding to the conventional plate tectonic regime in which crustal growth occurs in accordance with the Wilson cycle. (b) Deeply penetrative mantle overturn involving the downwelling of cold lithosphere into the lower mantle and the associated upwelling of major plumes. These MOMO (mantle overturn and major orogeny) episodes are believed to replenish the depleted upper mantle chemically and also to coincide with the major periods of orogenic activity and enhanced crustal growth.

during which continental growth occurs mainly by ocean subduction, arc construction, and accretion. In this model global tectonic patterns are reflected in terms of the Wilson cycle, in which oceans open and close in ≤ 500 million year periods. The other mode, called the MOMO (Mantle Overturn and Major Orogeny) model, involves significant exchange of material between lower and upper mantle and, accordingly, higher rates of crust formation (Figure 6.5b). This mode is considered to operate at longer periodicities than the Wilson cycle and produces magmatic activity that coincides with major orogenic events, such as those at circa 2.8, 2.0, 1.0, and 0.5 Ga (Figure 6.2b). From a metallogenic viewpoint, the proliferation of plume activity attributed to MOMO events might coincide with periods of alkaline magmatism and is, therefore, relevant to the ore deposits associated with such rocks.

Eustatic sea-level changes and "continental freeboard"

Continental freeboard, or the relative elevation of the continental land masses with respect to sea level or the geoid, is effectively a measure of the area of the exposed continents compared to that covered by the oceans. Continental freeboard is reduced when the average ocean depth is reduced, since this causes marine transgression and flooding of the continental shelf. This situation is linked to events of large-scale continental dispersal, which in turn reflects enhanced creation of oceanic crust, and active magmatism and uplift along mid-ocean ridges. By contrast, an increase in the area of the continents occurs when the oceans are deepened and the continental shelf exposed, a situation which tends to be associated with periods of tectonic stability and muted

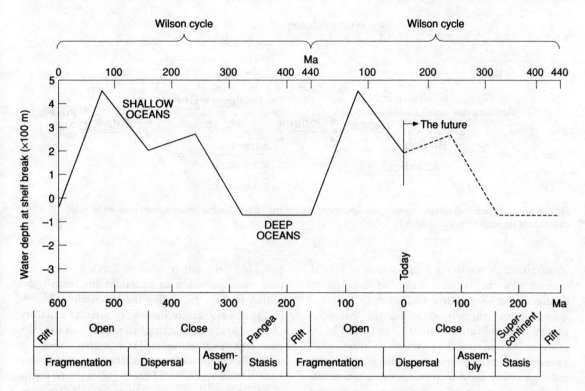

Figure 6.6 Pattern of Wilson cycles, reflecting Pangean assembly and fragmentation during the Phanerozoic Eon (and into the future), and showing water depth of the continental shelf (after Nance *et al.*, 1986).

mid-ocean ridge magmatic activity (Worsley *et al.*, 1984; Nance *et al.*, 1986). The cyclicity of continental freeboard and ocean depth in the Phanerozoic Eon is well documented (Figure 6.6) and shows that a period of maximum continental exposure and ocean low-stand (i.e. deep oceans) coincides with the amalgamation of the Pangean supercontinent in Permian–Triassic times. The nature and duration of Wilson cycles in the Phanerozoic, and their projection into the future, are also shown in Figure 6.6. A similar period of ocean lowstand may also have applied with respect to the amalgamation of an earlier super-continent, Rodinia, at approximately 1000 Ma (see section 6.5.2 below). From a metallogenic viewpoint, continental freeboard has its biggest influence on the nature and preservation of sediments forming on the continental shelves. Marine transgressions flood the continental shelf,

preserving the sediments within which deposits such as heavy mineral beach placers, SEDEX Pb–Zn ores, banded iron-formations, bedded manganese deposits, and phosphorites might have formed. Oceanic lowstand and maximal continental area, on the other hand, would tend to result in shelf exposure and erosion, with possible destruction of any ore deposits present in the sedimentary sequence.

6.5 METALLOGENY THROUGH TIME

The pattern of crustal evolution in the Phanerozoic Eon, involving the progressive amalgamation of large continental fragments to form the supercontinent of Pangea during Permian and Triassic times, and its subsequent dispersal to form the present day continental geography, is well

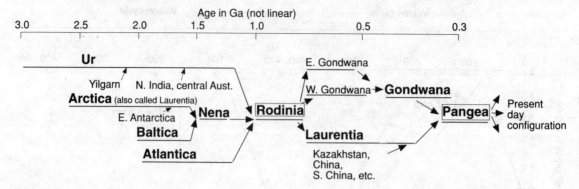

Figure 6.7 Schematic diagram showing the approximate timing of amalgamation and dispersal of the major continents through time (after Rogers, 1996).

constrained. A relatively high degree of confidence marks the reconstruction of continental configuration during the Phanerozoic Eon and geoscientists generally agree on the paleogeography of Gondwana, Laurentia, and Pangea. As one goes back in time, however, even into the late Precambrian, the situation becomes progressively more uncertain and disagreement often accompanies the reconstruction of continental geometry. There are many reasons for this, including the difficulties in acquiring and accurately dating apparent polar wander paths, the high rates of recycling (or destruction) of continental and oceanic crust, and progressive deformation and burial of crust with time.

Despite these difficulties, considerable progress has been made in reconstructing continental paleogeography during the latter stages of the Proterozoic Eon. There are indications that a Neoproterozoic supercontinent, generally referred to as Rodinia, was assembled from about 1000 Ma, and then dispersed again by about 700 Ma. There is also some evidence for the existence of a Mesoproterozoic supercontinent, although at this stage there is still considerable uncertainty as to the nature of its constituents, as well as its shape and position. It is also likely that substantial continents existed in the Paleoproterozoic and even into the late Archean, although at this stage the configuration of these continents is speculative. Windley (1995) has compiled a detailed account of the many ideas regarding the evolution of the

crust over the entire span of Earth history, and this work provides an excellent platform upon which to base the following discussion. Rogers (1996) has also attempted to reconstruct a history of the continents and their configuration over the past 3000 million years. He has also chosen to name the larger continental fragments over this time period and charted their evolution in terms of major periods of amalgamation and dispersal. In the sections that follow this scheme is summarized and complemented with more recent data pertaining to Neoproterozoic (Rodinia) and Phanerozoic (Pangea) continental evolution. Although still in its early stages of development and, therefore, speculative, the Rogers scheme nevertheless provides a useful framework upon which to base a discussion of metallogeny through time. It is also a working hypothesis that can be used to test ideas relating to crustal evolution and the link to global metallogeny. Figure 6.7 presents a schematic history of continental amalgamation and dispersal between 3000 and 300 Ma, together with names for suggested early continental fragments.

In brief, the Rogers model commences with an inferred Archean continent known as *Ur*, comprising the ancient Kaapvaal and Pilbara cratons of southern Africa and Western Australia, respectively, as well as parts of India and Antarctica. Ur is believed to have coalesced from about 3000 Ma and to have existed as a separate block throughout much of Earth history until it contributed to the assembly of a supercontinent at around 1000 Ma.

Another major continent, called *Arctica*, now largely preserved in parts of Canada, Greenland, and Siberia, is believed to have amalgamated toward the end of the Archean or in the early Proterozoic. At least two other substantial continental fragments are believed to have formed during the Paleoproterozoic, namely *Baltica* and *Atlantica*. Arctica (also commonly referred to as Laurentia in earlier reconstructions; Hoffman, 1988) and Baltica are suggested to have amalgamated at around 1500 Ma to form the first substantially consolidated mass of continental material (but not yet a supercontinent), called *Nena* (Figure 6.7). Nena, Ur, and Atlantica are considered to have been the founding blocks for what was arguably the first supercontinent, *Rodinia*, which existed largely in the Neoproterozoic and comprised an amalgamation of most continental mass at that time. Thereafter, the pattern of continental evolution is far better constrained. Rodinia broke up into essentially three large fragments known as *Laurentia* (i.e. an enlarged version of the Paleoproterozoic Laurentia) and east and west *Gondwana*, although it is likely that other smaller continental entities also existed at this time. The two sections of Gondwana amalgamated into a single entity during the Panafrican and Brasiliano orogenies at around 500 Ma. Laurentia collided with Baltica after the closure of the Iapetus Ocean in the early Paleozoic, at about 400 Ma, to form a transient entity known as *Laurasia*. It was the subsequent collision of Laurasia and Gondwana that gave rise to the second global supercontinent, *Pangea*, which formed at around 300 Ma. Since then continental fragments have dispersed to many parts of the globe, forming the present day geographic configuration. Some areas are currently undergoing reamalgamation, with collision of India with Asia, and the partial amalgamation of Africa and Europe, having been particularly active over the past 20 million years.

This pattern of continental evolution is used below as the framework around which to discuss global metallogenic trends. The discussion progresses from oldest to youngest, even though much more is known about processes in younger periods of time.

6.5.1 The Archean Eon

The Hadean (>4000 Ma) and Eoarchean (>3600 Ma) stages

The Hadean Era refers to that period of Earth history for which there is very little evidence in the rock record and which is nominally pre-Archean. It was a time of global differentiation and accretion, as well as intense meteorite bombardment. The Hadean was previously regarded as existing prior to 3800 Ma (Harland, 1989) although the growing evidence (from U–Pb zircon dating) for crustal remnants at close to 4000 Ma suggests that the latter date is perhaps a more accurate reflection of the Hadean boundary (Windley, 1995). The lack of any meaningful preservation of Hadean crust anywhere on the face of the Earth is a feature generally attributed to widespread destruction of this ancient material, either by intense meteorite bombardment or by subduction associated with a turbulent, rapidly convecting mantle, or both. There is also evidence to suggest that the early atmosphere and ocean formed only at the end of the Hadean era, once the main period of accretion and meteorite bombardment had terminated (Kasting, 1993). De Wit and Hynes (1995) have suggested that the Hadean Earth was also characterized by loss of heat direct to the atmosphere, in contrast to later periods of time when heat loss is largely buffered by a liquid hydrosphere. The implications for metallogenesis are that sedimentation and hydrothermal process are likely to have been inconsequential in the Hadean, and any ore deposits that did form at that time were, therefore, probably igneous in character. It is conceivable, for example, that oxide and sulfide mineral segregations accumulated from anorthositic and basaltic magmas at this time. The only preserved record of such rocks within reach of humankind at present is, however, likely to be on the Moon.

The Eoarchean refers to the dawn of Archean time and to rocks formed prior to 3600 Ma, although for the purposes of this discussion it is considered to extend between 4000 and 3600 Ma. The best preserved section of Archean crust that falls into this time bracket is the 3800 Ma Isua

Figure 6.8 Suggested configuration and paleogeography of the two major continental blocks, Ur and Arctica, that may have been in existence by the end of the Archean Eon at 2500 Ma (after Rogers, 1996). (a) The configuration of Ur at about 3.0 Ga relative to the continental outlines of southern Africa, India, Antarctica, and Australia in a Gondwana make-up and an enlarged configuration for Ur at about 1.5 Ga that includes accretion of continental crust (such as the Zimbabwe craton) formed largely at 2800–2600 Ma. (b) The configuration of Arctica at around 2500 Ma relative to continental outlines for North America and Greenland.

supracrustal belt and associated Itsaq (previously called Amitsoq) gneisses of western Greenland. The Isua belt comprises mafic and felsic metavolcanics, as well as metasediments, and resembles younger greenstone belts from elsewhere in the world. Although only 4 × 30 km in dimension, the Isua belt contains a major chert–magnetite banded iron-formation component as well as minor occurrences of copper–iron sulfides in banded amphibolites and in iron-formation (Appel, 1983). The largest iron-formation contains an estimated 2 billion tons of ore at a grade of 32% Fe. Scheelite mineralization has also been found in both amphibolite and calc–silicate rocks of the Isua belt, an association which suggests a submarine-exhalative origin. The coexistence of banded iron-formations and incipient volcanogenic massive sulfide style mineralization points to sea-floor processes not unlike those active throughout much of subsequent Earth history. Although the zones of known mineralization in the Isua belt are sub-economic, at 3800 million years old they clearly represent the oldest known ore deposits on Earth.

The Paleo-, Meso-, and Neoarchean stages (3600 to 2500 Ma)

The main stage of Archean crustal evolution took place over an extended duration of more than 1000 million years, during which time geological processes were probably not too dissimiliar to those of today – provided that allowances are made for features such as higher heat flow, thicker oceanic crust, and an anoxic atmosphere. De Wit *et al.* (1992) described the processes that took place during this period of time in terms of two principal stages, termed *"intra-oceanic shield formation"* (between about 3600 and 3100 Ma) and *"intra- and inter-continental craton formation"* (between about 3100 and 2500 Ma). The latter stage terminated, in the Neoarchean, in what might have been the most intense period of crustal development in Earth history (Figure 6.2b). The Neoarchean was also characterized by extremely active ore-forming processes representing igneous, hydrothermal, and sedimentary deposit types.

The Rogers model (Figure 6.7) suggests that by the end of the Archean (2500 Ma) there might have been two major continental blocks in existence, Ur and Arctica. The two blocks would have comprised segments of ancient crust now preserved in various parts of different present day continents and it is, therefore, doubtful that their configuration in the Archean can be known with any real certainty. A suggested configuration for Ur at around 3000 Ma is shown in Figure 6.8a and comprises the Kaapvaal and Pilbara cratons of southern Africa and Western Australia repectively, linked via a corridor made up of Archean segments from India and Antarctica. The existence of Ur receives some support from the similiarities that exist in the nature and ages of Archean greenstone belts and supracrustal sequences on the Pilbara and Kaapvaal cratons (Cheney, 1996; Martin *et al.*, 1998a), a feature that is especially striking in the similarities between the huge Superior-type banded iron-formations of the two regions. The unique occurrence of the Archean-aged Witwatersrand basin on the Kaapvaal Craton, and its apparent absence in Western Australia, on the other hand, would tend to question the relevance of comparative geology that far back in Earth history. Likewise, paleomagnetic data contradict a close fit of Pilbara and Kaapvaal (Wingate, 1998; Evans *et al.*, 2000) so that the real paleogeography, and perhaps even the very existence of Ur at all, must remain questionable. Nevertheless, as a working hypothesis, a possible 1500 Ma configuration for Ur is shown in Figure 6.8a, in which components of Neoarchean crustal growth, such as the highly mineralized Zimbabwe craton, are also shown. Arctica (Figure 6.8b) is considered to have been made up of several ancient continental fragments (including west Greenland and the Slave province with their remnants of circa 4000–3800 million year old crust), although the actual amalgamation and of this continent is considered to have postdated Ur, at around 2500 Ma. The fit between the Siberian and Canadian portions of Arctica was originally suggested on the basis of colinearity in the trends of the Paleoproterozoic Akitkan and Thelon magmatic arcs.

In a metallogenic context, Archean crustal evolution can be viewed in terms of a two stage model which suggests that early "shield" formation, in which amalgamation of oceanic basaltic terranes and emplacement of early tonalite–tronhjemite–granodiorite (TTG) magmas was followed by "cratonization," where modern plate tectonic processes such as subduction and continent collision occurred (De Wit *et al.*, 1992). The characteristics and relevant ore-forming processes of these two stages are illustrated in Figure 6.9.

Shield formation (circa 3600–3100 Ma)

This period conforms approximately with the Paleoarchean era and is typified by amalgamation of oceanic and arc-formed crust and the incipient stages of continental crust formation by emplacement of early, tonalite–trondhjemite–granodiorite (TTG) plutons (De Wit *et al.*, 1992; Choukroune *et al.*, 1997). This stage of Archean crustal evolution is characteized by the development of early continental shield areas comprising highly deformed (oceanic) greenstone remnants occurring as megaxenoliths within extensive TTG terranes (Figure 6.9a).

The styles of mineralization that formed during this stage of Earth evolution are limited and best exemplified by the deposits previously described for the Isua belt of west Greenland. Algoma type banded iron-formations are a common component of early greenstone belt assemblages and reflect the low oxygen levels of the atmosphere and the abundance of ferrous iron, sourced from exhalative activity at the mid-ocean ridges. The existence of oceans at this time and the likelihood of exhalative hydrothermal processes on the sea floor would have resulted in the formation of volcanogenic massive base metal sulfide deposits, although examples are rare. An exception is the well preserved Big Stubby VMS deposit, in the 3460 Ma Warrawoona Group metavolcanics of the Pilbara Craton in Western Australia (Barley, 1992).

Cratonization (circa 3100–2500 Ma)

This stage of Archean crust formation coincides broadly with the Meso- and Neoarchean eras and is illustrated in Figure 6.9b. It is suggested to be the most prolific period of crustal production

in Earth history (Figure 6.2b) and is also a time of major global mineralization. The processes active at this time were not unlike those taking place later on in Earth history and involved widespread plate subduction, arc magmatism, continent collision and rifting, and cratonic sedimentation. In Figure 6.9b two sketches are presented. An earlier sub-stage illustrates consecutive accretion of island arcs onto a previously formed continental shield and stabilization of the latter by intrusion of large granite batholiths. A later sub-stage envisages the existence of Archean cratons consisting of numerous terranes, each bordered by major suture zones (possibly the fossilized sites of subduction or arc collision) and flanked by both active and passive margins. Sites of intracratonic sedimentation are also envisaged in this stage of development. This scenario is consistent with the pattern of Archean crustal evolution envisaged, for example, in the Superior Province of Canada by Choukroune *et al.* (1997).

From a metallogenic viewpoint this stage of Archean crustal evolution gave rise to a wide variety of ore-forming processes (Figure 6.9b). Arc-related volcanism associated with plate subduction contributed large volumes of magma to the accreting terranes of the time. Well mineralized examples of continental crust formed in the period 3100–2500 Ma are represented by the granite–greenstone terranes of the Superior Province of Canada, as well as the Yilgarn and Zimbabwe cratons. Greenstone belts are hosts to numerous important volcanogenic massive sulfide (VMS) Cu–Zn ore bodies, such as those at Kidd Creek and Noranda in the Abitibi greenstone belt of the Superior Province. Off-shore, in more distal environments, chemical sedimentation gave rise to Algoma type banded iron-formations, examples of which include the Adams and Sherman deposits, also in the Abitibi greenstone belt. Greenstone belts formed at this time also often contain komatiitic basalts that, under conditions favorable for magma mixing and contamination, exsolved immiscible Ni–Cu–Fe sulfide fractions to form deposits such as Kambalda in Western Australia and Trojan in Zimbabwe. During periods of compressive deformation, major suture zones became the focus of hydrothermal fluid flow

(a)
SHIELD FORMATION (3600–3100 Ma)

(b)
CRATONIZATION (3100–2500 Ma)

① EARLY STAGES:

② LATER STAGES:

Figure 6.9 (a) Early stage of Archean crustal evolution, termed intra-oceanic shield formation, occurring in the interval 3600–3100 Ma. Mineralization in this period seems to have been restricted mainly to ocean floor exhalative processes and formation of Algoma-type banded iron-formations. (b) Later stage of Archean crustal evolution, termed intra- and inter-continental craton formation, occurring between 3100 and 2500 Ma. Mineralization processes were varied and resulted in the formation of many important ore deposit types, including lode- or orogenic gold, VMS Cu–Zn, paleoplacer Au–U, Algoma- and Superior-type iron ores and komatiite-hosted Ni–Cu deposits (after De Wit et al., 1992).

derived from either metamorphic devolatilization or late-orogenic magmatism. This resulted in the formation of the voluminous and characteristic styles of orogenic gold mineralization which are typical of most late Archean granite–greenstone terranes worldwide. Examples include important deposits such as the Golden Mile, Kalgoorlie district of Western Australia, the Hollinger–McIntyre deposits in the Abitibi greenstone belt, the Sheba–Fairview deposits of the Barberton greenstone belt, and the Freda–Rebecca mine in Zimbabwe. Early intracratonic styles of sedimentation, often in a foreland basinal setting, gave rise to concentrations of gold and uraninite represented by the Witwatersrand basin in South Africa. At least some of this mineralization is placer in origin and was derived by eroding a fertile Archean hinterland. The passive margins to these early continents would have developed stable platformal settings onto which laterally extensive Superior type banded iron-formations could have been deposited. A very significant period for deposition of iron ores such as those of the Hamersley and Transvaal basins of Western Australia and South Africa respectively, as well as the Mesabi range of Minnesota, seems to have been around the Archean–Proterozoic boundary at 2500 Ma.

6.5.2 The Proterozoic Eon

The period of time around 2500 Ma represents a major transition in the nature of crustal evolution, involving changes in the volume and composition of the continents, tectonic regimes, and atmospheric make-up. It is also clear from secular metallogenic patterns (Figure 6.1) that these evolutionary changes affected ore-forming processes and characteristics. The Proterozoic Eon spans a vast period of geological time, from 2500 to 540 Ma, including the period between 2000 and 1000 Ma that was marked by a relative paucity of orogenic and/or magmatic-hydrothermal deposit types, but abundant ores hosted in intracontinental sedimentary basins and anorogenic igneous complexes (Figure 6.1). The reasons for this pattern are multifaceted and complex, but, as a first order approximation, are related to a higher degree of continental stability and the existence

of major land masses which amalgamated and dispersed in relatively long-lived Wilson cycles (Windley, 1995). A substantial volume of continental crust must have been in existence by the beginning of the Proterozoic Eon (Figure 6.2) and it is widely held that the first supercontinent came into existence during this time, although its form and evolution are still largely speculative (Piper, 1976; Hoffman, 1988; Park, 1995).

The Rogers model (Figure 6.7) envisages that, in addition to Ur and Arctica, the Paleoproterozoic witnessed continuing amalgamation of land masses to form Atlantica (from about 2000 Ma and comprising parts of west Africa and South America; Figure 6.10a) and Baltica (the Paleoproterozoic basement to what is now western Europe). Further amalgamation of two (i.e. Arctica and Baltica) of the four continental land masses in existence at this time is believed to have occurred at about 1500 Ma, to form a new continent that Gower (1990) and Rogers (1996) called Nena (an acronym for Northern Europe and North America). Figure 6.10b shows a possible reconstruction of Nena, at about 1500 Ma, and is very similar to a scheme proposed by Park (1995) in which Laurentia and Baltica were joined together between 1900 and 1500 Ma. The process of continental amalgamation continued through the Mesoproterozoic, until approximately 1000 Ma, when virtually complete consolidation gave rise to the formation of a single supercontinent, now widely referred to as Rodinia (McMenamin and McMenamin, 1990). Rodinia formed largely by accretion of Ur and Atlantica to Nena (Figure 6.7) along a major, almost continuous (in some reconstructions) suture zone known, at least in North America, as the Grenville orogeny. In the Neoproterozoic, and certainly by about 700 Ma, Rodinia was broken apart again, mainly along two major rifts. One of these separated Atlantica from Nena, along a previous suture, to form two fragments known thereafter as Laurentia and west Gondwana. The other split Nena internally to separate Laurentia from east Gondwana. Figure 6.11a shows a configuration for Rodinia at 1000–700 Ma and Figure 6.11b illustrates a possible break-up scheme in which Laurentia has extricated itself, leaving a recombined west and east Gondwana at the end of

Figure 6.10 (a) Map showing a possible configuration for Atlantica at 2000 Ma, comprising mainly remnants of Archean crust in Brazil and west-central Africa. (b) Map showing the configuration envisaged for the possible amalgamation of Arctica, Baltica, and east Antarctica to form Nena at about 1500 Ma. Both maps are after Rogers (1996).

the Proterozoic Eon. This configuration, although still largely conjectural and the subject of continual modification and further research (Dalziel *et al.*, 2000), sets the scene for the subsequent pattern of crustal evolution and global tectonics in the Phanerozoic Eon.

In summary, crustal evolution through the Proterozoic Eon was characterized by intermittent continental growth (primarily at around 2000 and 1000 Ma; Figure 6.2) and amalgamation which ultimately gave rise to the existence of a stable and long-lived supercontinent in the Neoprotero-

zoic Era. Although geological processes were not significantly different from those of other periods of Earth history, the interval between 2000 and 1000 Ma is typified by ore deposits related to anorogenic magmatism and intracontinental basin deposition (Figure 6.1). These ore-forming processes point to a pattern in which a substantial part of Proterozoic crustal evolution was characterized by relatively long-lived periods of continental stability. Continental stability at this time may have been promoted by an asymmetry in the distribution of crustal type, where a largely

(a)

~750 Ma

UR

India

Australia

Rift

ARCTICA

East Antarctica

Siberia

Rift

Kalahari

Laurentia

0°

N

Congo

NENA

Amazonia

ATLANTICA

West Africa

Baltica

Phanerozoic belts

800–500 Ma belts

1000 Ma belts (Grenville)

pre-1000 Ma cratons

(b)

~500 Ma

EAST GONDWANA

Proto Pacific Ocean

East Antarctica

Laurentia

0°

Kalahari

India

Plate

Congo

Amazonia

N

Iapetus Ocean

West Africa

Baltica

WEST GONDWANA

oceanic hemisphere was antipodal to a static continental domain. This feature might have been further accentuated, at around 1000–700 Ma, by the presence of a Rodinia. A similar situation is suggested to have applied during the existence of the Pangean supercontinent in Permian–Triassic times (Nance *et al.*, 1986). The metallogenic contexts of the three Proterozoic eras are discussed in more detail below.

The Paleoproterozoic Era (2500–1600 Ma)

From a metallogenic viewpoint, the period of earth history between 2500 and 1600 Ma is very significant because of the major changes that occurred to the atmosphere, especially the rise in atmospheric oxygen levels at around 2200 Ma (Figure 6.3). Prior to this time, the major oxygen sink was the reduced deep ocean where any photosynthetically produced free oxygen was consumed by the oxidation of volcanic gases, carbon, and ferrous iron. In this environment banded iron-formations, as well as bedded manganese ores, developed, as is evident from the widespread preservation of both Algoma and Superior type iron deposits. The increase in ferric/ferrous iron ratio in the surface environment that accompanied oxyatmoinversion at 2200 Ma, and the accompanying depletion in the soluble iron content of the oceans at around this time, resulted in few BIFs forming after this time. The stability of easily oxidizable minerals such as uraninite and pyrite is also to a certain extent dependent on atmospheric oxygen levels and it is, therefore, relevant that major Witwatersrand-type placer deposits did not form after about 2000 Ma. Besides these non-

Figure 6.11 (*Opposite*) (a) Simplified map showing a possible configuration for Rodinia, comprising the amalgamated continental land-masses of Nena (previously Arctica and Baltica), Atlantica, and Ur, from about 1000 Ma. Rift lines and arrows show the way in which Rodinia might have started to break apart, from about 750 Ma onwards (details from Hoffman, 1991). (b) Simplified map showing how fragments of Rodinia might have reconsolidated by the end of the Proterozoic and early Phanerozoic (at about 500 Ma) to form an early Gondwana configuration. Both maps are after Rogers (1996).

recurrent changes, which only affected oxygen-sensitive ore-forming processes, the pattern of metallogeny in the Paleoproterozoic followed normal global tectonic constraints.

The continent of Ur remained tectonically quiescent throughout much of the Proterozoic period although it witnessed episodic growth at around 2000 Ma (possible amalgamation with the Yilgarn and Zimbabwe cratons) and again at about 1500 Ma (amalgamation with parts of northern India and central Australia; Figure 6.7). This early stability is reflected in the widespread deposition and preservation of banded iron-formations along shallow continental platforms at the Archean–Proterozoic boundary, already mentioned. On the Zimbabwe craton, rifting at around 2500 Ma gave rise to intrusion of the Great Dyke, with its significant Cr and PGE reserves. At 2060 Ma on the Kaapvaal craton, the enormous Bushveld complex with its world-class PGE, Cr, and Fe–Ti–V reserves was emplaced, as was the Phalaborwa alkaline complex with its contained Cu–P–Fe–REE mineralization. The period between 2000 and 1800 Ma, however, was characterized by a global orogeny, largely accretionary in nature (Windley, 1995), which also affected Ur. The Australian Barramundi and southern African Kheis orogenies are events which contributed to the growth of Ur and, in the latter region, for example, gave rise to the Haib porphyry Cu deposit and small MVT-type Pb–Zn deposits along the western edge of the Kaapvaal craton. A further long period of cratonic stability ensued and Ur was subjected to rifting and intracontinental sedimentation. The period between 1700 and 1600 Ma saw the deposition of large dominantly clastic sedimentary basins that host the world-class SEDEX Pb–Zn ores of eastern Australia (Mount Isa, Broken Hill, and McArthur River) and South Africa (Aggeneys and Gamsberg). Elsewhere on Ur at this time, anorogenic magmatism was also occurring, importantly in the form of the 1600 Ma Roxby Downs granite–rhyolite complex, host to the enormous magmatic-hydrothermal Olympic Dam iron oxide–Cu–Au deposit in South Australia.

A slightly different pattern of Paleoproterozoic metallogeny is evident with respect to the continental fragments of Arctica and Baltica, which had combined by about 1500 Ma to form Nena (Figure 6.7). Early cratonic stability of Arctica is evident in the deposition of the Huronian Supergroup at 2450 Ma which contains the paleoplacer uranium ores of the Eliot Lake–Blind River regions of the Superior province, Canada. Both Arctica and Baltica were, however, subjected to extensive accretionary orogenies between 2000 and 1700 Ma. The Trans-Hudson, Yavapai–Mazatzal and Svecofennian orogenies, for example, produced significant new crust within which volcanogenic massive sulfide Cu–Zn deposits such as Flin Flon in Canada, Jerome, Arizona, and the Skellefte (Sweden)–Lokken (Norway) ores of Scandanavia are preserved. Relative stability followed this period of orogenesis, during which time large intracontinental sedimentary sequences such as the Athabasca basin formed at around 1700 Ma. It should be noted that the very rich uranium ores in the latter are epigenetic and probably formed during several later episodes of fluid flow between 1500 and 1000 Ma (Hecht and Cuney, 2000).

The continent of Atlantica (Figure 6.10a) was consolidated only after 2000 Ma, subsequent to a major compressional event reflected in west Africa as the Birimian orogeny at 2100–2000 Ma. This major crust-forming event gave rise to the important orogenic or lode-gold deposits of Ghana, such as Ashanti. Atlantica was relatively stable for the remainder of the Paleoproterozoic and saw the emplacement of anorogenic type granite magmatism at around 1900–1800 Ma, with which the large iron oxide–Cu–Au deposits of the Carajas region, Brazil, are associated.

The Mesoproterozoic Era (1600–1000 Ma)

The period of geological time after the formation of Nena (i.e. the amalgamation of Arctica and Baltica) at around 1500 Ma appears to have been one of tectonic quiescence and continental stability which lasted for several hundred million years. It culminated at around 1000 Ma in an episode of widespread orogenic activity (the Grenville orogeny and its many analogues worldwide) which resulted in the final amalgamation of the Rodinia supercontinent. Although this period of orogenesis affected the continental margins of Ur

it appears to have contributed little to the formation of mineral deposits. An exception is provided in South Africa by the magmatic Cu–sulfide ores associated with mafic intrusions of the Okiep copper district in the 1060–1030 Ma Namaqualand belt. In Nena, by contrast, enormous volumes of anorogenic magmatism, especially in the period 1500–1300 Ma, provided the host rocks to a number of very important deposits. In a belt stretching from southern California through Labrador into Scandinavia, numerous intrusions of gabbro–anorthosite host the large magmatic Fe–Ti (ilmenite) ore bodies of the Marcy massif in the Adirondacks and Lac Allard in Quebec. The same belt also contains alkali granite–rhyolite complexes which give rise to Fe–Au–REE resources such as those of the St Francois mountains of Missouri. The granite–rhyolite magmatic complexes were also eroded to form the sediments of the 1440 Ma Belt basin in the northwest USA, host to the Sullivan Pb–Zn SEDEX deposit in British Columbia in Canada. In addition, intracontinental rifting at around 1100 Ma in Nena gave rise to the formation of the 2000 km long Keweenawan mid-continental rift, stretching from Michigan to Kansas and filled with a thick sequence of bimodal basalt–rhyolite volcanics overlain by rift sediments. The latter form the host rocks to the stratiform Cu–Ag White Pine deposit in Michigan.

The Neoproterozoic Era (1000–540 Ma)

The Neoproterozoic commenced with the formation, at around 1000 Ma, of the supercontinent Rodinia, arguably the first substantially consolidated land-mass in Earth history. Rodinia was long-lived and only started to partially fragment after a static period of more than 250 million years. Substantial parts of what had been Rodinia then reconvened toward the end of the Proterozoic (at 540 Ma) to form the very substantial Gondwanan land-mass during the Pan-African orogeny (Figure 6.11b). Break-up of Rodinia started at around 750 Ma when east Gondwana (previously referred to as Ur) rifted away from the western edge of Laurentia to initiate the opening of the proto-Pacific ocean. The remaining portion of Rodinia (i.e. Laurentia, west Gondwana, Siberia, and Baltica) drifted southwards, remaining intact while at the same time rotating clockwise (Torsvik *et al.*, 1996). At about 650–600 Ma both Baltica and Siberia started to break away from Laurentia and the Iapetus Ocean formed. By the end of the Proterozoic Eon, the amalgamation of east and west Gondwana had taken place and this large continental mass was situated at polar latitudes and across the Iapetus seaway from an equatorially located Laurentia (Figure 6.11b). In detail, the assembly of Gondwana was long-lived and polyphase and occurred progressively from about 750 to 550 Ma. The Neoproterozoic is, therefore, sometimes referred to as the period of two supercontinents and was notable for its protracted periods of continental amalgamation, enhanced freeboard, and tectonic stability. The time between about 750 and 550 Ma was also characterized by the development of at least two, and in places possibly four, major ice ages, one or more of which was near global in cover and extended to equatorial latitudes. The concept of the Neoproterozoic "Snowball Earth" (Harland, 1965; Hoffman *et al.*, 1998) has important implications for understanding climate change and, especially, for the proliferation and diversification of organic life at the Precambrian–Cambrian boundary. Global glaciations also have implications for the nature and formation of ore deposits in the Neoproterozoic Era.

The major ore deposits of the Neoproterozoic reflect the conditions of continental stability, as well as the periods of near global ice cover and attendant anoxia, that prevailed at this time. The extensively developed ironstone ores of northwest Canada and South Australia, associated with the 750–725 Ma Rapitan and Sturtian glaciogenic rocks respectively, are considered to be the result of the build-up of ferrous iron derived from offshore hydrothermal vents in the reduced ocean waters that accompanied the development of vast continental and oceanic ice sheets at this time. Receding glaciers and a return to more oxidizing conditions would have resulted in conversion of labile ferrous iron to insoluble ferric iron and precipitation of the latter from the ocean water column, together with clastic and glaciomarine

detritus to form the ironstones (Lottermoser and Ashley, 2000). Even more oxidizing conditions would also have resulted in the precipitation of manganese oxides or carbonates in the succession.

In a similar vein, the Precambrian–Cambrian boundary at around 540 Ma is also characterized by the first major global phosphogenic event that resulted in the development of vast deposits of phosphatic sedimentary rock (phosphorites) in several parts of the world (Cook and Shergold, 1984). As with sedimentary iron ores, phosphorites reflect the upwelling of deep, nutrient-rich ocean waters onto shallow continental shelves with the syn-sedimentary precipitation of carbonate–apatite (or collophane) onto the shelf floor. Although the actual formation of phosphate ores is a complex process (see Chapter 5), there is compelling evidence to suggest that the onset of phosphogenesis at 540 Ma was related to conditions prevailing toward the end of the Neoproterozoic. Many phosphorite deposits worldwide immediately overlie glaciogenic sediments, suggesting that upwelling of phosphorus-rich ocean waters was promoted by overturn of a stagnant ocean during the widespread blanketing of sea-ice associated with a Snowball Earth scenario. The Precambrian–Cambrian phosphogenic event also coincides with the proliferation and diversification of organic life and it is pertinent that a significant proportion of organisms that evolved at this time developed calcium phosphate skeletal structures. Phosphorus is, in addition, a universal nutrient (unlike oxygen) and its concentration in the oceans at the end of the Proterozoic, and in the Cambrian, may also be linked to the evolution of organic life.

The formation of the vast, stratiform Cu–Co clastic sediment hosted ores of the Central African Copperbelt is also considered to have formed in an environment influenced by the Snowball Earth. The host Katangan sediments were deposited on a fertile Paleoproterozoic basement in an intracontinental rift, the development of which overlapped with both the Sturtian and Marinoan glacial events. The Grand and Petit Conglomerats of the Katangan sequence, for example, represent glaciogenic sediments capped by carbonates which are correlated, respectively, with the Sturtian and Marinoan events (Windley, 1995). Influx of oxide-soluble Cu and Co, perhaps derived from the local basement, might have occurred as diagenetic fluids migrated along growth faults and through the basin during the postglacial stages of deposition. Precipitation of ore sulfides would have occurred when the metal-charged oxidized fluids encountered reduced sediments or fluids.

The enormous proliferation and diversification of organic life in the late Neoproterozoic also resulted in the first substantial development of highly carbonaceous sediments. A good example of these are the Hormuz sediments that flank the eastern Arabian shield and which could represent some of the source rocks for the vast Mesozoic oil and gas fields of the Arabian Gulf (Chapter 5, Box 5.3; Windley, 1995). The Neoproterozoic is notable for the paucity of orogenic type deposits (Figure 6.1). Even the extensive Pan-African orogenic belts representing the suturing of continental fragments during Gondwanan assembly are strangely devoid of, for example, world-class volcanogenic massive sulfide deposits, the latter being relatively abundant in the Paleoproterozoic orogenic belts of the world. A few small examples do nevertheless occur, such as the deposits of the Matchless amphibolite belt in Namibia, Bleïda in Morrocco, and the Ducktown, Tennessee deposit (Titley, 1993). The global shortage of these ores in the Neoproterozoic perhaps reflects either a preservation factor or simply lack of exploration success.

6.5.3 The Phanerozoic Eon

By comparison with earlier eons, crustal evolution during the Phanerozoic is well understood and there is a large measure of confidence that accompanies the interpretation of tectonic, chemical, and biological processes over the past 540 million years. The latter half of this period, the Mesozoic and Cenozoic eras, has been accompanied by a prolific development of mineralization, the likes of which has probably not been seen since the late Archean bonanza, despite the influence of a preservation factor. Ore-forming processes and their relationships to the pattern of Earth evolution in the Phanerozoic are also reasonably well understood and additional details

regarding some of the topics discussed below can be found in Nance *et al.* (1986), Larson (1991), Barley and Groves (1992), Titley (1993), Kerrich and Cassidy (1994), Windley (1995), and Barley *et al.* (1998).

A significant proportion of the Phanerozoic was characterized by geological processes that reflect a Wilson cycle, namely the sequence of events that saw the dispersal of Gondwana in the early Paleozoic, followed by reamalgamation of continental material to form the Pangean supercontinent, by the early Mesozoic. The remainder of the Phanerozoic has witnessed the start of another Wilson cycle, involving the dispersal of Pangea to form the present day continental geography. It seems likely that we are presently about half way through this Wilson cycle (Nance *et al.*, 1986) and that it will be responsible for reassembling a significant proportion of the continents over the next 100–200 million years (Figure 6.6). Continued continental amalgamation in the future will extend processes currently taking place, such as the collision of the Indo-Australian plate (previously part of east Gondwana) with the combined Baltica–Siberia (now called the Eurasian plate) and closure of the Mediterranean Sea.

As previously mentioned, break-out of Laurentia from Rodinia and rotation of Ur at around 725 Ma (Figure 6.11) led to the formation of a Gondwanan land-mass by the end of the Proterozoic. Dispersal of Gondwana in the Cambrian–Ordovician may have been facilitated by the earlier development of a superplume (Larson, 1991), evidence for which is seen in the formation of major dyke swarms in different parts of Gondwana at 650–580 Ma (Torsvik *et al.*, 1996). The Iapetus Ocean formed as Laurentia drifted away from Baltica and Gondwana from the late Precambrian onwards. The pattern of continental fragmentation is illustrated in Figure 6.12a and was accompanied by a

Figure 6.12 (*Opposite*) The paleogeographic patterns of Gondwanan and Pangean dispersal in the Phanerozoic Eon. (a) and (b) Two reconstructions in the early Ordovician and Silurian (modified after Torsvik *et al.*, 1996). (c) A reconstruction of Pangea at its peak amalgamation in the Permian–Triassic. (d) and (e) Two instants of Pangean dispersal in the mid-Cretaceous and Eocene (after Windley, 1995).

(a) Ordovician (490 Ma)

GONDWANAN DISPERSAL

(b) Silurian (420 Ma)

(c) Permian–Triassic (250 Ma)

PANGEA

Panthalassan Ocean

Tethys Ocean

PANGEAN DISPERSAL

(d) Mid-Cretaceous (100 Ma)

(e) Eocene (50 Ma)

decrease in continental freeboard, sea-level high-stand and marine transgression. This was followed by progressive basin closure, terrane accretion, and granitoid magmatism during the period extending from the Silurian through to the early Carboniferous (about 420–300 Ma). This collisional phase commenced with the rapid consumption of Iapetus as Baltica and Avalonia (i.e. a small terrane comprising England, Wales, southern Ireland, and eastern Newfoundland) moved toward lower latitudes and collided with Laurentia in Silurian times (Figure 6.12b). The orogenies that reflect this collision phase are referred to as the Caledonian in Scandanavia and Scotland/Ireland and Appalachian in the eastern USA. Continental amalgamation continued as Gondwana drifted northwards toward lower latitudes, consuming the Rheic Ocean during the Devonian and Carboniferous, and eventually colliding with Laurentia–Avalonia–Baltica in the late Carboniferous–Permian. These complex and polyphase collisions are referred to as the Variscan and Hercynian orogenies (the terms are essentially synonomous) in present day Europe and the Alleghanian orogeny in the eastern USA. Continental amalgamation continued into the Permian with the accretion of Siberia to Baltica along the Urals suture, after which the Pangean supercontinent had essentially formed (Figure 6.12c).

The break-up of Pangea commenced soon after the time of its maximum coalescence in the Triassic at around 230 ± 5 Ma (Veevers, 1989). It was, therefore, a very short-lived supercontinent compared to Rodinia, which appears to have endured during much of the early Neoproterozoic. One reason for this might have been the development of a superplume, or plumes, that existed for some 70 million years, in Carboniferous and Permian times (320–250 Ma), an interval that also coincided with a protracted period of constant reversed magnetic polarity (Larson, 1991). The effects are seen geologically by increased production of oceanic crust and global volcanism (e.g. the outpouring of the Siberian continental flood basalt province and also the central Atlantic magmatic province), eustatic sea-level rise, increased atmospheric greenhouse gas production (with associated warming and organic proliferation),

and enhanced deposition of organic-rich black shales. The first land-masses to actually drift apart, more than 70 million years after initial plume-related rifting, were Laurentia from Gondwana in the Jurassic at around 180 Ma. West and east Gondwana also started to split at this time, with the development of the proto-Indian Ocean and outpouring of the Karoo igneous province. The opening of the Atlantic Ocean was particularly prevalent in the early Cretaceous (around 130 Ma) and this extensional phase was also marked by continental flood basalt volcanism of the Etendeka–Parana provinces in Namibia and Brazil respectively. Continued dispersal of Pangea was stimulated by a second superplume event in the mid-Cretaceous between 120 and 80 Ma (Figure 6.12d). The evidence for this event is again seen in a 40 million year period of constant, normal magnetic polarity, as well as the expected increases in oceanic crust production, eustatic sea level, atmospheric temperatures, organic productivity, and black shale deposition. The very large oceanic plateaux of the western Pacific (e.g. Ontong–Java) are a magmatic reflection of this mid-Cretaceous event, as is the development of very significant global oil reserves related to the surges in nutrient supply and organic productivity on the voluminous continental shelves formed by the rise in sea level (Larson, 1991). In post-plume times the late Cretaceous saw the final separation of Indo-Australia from Antarctica (Figure 6.13e), propelling the former northwards and resulting in continent–continent collision with Eurasia and the formation of the Himalayan orogeny in the Cenozoic. The Alpine orogeny of southern Europe was more or less coeval with its Himalayan counterpart and resulted from the collision of the African and Arabian plates with Eurasia after consumption of the Tethyan Ocean.

A very important component of Pangean break-up in the Mesozoic–Cenozoic is reflected in the development of new crust that accompanied the Cordilleran and Andean orogenies along the western margins of North and South America (Windley, 1995). This huge and complex orogeny, extending along the ocean–continent interface of western Pangea (Figure 6.12c), occurred in response to subduction and translocation of the original Panthalassan Ocean (now the eastern Pacific) beneath Laurentia (now North America), the Cocos plate (now central America), and segmented west Gondwana (now South America). An island arc lay to the west of North America during Pangean times and this was accreted onto the continental margin, together with numerous other exotic terranes, during the consumption of several thousand kilometers of the Pacific beneath North America during the Mesozoic Era. The enormous continent-floored magmatic arc that resulted from this subduction gave rise to the 130–80 Ma granite batholiths and felsic volcanic rocks (such as the Sierra Nevada batholith) of the Cordillera. Continued subduction, albeit at a shallower angle than previously, and crustal thickening during the early Cenozoic, gave rise to in-board extension and exhumation of metamorphic core complexes. Ongoing subduction during the Laramide orogeny (80–40 Ma) continued to feed the magmatic arc and numerous, metallogenically important I-type granite batholiths were emplaced at this time. As subduction waned in the late Eocene–Oligocene the magmatic arc migrated westwards, resulting in continued calc–alkaline magmatism. Thermal collapse commenced in the Neogene and the resulting crustal extension ultimately led to the formation of the Basin and Range province. In South America, Andean evolution was analogous, but less complex, than further north, and was also characterized by a lesser degree of accretionary and extensional processes. Subduction of the Nazca plate beneath a Paleozoic sedimentary margin, in the late Cretaceous, gave rise to a volcanic arc, behind which back-arc sedimentation took place (Lamb et al., 1997). This arc was the site of protracted magmatism that built the Western Cordillera and gave rise to the volcanic edifices which host the very important porphyry and epithermal styles of polymetallic mineralization in Peru, Bolivia, and Chile. Continued subduction transferred compressional stresses in-board and created a thin-skin fold and thrust belt in what is now referred to as the Eastern Cordillera. In the late Oligocene, crust was shortened even more and uplift gave rise to rapid erosion of the mountain belt to form a thick sedimentary plateau of dominantly

Miocene-aged gravel and red-bed sequences known as the Altiplano. Subduction-related volcanism continued throughout this period in the Western Cordillera, which was also elevated to form the high Andes and then eroded to contribute sediment into the Altiplano basin as well as westwards onto the coastal plain. Further to the east, magmatism commenced in the early Miocene as a result of convective removal of the basal lithosphere and crustal melting beneath the Altiplano (Lamb et al., 1997). The buoyancy and elevated profile of the Andes is maintained by present day underthrusting of the Brazilian shield beneath the Eastern Cordillera.

Tectonic cycles and metallogeny

The relatively well defined global tectonic cycles of the Phanerozoic Eon, summarized above, are also clearly reflected in secular metallogenic trends. Titley (1993), for example, noted that the distribution of stratabound ores (i.e. volcanogenic massive sulfide, clastic sediment hosted Pb–Zn (SEDEX), and Cu (red-bed) deposit types) could be related to the tectonic cycles of Pangean amalgamation and break-up (Figure 6.13). Preferential development of VMS deposits appears to be associated with periods in the Wilson cycle of elevated sea levels (highstand) associated with continental dispersal, namely, *after* Gondwana break-up in the early Paleozoic and in *post-Pangean* Mesozoic times. This association was considered to reflect the processes of rifting, enhanced ocean crust production, and hydrothermal exhalation that accompany continental dispersal. Similar patterns are also evident in the accumulation of organic-rich shales and oolitic ironstone ores, which preferentially occur in the same two intervals, namely after Gondwana break-up in the Ordovician–Devonian and in post-Pangean Jurassic–Cretaceous times (Figure 6.13). In these cases, increased exhalative activity, carbon dioxide production, global warming, and organic productivity are interrelated processes which result in suitable conditions for black shale and ironstone precipitation in the oceans. In contrast, clastic sediment hosted base metal ores of the SEDEX Pb–Zn–Ag and red-bed Cu types tend to form at different

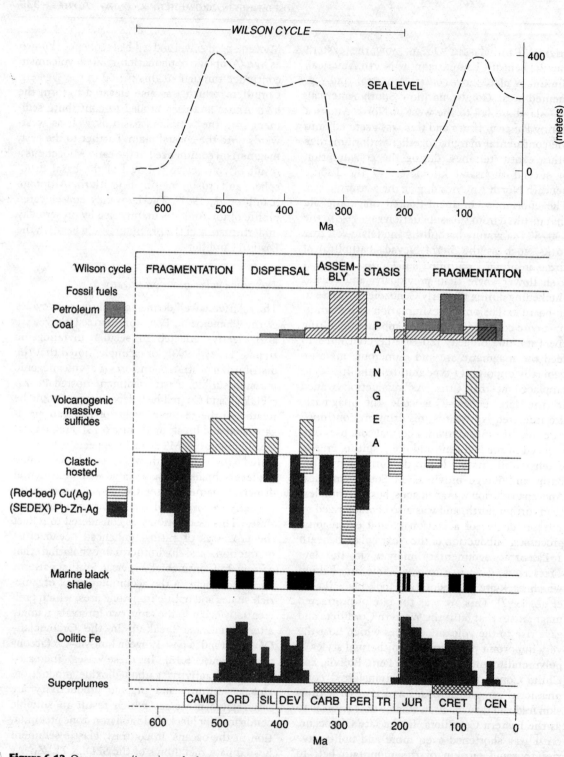

Figure 6.13 Occurrences (in terms of relative abundances) of a variety of different ore types with time and with respect to major Wilson tectonic cycles in the Phanerozoic (modified after Titley, 1993; with information from Nance *et al.*, 1986; Larson, 1991).

stages of the Wilson tectonic cycle. These ores are preferentially developed *at the time* of maximum continental amalgamation and stasis, namely in Gondwana during the Precambrian–Cambrian transition and in Pangea during the late Paleozoic–early Mesozoic (Figure 6.13). These ore types appear to have evolved preferentially during intracratonic rifting and sea-level lowstand (Titley, 1993).

The two Phanerozoic superplume events described above are also related in time to periods of enhanced organic productivity and formation of fossil fuels (Figure 6.13). The mid-Cretaceous superplume, active between 120 and 80 Ma, coincides with the formation of voluminous organic-rich shales deposited largely in the low-latitude Tethyan seaway. These shales are thought to be genetically linked to some 60% of the world's oil reserves (Larson, 1991). The late Carboniferous–Permian superplume is similarly associated with deposition of a large proportion of the world's coal reserves, formed between 320 and 250 Ma, again at a time when organic productivity increased and tropical, swampy conditions prevailed along flooded continental margins associated with the corresponding sea-level rise. Continental hotspots, or beheaded plumes, are also possibly related to the preferential development of alkaline and kimberlitic magmatism associated with enhanced igneous activity in the mid-Cretaceous and again in the Cenozoic. Many of these intrusions, important for Cu–REE–P–Fe–Au mineralization and also diamonds, are found on old, stable cratons and located along ancient lineaments that might have been reactivated during extension and crustal thinning associated with hotspot activity.

Time-bound and regional aspects of Phanerozoic metallogeny

A summary of ore deposit trends as a function of the major Phanerozoic tectonic events reveals that the metallogenic inventory, especially of convergent margin lithosphere, increases with time and with each tectonic cycle (Barley *et al.*, 1998). The distribution of ore deposit types also very often has a regional character to it and, as mentioned previously, may reflect the extent of erosion in different regions and the preservation potential of ores.

The large-scale development of new crust along the convergent Mesozoic–Cenozoic plate margins of the Americas did not occur on the same scale during the Paleozoic dispersal stage. Hence, a cyclic pattern in the development of orogenic magmatic-hydrothermal ores is not as evident as it is for statabound deposits, where controls on ore formation are different. There are, for example, few known porphyry Cu–Mo type deposits of Paleozoic age, although sub-economic examples are recognized along convergent margins such as the Caledonides of Scotland. Orogenic gold mineralization is also related to the late stages of collisional orogens. Cretaceous examples of this style of gold mineralization are evident in California, British Columbia, China, and New Zealand and could conceivably be related to the enhanced thermal regime related to the superplume break-out at this time. It has also been suggested that these gold provinces might rather have been linked to areas where mid-ocean ridge, as opposed to normal oceanic crust, was subducted. Scenarios in which hot crust was subducted, compared to periods when normal subduction of cold oceanic crust prevailed, have been suggested as an explanation for the anomalous thermal conditions required for widespread gold mineralization (Haeussler *et al.*, 1995).

The amalgamation stage of Pangea commenced with the collision of Avalonia–Baltica with Laurentia during the polyphase Paleozoic Caledonian–Appalachian orogenies. VMS deposits formed in response to these processes in, for example, the Bathurst–Newcastle district of New Brunswick, the Buchans area of Newfoundland, and Scandanavia. New Brunswick also has examples of Devonian aged Sn–W–Mo–F granites, some of which are mineralised. The carbonate-hosted MVT Pb–Zn deposits of the southeastern USA are also related to the Appalachian orogeny and formed when the thrust front expelled basinal fluids into the carbonate platform on the continental margin, giving rise to epigenetic hydrothermal mineralization. The Variscan orogeny, formed when Gondwana collided with an already amalgamated Laurentia–Baltica–Avalonia, is also characterized by carbonate-hosted ore bodies. Some of these, particularly the Irish deposits at Navan, are transitional in style between MVT and SEDEX-type Pb–Zn deposits, but are also related to compression-related, gravity- and tectonic-driven, basinal fluid flow. The Variscan orogeny of Europe is particularly well known for its association with widespread, 300–275 Myr old, S-type Sn–W–U granites. These are well mineralized in many of the historic European mining districts, such as Cornwall in southwest England (South Crofty, St Just, etc.), the Massif Central of France (Bellezane), the Bohemian massif of the Czech Republic, and Portugal (Panasqueira). Other deposits associated with the Variscan of Europe include the Devonian aged Rammelsberg and Meggen SEDEX-type deposits of Germany and the numerous VMS deposits of the Iberian Pyrite Belt (Rio Tinto, Neves Corvo, etc.). The brief interval in the Permian–Triassic of relative stability that accompanied the existence of the Pangean supercontinent was one in which little mineralization formed. An exception to this was the stratiform red-bed hosted Cu–Ag ores of the Permian Kupferschiefer in Poland and Germany.

Mineralization associated with post-Pangean break-up and orogenesis is both spectacular and widespread. Exceptions to this would appear to be the products of continent–continent collision, such as regions affected by the Himalayan orogeny, which appear to be devoid of any world-class ore deposits. The Karakoram mountains of Pakistan, for example, contain rich gemstone deposits (such as the rubies of the Hunza area), but otherwise only minor MVT and vein-related precious and base metal type ores, as well as a few small hydrothermal uranium deposits, occur (Windley, 1995). More significant stratabound and ophiolite-hosted styles of mineralization are contained in rocks caught up in the Himalayan orogeny, but the ore-forming processes probably predate the latter. Regions affected by the Alpine orogeny are, likewise, not particularly well mineralized, although exceptions do occur. MVT-type Pb–Zn deposits occur in mid-Triassic limestones of the eastern Alps and north Africa. The Carpathian arc of southeastern Europe contains porphyry Cu–Mo styles of mineralization, such as at Sar Cheshmeh

in Iran and Bor in the former Yugoslavia, and also contains significant potential for epithermal gold mineralization. Important ophiolite-hosted VMS Cu–Zn and chromite mineralization occurs in numerous obducted remnants of ocean floor, in places such as Troodos, Cyprus and in Albania and Turkey. Again, however, these deposits are likely related to ore-forming processes that predate the Alpine orogeny.

The Andean and Cordilleran orogens of the western Americas contain the greatest concentration of metals on Earth, and are pervasively mineralized from one end to the other. During the Jurassic–Cretaceous period of terrane accretion in North America, small VMS-type Cu–Zn deposits were formed, as were the "mother-lode" hydrothermal gold systems, hosted in obducted oceanic material in California, British Columbia, and Mexico. Mesozoic and early Cenozoic plutonism gave rise to the numerous world-class porphyry Cu–Mo deposits of the USA and Canada, as well as the related skarn and polymetallic epithermal vein deposits, such as the Bingham system in Utah. Thermal collapse and the development of Basin and Range extension gave rise to the enormous Eocene (40 Ma), hydrothermal, sediment-hosted Carlin-type Au deposits of northeast Nevada, followed by Miocene volcanism and widespread development of epithermal Au–Ag mineralization such as the Comstock Lode of Virginia City, Nevada. Similarly, in South America a wide variety of mineralization styles are associated with Mesozoic–Cenozoic orogeny. During the Jurassic–Cretaceous period island arc volcanism and associated hydrothermal activity gave rise to the Fe oxide–phosphate ores now preserved in the western, coastal portions of the belt. The axis of subduction related magmatism commenced in the west during the late Triassic and early Jurassic and then migrated eastwards with time through the Cretaceous and early Cenozoic (Sillitoe, 1976). In the Eastern Cordillera, however, minor magmatism occurred early in the Mesozoic, but most of the magmatism took place in the Miocene. The enormous porphyry copper deposits of Chile (such as Chuquicamata and El Teniente) and Peru (Morococha and Toquepala) formed in response to diachronous episodes of subduction-related magmatism. Many of the important porphyry copper deposits in Peru are Paleocene in age, whereas in northern Chile they are Eocene–Oligocene and, further south, Miocene–Pliocene (Sillitoe, 1976). East of the porphyry copper belt a broad zone of vein-related and skarn type Cu–Pb–Zn–Ag mineralization occurs, spatially related to Eocene–Oligocene calc–alkaline plutons. The deposits are most prolific in Peru (Antamina and Cerro de Pasco) but the belt continues southwards into Bolivia and Argentina. Finally, a distinct zone of Sn–W–Ag–Bi mineralization occurs mainly in the Eastern Cordillera of Bolivia and southern Peru, in the elbow of the central Andes. These ores occur as both vein-types associated mainly with Mesozoic intrusions, and disseminated porphyry type deposits (such as Llallagua and Potosi in Bolivia) associated with Oligocene–Miocene granites.

Also extremely important with respect to mineralization associated with post-Pangean orogenesis is the extensive chain of island arcs in the northern and western Pacific. The northern and western Pacific is predominantly characterized by collisions of oceanic crust (as opposed to the ocean–continent collisions of the western Americas) which form island arcs that build new crust on oceanic (simatic) basement rather than on continental (sialic) basement. There are several types of island arc, each with its particular metallogenic character. These include intra-oceanic arcs (such as Tonga, New Hebrides, and the Solomons), island arcs separated from continental crust by a narrow back-arc sea (such as Japan), and those built directly against a continent (such as Java–Sumatra). Soon after initiation of ocean–ocean collision in the western circum-Pacific region, early, relatively mafic (andesitic–dacitic), stages of calc–alkaline magmatism resulted in porphyry Cu–Au deposit formation, examples of which include Grasberg, Indonesia, and Bougainville in Papua New Guinea. Besshi-type VMS deposits also occur in back arc settings where andesite–dacite volcanism and ocean floor exhalative activity occurs synchronously with deep water sedimentation. During the main stages of arc construction and calc–alkaline magmatism, dacite–rhyolite volcanism occurred and is asso-

ciated with the development of Kuroko-type VMS deposits, examples of which are known from the Miocene-aged Green Tuff belt of Japan. Also very important, in geologically more recent times, is the formation of large epithermal Au–Ag deposits. Several world-class ore deposits of this type occur in the western circum-Pacific region, such as Baguio and Lepanto in the Phillipines, Hishikari in Japan, Ladolam and Porghera in Papua New Guinea, and Emperor in Fiji. Porphyry Cu–Au styles of mineralization are commonly known to occur beneath such epithermal deposits, such as at Baguio and Ladolam.

As a final comment, it is interesting to note that the Central Asian orogenic belts are characterized by many of the features, both temporal and tectonic, of the Andean and Cordilleran orogens. Still somewhat underexplored, these terranes probably represent particularly attractive metallotects for future mineral exploration.

6.6 Plate tectonics and ore deposits – a summary

The description of ore deposits in the context of their plate tectonic setting has been carried out in considerable detail in numerous publications (Mitchell and Garson, 1981; Tarling, 1981; Hutchison, 1983; Sawkins, 1990). A useful diagrammatic summary is presented in Mitchell and Garson (1981), from which Figures 6.14 and 6.15 are extracted. The latter two diagrams serve as a useful overview of the major plate-related tectonic settings and the ore deposit types associated with each.

6.6.1 Extensional settings

Incipient rifting of stable continental crust is represented in Figure 6.14a, where thinning and extension may be related to hotspot activity. Magmatism is often localized along old sutures and is alkaline or ultrapotassic (kimberlites and lamproites) in character. Anorogenic granites such as those of the Bushveld Complex (Sn, W, Mo, Cu, F, etc.), pyroxenite–carbonatite intrusions such as Phalaborwa (Cu–Fe–P–U–REE etc.), and kimberlites (diamonds) represent ore deposit types formed in

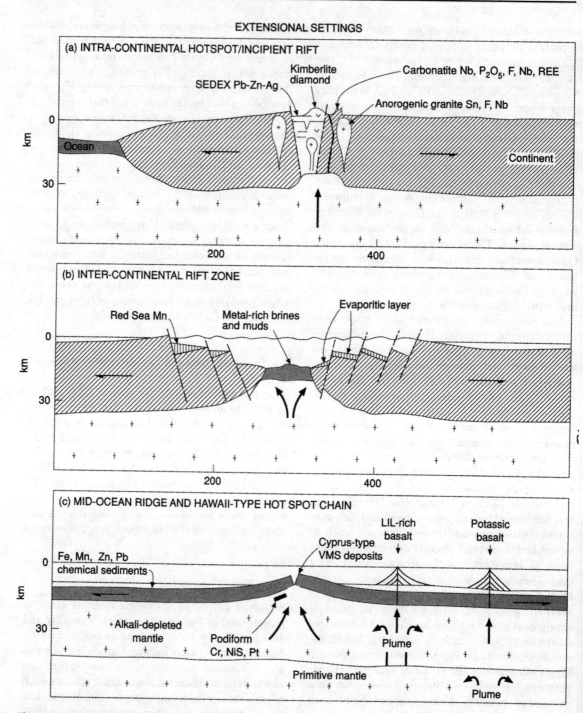

Figure 6.14 Simplified illustrations of the major extensional tectonic settings and the ore deposit types associated with each (modified after Mitchell and Garson, 1981).

COLLISIONAL SETTINGS

Figure 6.15 Simplified illustrations of the major compressional tectonic settings and the ore deposit types associated with each (modified after Mitchell and Garson, 1981).

this setting. Intracontinental rifts can host SEDEX-type Pb–Zn–Ba–Ag deposits. As continental rifting extends to the point that incipient oceans begin to open (such as the Red Sea; Figure 6.14b), basaltic volcanism marks the site of a mid-ocean ridge and this site is also accompanied by exhalative hydrothermal activity and plentiful VMS deposit formation. Such settings also provide the environments for chemical sedimentation and precipitation of banded iron-formations and manganiferous sediments. Continental platforms commonly host organic accumulations that on

catagenesis give rise to oil deposits. Carbonate sedimentation ultimately provides the rocks which host MVT deposits, although the hydrothermal processes that give rise to these epigenetic Pb–Zn ores are typically associated with circulation during compressional stages of orogeny. Mid-ocean ridges are the culmination of extensional processes (Figure 6.14c). Exhalative activity at these sites gives rise to "black-smoker" vents (such as those at 21° N on the East Pacific Rise) that provide the environments for the fomation of Cyprus type VMS deposits. The basalts which form at

Figure 6.15 (cont'd)

mid-ocean ridges also undergo fractional crystallization at sub-volcanic depths to form podiform chromite deposits as well as Cu–Ni–PGE sulfide segregations.

6.6.2 Compressional settings

The highly significant Andean type collisional margins are represented in Figure 6.15a. These are the sites of the great porphyry Cu–Mo provinces of the world, while inboard of the arc significant Sn–W granitoid-hosted mineralization also occurs. The volcanic regions above the porphyry systems are also the sites of epithermal precious metal mineralization. A similar tectonic setting can exist between two slabs of oceanic crust, as represented by the island arc environment in Figure 6.15b. Porphyry Cu–Au deposits occasionally occur associated with the early stages of magmatism in these settings, whereas the later, more evolved calc–alkaline magmatism gives rise to Kuroko-type VMS deposits. The back-arc basins represent the sites of Besshi type VMS deposition. Arc–arc collision in the back-arc environment can also result in the preservation of obducted oceanic spreading centers within which podiform Cr and sulfide segregations might be preserved. In the Japanese setting, where the island arc develops fairly close to a continent (Figure 6.15c), marginal sedimentary basins floored by oceanic crust occur.

This setting typically hosts Besshi- and Cyprus-type VMS deposits. As the arc and continent accrete, ophiolite obduction can occur, and felsic magmatism may give rise to large-ion lithophile element mineralization. Ultimately, the oceanic crust is totally consumed to form a zone of continent–continent collision (Figure 6.15d). Modern examples such as the Himalayas and Alps do not appear to be significantly mineralized, but this may be an expression of insufficient exhumation of mineralized zones. Older examples preserve Sn–W–U mineralization in S-type granites, whereas orogeny-driven fluids give rise to orogenic vein-related lode Au systems and MVT Pb–Zn deposits in suitably preserved platformal sediments.

SUMMARY

Broad trends emerge when relating ore deposit types to geological time and global tectonic setting. The mechanisms by which the crust has evolved, and the amalgamation and dispersal of continents over time, have played an overriding role in the formation of all deposit types. Although the processes are obscure in the early periods of Earth history, it appears that primitive continents started to form after the late heavy meteorite bombardment, from about 4000 Ma. Only a limited range of ore deposit types, mainly related to ocean floor hydrothermal processes, appears to have developed at this stage. As more evolved continents formed in the Mesoarchean and conventional plate tectonic processes were entrenched, the range of ore deposit types broadened, although many of the near-surface variants may not be preserved due to erosion. The Neoarchean Era was a period of intense global orogenesis and ore deposits formed at this time tend to be arc-related and magmatic-hydrothermal to hydrothermal in nature, not unlike those typifying the latter part of the Phanerozoic Eon. Although global tectonic processes continued unabated in the Proterozoic Eon, and a number of major crust-forming orogenies occurred, this extensive period of time appears to have been characterized by longer periods of tectonic quiescence and continental stability. Consequently, deposits reflect hydrothermal and sedimentary ore-forming processes in intracratonic settings or passive margins. Likewise, magmatism is more commonly anorogenic or post-tectonic in nature and is associated with an entirely different suite of metal deposits than those found in arc-related provinces. Global tectonic processes are much better understood in the Phanerozoic Eon and the distribution of continental land masses is well documented in terms of Wilson cycles. Certain deposit types (such as VMS Cu–Zn ores) are preferentially associated with break-up and dispersal stages of the cycle, such as Gondwana in the early Paleozoic and Pangea in the Mesozoic. Other ores (such as SEDEX Pb–Zn and red-bed Cu deposit types) exhibit a complementary association in terms of the Wilson cycle and are linked with peak continental amalgamation and stasis. The biggest concentration of metals on the Earth's surface is, however, linked to subduction along the western margins of Pangea, commencing in the Mesozoic and extending through the Cenozoic Era. The present day Pacific Ocean has been, and still is being, consumed beneath North and South America and has given rise to a large variety of world-class deposit types, of which the porphyry and epithermal ores are the most prolific. The skew in the distribution of these and other deposit types is, however, also related to the enhanced preservation of young ore bodies that have not yet been eroded or consumed at a plate margin.

FURTHER READING

Goldfarb, R.J., Groves, D.I. and Gardoll, S. (2001) Orogenic gold and geologic time: a global synthesis. *Ore Geology Reviews*, 18, 1–75.

Hutchison, C.S. (1983) *Economic Deposits and Their Tectonic Setting*. London: Macmillan Press, 365 pp.

Kesler, S. (1997) Metallogenic evolution of convergent margins: selected ore deposit models. *Ore Geology Reviews*, 12, 153–71.

Pattrick, R.A.D. and Polya, D.A. (1993) *Mineralization in the British Isles*. London: Chapman and Hall, 499 pp.

Sawkins, F.J. (1990) *Metal Deposits in Relation to Plate Tectonics*, 2nd edn. New York: Springer-Verlag, 461 pp.

Solomon, M., Groves, D.I. and Jacques, A.L. (2000) *The Geology and Origin of Australia's Mineral Deposits*. Hobart: University of Tasmania and University of Western Australia, 1002 pp.

Windley, B.F. (1995) *The Evolving Continents*. New York: John Wiley and Sons, 526 pp.

References

Ague, J.J. and Brimhall, G.H. (1989) Geochemical modeling of steady state fluid flow and chemical reactions during supergene enrichment of porphyry copper deposits. *Economic Geology*, 84, 506–28.

Albarede, F. (1996) *Introduction to Geochemical Modeling.* Cambridge University Press, 543 pp.

Alderton, D.H.M. (1993) Mineralization associated with the Cornubian Granite Batholith. In R.A.D. Pattrick and D.A. Polya (eds), *Mineralization in the British Isles.* Chapman & Hall, pp. 270–354.

Aldous, R.T.H. (1986) Copper-rich fluid inclusions in pyroxenes from the Guide Copper Mine, a satellite intrusion of the Palabora Igneous Complex, South Africa. *Economic Geology*, 81, 143–55.

Allen, J.R.L. (1985) *Principles of Physical Sedimentation.* Allen and Unwin, 272 pp.

Allen, P.A. (1997) *Earth Surface Processes.* Blackwell Science, 404 pp.

Alpers, C.N. and Brimhall, G.H. (1989) Paleohydrological evolution and geochemical dynamics of cumulative metal supergene enrichment at La Escondida, Atacama Desert, northern Chile. *Economic Geology*, 84, 229–55.

Anderson, G.M. (1975) Precipitation of Mississippi Valley type ores. *Economic Geology*, 70, 937–42.

Anderson, G.M. and Burnham, C.W. (1965) The solubility of quartz in supercritical water. *American Journal of Science*, 263, 494–511.

Anderson, J.C.Ø., Rasmussen, H., Nielsen, T.F.D. and Ronsbo, J.G. (1998) The Triple Group and the Platinova gold and palladium reefs in the Skaergaard Intrusion: stratigraphic and petrographic relations. *Economic Geology*, 91, 488–509.

Annels, A.E. (1984) The geotectonic environment of Zambian copper-cobalt mineralization. *Journal of the Geological Society London*, 141, 279–89.

Annels, A.E. (1989) Ore genesis in the Zambian copperbelt with particular reference to the northern sector of the Chambishi basin. Geological Association of Canada, Special Paper, 36, 427–52.

Appel, P.W.U. (1983) Mineral occurrences in the 3.6 Ga old Isua supracrustal belt, west Greenland. In A.F. Trendall and R.C. Morris (eds), *Iron Formation: Facts and Problems.* Developments in Precambrian Geology, 6. Elsevier, pp. 593–603.

Arribas, A., Hedenquist, J.W., Itaya, T., Okada, T. Concecion, R.A. and Garcia, J.S. (1995) Contemporaneous formation of adjacent porphyry and epithermal Cu–Au deposits over 300 ka in northern Luzon, Philippines. *Geology*, 23, 337–40.

Atkinson, D. and Baker, D.J. (1986) Geology of the MacTung tungsten skarn deposit. In J.G. Abbott and R.J.W. Turner (eds), *Mineral Deposits of the Northern Canadian Cordillera, Yukon–North Eastern British Columbia.* Geological Survey of Canada Open File 2169, 279 pp.

Bagnold, R.A. (1941) *The Physics of Blown Sand and Desert Dunes.* Methuen, 265 pp.

Baker, W.E. (1978) The role of humic acid in the transport of gold. *Geochimica et Cosmochimica Acta*, 42, 645–9.

Baldridge, W.S., McGetchin, T.R. and Frey, F.A. (1973) Magmatic evolution of Hekla, Iceland. *Contributions to Mineralogy and Petrology*, 42, 245–58.

Ballhaus, C. (1998) Origin of podiform chromite deposits by magma mingling. *Earth and Planetary Science Letters*, 156, 185–93.

Ballhaus, C. and Sylvester, P. (2000) Noble metal enrichment processes in the Merensky Reef, Bushveld Complex. *Journal of Petrology*, 41, 545–61.

Barley, M.E. (1992) A review of Archean volcanic-hosted massive sulfide and sulfate mineralization in Western Australia. *Economic Geology*, 87, 855–72.

Barley, M.E. and Groves, D.I. (1992) Supercontinent cycles and distribution of metal deposits through time. *Geology*, 20, 291–94.

Barley, M.E., Krapez, B., Groves, D.I. and Kerrich, R. (1998) The late Archaean bonanza: metallogenic and environmental consequences of the interaction between mantle plumes, lithospheric tectonics and global cyclicity. *Precambrian Research*, 91, 65–90.

Barley, M.E., Pickard, A.L., Hagemann, S.G. and Folkert, S.L. (1999) Hydrothermal origin for the 2 billion year old Mount Tom Price giant iron ore deposit, Hamersley Province, Western Australia. *Mineralium Deposita*, 34, 784–9.

Barley, M.E., Pickard, A.L. and Sylvester, P.J. (1997) Emplacement of a large igneous province as a possible cause of banded iron formation 2.45 billion years ago. *Nature*, 385, 55–8.

Barnes, H.L. (1967) *Geochemistry of Hydrothermal Ore Deposits*. Holt, Rinehart and Winston. 670 pp.

Barnes, H.L. (1975) Zoning of ore deposits: types and causes. *Transactions of the Royal Society Edinburgh*, 69, 295–311.

Barnes, H.L. (1979a) *Geochemistry of Hydrothermal Ore Deposits*, 2nd edn. John Wiley & Sons, 798 pp.

Barnes, H.L. (1979b) Solubilities of ore minerals. In H.L. Barnes (ed.), *Geochemistry of Hydrothermal Ore Deposits*, 2nd edn. John Wiley & Sons, pp. 404–60.

Barnes, H.L. (1997) *Geochemistry of Hydrothermal Ore Deposits*, 3rd edn. John Wiley & Sons, 972 pp.

Barnes, S.-J., von Achterbergh, E., Makovicky, E. and Li, C. (2001) Proton microprobe results for the partitioning of platinum group elements between monosulphide solid solution and sulphide liquid. *South African Journal of Geology*, 104, 275–86.

Barnes, S.-J. and Francis, D. (1995) The distribution of the platinum-group elements, nickel, copper, and gold in the Muskox Layered Intrusion, Northwest Territories, Canada. *Economic Geology*, 90, 135–54.

Barnes, S.-J. and Maier, W.D. (2002) Platinum group elements and microstructures of normal Merensky Reef from Impala Platinum Mines, Bushveld Complex. *Journal of Petrology*, 43, 103–28.

Barnicoat, A.C. and 11 others (1997) Hydrothermal gold mineralization in the Witwatersrand basin. *Nature*, 386, 820–4.

Barshad, I. (1966) The effect of a variation in precipitation on the nature of clay mineral formation in soils from acid and basic igneous rocks. *Proceedings of the International Clay Conference*, 1, 167–73.

Barton, M.D. (1996) Granitic magmatism and metallogeny of southwestern North America. *Transactions of the Royal Society Edinburgh: Earth Sciences*, 87, 261–280.

Bates, R.L. and Jackson, J.A. (1987) *Glossary of Geology*. American Geological Institute, 788 pp.

Bavinton, O. (1981) The nature of sulfidic metasediments at Kambalda and their broad relationships with associated ultramafic rocks and nickel ores. *Economic Geology*, 76, 1606–28.

Battey, M.H. and Pring, A. (1997) *Mineralogy for Students*. Longman, 363 pp.

Beales, F.W. and Jackson, S.A. (1966) Precipitation of lead-zinc ores in carbonate reservoirs as illustrated in Pine Point ore field, Canada. *Transactions of the Institute of Mining Metallurgy B*, 75, 278–85.

Beeson, R. (1990) Broken Hill-type lead-zinc deposits – an overview of their occurrence and geological setting. *Transactions of the Institute of Mining Metallurgy B*, 99, B163–B175.

Bentor, Y.K. (1980) Phosphorites – the unsolved problems. In Y.K. Bentor (ed.), *Marine Phosphorites*. Special Publication of the Society of Economic Palaeontologists and Mineralogists, 29, 3–18.

Berner, R.A. (1970) Sedimentary pyrite formation. *American Journal of Science*, 268, 1–23.

Berner, R.A. (1971) *Principles of Chemical Sedimentology*. McGraw-Hill, 240 pp.

Berner, R.A. (1984) Sedimentary pyrite formation: an update. *Geochimica Cosmochimica Acta*, 48, 605–15.

Berner, E.K. and Berner, R.A. (1987) *The Global Water Cycle: Geochemistry and Environment*. Prentice Hall.

Berry, L.G., Mason, B. and Dietrich, R.V. (1983) *Mineralogy*. W.H. Freeman and Co., 561 pp.

Best, J.L. and Brayshaw, A.C. (1985) Flow separation – a physical process for the concentration of heavy minerals within alluvial channels. *Journal of the Geological Society*, 142, 747–55.

Best, M.G. (2003) *Igneous and Metamorphic Petrology*. Blackwell Publishing, 729 pp.

Bierlein, F.P. and Crowe, D.E. (2000) Phanerozoic orogenic lode gold deposits. *Reviews in Economic Geology*, 13, 103–40.

Birch, G.F. (1980) A model of penecontemporaneous phosphatization by diagenetic and authigenic mechanisms from the western margin of Southern Africa. In Y.K. Bentor (ed.), *Marine Phosphorites*. Special Publication of the Society of Economic Palaeontologists and Mineralogists, 29, 79–100.

Bird, D.K., Brooks, C.K., Gannicott, R.A. and Turner, T.A. (1991) A gold bearing horizon in the Skaergaard Intrusion, east Greenland. *Economic Geology*, 86, 1083–92.

Bischoff, J.L. (1969) Red Sea geothermal brine deposits: their mineralogy, geochemistry and genesis. In E.T. Degens and D.A. Ross (eds), *Hot Brines and Recent Heavy Metal Deposits in the Red Sea*. Springer-Verlag, pp. 368–401.

Bjørlykke, K. (1989) *Sedimentology and Petroleum Geology*. Springer-Verlag, 363 pp.

Bjørlykke, K. (1994) Fluid-flow processes and diagenesis in sedimentary basins. In J. Parnell (ed.), *Geofluids: Origin, Migration and Evolution of Fluids in Sedimentary Basins*. Geological Society, Special Publication, 78, 127–40.

Bland, W. and Rolls, D. (1998) *Weathering: an Introduction to the Scientific Principles*. Arnold, 271 pp.

Blevin, P.L. and Chappell, B.W. (1992) The role of magma sources, oxidation states and fractionation in determining the granite metallogeny of eastern Australia. *Transactions of the Royal Society Edinburgh: Earth Sciences*, 83, 305–16.

Blevin, P.L., Chappell, B.W. and Allen, C.M. (1996) Intrusive metallogenic provinces in eastern Australia based on granite source and composition. *Transactions of the Royal Society Edinburgh: Earth Sciences*, 87, 281–90.

Blunden, J. (1983) *Mineral Resources and Their Management*. Longman, 302 pp.

Bodnar, R., Reynolds, T.J. and Kuehn, C.A. (1985) Fluid inclusion systematics in epithermal systems. In B.R. Berger and P.M. Bethke (eds), *Geology and Geochemistry of Epithermal Systems*. Reviews in Economic Geology, 2, 73–97.

Boer, R., Meyer, F.M., Robb, L.J., Graney, J.R., Vennemann, T.W. and Kesler, S.E. (1995) Mesothermal-type mineralization in the Sabie–Pilgrim's Rest Goldfield, South Africa. *Economic Geology*, 90(4), 860–76.

Bottinga, Y. and Javoy, M. (1990) The degassing of Hawaaian tholeiite. *Bulletin of Volcanology*, 53, 73–85.

Boudreau, A.E. and Meurer, W.P. (1999) Chromatographic separation of the platinum-group elements, gold, base metals and sulphur during degassing of a compacting and solidifying igneous crystal pile. *Contributions to Mineralogy and Petrology*, 134, 174–85.

Bowles, J.F.W. (1986) The development of platinum-group minerals in laterites. *Economic Geology*, 81, 1276–85.

Bowles, J.F.W., Gize, A.P., Vaughan, D.J. and Norris, S.J. (1994) Development of platinum-group minerals in laterites – initial comparison of organic and inorganic controls. *Transactions of the Institution of Mining Metallurgy*, 103, B53–B56.

Boxer, G.L., Lorenz, V. and Smith, C.B. (1989) The geology and volcanology of the Argyle (AK1) Lamproite Diatreme, Western Australia. Geological Society of Australia, Special Publication, 14, 140–52.

Boyce, A.J., Fallick, A.E., Little, C.T.S., Wilkinson, J.J. and Everett, C.E. (1999) A hydrothermal vent tube worm in the Ballynoe barite deposit, Silvermines, Ireland: implications for timing and ore genesis. In C. Stanley and 39 others (eds), *Mineral Deposits: Processes to Processing*. Balkema, pp. 825–7.

Brathwaite, R.L. and Faure, K. (2002) The Waihi epithermal gold-silver-base metal sulfide-quartz vein system, New Zealand. *Economic Geology*, 97, 269–90.

Brown, P.E. (1998) Fluid inclusion modeling for hydrothermal systems. *Reviews in Economic Geology*, 10, 151–171.

Buntin, T.J., Grandstaff, D.E., Ulmer, G.C. and Gold, D.P. (1985) A pilot study of geochemical and redox relationships between potholes and adjacent normal Merensky Reef of the Bushveld Complex. *Economic Geology*, 80, 975–87.

Burnham, C.W. (1967) Hydrothermal fluids in the magmatic stage. In H.L. Barnes (ed.), *Geochemistry of Hydrothermal Ore Deposits*. Holt, Rinehart and Winston, pp. 34–76.

Burnham, C.W. (1979) Magmas and hydrothermal fluids. In H.L. Barnes (ed.), *Geochemistry of Hydrothermal Ore Deposits*, 2nd edn. John Wiley & Sons, pp. 71–136.

Burnham, C.W. (1997) Magmas and hydrothermal fluids. In H.L. Barnes (ed.), *Geochemistry of Hydrothermal Ore Deposits*, 3rd edn. John Wiley & Sons, pp. 63–123.

Burnham, C.W. and Ohmoto, H. (1980) Late-stage processes of felsic magmatism. *Mining Geology*, Special Issue, 8, 1–11.

Burrows, D.R. and Spooner, E.T.C. (1987) Generation of a magmatic H_2O-CO_2 fluid enriched in Mo, Au and W within an Archaean sodic granodiorite stock, Mink Lake, northwestern Ontario. *Economic Geology*, 82, 1931–57.

Butt, C.R.M., Lintern, M.J. and Anand, R.R. (2000) Evolution of regoliths and landscapes in deeply weathered terrain – implications for geochemical exploration. *Ore Geology Reviews*, 16, 167–83.

Cairns-Smith, A.G. (1978) Precambrian solution photochemistry, inverse segregation and banded iron-formation. *Nature*, 276, 807–8.

Campbell I.H. and Naldrett, A.J. (1979) The influence of silicate:sulphide ratios on the geochemistry of magmatic sulphide deposits. *Economic Geology*, 74, 2248–53.

Campbell, I.H., Naldrett, A.J. and Barnes, S.J. (1983) A model for the origin of the platinum-rich sulfide horizons in the Bushveld and Stillwater Complexes. *Journal of Petrology*, 24, 133–65.

Camus, F. and Dilles, J.H. (2001) A special issue devoted to porphyry copper deposits of northern Chile: Preface. *Economic Geology*, 96, 233–7.

Candela, P.A. (1989a) Felsic magmas, volatiles and metallogenesis. *Reviews in Economic Geology*, 4, 223–33.

Candela, P.A. (1989b) Magmatic ore-forming fluids: thermodynamic and mass transfer calculations of metal concentrations. *Reviews in Economic Geology*, 4, 302–21.

Candela, P.A. (1991) Physics of aqueous phase evolution in plutonic environments. *American Mineralogist*, 76, 1081–91.

Candela, P.A. (1992) Controls on ore metal ratios in granite related ore systems: an experimental and computational approach. *Transactions of the Royal Society Edinburgh: Earth Sciences*, 83, 317–26.

Candela, P.A. (1997) A review of shallow, ore-related granites: textures, volatiles and ore metals. *Journal of Petrology*, 38, 1619–33.

Candela, P.A. and Holland, H.D. (1984) The partitioning of copper and molybdenum between silicate melts and aqueous fluids. *Geochimica et Cosmochimica Acta*, 48, 373–80.

Candela, P.A. and Holland, H.D. (1986) A mass transfer model for copper and molybdenum in magmatic hydrothermal systems: the origin of porphyry-type copper deposits. *Economic Geology*, 81, 1–18.

Candela, P.A. and Piccoli, P.M. (1995) Model ore-metal partitioning from melts into vapor and vapor-brine mixtures. In J.F.H. Thompson (ed.), *Magmas, Fluids and Ore Deposits*. Short Course, Mineralogical Association of Canada, 23, 101–28.

Carlisle, D. (1983) Concentration of uranium and vanadium in calcretes and gypcretes. In R.C.L. Wilson (ed.), *Residual Deposits: Surface Related Weathering Processes and Materials*. The Geological Society of London and Blackwell Scientific Publications, pp. 185–95.

Carr, H.W., Kruger, F.J., Groves, D.I. and Cawthorn, R.G. (1999) The petrogenesis of Merensky Reef potholes at the Western Platinum Mine, Bushveld Complex: Sr-isotopic evidence for the synmagmatic deformation. *Mineralium Deposita*, 34, 335–47.

Cathles, L.M. (1981) Fluid flow and genesis of hydrothermal ore deposits. *Economic Geology*, 75th Anniversary Volume, 424–57.

Cawthorn, R.G. (1999) Platinum group element mineralization in the Bushveld Complex – a critical reassessment of geochemical models. *South African Journal of Geology*, 102, 268–81.

Cawthorn, R.G. (2002) The role of magma mixing in the genesis of PGE mineralization in the Bushveld Complex: thermodynamic calculations and new interpretations – a discussion. *Economic Geology*, 97, 663–7.

Cawthorn, R.G., Harrison, C. and Kruger, F.J. (2000) Discordant ultramafic pegmatoidal pipes in the Bushveld Complex. *Contributions to Mineralogy and Petrology*, 140, 119–33.

Cawthorn, R.G., Lee, C.A., Schouwstra, R.P. and Mellowship, P. (2002) Relationship between PGE and PGM in the Bushveld Complex. *Canadian Mineralogist*, 40, 311–28.

Cawthorn, R.G. and McCarthy, T.S. (1985) Incompatible trace element behavior in the Bushveld Complex. *Economic Geology*, 80, 1016–26.

Cerny, P. (1991) Fertile granites of Precambrian rare-element pegmatite fields: is geochemistry controlled by tectonic setting or source lithologies? *Precambrian Research*, 51, 429–68.

Cerny, P and Meintzer, R.E. (1988) Fertile granites in the Archean and Proterozoic fields of rare-element pegmatites: crustal environment, geochemistry and petrogenetic relationships. In R.P. Taylor and D.F. Strong (eds), *Recent Advances in the Geology of Granite Related Mineral Deposits*. Canadian Institution of Mining, Special Volume, 39, 170–207.

Chan, M.A. and Kocurek, G. (1988) Complexities in eolian and marine interactions: processes and eustatic controls on erg development. *Sedimentary Geology*, 56, 283–300.

Chappell, B.W. and White, A.J.R. (1974) Two contrasting granite types. *Pacific Geology*, 8, 173–4.

Chávez, W.X. (2000) Supergene oxidation of copper deposits: zoning and distribution of copper oxide minerals. *Society of Economic Geologists Newsletter*, 41.

Cheney, E.S. (1996) Sequence stratigraphy and plate tectonic significance of the Transvaal succession of southern Africa and its equivalent in Western Australia. *Precambrian Research*, 79, 3–24.

Choukroune, P., Ludden, J.N., Chardon, D., Calvert, A.J. and Bouhallier, H. (1997) Archaean crustal growth and tectonic processes: a comparison of the Superior Province, Canada and the Dharwar craton, India. In J.-P. Burg and M. Ford (eds), *Orogeny through Time*. Geological Society, Special Publication, 121, 63–98.

Clark, A.H. and 10 others (1990) Geologic and geochronologic constraints on the metallogenic evolution of the Andes of southeastern Peru. *Economic Geology*, 85, 1520–83.

Clemens, J.D. and Vielzeuf, D. (1987) Constraints on melting and magma production in the crust. *Earth and Planetary Science Letters*, 86, 287–306.

Clemmey, H. (1985) Sedimentary ore deposits. In P.J. Brenchley and B.P.J. Williams (eds), *Sedimentology: Recent Developments and Applied Aspects*. Geological Society London and Blackwell Scientific Publications, pp. 229–47.

Cloke, P.L. and Kelly, W.C. (1964) Solubility of gold under inorganic supergene conditions. *Economic Geology*, 59, 259–70.

Coetzee, F. (1965) Distribution and grain size of gold, uraninite, pyrite and certain other heavy minerals In gold-bearing reefs of the Witwatersrand basin. *Transactions of the Geological Society of South Africa*, 68, 61–8.

Coetzee, J. and Twist, D. (1989) Disseminated tin mineralization in the roof of the Bushveld granite pluton at the Zaaiplaats Mine, with implications for the genesis of magmatic-hydrothermal tin systems. *Economic Geology*, 84, 85–102.

Colvine, A.C. (1989) An empirical model for the formation of Archean gold deposits: products of final cratonization of the Superior Province, Canada. *Monograph in Economic Geology*, 6, 37–53.

Comer, J.B. (1974) Genesis of Jamaican bauxite. *Economic Geology*, 69, 1251–64.

Connan, J. (1974) Time–temperature relations in oil genesis. *Bulletin of the American Association of Petroleum Geologists*, 58, 2516–21.

Constantinou, G. and Govett, G.J.S. (1973) Geology, geochemistry and genesis of Cyprus sulfide deposits. *Economic Geology*, 68, 843–58.

Cook, P.J. and McElhinny, W. (1979) A reevaluation of the spatial and temporal distribution of sedimentary phosphate deposits in the light of plate tectonics. *Economic Geology*, 74, 315–30.

Cook, P.J. and Shergold, J.H. (1984) Phosphorus, phosphorites and skeletal evolution at the Precambrian-Cambrian boundary. *Nature*, 308, 2331–7.

Cooke, D.R. and Simmons, S.F. (2000) Characteristics and genesis of epithermal gold deposits. *Reviews in Economic Geology*, 13, 221–44.

Corbett, G.J. and Leach, T.M. (1998) Southwest Pacific rim gold–copper systems: structure, alteration and mineralization. Society of Economic Geologists, Special Publication, 6, 237 pp.

Cornford, C. (1998) Source rocks and hydrocarbons of the North Sea. In K.W. Glennie (ed.), *Petroleum Geology of the North Sea: Basic Concepts and Recent Advances*. Blackwell Science, 636 pp.

Cox, K.G., Bell, J.D. and Pankhurst, R.J. (1979) *The Interpretation of Igneous Rocks*. George Allen & Unwin, 450 pp.

Cox, S.F., Knackstedt, M.A. and Braun, J. (2001) Principles of structural control on permeability and fluid flow in hydrothermal systems. In J.P. Richards and R.M. Tosdal (eds), *Structural Controls on Ore Genesis*. Reviews in Economic Geology, 14, 1–24.

Craig, H. (1961) Isotopic variations in meteoric waters, *Science*, 133, 1702–3.

Craig, J.R., Vaughan, D.J. and Skinner, B.J. (1996) *Resources of the Earth: Origin, Use and Environmental Impact*. Prentice Hall, 472 pp.

Craig, J.R. and Vaughan, D.J. (1994) *Ore Microscopy and Ore Petrography*. John Wiley & Sons, 434 pp.

Creaser, R.A. and Cooper, J.A. (1993) U-Pb geochronology of middle Proterozoic felsic magmatism surrounding the Olympic Dam Cu-U-Au-Ag and Moonta Cu-Au-Ag deposits, South Australia. *Economic Geology*, 88, 186–97.

Dalziel, I.W.D., Mosher, S. and Gahagan, L.M. (2000) Laurentia–Kalahari collision and the assembley of Rodinia. *Journal of Geology*, 108, 499–513.

Davies, G. and Tredoux, M. (1985) The platinum group element and gold contents of the marginal rocks and sills of the Bushveld Complex. *Economic Geology*, 80, 838–48.

Deer, W.A., Howie, R.A. and Zussman, J. (1982) *Rock Forming Minerals, Volumes 1–5*, 2nd edn. Longman.

Delaney, J.R. and Cosens, B.A. (1982) Boiling and metal deposition in submarine hydrothermal systems. *Marine Technology Society Journal*, 16(3), 62–6.

De Voto, R.H. (1978) *Uranium Geology and Exploration*. Colorado School of Mines, 188 pp.

De Wit, M.J. and 11 others (1992) Formation of an Archaean continent. *Nature*, 357, 553–62.

De Wit, M.J. and Hynes, A. (1995) The onset of interaction between the hydrosphere and oceanic crust, and the origin of the first continental lithosphere. In M.P. Coward and A.C. Ries (eds), *Early Precambrian Processes*. Geological Society, Special Publication, 95, 1–9.

Dingwell, D.B., Holtz, F. and Behrens, H. (1997) The solubility of H_2O in peralkaline and peraluminous granitic melts. *American Mineralogist*, 82, 3–4.

Drennan, G.R., Cathelineau, M., Boiron, M.-C., Dubessy, J. and Robb, L.J. (1999) Characteristics of post-depositional fluids in the Witwatersrand Basin. *Mineralogy and Petrology*, 66, 83–109.

Duane, M.J. and De Wit, M.J. (1988) Pb–Zn ore deposits of the northern Caledonides: products of continental-scale fluid mixing and tectonic expulsion during tectonic collision. *Geology*, 16, 999–1002.

Durrance, E.M. and Bristow, C.W. (1986) Kaolinisation and isostatic readjustment in southwest England. *Proceedings of the Ussher Society*, 6, 318–22.

Eddy, C.A., Dilek, Y., Hurst, S. and Moores, E.M. (1998) Seamount formation and associated caldera complex and hydrothermal mineralization in ancient oceanic crust, Troodos ophiolite (Cyprus). *Tectonophysics*, 292, 189–210.

Eidel, J.J. (1991) Basin analysis for the mineral industry. *Reviews in Economic Geology*, 5, 1–15.

Einaudi, M. (1982) Description of skarns associated with porphyry copper plutons: southwestern North America. In S.R. Titley (ed.), *Advances in Geology of the Porphyry Copper Deposits: Southwestern North America*. University of Arizona Press, pp. 139–83.

Einaudi, M. (2000) Mineral resources: assets and liabilities. In W.G. Ernst (ed.), *Earth Systems: Processes and Issues*. Cambridge University Press, pp. 346–72.

Einaudi, M., Meinert, L.D. and Newberry, R.J. (1981) Skarn deposits. *Economic Geology*, 75th Anniversary Volume, 317–91.

Eldridge, C.S., Compston, W., Williams, I.S., Harris, J.W., Bristow, J.W. and Kinny, P.D. (1995) Applications of the SHRIMP I Ion Microprobe to the understanding of processes and timing of diamond formation. *Economic Geology*, 90, 271–80.

Emmons, W.H. (1936) Hypogene zoning in metalliferous lodes. *Report 1 of the 16th International Geological Congress*, 417–32.

England, G.L., Rasmussen, B., Krapez, B. and Groves, D.I. (2001) The origin of uraninite, bitumen nodules and carbon seams in Witwatersrand gold–uranium–pyrite ore deposits, based on a Permo-Triassic analogue. *Economic Geology*, 96, 1907–20.

England, P. and Houseman, G. (1984) On the geodynamic setting of kimberlite genesis. *Earth and Planetary Science Letters*, 67, 109–22.

Engel, M.H. and Mack, S.A. (1993) *Organic Geochemistry: Principles and Applications*. Plenum Press, 861 pp.

Eriksson, K.A. and Donaldson, J.A. (1986) Basinal and shelf sedimentation in relation to the Archaean–Protozoic boundary. *Precambrian Research*, 33, 103–21.

Eriksson, S. C. (1989) Palaborwa: a saga of magmatism, metasomatism and miscibility. In J.D. Bell (ed.), *Carbonotites: Genesis and Evolution*, Unwin Hyman, 618 pp.

Ernst, W.G. (2000) *Earth Systems: Processes and Issues*. Cambridge University Press, 566 pp.

Evans, A.M. (2001) *An Introduction to Economic Geology and Its Environmental Impact*. Blackwell Science, 364 pp.

Evans, D.A.D., Martin, D.McB., Nelson, D.R., Powell, C.McA. and Wingate, M.T.D. (2000) The Vaalbara hypothesis reviewed. Extended Abstract, 31st International Geological Congress, Brazil.

Exley, C.S. (1976) Observations on the formation of kaolinite in the St Austell granite, Cornwall. *Clay Minerals*, 11, 51–63.

Fallick, A.E., Ashton, J.H., Boyce, A.J., Ellam, R.B. and Russell, M.J. (2001) Bacteria were responsible for the magnitude of the world-class hydrothermal base metal sulphide ore body at Navan, Ireland. *Economic Geology*, 96, 885–90.

Ferguson, J. and Currie, K.L. (1971) Evidence of liquid immiscibility in alkaline ultrabasic dikes at Callander Bay, Ontario. *Journal of Petrology*, 12, 561–85.

Field, M., Gibson, T.A., Wilkes, J., Gabobetse, G. and Khutwe, P. (1997) The geology of the Orapa A/K1 kimberlite, Botswana: further insight into the emplacement of kimberlite pipes. *Russian Geology and Geophysics*, 38(1), 261–76.

Fleischer, V.D. (1984) Discovery, geology and genesis of copper-cobalt mineralization at Chambishi Southeast prospect, Zambia. *Precambrian Research*, 25, 119–33.

Fleischer, V.D., Garlick, W.G. and Haldane, R. (1976) Geology of the Zambian Copper Belt. In K.H. Wolff (ed.), *Handbook of Strata-bound and Stratiform Ore Deposits: II Regional Studies and Specific Deposits, Volume 6*. Elsevier, pp. 223–352.

Foose, M.P. and McLelland, J.M. (1995) Proterozoic low-Ti iron-oxide deposits in New York and New Jersey: relation to Fe-oxide (Cu-U-Au-rare earth element) deposits and tectonic implications. *Geology*, 23, 665–68.

Force, E.C. (1991a) Geology of titanium deposits. *Bulletin Geological Society of America*, 129, 19–37.

Force E.C. (1991b) Placer deposits in shoreline-related sands of Quaternary Age. United States Geological Survey, Special Publication.

Force, E.C., Eidel, J.J. and Maynard, J.B. (1991) *Sedimentary and Diagenetic Mineral Deposits: A Basin Analysis Approach to Exploration*. Society of Economic Geologists, Reviews in Economic Geology, 5, 216 pp.

Force, E.C. and Maynard, J.B. (1991) Manganese: syngenetic deposits on the margins of anoxic basins. *Reviews in Economic Geology*, 5, 147–57.

Forsman, J.P. and Hunt, J.M. (1958) Insoluble organic matter (kerogen) in sedimentary rocks. *Geochimica et Cosmochimica Acta*, 15, 170–82.

Förster, H. and Jafarzadeh, A. (1994) The Bafq Mining District in central Iran: a highly mineralized infracambrian volcanic field. *Economic Geology*, 89, 1697–721.

Francheteau, J. and 14 others (1979) Massive deep-sea sulphide ore deposits discovered on the East Pacific Rise. *Nature*, 277, 523–8.

Franklin, J.M. (1993) Volcanic-associated massive sulfide deposits. Geological Association of Canada, Special Paper, 40, 315–34.

Franklin, J.M., Lydon, J.W. and Sangster, D.F. (1981) Volcanic-associated massive sulfide deposits. *Economic Geology*, 75th Anniversary Volume, 485–627.

Freitsch, R. (1978) On the origin of iron ores of the Kiruna Type. *Economic Geology*, 73, 478–85.

Friedman, G.M., Sanders, J.E. and Kopaska-Merkel, D.C. (1992) *Principles of Sedimentary Deposits*. Macmillan, 717 pp.

Frimmel, H.E. (1997) Detrital origin of hydrothermal Witwatersrand gold: a review. *Terra Nova*, 9(4), 192–7.

Frimmel, H., Hallbauer, D.K. and Gartz, V.H. (1999) Gold mobilizing fluids in the Witwatersrand Basin: composition and possible sources. *Mineralogy and Petrology*, 66, 55–81.

Frimmel, H.E. and Minter, W.E.L. (2002) Recent developments concerning the geological history and genesis of the Witwatersrand gold deposits, South Africa. Society of Economic Geologists, Special Publication, 9, 17–45.

Fuchs, W.A. and Rose, A.W. (1974) The geochemical behaviour of platinum and palladium in the weathering cycle in the Stillwater Complex, Montana. *Economic Geology*, 69, 332–46.

Fyfe, W.S. (2000) The life support system: toward Earth sense. In W.G. Ernst (ed.), *Earth Systems: Processes and Issues*. Cambridge University Press, pp. 506–15.

Gaál, G. (1987) An outline of the Precambrian Evolution of the Baltic Shield. *Precambrian Research*, 35, 15–52.

Gaál, G. (1990) Tectonic styles of Early Proterozoic ore deposition in the Fennoscandian Shield. *Precambrian Research*, 46, 83–114.

Galloway, W.E. and Hobday, D.K. (1983) *Terrigeneous Clastic Depositional Systems*. Springer-Verlag, 423 pp.

Gammons, C.H. (1996) Experimental investigations of the hydrothermal geochemistry of Pt and Pd: V. Equilibria between platinum metal, Pt(II), and Pt(IV) chloride complexes at 25 to 300 °C. *Geochimica et Cosmochimica Acta*, 60, 1683–94.

Garlick, W.G. (1982) Erosion of the folded copper-rich arenite filling of a rolled-up algal mat, Mufulira, Zambia. *Economic Geology*, 77, 1934–50.

Garrels, R.M. and Christ, C.L. (1965) *Solutions, Minerals and Equilibria*. Harper and Row, 450 pp.

Garven, G., Ge, S., Person, M.A. and Sverjensky, D.A. (1993) Genesis of stratabound ore deposits in the mid-continent basins of North America. *American Journal of Science*, 293, 497–568.

Garven, G. and Raffensberger, (1997) Hydrogeology and geochemistry of ore genesis in sedimentary basins. In H.L. Barnes (ed.), *Geochemistry of Hydrothermal Ore Deposits*, 3rd edn. John Wiley, pp. 125–90.

Gibson, R.L. and Reimold, W.U. (1999) The significance of the Vredefort dome for the thermal and structural evolution of the Witwatersrand Basin, South Africa. *Mineralogy and Petrology*, 66, 5–23.

Giggenbach, W. (1997) The origin and evolution of fluids in magmatic-hydrothermal systems. In H.L. Barnes (ed.), *Geochemistry of Hydrothermal Ore Deposits*, 3rd edn. John Wiley, pp. 737–96.

Gill, R. (1996) *Chemical Fundamentals of Geology*. Chapman & Hall, 290 pp.

Gilmour, P. (1976) Some transitional types of mineral deposits in volcanic and sedimentary rocks. In K.H. Wolf (ed.), *Handbook of Strata-bound and Stratiform Ore Deposits, Volume 1*. Elsevier, pp. 111–60.

Giordano, T.H. (1994) Metal transport in ore fluids by organic ligand complexation. In E.D. Pittman and M.D. Lewan (eds), *Organic Acids in Geological Processes*. Springer-Verlag, pp. 319–54.

Giordano, T.H. and Kharaka, Y.K. (1994) Organic ligand distribution and speciation in sedimentary basin brines, diagenetic fluids and related ore solutions. In J. Parnell (ed.), *Geofluids: Origin, Migration and Evolution of Fluids in Sedimentary Basins*. Geological Society, Special Publication, 78, pp. 175–202.

Gize, A.P. (1999) Organic alteration in hydrothermal sulfide ore deposits. *Economic Geology*, 94, 967–80.

Gize, A.P. and Hoering, T.C. (1980) The organic matter in Mississippi Valley-type deposits. *Carnegie Institute Washington Yearbook*, 79, 384–8.

Glennie, K.W. (1998) *Petroleum Geology of the North Sea: Basic Concepts and Recent Advances*. Blackwell Science, 636 pp.

Glennie, K.W. (2000) Cretaceous tectonic evolution of Arabia's eastern plate margin: a tale of two oceans. SEPM, Special Publication, 69, 9–20.

Goldfarb, R.J., Groves, D.I. and Gardoll, S. (2001) Orogenic gold and geologic time: a global synthesis. *Ore Geology Reviews*, 18, 1–75.

Goldhaber, M.B., Reynolds, R.L. and Rye, R.O. (1978) Origin of a south-Texas roll-type uranium deposit: II. Sulfide petrology and sulfur isotope studies. *Economic Geology*, 73, 1690–705.

Goldhaber, M.B., Reynolds, R.L. and Rye, R.O. (1983) Role of fluid mixing and fault-related sulfide in the origin of the Ray Point uranium district, south Texas. *Economic Geology*, 78, 1043–63.

Golightly, J.P. (1981) Nickeliferous laterite deposits. *Economic Geology*, 75th Anniversary Volume, 710–35.

Goodfellow, W.D., Lydon, J.W. and Turner, R.J.W. (1993) Geology and genesis of stratiform sediment-hosted (SedEx) zinc-lead-silver sulfide deposits. Geological Association Canada, Special Paper, 40, 201–52.

Gower, C.F., Ryan, A.B. and Rivers, T. (1990) Mid-Proterozoic Laurentia-Baltica: an overview of its geological evolution and a summary of the contributions made by this volume. In C.F. Gower, T. Rivers and A.B. Ryan (eds), Mid-Proterozoic Laurentia-Baltica. Geological Association Canada Special Paper, 38, 1–20.

Grainger, C.J., Groves, D.I. and Costa, C.H.C. (2002) The epigenetic sediment-hosted Serra Pelada Au-PGE deposit and its potential genetic association with Fe oxide Cu-Au mineralization within the Carajás Mineral Province, Amazon Craton, Brazil. Society of Economic Geologists, Special Publication, 19, 47–64.

Grinenko, L.N. (1985) Sources of sulphur of the nickeliferous and barren gabbro-dolerite intrusions of the northwest Siberian platform. International Geological Reviews, 27, 695–708.

Gross, G.A., Gower, C.F. and Lefebure, D.V. (1997) Magmatic Ti–Fe–V oxide deposits. In Geological Fieldwork 1997, British Columbia Ministry of Employment and Investment, Paper 1998-1, 24J-1-3.

Groves, D.I. (1993) The crustal continuum model for late-Archaean lode-gold deposits of the Yilgarn block, Western Australia. Mineralium Deposita, 28, 366–74.

Groves, D.I., Goldfarb, R.J., Gebre-Mariam, M., Hagemann, S.G. and Robert, F. (1998) Orogenic gold deposits: a proposed classification in the context of their crustal distribution and relationship to other gold deposit types. Ore Geology Reviews, 13, 7–27.

Groves, D.I. and McCarthy, T.S. (1978) Fractional crystallization and the origin of tin deposits in granitoids. Mineralium Deposita, 13, 11–26.

Guilbert, J.M. and Park, C.F. (1986) The Geology of Ore Deposits. W.H. Freeman and Co., 985 pp.

Guild, P.W. (1978) Metallogenesis in the western United States. Journal of the Geological Society London, 135, 355–76.

Gustafson, L.B. and Williams, N. (1981) Sediment-hosted stratiform deposits of copper, lead and zinc. Economic Geology, 75th Anniversary Volume, 139–78.

Haeussler, P.J., Bradley, D., Goldfarb, R., Snee, L. and Taylor, C. (1995) Link between ridge subduction and gold mineralization in southern Alaska. Geology, 23, 995–8.

Hagemann S.G. and Brown, P.E. (2000) Gold in 2000. Society of Economic Geologists, Reviews in Economic Geology, 13, 559 pp.

Hagemann, S.G. and Cassidy, K.F. (2000) Archean orogenic lode gold deposits. Reviews in Economic Geology, 13, 9–68.

Haggerty, S.E. (1989) Mantle metasomes and the kinship between carbonatites and kimberlites. In J.D. Bell (ed.), Carbonatites Genesis and Evolution. Unwin Hyman, 618 pp.

Haggerty, S.E. (1999) A diamond trilogy: superplumes, supercontinents and supernovae. Science, 285, 851–60.

Hall, A. (1996) Igneous Petrology. Longman, 551 pp.

Hall, R.P. and Hughes, D.J. (1993) Early Precambrian crustal development: changing styles of mafic magmatism. Journal of the Geological Society, 150, 625–35.

Hannah, J.L. and Stein, H.J. (1990) Magmatic and hydrothermal processes in ore-bearing systems. Geological Society of America, Special Paper, 246, 1–10.

Hanor, J.S. (1979) The sedimentary genesis of hydrothermal fluids. In H.L. Barnes (ed.), Geochemistry of Hydrothermal Ore Deposits. Wiley-Interscience, pp. 137–72.

Hanor, J.S. (1994) Origin of saline fluids in sedimentary basins. In J. Parnell (ed.), Geofluids: Origin, Migration and Evolution of Fluids in Sedimentary Basins. Geological Society, Special Publication, 78, 151–74.

Hardisty, J. (1994) Beach and nearshore sediment transport. In K. Pye (ed.), Sediment Transport and Depositional Processes. Blackwell Scientific, pp. 219–55.

Harland, W.B. (1965) Critical evidence for a great infra-Cambrian glaciation. Geologische Rundschau, 54, 45–61.

Harland, W.B. (1989) A Geologic Time Scale. Cambridge University Press, 263 pp.

Haynes, D.W. (1986a) Stratiform copper deposits hosted by low-energy sediments: I. Timing of sulfide precipitation – an hypothesis. Economic Geology, 81, 250–65.

Haynes, D.W. (1986b) Stratiform copper deposits hosted by low-energy sediments: II. Nature of source rocks and composition of metal-transporting water. Economic Geology, 81, 266–80.

Haynes, D.W., Cross, K.C., Bills, R.T. and Reed, M.H. (1995) Olympic Dam ore genesis: a fluid-mixing model. Economic Geology, 90, 281–307.

Heath, G.R. (1981) Ferromanganese nodules of the deep sea. Economic Geology, 75th Anniversary Volume, 736–65.

Hecht, L. and Cuney, M. (2000) Hydrothermal alteration of monazite in the Precambrian crystalline basement of the Athabasca Basin (Saskatchewan, Canada); implications for the formation of unconformity-related uranium deposits. Mineralium Deposita, 35, 791–5.

Hedenquist, J.W. and Aoki, M. (1991) Meteoric interaction with magmatic discharges in Japan and the significance for mineralization. *Geology*, 14, 1041–4.

Hedenquist, J.W., Arribas, R.A. and Gonzalez, U.E. (2000) Exploration for epithermal gold deposits. In S. Hagemann and P.E. Brown (eds), *Gold in 2000*. Society of Economic Geologists, Reviews in Economic Geology, 13, 245–77.

Hedenquist, J.W., Izawa, E., White, N.C., Giggenbach, W.F. and Saoki, M. (1994) Geology, geochemistry and origin of high sulfidation Cu-Au mineralization in the Nansatsu district, Japan. *Economic Geology*, 89, 1–30.

Hedenquist, J.W., Simmons, S.F., Giggenbach, W.F. and Eldridge, C.S. (1993) White Island, New Zealand, volcanic-hydrothermal system represents the geochemical environment of high-sulfidation Cu and Au ore deposition. *Geology*, 21, 731–4.

Hedenquist, J.W., Arribas, A. and Reynolds, T.J. (1998) Evolution of an intrusion-centred hydrothermal system: Far Southeast-Lepanto porphyry – epithermal Cu–Au deposits, Phillipines. *Economic Geology*, 93, 373–404.

Hedenquist, J.W., Izawa, E, Arribas, A. and White, N.C. (1996) Epithermal gold deposits: styles, characteristics and exploration. Resource Geology, Special Publication, 1, 17 pp.

Hekinian, H. and Fouquet, Y. (1985) Volcanism and metallogenesis of axial and off-axial structures on the East Pacific Rise near 13° N. *Economic Geology*, 80, 221–49.

Heinrich, C.A., Gunther, D., Audetat, A., Ulrich, T. and Frischknecht, R. (1999) Metal fractionation between magmatic brine and vapor, determined by microanalysis of fluid inclusions. *Geology*, 27, 755–8.

Helgeson, H. (1964) *Complexing and Hydrothermal Ore Deposition*. Pergamon Press, 128 pp.

Herzig, P.M. and Hannington, M.D. (1995) Polymetallic massive sulfides at the modern seafloor; a review. *Ore Geology Reviews*, 10, 95–115.

Hiemstra, S.A. (1979) The role of collectors in the formation of the platinum deposits in the Bushveld Complex. In A.J. Naldrett (ed.), *Nickel-Sulfide and Platinum-group-element Deposits*. Canadian Mineralogist, 17, 469–82.

Hilderbrand, R.S. (1986) Kiruna-type deposits: their origin and relationship to intermediate subvolcanic plutons in the Great Bear Magmatic Zone, Northwest Canada. *Economic Geology*, 81, 640–59.

Hoffman, P.F. (1988) United plates of America, the birth of a craton: early Proterozoic assembly and growth of Laurentia. *Annual Reviews of Earth and Planetary Science*, 16, 543–603.

Hoffman, P.F. (1991) Did the breakout of Laurentia turn Gondwanaland inside-out? *Science*, 252, 1409–11.

Hoffman, P.F., Kaufman, A.J., Halverson, G.P. and Schrag, D.P. (1998) A Neoproterozoic snowball Earth. *Science*, 281, 1342–6.

Hofmann, B.A. (1990) Reduction spheroids from northern Switzerland: mineralogy, geochemistry and genetic models. *Chemical Geology*, 81, 55–81.

Hofstra, A. and Cline, J. (2000) Characteristics and models for Carlin type gold deposits. *Reviews in Economic Geology*, 13, 163–220.

Holland, H.D. (1972) Granites, solutions and base metal deposits. *Economic Geology*, 67, 281–301.

Holland, H.D. (1984) *The Chemical Evolution of the Atmosphere and the Oceans*. Princeton University Press, 598 pp.

Holloway, J.R. (1987) Igneous fluids. In I.S.E. Carmichael and H.P. Eugster (eds), *Thermodynamic Modelling of Geologic Materials: Minerals, Fluids and Melts*. Reviews in Mineralogy, Mineralogical Society of America, 17, 211–34.

Holzheid, A., Sylvester, P., O'Neill, H.StC., Rubie, D.C. and Palme, H. (2000) Evidence for a late chondritic veneer in the Earth's mantle from high-pressure partitioning of palladium and platinum. *Nature*, 406, 396–9.

Hughes, M.G., Keene, J.B. and Joseph, R.G. (2000) Hydraulic sorting of heavy mineral grains by swash on a medium-sand beach. *Journal of Sedimentary Research*, 70, 994–1004.

Hunt, J.M. (1979) *Petroleum Geochemistry and Geology*. W.H. Freeman and Company, 617 pp.

Huppert, H.H. and Sparks, R.S.J. (1980) Restrictions on the compositions of mid-ocean ridge basalts; a fluid dynamical investigation. *Nature*, 286, 46–8.

Hutchison, C.S. (1983) *Economic Deposits and Their Tectonic Setting*. Macmillan Press, 365 pp.

Hutchison, C. S., and Taylor, D. (1987) Metallogenesis in SE Asia. *Journal of the Geological Society London*, 135, 407–28.

Hutchinson, R.W. and Searle, D.L. (1971) Stratabound pyrite deposits in Cyprus and relation to other sulphide ores. Mining Geology Society of Japan, Special Publication, 3, 198–205.

Hyndman, D.W. (1981) Controls on source and depth of emplacement of granitic magma. *Geology*, 9, 244–9.

International Commission on Stratigraphy (2000) A Geologic Time Scale. Chart published by International Commission on Stratigraphy (ICS) of the International Union of Geological Sciences (IUGS) (www.micropress.org/stratigraphy/).

Irvine, T.N. (1977) Origin of chromitite layers in the Muskox Intrusion and other stratiform intrusions: a new interpretation. *Geology*, 5, 273–7.

Irvine, T.N., Anderson, J.C.Ø. and Brooks, K. (1998) Included blocks (and blocks within blocks) in the Skaergaard Intrusion: geologic relations and the origins of rhythmic modally graded layers. *Bulletin of the Geological Society of America*, 110, 1398–447.

Irvine, T.N., Keith, D.W. and Todd, S.G. (1983) The J-M platinum–palladium reef of the Stillwater Complex, Montana: II. origin by double-diffusive convective magma mixing and implications for the Bushveld Complex. *Economic Geology*, 78, 1287–334.

Isachsen, C.E. and Bowring, S.A. (1994) Evolution of the Slave craton. *Geology*, 2, 917–20.

Ishihara, S. (1977) The magnetite-series and ilmenite-series granitic rocks. *Mining Geology*, 26, 293–305.

Ishihara, S. (1978) Metallogenesis in the Japanese island arc system. *Journal of the Geological Society London*, 135, 389–406.

Ishihara, S. (1981) The granitoid series and mineralization. *Economic Geology*, 75th Anniversary Volume, 458–84.

Ishihara, S. and Takenouchi, S. (1980) *Granitic Magmatism and Related Mineralization*. Society of Mining Geologists of Japan, Special Issue Mining Geology, 8, 247 pp.

Ixer, R.A. (1990) *Atlas of Opaque and Ore Minerals in Their Associations*. Open University Press, 208 pp.

Izawa, E., Etho, J., Misuzu, H., Motomura, Y. and Sekine, R. (2001) Hishikari gold mineralization: a case study of the Hosen No. 1 vein hosted by basement Shimanto rocks, southern Kyushu, Japan. Society of Economic Geologists, Guidebook Series, 34, 21–30.

Jackson, N.J., Willis-Richards, J., Manning, D.A.C. and Sams, M. (1989) Evolution of the Cornubian Ore Field, southwest England: part II. Mineral deposits and ore-forming processes. *Economic Geology*, 84, 1101–33.

Jahns, R.H. and Burnham, C.W. (1969) Experimental studies of pegmatite genesis: I. A model for the derivation and crystallization of granitic pegmatites. *Economic Geology*, 64, 843–64.

James, H.L. (1954) Sedimentary facies of iron-formation. *Economic Geology*, 49, 235–93.

Jean, G.E. and Bancroft, G.M. (1985) An XPS and SEM study of gold deposition at low temperatures on sulphide mineral surfaces: concentration of gold by adsorption/reduction. *Geochimica et Cosmochimica Acta*, 49, 979–87.

Jean, G.E. and Bancroft, G.M. (1986) Heavy metal adsorption by sulphide mineral surfaces. *Geochimica et Cosmochimica Acta*, 50, 1455–63.

Johnson, J.P. and Cross, K.C. (1991) Geochronological and Sm–Nd isotopic constraints on the genesis of the Olympic Dam Cu–U–Au–Ag deposit, South Australia. In M. Pagel (ed.), *Source, Transport and Deposition of Metals*. Balkema, pp. 395–400.

Johnson, J.P. and McCulloch, M.T. (1995) Sources of mineralizing fluids for the Olympic Dam deposit (South Australia): Sm–Nd isotopic constraints. *Chemical Geology*, 121, 177–99.

Jones, H.D. and Kesler, S.E. (1992) Fluid inclusion gas chemistry in east Tennessee Mississippi Valley-type districts: evidence for immiscibility and implications for depositional mechanisms. *Geochimica et Cosmochimica Acta*, 56, 137–54.

Jowett, E.C., Rydzewski, A. and Jowett, R.J. (1987) The Kupferschiefer Cu–Ag deposits in Poland: a re-appraisal of the evidence of their origin and presentation of a new genetic model. *Canadian Journal of Earth Sciences*, 24, 2016–37.

Kasting, J.F. (1993) Evolution of the Earth's atmosphere and hydrosphere. In M.H. Engel and S.A. Macko (eds), *Organic Geochemistry*. Plenum Press, 821 pp.

Kearey, P. (ed.-in-chief) (1993) *The Encyclopedia of the Solid Earth Sciences*. Blackwell Scientific Publications, 713 pp.

Kearey, P. and Vine, F. (1996) *Tectonics*. Blackwell Science, 333 pp.

Keith, M.L. (1982) Violent volcanism, stagnant oceans and some inferences regarding petroleum, strata-bound ores and mass extinctions. *Geochimica et Cosmochimica Acta*, 46, 2621–37.

Kendall, A.C. and Harwood, G.M. (1996) Marine evaporites; arid shorelines and basins. In H.G. Reading (ed.), *Sedimentary Environments, Processes, Facies and Stratigraphy*. Blackwell Science, pp. 281–324.

Kennicutt, M.C., Brooks, J.M. and Cox, H.B. (1993) The origin and distribution of gas hydrates in marine sediments. In M.H. Engel and S.A. Macko (eds), *Organic Geochemistry*. Plenum Press, 861 pp.

Keppler, H. and Wyllie, P.J. (1991) Partitioning of Cu, Sn, Mo, W, U, and Th between melt and aqueous fluid in the systems haplogranite–H_2O–HCl and haplogranite–H_2O–HF. *Contributions to Mineralogy and Petrology*, 109, 139–50.

Kerrich, R. and Cassidy, K.F. (1994) Temporal relationships of lode-gold mineralization to accretion, magmatism, metamorphism and deformation – Archean to present: a review. *Ore Geology Reviews*, 9, 263–310.

Kesler, S.E. (1994) *Mineral Resources, Economics and the Environment*. Macmillan, 400 pp.

Kesler, S.E. (1997) Metallogenic evolution of convergent margins: selected ore deposit models. *Ore Geology Reviews*, 12, 153–71.

Key, R., Liyungu, A.K., Njamu, F.M., Somwe, V., Banda, J., Moseley, P.N. and Armstrong, R.A. (2001) The western arm of the Lufilian arc, NW Zambia and its potential for Cu mineralization. *Journal of African Earth Sciences*, 33, 503–28.

Kilinc, I.A. and Burnham, C.W. (1972) Partitioning of chloride between a silicate melt and coexisting aqueous phase from 2 to 8 kilobars. *Economic Geology*, 67, 231–5.

Kimura, K., Lewis, R.S. and Anders, S. (1974) Distribution of gold and rhenium between nickel-iron and silicate melts; implications for the abundance of siderophile elements on the Earth and Moon. *Geochimica et Cosmochimica Acta*, 38, 683–701.

Kinloch, E.D. (1982) Regional trends in the platinum group mineralogy of the Critical Zone of the Bushveld Complex, South Africa. *Economic Geology*, 77, 1328–47.

Kinnaird, J.A., Kruger, F.J., Nex, P.A.M. and Cawthorn, R.G. (2002) Chromitite formation: a key to understanding processes of platinum enrichment. In I. McDonald, A.G. Gunn and H.M. Prichard (eds), *21st Century of Pt–Pd Deposits: Current and Future Potential*. Transactions of the Institute of Mining Metallurgy, pp. 23–35.

Kirschvink, J.L. and Hagadorn, J.W. (2000) A grand unified theory of biomineralization. In E. Bauerlein (ed.), *The Biomineralization of Nano- and Microstructures*. Wiley-VCH Verlag GmbH, pp. 139–50.

Kirk, J., Ruiz, J., Chesley, J., Titley, S. and Walshe, J. (2001) A detrital model for the origin of gold and sulfides in the Witwatersrand basin based on Re–Os isotopes. *Geochimica et Cosmochimica Acta*, 65, 2149–59.

Kirk, J., Ruiz, J., Chesley, J., Walshe, J. and England, G. (2002) A major Archean, gold- and crust-forming event in the Kaapvaal Craton, South Africa. *Science*, 297, 1856–8.

Kirkham, R.V. (1989) Distribution, settings and genesis of sediment-hosted stratiform copper deposits. Geological Association Canada, Special Paper, 36, 3–38.

Kirkham, R.V. and Roscoe, S.M. (1993) Atmospheric evolution and ore deposit formation. In S. Ishihara and 9 others (eds), *Resource Geology*, Special Issue 15, 1–17.

Kisvarsanyi, G. (1977) The role of the Precambrian igneous basement in the formation of stratabound lead-zinc-copper deposits in southeast Missouri. *Economic Geology*, 72, 435–42.

Klappa, C.F. (1983) A process-response model for the formation of pedogenic calcretes. In R.C.L. Wilson (ed.), *Residual Deposits: Surface Related Weathering Processes and Materials*. Special Publication, Geological Society of London, 11, 211–20.

Klein, C. and Beukes, N.J. (1993) Sedimentology and geochemistry of the glaciogenic late Proterozoic Rapitan Iron-Formation in Canada. *Economic Geology*, 88, 542–65.

Klemd, R., Hirdes, W., Olesch, M. and Oberthür, T. (1993) Fluid inclusions in quartz-pebbles of the gold-bearing Tarkwaian conglomerates of Ghana as guides to their provenance area. *Mineralium Deposita*, 28, 334–43.

Kneeshaw, M. (2002) *Guide to the Geology of the Hamersley and Northeast Pilbara Iron Ore Provinces*. Handbook, BHP Billiton, 34 pp.

Kneeshaw, M. and Kepert, D.A. (2002) Genesis of high grade hematite orebodies of the Hamersley Province, Western Australia – a discussion. *Economic Geology*, 97, 173–6.

Knipe, S.W., Foster, R.P. and Stanley, C.J. (1992) Role of sulphide surfaces in sorption of precious metals from hydrothermal fluids. *Transactions of the Institute of Mining Metallurgy Section B*, 101, B83–B88.

Kocurek, G.A. (1996) Desert aeolian systems. In H.G. Reading (ed.), *Sedimentary Environments, Processes, Facies and Stratigraphy*. Blackwell Science, pp. 125–53.

Kojima, S., Takeda, S. and Kogita, S. (1994) Chemical factors controlling the solubility of uraninite and their significance in the genesis of unconformity-related uranium deposits. *Mineralium Deposita*, 29, 353–60.

Komar, P.D. (1989) Physical processes of waves and currents and the formation of marine placers. *Reviews in Aquatic Sciences*, 1(3), 393–423.

Komar, P.D. and Wang, C. (1984) Processes of selective grain transport and the formation of placers on beaches. *Journal of Geology*, 92, 637–55.

Konhauser, K.O. (1998) Diversity of bacterial iron mineralization. *Earth-Science Reviews*, 43, 91–121.

Konhauser, K.O. (2003) *Introduction to Geomicrobiology*. Blackwell Publishing.

Konhauser, K.O. and Ferris, F.G. (1996) Diversity of iron and silica precipitation by microbial mats in hydrothermals waters, Iceland: implications for Precambrian iron-formations. *Geology*, 24, 323–6.

Krauskopf, K.B. and Bird, D.K. (1995) *Introduction to Geochemistry*. McGraw-Hill, 647 pp.

Krogh, T.E., Davis, D.W. and Corfu, F. (1984) Precise U-Pb zircon and baddeleyite ages for the Sudbury area. In E.G. Pye, A.J. Naldrett and P.E. Giblin (eds), *The Geology and Ore Deposits of the Sudbury Structure*, Ontario Geological Survey Special Publication 1, 431–46.

Kröner, A. and Layer, P.W. (1992) Crust formation and plate motion in the Early Archean. *Science*, 256, 1405–11.

Kruger, F.J. and Marsh, J.S. (1982) Significance of Sr[87/86] ratios in the Merensky cyclic unit of the Bushveld igneous Complex, South Africa. *Nature*, 298, 53–5.

Kruger, F.J. and Marsh, J.S. (1985) The mineralogy, petrology, and origin of the Merensky Cyclic Unit in the western Bushveld Complex. *Economic Geology*, 80, 958–74.

Kushiro, I. (1980) Viscosity, density and structure of silicate melts at high pressure and their petrologic implications. In R.B. Hargraves (ed.), *Physics of Magmatic Processes*, Princeton University Press, pp. 93–120.

Kutina, J., Telupil, A., Adam, J. and Pacesova, M. (1967) On the vertical extent of ore deposition of the Prbram ore veins. *Transactions of the Institution of Mining and Metallurgy, Section B: Applied Earth Science*, 76, 732.

Kvenvolden, K.A. (1988) Methane hydrate: a major reservoir of carbon in the shallow geosphere. *Chemical Geology*, 71, 41–51.

Kvenvolden, K.A. and McMenamin, M.A. (1980) Hydrates of natural gas: a review of their geologic occurrence. United States Geological Survey, Circular, 825.

LaBerge, G.L. (1973) Possible biologic origin of Precambrian iron-formations. *Economic Geology*, 68, 1098–109.

Lamb, S., Hoke, L., Kennan, L. and Dewey, J. (1997) Cenozoic evolution of the central Andes in Bolivia and northern Chile. In J.-P. Burg and M. Ford (eds), *Orogeny through Time*. Geological Society Special Publication, 121, 237–64.

Langmuir, C.H. (1989) Geochemical consequences of in situ crystallization. *Nature*, 340, 199–205.

Langmuir, D. (1978) Uranium solution–mineral equilibria at low temperatures with applications to sedimentary ore deposits. In M.M. Kimberley (ed.), *Uranium Deposits, Their Mineralogy and Origin*. Mineralogical Association of Canada, Short Course Handbook, 3, 17–55.

Large, R.R. (1992) Australian volcanic-hosted massive sulfide deposits: features, styles and genetic models. *Economic Geology*, 87, 471–510.

Larsen, K.G. (1977) Sedimentology of the Bonneterre Formation, Southeast Missouri. *Economic Geology*, 72, 408–19.

Larson, R.L. (1991) Geological consequences of superplumes. *Geology*, 19, 963–6.

Le Bas, M.J. (1987) Nephelinites and carbonatites. In J.G. Fitton and B.G.J. Upton (eds), *Alkaline Igneous Rocks*. Geological Society of London, Special Publication, 30, 53–83.

Leach, D.L., Bradley, D., Lewchuk, M.T., Symons, D.T.A., de Marsily, G. and Brannon, J. (2001) Mississippi Valley-type lead-zinc deposits through geologic time: implications from recent age-dating research. *Mineralium Deposita*, 36, 711–40.

Lee, C.A. and Butcher, A.R. (1990) Cyclicity in the Sr isotope stratigraphy through the Merensky and Bastard reef units, Atok section, eastern Bushveld Complex. *Economic Geology*, 85, 877–83.

Leeder, M. (1999) *Sedimentology and Sedimentary Basins from Turbulence to Tectonics*. Blackwell Science, 592 pp.

Le Fort, P. (1975) Himalayas: the collided range. Present knowledge of the continental arc. *American Journal Science*, 275A, 1–44.

Lesher, C.M. (1989) Komatiite-hosted nickel sulfide deposits. *Reviews Economic Geology*, 4, 45–101.

Leventhal, J. (1993) Metals in black shales. In M.H. Engel and S.A. Macko (eds), *Organic Geochemistry*. Plenum Press, pp. 581–92.

Li, C., Maier, W.D. and de Waal, S.A. (2001) Magmatic Ni–Cu versus PGE deposits: contrasting genetic controls and exploration implications. *South African Journal of Geology*, 104, 309–18.

Li, C. and Naldrett, A.J. (1994) A numerical model for the compositional variations of Sudbury sulfide ores and its application to exploration. *Economic Geology*, 89, 1599–607.

Lightfoot, P.C., Keays, R.R. and Doherty, W. (2001) Chemical evolution and origin of nickel sufide mineralization in the Sudbury Igneous Complex, Ontario, Canada. *Economic Geology*, 96, 1855–75.

Lindgren, W. (1933) *Mineral Deposits*. McGraw-Hill, 930 pp.

Lipin, B.R. (1993) Pressure increases, the formation of chromite seams, and the development of the Ultramafic Series in the Stillwater Complex, Montana. *Journal of Petrology*, 34, 955–76.

London, D. (1990) Internal differentiation of rare-element pegmatites: a synthesis of recent research. Geological Society of America, Special Paper, 246, 35–50.

London, D. (1992) The application of experimental petrology to the genesis and crystallization of granitic pegmatites. *Canadian Mineralogist*, 30, 499–540.

London, D. (1996) Granitic pegmatites. *Transactions of the Royal Society Edinburgh: Earth Sciences*, 87, 305–19.

Lottermoser, B.G. and Ashley, P.M. (2000) Geochemistry, petrology and origin of Neoproterozoic ironstones in the eastern part of the Adelaide Geosyncline, South Australia. *Precambrian Research*, 101, 49–67.

Lowenstam, H.A. (1981) Minerals formed by organisms. *Science*, 211, 1126–31.

Lowenstern, J.B. (1994) Dissolved volatile concentrations in an ore-forming magma. *Geology*, 22, 893–6.

Lowenstern, J.B. (2001) Carbon dioxide in magmas and implications for hydrothermal systems. *Mineralium Deposita*, 36, 490–502.

Lowenstern, J.B., Mahood, G.A., Rivers, M.L. and Sutton, S.R. (1991) Evidence for extreme partitioning of copper into a magmatic vapor phase. *Science*, 252, 1405–8.

Lydon, J.W. (1988) Volcanogenic massive sulphide deposits. Part 2: Genetic models. *Geoscience Canada*, 15, 43–65.

Lynn, M.D., Wipplinger, P.E. and Wilson, M.G.C. (1998) Diamonds. In C.R. Anhaeusser and M.G.C. Wilson (eds), *The Mineral Resources of South Africa*. Handbook, Council for Geoscience, 16, 232–58.

McBirney, A.R. (1985) Further considerations of double-diffusive stratification and layering in the Skaergaard Intrusion (Greenland). *Journal of Petrology*, 26, 993–1001.

McBirney, A.R. and Noyes, R.M. (1979) Crystallization and layering of the Skaergaard Intrusion. *Journal of Petrology*, 20, 487–554.

McCandless, T.E., Ruiz, J., Adair, A.I. and Freydier, C. (1999) Re–Os isotope and Pd/Ru variations in chromitites from the Critical Zone, Bushveld Complex, South Africa. *Geochimica et Cosmochimica Acta*, 63, 911–23.

McCabe, P.J. (1984) Depositional environments of coal and coal-bearing strata. In R.A. Rahmani and R.M. Flores (eds), *Special Publication 7, International Association of Sedimentologists*. Blackwell Scientific Publications, pp. 13–42.

McCarthy, T.S., Cawthorn, R.G., Wright, C.J. and McIver, J.R. (1985) Mineral layering in the Bushveld Complex: implications of Cr abundances in magnetitite and intervening silicate-rich layers. *Economic Geology*, 80, 1062–74.

McCarthy, T.S. and Hasty, R.A. (1976) Trace element distribution patterns and their relationship to the crystallization of granitic melts. *Geochimica et Cosmochimica Acta*, 40, 1351–8.

McCuaig, T.C. and Kerrich, R. (1998) P–T–t deformation-fluid characteristics of lode gold deposits: evidence from alteration systematics. *Ore Geology Reviews*, 12, 381–453.

McCulloch, M.T. and Bennett, V.C. (1994) Progressive growth of the Earth's continental crust and depleted mantle: geochemical constraints. *Geochimica et Cosmochimica Acta*, 58, 4717–38.

McInnes, B.I.A., McBride, J.S., Evans, N.J., Lambert, D.D. and Andrew, A.S. (1999) Osmium isotope constraints on ore metal recycling in subduction zones. *Science*, 286, 512–16.

MacKenzie, F.T. (1975) Sedimentary cycling and the evolution of sea water. In J.P. Riley and G. Skirrow (eds), *Chemical Oceanography*. Academic Press, pp. 309–64.

McKibben, M.A., Andes, J.P. and Williams, A.E. (1988) Active ore formation at a brine interface in metamorphosed deltaic lacustrine sediments: the Salton Sea geothermal system, California. *Economic Geology*, 83, 511–23.

McKibben, M.A. and Hardie, L.A. (1997) Ore-forming brines in active continental rifts. In H.L. Barnes (ed.), *Geochemistry of Hydrothermal Ore Deposits*. Wiley-Interscience, pp. 877–930.

MacLean, W.H. (1969) Liquidus phase relationships in the FeS-FeO-Fe$_3$O$_4$-SiO$_2$ system, and their application in geology. *Economic Geology*, 64, 865–84.

McMenamin, M.A.S. and McMenamin, D.L.S. (1990) *The Emergence of Animals: The Cambrian Breakthrough*. Columbia University Press, 217 pp.

Mann, A.W. (1984) Mobility of gold and silver in lateritic weathering profiles: some observations from Western Australia. *Economic Geology*, 79, 38–49.

Mann, A.W. and Deutscher, R.L. (1978) Genesis principles for the precipitation of carnotite in calcrete drainages in Western Australia. *Economic Geology*, 73, 1724–37.

Manning, D.A.C. and Henderson, P. (1984) The behaviour of tungsten in granitic melt–vapour systems. *Contributions to Mineralogy and Petrology*, 76, 257–62.

Mariano, A.N. (1989) Nature of economic mineralization in carbonatites and related rocks. In J.D. Bell (ed.), *Carbonatites: Genesis and Evolution*. Unwyn Hyman, 618 pp.

Martin, D.M., Clendenin, C.W., Krapez, B. and McNaughton, N.J. (1998a) Tectonic and geochronological constraints on late Archaean and Palaeoproterozoic stratigraphic correlation within and between the Kaapvaal and Pilbara cratons. *Journal of the Geological Society London*, 155, 311–22.

Martin, D.M., Li, Z.X., Nemchin, A.A. and Powell, C.M. (1998b) A pre-2.2 Ga age for the giant hematite ores of the Hamersley Province, Australia? *Economic Geology*, 93, 1064–90.

Martini, I.P. and Chesworth, W. (1992) *Weathering, Soils and Paleosols*. Developments in Earth Surface Processes 2. Elsevier, 618 pp.

Mathez, E.A. (1989a) Vapor associated with mafic magma and controls on its composition. *Reviews in Economic Geology*, 4, 21–31.

Mathez, E.A. (1989b) Interactions involving fluids in the Stillwater and Bushveld Complexes: observations from the rocks. *Reviews in Economic Geology*, 4, 167–79.

Mathez, E.A. (1999) On factors controlling the concentrations of platinum group elements in layered intrusions and chromitites. In R.R. Keays, C.M. Lesher, P.C. Lightfoot and C.E.G. Farrow (eds), *Dynamic Processes in Magmatic Ore Deposits and Their Application to Mineral Exploration*. Short course notes, Geological Society Canada, 13, 251–85.

Maynard, J.B. (1983) *Geochemistry of Sedimentary Ore Deposits*. Springer-Verlag, 305 pp.

Maynard, J.B. (1991) Uranium: syngenetic to diagenetic deposits in foreland basins. *Reviews in Economic Geology*, 5, 187–97.

Meinert, L.D. (1992) Skarns and skarn deposits. *Geoscience Canada*, 19, 145–62.

Meinert, L.D. (2000) Gold in skarns related to epizonal intrusions. *Reviews in Economic Geology*, 13, 347–75.

Meland, N. and Norman, J.O. (1966) Transport velocities of single particles in bed-load motion. *Geografisca Annaler*, 48A, 165–82.

Mel'nik, Y.P. (1982) *Precambrian Banded Iron-formations: Physicochemical Conditions of Formation*. Developments in Precambrian Geology 5. Elsevier, 310 pp.

Melvin, J.L. (1991) Evaporites, petroleum and mineral resources. In *Developments in Sedimentology, 50*. Elsevier, Chapter 4.

Merkle, R. (1992) Platinum-group minerals in the middle group of chromitite layers at Marikana, western Bushveld complex: indications for collection mechanism and postmagmatic modification. *Canadian Journal of Earth Sciences*, 29, 209–21.

Metcalfe, R., Rochelle, C.A., Savage, D. and Higgo, J.W. (1994) Fluid–rock interactions during continental red-bed diagenesis: implications for theoretical models of mineralization in sedimentary basins. In J. Parnell (ed.), *Geofluids: Origin, Migration and Evolution of Fluids in Sedimentary Basins*. Geological Society, Special Publication, 78, 301–24.

Meyer, C. (1981) Ore-forming processes in geologic history. *Economic Geology*, 75th Anniversary Volume, 6–41.

Meyer, C. (1988) Ore deposits as guides to the geologic history of the Earth. *Annual Reviews in Earth Planetary Science*, 16, 147–71.

Meyer, C. and Hemley (1967) Wall rock alteration. In H.L. Barnes (ed.), *Geochemistry of Hydrothermal Ore Deposits*. Holt, Rinehart and Winston, pp. 166–235.

Meyer, F.M., Happel, U., Hausberg, J. and Wiechowski, A. (2002) The geometry and anatomy of the Los Pijiguaos bauxite deposit, Venezuela. *Ore Geology Reviews*, 20, 27–54.

Miall, A.D. (1978) Fluvial sedimentology: an historical review. In A.D. Miall (ed.), *Fluvial Sedimentology*. Canadian Society for Petroleum Geology, Memoir 5, 1–47.

Mikucki, E.J. (1998) Hydrothermal transport and depositional processes in Archean lode-gold systems: a review. *Ore Geology Reviews*, 13, 307–21.

Milési, J.P. and 9 others (2002) The Jacobina Paleoproterozoic gold-bearing conglomerates, Bahia, Brazil: a "hydrothermal shear–reservoir" model. *Ore Geology Reviews*, 19, 95–136.

Minter, W.E.L. (1978) A sedimentological synthesis of placer gold, uranium and pyrite concentrations in Proterozoic Witwatersrand deposits. In A.D. Miall (ed.), *Fluvial Sedimentology*. Canadian Society for Petroleum Geology, Memoir 5, 801–29.

Misra, K.C. (2000) *Understanding Mineral Deposits*. Kluwer Academic Publishers, 845 pp.

Mitchell, A.H.G. and Garson, M.S. (1981) *Mineral Deposits and Global Tectonic Settings*. Academic Press, 457 pp.

Mitchell, A.H.G. and Leach, T.M. (1991) *Epithermal Gold in the Phillipines: Island Arc Metallogenesis, Geothermal Systems and Geology*. Academic Press, 457 pp.

Moore, D.W., Young, L.E., Modene, J.S. and Plahuta, J.T. (1986) Geologic setting and genesis of the Red Dog zinc-lead-silver deposit, Western Brooks range, Alaska. *Economic Geology*, 81, 1696–727.

Moores, E.M. (1993) Neoproterozoic oceanic crustal thinning, emergence of continents, and the origin of the Phanerozoic ecosystem: a model. *Geology*, 21, 5–8.

Moores, E.M. (1991) Southwest US–east Antarctic (SWEAT) connection: a hypothesis. *Geology*, 19, 425–8.

Morris, R.C. (1985) Genesis of iron ore in banded iron-formation by supergene and supergene-metamorphic processes – a conceptual model. In K.H. Wolf (ed.), *Handbook of Strata-bound and Stratiform Ore Deposits, Volume 13*. Elsevier, pp. 33–235.

Morris, R.C., Thornber, M.R. and Ewers, W.E. (1980) Deep-seated iron ores from banded iron formation. *Nature*, 288, 250–2.

Mote, T.I., Brimhall, G.H., Tidy-Finch, E., Muller, G. and Carrasco, P. (2001) Application of mass balance modeling of sources and sinks of supergene enrichment to exploration and discovery of the Quebrada Turquesa exotic Cu ore body, El Salvador district, Chile. *Economic Geology*, 96, 367–86.

Muir Wood, R. (1994) Earthquakes, strain-cycling and the mobilization of fluids. In J. Parnell (ed.), *Geofluids: Origin, Migration and Evolution of Fluids in Sedimentary Basins*. Geological Society, Special Publication 78, 85–98.

Murck, B.W. and Campbell, I.H. (1986) The effects of temperature, oxygen fugacity and melt composition on the behavior of chromium in basic and ultrabasic melts. *Geochimica et Cosmochimica Acta*, 50, 1871–87.

Murphey, J.B. and Nance, R.D. (1991) Supercontinent model for the contrasting character of Late Proterozoic orogenic belts. *Geology*, 19, 469–72.

Mysen, B.O. and Kushiro, I. (1976) Melting behaviour of peridotite at high pressure. *Eos*, 57, 354.

Nahon, D.B., Boulangé, B. and Colin, F. (1992) Metallogeny of weathering: an introduction. In I.P. Martini and W. Chesworth (eds), *Weathering, Soils and Paleosols*. Developments in Earth Surface Processes, 2. Elsevier, pp. 445–71.

Naldrett, A.J. (1989a) *Magmatic Sulphide Deposits*. Oxford Monographs on Geology and Geophysics. Clarendon Press, 186 pp.

Naldrett, A.J. (1989b) Stratiform PGE deposits in layered intrusions. *Reviews in Economic Geology*, 4, 135–65.

Naldrett, A.J. (1997) Models for the formation of stratabound concentrations of platinum group elements in layered intrusions. In R.V. Kirkham, W.D. Sinclair, R.I. Thorpe and J.M. Duke (eds), *Mineral Deposit Modelling*. Geological Association of Canada Special Paper, 40, 373–88.

Naldrett, A.J. (1999) World-class Ni-Cu-PGE deposits: key factors in their genesis. *Mineralium Deposita*, 34, 227–40.

Naldrett, A.J. and Lehmann, J. (1988) Spinel non-stoichiometry as the explanation for Ni-, Cu-, and PGE-enriched sulphides in chromitites. In H.M. Prichard (ed.), *Geo-platinum*, 87, 93–109.

Naldrett, A.J. and MacDonald, A.J. (1980) *Tectonic Setting of Some Ni-Cu Sulphide Ores: Their Importance in Genesis and Exploration*. Geological Association Canada, Special Paper, 20, 633–57.

Naldrett, A.J., Rao, B.V. and Evensen, N.M. (1986) Contamination at Sudbury and its role in ore formation. In M.J. Gallager, R.A. Ixer, C.R. Neary and H.M. Prichard (eds), *Metallogeny of Basic and Ultrabasic Rocks*. Institution of Mining Metallurgy, pp. 75–91.

Naldrett, A.J. and von Grünewaldt, G. (1989) Association of platinum-group elements with chromitite in layered intrusions and ophiolite complexes. *Economic Geology*, 84, 180–7.

Naldrett, A.J. and Wilson, A.H. (1991) Horizontal and vertical variation in the noble metal distribution in the Great Dyke of Zimbabwe: a model for the origin of the PGE mineralization by fractional segregation of sulfide. *Chemical Geology*, 88, 279–300.

Nami, M. and Ashworth, S.G.E. (1993) Principles of a sediment sorting model and its application for predicting economic values in placer deposits. International Association Sedimentology, Special Publication, 17, 543–51.

Nami, M. and James, C.S. (1987) Numerical simulation of gold distribution in the Witwatersrand placers. Society of Economic Palaeontologists and Mineralogists, Special Publication, 39, 353–70.

Nance, R.D., Worsley, T.R. and Moody, J.B. (1986) Post-Archean biogeochemical cycles and long-term episodicity in tectonic processes. *Geology*, 14, 514–18.

Nash, J.T., Granger, H.C. and Adams, S.S. (1981) Geology and concepts of genesis of important types of uranium deposits. *Economic Geology*, 75th Anniversary Volume, 63–116.

Naslund, H.R. (1976) Liquid immiscibility in the system $KalSi_3O_8$-$NaAlSi_3O_8$-FeO-Fe_2O_3-SiO_2 and its application to natural magmas. *Year Book, Carnegie Institution of Washington*, 75, 592–7.

Naslund, H.R. (1983) The effect of oxygen fugacity on liquid immiscibility in iron bearing silicate melts. *American Journal of Science*, 283, 1034–59.

Naslund, H.R., Henriquez, F., Nystrom, J.O., Vivallo, W. and Dobbs, F.M. (2002) Magmatic iron ores and associated mineralization: examples from the Chilean high Andes and coastal Cordillera. In T.M. Porter (ed.), *Hydrothermal Iron Oxide-Copper-Gold and Related Deposits: A Global Perspective*. PGC Publishing, pp. 207–26.

Nex, P. (2002) Bifurcating chromitites: analogues to sedimentary structures in the Bushveld Complex, South Africa. Extended Abstract, 11th Quadrennial IAGOD Symposium and Geocongress, Geological Survey of Namibia, Windhoek.

Nex, P.A.M., Kinnaird, J.A. and Oliver, G.J.H. (2001) Petrology, geochemistry and uranium mineralization of post-collisional magmatism around Goanikontes, southern Central Zone, Namibia. *Journal of African Earth Sciences*, 33, 481–502.

Nixon, P.H. (1995) The morphology and nature of primary diamondiferous occurrences. *Journal Geochemical Exploration*, 53, 41–71.

North, F.K. (1985) *Petroleum Geology*. Allen & Unwin, 607 pp.

Northrop, H.R. and Goldhaber, M.B. (1990) Genesis of the tabular-type vanadium–uranium deposits of the Henry Basin, Utah. *Economic Geology*, 85, 215–68.

Norton, I. and Cathles, L.M. (1979) Thermal aspects of ore deposition. In H.L. Barnes (ed.), *Geochemistry of Hydrothermal Ore Deposits*. John Wiley & Sons, pp. 611–31.

Norton, S.A. (1973) Laterite and bauxite formation. *Economic Geology*, 68, 353–61.

Nyström, J.O. and Henríquez, R. (1992) Magmatic features of iron ore of the Kiruna Type in Chile and Sweden: ore textures and magnetite geochemistry. *Economic Geology*, 89, 820–39.

Odling, N.E. (1997) Fluid flow in fractured rocks at shallow levels in the Earth's crust: an overview. In M.B. Holness (ed.), *Deformation-enhanced Fluid Transport in the Earth's Crust and Mantle*. Chapman & Hall, pp. 289–98.

Ohmoto, H., Mizukami, M., Drummond, S.E., Eldridge, C.S., Pisutha-Arnond, V. and Lenagh, T.C. (1983) Chemical processes of Kuroko formation. *Economic Geology Monograph*, 5, 570–604.

Oliver, J. (1986) Fluids expelled tectonically from orogenic belts: their role in hydrocarbon migration and other geologic phemomena. *Geology*, 14, 99–102.

Oliver, N.H.S. (1996) Review and classification of structural controls on fluid flow during regional metamorphism. *Journal of Metamorphic Geology*, 14, 477–92.

Oreskes, N. and Einaudi, M.T. (1990) Origin of rare earth element-enriched hematite breccias at the Olympic Dam Cu-U-Au-Ag deposit, Roxby Downs, South Australia. *Economic Geology*, 85, 1–28.

Oreskes, N. and Einaudi, M.T. (1992) Origin of hydrothermal fluids at Olympic Dam: preliminary results from fluid inclusions and stable isotopes. *Economic Geology*, 87, 64–90.

Osborn, E.F. (1979) The reaction principle. In H.S. Yoder (ed.), *The Evolution of the Igneous Rocks: Fiftieth Anniversary Perspective*. Princeton University Press, pp. 133–69.

Ossandón, G.C., Freraut, C.R., Gusttafson, L.B., Lindsay, D.D. and Zentilli, M. (2001) Geology of the Chuquicamata Mine: a progress report. *Economic Geology*, 96, 249–70.

Paarlberg, N.L. and Evans, L.L. (1977) Geology of the Fletcher Mine, Viburnum Trend, southeast Missouri. *Economic Geology*, 72, 391–407.

Padilla Garza, R.A., Titley, S.R. and Pimental, F.B. (2001) Geology of the Escondida porphyry Cu deposit, Antofagasta region, Chile. *Economic Geology*, 96, 307–24.

Park, R.G. (1995) Palaeoproterozoic Laurentia–Baltica relationships: a view from the Lewisian. In M.P. Coward and A.C. Ries (eds), *Early Precambrian Processes*. Geological Society, Special Publication, 95, 211–24.

Parnell, J. (ed.) (1994) Geofluids: origin, migration and evolution of fluids in sedimentary basins. Geological Society, Special Publication, 78, 372 pp.

Parnell, J., Ye, L. and Chen, C. (1990) *Sediment-hosted Mineral Deposits*. Special Publication, 11, International Association of Sedimentologists. Blackwell Scientific Publications, 227 pp.

Partington, G.A. and Williams, P.J. (2000) Proterozoic lode gold and (iron)-copper-gold deposits: a comparison of Australian and global examples. *Reviews in Economic Geology*, 13, 69–101.

Patterson, C. (1999) *Evolution*. Cornell University Press, 166 pp.

Pattrick, R.A.D. and Polya, D.A. (1993) The mineralization and geological evolution of the British Isles. In R.A.D. Pattrick and D.A. Polya (eds), *Mineralization in the British Isles*. Chapman & Hall, 499 pp.

Pearson, R.G. (1963) Hard and soft acids and bases. *Journal of the American Chemical Society*, 85, 3533–9.

Perkins, W.G. (1997) Mount Isa lead-zinc ofe bodies: replacement lodes in a zoned syndeformational copper-lead-zinc system? *Ore Geology Reviews*, 12, 61–110.

Peyerl, W. (1982) The influence of the Driekop dunite pipe on the platinum-group mineralogy of the UG-2 chromitite in its vicinity. *Economic Geology*, 77, 1432–8.

Phillips, G.N. (1986) Geology and alteration in the Golden Mile, Kalgoorlie. *Economic Geology*, 91, 779–808.

Phillips, G.N. and Law, J.D.M. (2000) Witwatersrand gold fields: geology, genesis and exploration. *Reviews Economic Geology*, 13, 439–500.

Phillips, G.N., Williams, P.J. and De-Jong, G. (1994) The nature of metamorphic fluids and significance for metal exploration. In J. Parnell (ed.), *Geofluids: Origin, Migration and Evolution of Fluids in Sedimentary Basins*. Geological Society, Special Publication, 78, 55–68.

Philpotts, A.R. (1967) Origin of certain iron-titanium oxide and apatite rocks. *Economic Geology*, 62, 303–15.

Philpotts, A.R. (1982) Compositions of immiscible liquids in volcanic rocks. *Contributions to Mineralogy and Petrology*, 80, 201–18.

Piper, J.D. (1976) Palaeomagnetic evidence for a Proterozoic super-continent. In J. Sutton, R.M. Shackleton and J.C. Briden (eds), *A Discussion on Global Tectonics in Proterozoic Times.* Philosophical Transactions of the Royal Society London, 280, 469–90.

Pitcher, W.S. (1997) *The Nature and Origin of Granite.* Chapman & Hall, 387 pp.

Pirajno, F. (1992) *Hydrothermal Mineral Deposits.* Springer-Verlag, 709 pp.

Plimer, I.R. (1978) Proximal and distal stratabound ore deposits. *Mineralium Deposita,* 13, 345–53.

Plumlee, G.S. (1994) Fluid chemistry evolution and mineral deposition in the main-stage Creede epithermal system. *Economic Geology,* 89, 1860–82.

Powell, C.M., Li, Z.X., McElhinny, M.W., Meert, J.G. and Park, J.K. (1993) Paleomagnetic constraints on timing of the Neoproterozoic breakup of Rodinia and the Cambrian formation of Gondwana. *Geology,* 21, 889–92.

Powell, C.M., Oliver, N.H., Li, Z.X., Martin, D.M. and Ronaszeki, J. (1999) Synorogenic hydrothermal origin for the giant Hamersley iron oxide ore bodies. *Geology,* 27, 175–8.

Prevec, S.A., Lightfoot, P.C. and Keays, R.R. (2000) Evolution of the sublayer of the Sudbury Igneous Complex: geochemical, Sm-Nd isotopic and petrologic evidence. *Lithos,* 51, 271–92.

Pretorius, D.A. (1976) The stratigraphic, geochronologic, ore-type and geologic-environment sources of mineral wealth in the Republic of South Africa. *Economic Geology,* 71, 5–15.

Pye, K. (1994) *Sediment Transport and Depositional Processes.* Blackwell Scientific Publications, 397 pp.

Rainaud, C., Armstrong, R.A., Master, S. and Robb, L.J. (1999) A fertile Palaeoproterozoic magmatic arc beneath the Central African Copperbelt. In C. Stanley and 39 others (eds), *Mineral Deposits: Processes to Processing.* Balkema, 1427–30.

Rainaud, C., Armstrong, R.A., Master, S., Robb, L.J. and Mumba, P.A.C.C. (2002a) Contributions to the geology and mineralization of the Central African Copperbelt: I. Nature and geochronology of the pre-Katangan basement. In C.R. Anhaeusser (ed.), *Economic Geology Research Institute, Information Circular 362.* University of the Witwatersrand, pp. 19–23.

Rainaud, C., Master, S., Armstrong, R.A., Phillips, D. and Robb, L.J. (2002b) Contributions to the geology and mineralization of the Central African Copperbelt: IV. Monazite U-Pb dating and ^{40}Ar-^{39}Ar thermochronology of metamorphic events during the Lufilian Orogeny. In C.R. Anhaeusser (ed.), *Economic Geology Research Institute, Information Circular 362.* University of the Witwatersrand, pp. 33–7.

Rainault, C.R.L., Master, S., Armstrong, R., Robb, L.J. (1999) A fertile Palaeoproterozoic magmatic arc

beneath the Central African copperbelt. Extended Abstract, SGA-IAGOD Conference, London, 4 pp.

Raiswell, R.W., Brimblecombe, P., Dent, D.L. and Liss, P.S. (1980) *Environmental Chemistry: The Earth–Air–Water Factory.* J. Wiley & Sons, 184 pp.

Reading, H.H. (ed.) (1996) *Sedimentary Environments: Processes, Facies and Stratigraphy.* Blackwell Science, 688 pp.

Reading, H.H. and Collinson, J.D. (1996) Clastic coasts. In H.H. Reading (ed.), *Sedimentary Environments: Processes, Facies and Stratigraphy.* Blackwell Science, pp. 154–231.

Reed, M.H. (1982) Calculation of multicomponent equilibria and reaction processes involving minerals, gases and an aqueous phase. *Geochimica et Cosmochimica Acta,* 46, 513–28.

Reed, M.H. (1997) Hydrothermal alteration and its relationship to ore fluid composition. In H.L. Barnes (ed.), *Geochemistry of Hydrothermal Ore Deposits.* John Wiley, pp. 303–66.

Reeve, J.S., Cross, K.C., Smith, R.N. and Oreskes, N. (1990) Olympic Dam copper-uranium-gold-silver deposit. In F.E. Hughes (ed.), *Geology of the Mineral Deposits of Australia and Papua New Guinea.* Monograph Series, Australasian Institute Mining Metallurgy, 14, 1009–35.

Reid, I. and Frostick, L.E. (1994) Fluvial sediment transport and deposition. In K. Pye (ed.), *Sediment Transport and Depositional Processes.* Blackwell Scientific Publications, pp. 89–156.

Reynolds, R.L. and Goldhaber, M.B. (1978) Origin of a south-Texas roll-type uranium deposit: I. Alteration of iron-titanium oxide minerals. *Economic Geology,* 73, 1677–89.

Reynolds, R.L. and Goldhaber, M.B. (1983) Iron disulfide minerals and the genesis of roll-type uranium deposits. *Economic Geology,* 78, 105–20.

Rhodes, A.L. and Oreskes, N. (1999) Oxygen isotope compositions of magnetite deposits at El Laco, Chile: evidence of formation from isotopically heavy fluids. Society of Economic Geologists, Special Publication, 7, 333–51.

Rice, A. (1997) A model for PGE enrichment due to the splitting of freezing magma chambers by suspended crystal loads. *Exploration and Mining Geology,* 6, 129–37.

Rice, A. and von Grünewaldt, G. (1995) Shear aggregation (convective scavenging) and cascade enrichment of PGEs and chromite in mineralized layers of large layered intrusions. *Mineralogy and Petrology,* 54, 105–17.

Richards, J.P., Boyce, A.J. and Pringle, M.S. (2001)

Geologic evolution of the Escondida area, northern Chile: a model for spatial and temporal localization of porphyry Cu mineralization. *Economic Geology*, 96, 271–306.

Richards, J.P. and Larson, P.B. (eds) (1998) Techniques in hydrothermal ore deposit geology. *Reviews in Economic Geology*, 10, Society of Economic Geologists, 256 pp.

Richardson, S.H., Gurney, J.J., Erlank, A.J. and Harris, J.W. (1984) Origin of diamonds in old enriched mantle. *Nature*, 310, 198–202.

Rickard, D. (1976) Hydrocarbons associated with lead-zinc ores at Laisvall, Sweden. *Nature*, 255, 131–3.

Rickard, D., Willden, M.Y., Marinder, N.E. and Donnelly, T.H. (1979) Studies on the genesis of the Laisvall sandstone lead-zinc deposit, Sweden. *Economic Geology*, 74, 1255–85.

Ridley, J.R. and Diamond, L.W. (2000) Fluid chemistry of orogenic lode gold deposits and implications for genetic models. *Reviews in Economic Geology*, 13, 141–62.

Riggs, S.R. (1979) Phosphorite sedimentation in Florida; a model phosphogenic system. In P.F. Howard, J.C. Dunlap, R.J. Hite and A.J. Bodenlos (eds), *An Issue Devoted to Phosphate, Potash and Sulfur*. Economic Geology, 74, 285–314.

Rimstidt, J.D. (1979) The kinetics of silica–water reactions. Doctoral Thesis, Pennsylvania State University, University Park, PA, 148 pp.

Rimstidt, J.D. (1997) Gangue mineral transport and deposition. In H.L. Barnes (ed.), *Geochemistry of Hydrothermal Ore Deposits*. John Wiley & Sons, pp. 487–516.

Ripley, E.M. and Al-Jassar, T.J. (1987) Sulfur and oxygen isotope studies of melt-country rock interaction, Babbitt Cu-Ni deposit, Duluth Complex, Minnesota, USA. *Economic Geology*, 82, 87–107.

Ripley, E.M., Severson, M.J. and Hauck, S.A. (1998) Evidence for sulfide and Fe-Ti-P rich liquid immiscibility in the Duluth Complex, Minnesota. *Economic Geology*, 93, 1052–62.

Ripley, E.M., Merino, E., Moore, C. and Ortoleva, P. (1985) Mineral zoning in sediment-hosted copper deposits. In K.H. Wolf (ed.), *Handbook of Stratabound and Stratiform Ore Deposits, Volume 6*. Elsevier, pp. 237–60.

Robb, L.J., Charlesworth, E.G., Drennan, G.R., Gibson, R.L. and Tongu, E.L. (1997) Tectono-metamorphic setting and paragenetic sequence of Au-U mineralization in the Archaean Witwatertsrand Basin, South Africa. *Australian Journal of Earth Sciences*, 44, 353–71.

Robb, L.J., Freeman, L.A. and Armstrong, R. (2000) Nature and longevity of hydrothermal fluid flow and mineralization in granites of the Bushveld Complex, South Africa. *Transactions of the Royal Society Edinburgh: Earth Sciences*, 91, 269–81.

Robb, L.J., Master, S., Greyling, L., Yao, Y. and Rainaud, C. (2002) Contributions to the geology and mineralization of the Central African Copperbelt: V. Speculations regarding the "Snowball Earth" and redox controls on stratabound Cu-Co and Pb-Zn mineralization. In C.R. Anhaeusser (ed.), *Economic Geology Research Institute, Information Circular 362*. University of the Witwatersrand, pp. 38–42.

Roedder, E. (1984) *Fluid Inclusions*. Reviews in Mineralogy, 12, Mineralogical Society of America, 644 pp.

Roedder, E. and Bodnar, R.J. (1980) Geologic pressure determinations from fluid inclusion studies. *Annual Reviews of Earth Planetary Sciences*, 8, 263–301.

Rogers, J.J.W. (1996) A history of continents in the past three billion years. *Journal of Geology*, 104, 91–107.

Rollinson, H. (1993) *Using Geochemical Data: Evaluation, Presentation, Interpretation*. Longman, 352 pp.

Rose, A.W. (1976) The effect of cuprous chloride complexes in the origin of red-bed copper and related deposits. *Economic Geology*, 71, 1036–48.

Rose, A.W. and Bianchi-Mosquera, G.C. (1993) Adsorption of Cu, Pb, Zn, Co, Ni, and Ag on goethite and hematite: control on metal mobilization from redbeds into stratiform copper deposits. *Economic Geology*, 88, 1226–36.

Rose, A.W. and Burt, D. (1979) Hydrothermal alteration. In H.L. Barnes (ed.), *Geochemistry of Hydrothermal Ore Deposits*. John Wiley & Sons, pp. 173–235.

Ross Heath, G. (1981) Ferromanganese nodules of the deep sea. *Economic Geology*, 75th Anniversary Volume, 736–65.

Rowins, S.M., Groves, D.I., McNaughton, M.J., Palmer, M.R. and Stewart, C.S. (1997) A reinterpretation of the role of granitoids in the genesis of Neoproterozoic gold mineralization in the Telfer Dome, Western Australia. *Economic Geology*, 92, 133–60.

Rye, R. and Holland, H.D. (1998) Paleosols and the evolution of the atmosphere: a critical review. *American Journal of Science*, 298, 621–72.

Sallenger, A.H. (1979) Inverse grading and hydraulic equivalence in grain-flow deposits. *Journal of Sedimentary Petrology*, 49, 553–62.

Sams, M.S. and Thomas-Betts, A. (1988) Models of convective fluid flow and mineralization in southwest England. *Journal of the Geological Society London*, 145, 809–17.

Sasaki, A., Ishihara, S. and Seki, Y. (1985) *Mineral Resources and Engineering Geology*. J. Wiley & Sons. 299 pp.

Sassani, D.C. and Shock, E.L. (1990) Speciation and solubility of palladium in aqueous magmatic-hydrothermal solutions. *Geology*, 18, 925–8.

Sato, T. (1972) Behavior of ore forming solutions in sea water. *Mining Geology*, 22, 31–42.

Sawkins, F.J. (1990) *Metal Deposits in Relation to Plate Tectonics*. Springer-Verlag, 461 pp.

Sawlowicz, Z. (1992) Primary sulphide mineralization in Cu-Fe-S zones of the Kupferschiefer, Fore-Sudetic monocline, Poland. *Transactions of the Institute of Mining Metallurgy Section B*, 101, B1–B8.

Schiffries, C.M. (1982) The petrogenesis of a platiniferous dunite pipe in the Bushveld Complex: infiltration metasomatism by a chloride solution. *Economic Geology*, 77, 1439–53.

Schiffries, C.M. and Rye, D.M. (1990) Stable isotope systematics of the Bushveld Complex: II. Constraints on hydrothermal processes in layered intrusions. *American Journal of Science*, 290, 209–45.

Schoenberg, R., Kruger, F.J., Nagler, T.F., Meisel, T. and Kramers, J.D. (1999) PGE enrichment in chromitite layers and the Merensky Reef of the western Bushveld Complex: a Re-Os and Rb-Sr isotope study. *Earth and Planetary Science Letters*, 172, 49–64.

Schmid, G. (1994) Physics and chemistry of metal cluster compounds. In L.J. de Jongh (ed.), *Ligand Stabilized Giant Metal Clusters and Colloids*. Kluwer, 107 pp.

Schwartz, A.W. (1971) Phosphate; solubilization and activation on the primitive Earth. In *Molecular Evolution, Volume 1*. Elsevier, pp. 207–15.

Scoon, R.N. and Teigler, B. (1994) Platinum group element mineralization in the Critical Zone of the western Bushveld Complex: I. Sulfide poor chromitites below the UG-2. *Economic Geology*, 89, 1094–121.

Scott, S.D. (1997) Submarine hydrothermal systems and deposits. In H.L. Barnes (ed.), *Geochemistry of Hydrothermal Ore Deposits*, 3rd edn John Wiley, pp. 797–875.

Selley, R.C. (1988) *Applied Sedimentology*. Academic Press, 446 pp.

Selley, R.C. (1998) *Elements of Petroleum Geology*. Academic Press, 470 pp.

Seward, T.M. (1981) Metal complex formation in aqueous solutions at elevated temperatures and pressures. In D. Rickard and F. Wickman (eds), *Chemistry and Geochemistry of Solutions at High Temperatures and Pressures*. Physics and Chemistry of the Earth, Volumes 13 and 14, pp. 113–28.

Seward, T.M. (1991) The hydrothermal geochemistry of gold. In R.P. Foster (ed.), *Gold Metallogeny and Exploration*. Blackie, pp. 37–62.

Seward, T.M. and Barnes, H.L. (1997) Metal transport by hydrothermal ore fluids. In H.L. Barnes (ed.), *Geochemistry of Hydrothermal Ore Deposits*. John Wiley & Sons, pp. 435–86.

Sheldon, R.P. (1980) Episodicity of phosphate deposition and deep ocean circulation: a hypothesis. In Y.K. Bentor (ed.), *Marine Phosphorites*. Special Publication, Society of Economic Palaeontologists and Mineralogists, 29, 239–47.

Sheppard, S.M.F. (1977) The Cornubian batholith, south-west England: D/H and $^{18}O/^{16}O$ studies of kaolinite and other alteration minerals. *Journal of the Geological Society London*, 133, 573–91.

Sheppard, S.M.F., Nielsen, R.L. and Taylor, H.P. (1971) Hydrogen and oxygen isotope ratios in minerals from porphyry copper deposits. *Economic Geology*, 66, 515–42.

Shannon, P.M. and Naylor, D. (1989) *Petroleum Basin Studies*. Graham & Trotman, 206 pp.

Shinohara, H. (1994) Exsolution of immiscible vapor and liquid phases from a crystallizing silicate melt: implications for chlorine and metal transport. *Geochimica et Cosmochimica Acta*, 58, 5215–21.

Shinohara, H. and Hedenquist, J.W. (1997) Constraints on magma degassing beneath the Far Southeast Porphyry Cu-Au Deposit, Philippines. *Journal of Petrology*, 38, 1741–52.

Shinohara, H., Iiyama, J.T. and Matso, S. (1989) Partition of chlorine compounds between silicate melt and hydrothermal solutions: I. partition of NaCl-KCl. *Geochimica et Cosmochimica Acta*, 53, 2517–630.

Shuey, R.T. (1975) *Semiconducting Ore Minerals*. Developments in Economic Geology, 4. Elsevier, 364 pp.

Sibson, R.H. (1986) Earthquakes and rock deformation in crustal fault zones. *Annual Reviews in Earth Planetary Sciences*, 14, 149–75.

Sibson, R.H. (1987) Earthquake rupturing as a mineralizing agent in hydrothermal systems. *Geology*, 15, 701–4.

Sibson, R.H. (1994) Crustal stress, faulting and fluid flow. In J. Parnell (ed.), *Geofluids: Origin, Migration and Evolution of Fluids in Sedimentary Basins*. Geological Society, Special Publication, 78, 69–84.

Sibson, R.H., Moore, J.M. and Rankin, A.H. (1975) Seismic pumping: a hydrothermal fluid transport mechanism. *Journal of the Geological Society London*, 131, 653–9.

Sibson, R.H., Robert, F. and Poulsen, K.H. (1988) High-angle reverse faults, fluid-pressure cycling, and meso-thermal gold-quartz deposits. *Geology*, 16, 551–5.

Siehl, A. and Thein, J. (1989) Minette-type ironstones. In T.P. Young and W.E.G. Taylor (eds), *Phanerozoic Ironstones*. Geological Society London, Special Publication, 46, 175–93.

Sillitoe, R.H. (1976) Andean mineralization: a model for the metallogeny of unconvergent plate margins. In D.F. Strong (ed.), *Metallogeny and Plate Tectonics*. Geological Association of Canada, Special Paper, 14, 59–100.

Sillitoe, R.H. and Burrows, D.R. (2002) New field evidence bearing on the origin of the El Laco magnetite deposit northern Chile. *Economic Geology*, 97, 1101–9.

Sillitoe, R.H. and McKee, E.H. (1996) Age of supergene oxidation and enrichment in the Chilean porphyry copper province. *Economic Geology*, 91, 164–79.

Skinner, B.J. (1976) A second iron age ahead? *Scientific American*, 64, 258–69.

Skinner, B.J. (1997) Hydrothermal mineral deposits: what we do and don't know. In H.L. Barnes (ed.), *Geochemistry of Hydrothermal Ore Deposits*. John Wiley & Sons, pp. 1–29.

Skinner, B.J., White, D.E., Rose, H.J. and Mays, R.E. (1969) Sulfides associated with the Salton Sea geothermal brine. *Economic Geology*, 62, 316–30.

Skinner, B.J. and Peck, D.L. (1969) An immiscible sulfide melt from Hawaii. *Economic Geology Monograph*, 4, 310–22.

Slingerland, R. (1984) Role of hydraulic sorting in the origin of fluvial placers. *Journal of Sedimentary Petrology*, 54, 137–50.

Slingerland, R. and Smith, N.D. (1986) Occurrence and formation of water-laid placers. *Annual Review of Earth and Planetary Sciences*, 14, 133–47.

Smirnov, V.I. (1977) *Ore Deposits of the USSR*. Pitman, 3 volumes.

Smith, C.B., McCallum, M.E., Coppersmith, H.G. and Eggler, D.H. (1979) Petrochemistry and structure of kimberlites in the Front Range and Laramie Range, Colorado–Wyoming. In F.R. Boyd and H.O.A. Meyer (eds), *Kimberlites, Diatremès, and Diamonds: Their Geology, Petrology, and Geochemistry*. Proceedings International Kimberlite Conference, 2, 178–89.

Smith, N.D. and Beukes, N.J. (1983) Bar to bank flow convergence zones: a contribution to the origin of alluvial placers. *Economic Geology*, 78, 1342–9.

Smith, N.D. and Minter, W.E.L. (1980) Sedimentological controls of gold and uranium in two Witwatersrand paleoplacers. *Economic Geology*, 75, 1–14.

Solomon, M. and Groves, D.I. (1994) *The Geology and Origin of Australia's Mineral Deposits*. Oxford University Press, 951 pp.

Solomon, M., Groves, D.I. and Jaques, A.L. (2000) *The Geology and Origin of Australia's Mineral Deposits*. University of Tasmania and University of Western Australia, 1002 pp.

Southam, G. and Beveridge, T.J. (1994) The in vitro formation of placer gold by bacteria, *Geochimica et Cosmochimica Acta*, 58, 4527–30.

Spackman, W., Davis, A. and Mitchell, G.D. (1976) The fluorescence of liptinite macerals. *Geology Studies*, 22, 59–75.

Spear, F.S. (1995) *Metamorphic Phase Equilibria and Pressure–Temperature–Time Paths*. Mineralogical Society of America Monograph, 799 pp.

Spooner, E.T.C. (1980) Cu-pyrite mineralization and sea water convection in oceanic crust: the ophiolitic ore deposits of Cyprus. Geological Association of Canada, Special Paper, 20, 685–704.

Stach, E. (1975) *Textbook of Coal Petrography*. Borntraeger, 428 pp.

Stanton, R.L. (1972) *Ore Petrology*. McGraw-Hill, 771 pp.

Stein, M. and Hofmann, A.W. (1994) Mantle plumes and episodic crustal growth. *Nature*, 372, 63–8.

Stevens, G., Boer, R. and Gibson, R.L. (1997) Metamorphism, fluid flow and gold remobilization in the Witwatersrand Basin: towards a unifying model. *South African Journal of Geology*, 100, 363–75.

Stolper, E. (1982) The speciation of water in silicate melts. *Geochimica et Cosmochimica Acta*, 46, 2609–20.

Strong, D.F. (1981) Ore deposit models: 5. A model for granophile mineral deposits. *Geoscience Canada*, 8, 155–61.

Strong, D.F. (1988) A review and model for granite-related mineral deposits. In Taylor R.P. and Strong D.F. (eds), *Recent Advances in the Geology of Granite-related Mineral Deposits*. Canadian Institute of Mining Metallurgy, Special Volume, 39, 424–45.

Sundborg, A. (1956) The River Klaralven: a study of fluvial processes. *Geographic Annals*, 38, 127–316.

Susak, N.J. and Crerar, D.A. (1981) Factors controlling mineral zoning in hydrothermal ore deposits. *Economic Geology*, 76, 476–82.

Sverjensky, D.A. (1981) The origin of a Mississippi Valley-type deposit in the Viburnum Trend, southeast Missouri. *Economic Geology*, 76, 1848–72.

Sverjensky, D.A. (1986) Genesis of Mississippi Valley-type lead-zinc deposits. *Annual Reviews of Earth and Planetary Sciences*, 14, 177–99.

Sverjensky, D.A. (1989) Chemical evolution of basinal brines that form sediment hosted Cu-Pb-Zn deposits. *Geological Association Canada, Special Paper*, 36, 499–518.

Sweeney, M.A., Binda, P.L. and Vaughan, D.J. (1991) Genesis of the ores of the Zambian Copperbelt. *Ore Geology Reviews*, 6, 51–76.

Tardy, Y. (1992) Diversity and terminology of lateritic profiles. In I.P. Martini and W. Chesworth (eds), *Weathering, Soils and Paleosols*. Developments in Earth Surface Processes, 2. Elsevier, pp. 379–403.

Tardy, Y. and Roquin, C. (1992) Geochemistry and evolution of lateritic landscapes. In I.P. Martini and W. Chesworth (eds), *Weathering, Soils and Paleosols*. Developments in Earth Surface Processes, 2. Elsevier, pp. 415–39.

Tarling, D.H. (1981) *Economic Geology and Geotectonics*. Blackwell Scientific, 213 pp.

Taylor, H.P. (1997) O and H isotope relationships in hydrothermal mineral deposits. In H.L. Barnes (ed.), *Geochemistry of Hydrothermal Ore Deposits*. John Wiley and Sons, 229–302.

Taylor, J.R. and Wall, V.J. (1992) The behavior of tin in granitoid magmas. *Economic Geology*, 87, 403–20.

Taylor, S.R. (1964) Abundance of chemical elements in the continental crust: a new table. *Geochimica et Cosmochimica Acta*, 28, 1273–85.

Taylor, R.P. and Strong, D.F. (1988) *Recent Advances in the Geology of Granite-Related Mineral Deposits*. Canadian Institute of Mining and Metallurgy, Special Volume, 39, 445 pp.

Thomas, L. (1992) *Handbook of Practical Coal Geology*. John Wiley.

Thomas, A.V., Bray, C.J. and Spooner, E.T.C. (1988) A discussion of the Jahns–Burnham proposal for the formation of zoned granitic pegmatites using solid–liquid–vapour inclusions from the Tanco pegmatite, SE Manitoba, Canada. *Transactions of the Royal Society Edinburgh: Earth Sciences*, 79, 299–315.

Thomas, R., Webster, J.D. and Heinrich, W. (2000) Melt inclusions in pegmatite quartz: complete miscibility between silicate melts and hydrous fluids at low pressure. *Contributions to Mineralogy and Petrology*, 139, 394–401.

Thomas, R. and Webster, J.D. (2000) Strong tin enrichment in a pegmatite forming melt. *Mineralium Deposita*, 35, 570–82.

Thompson, A.J.B. and Thompson, J.F.H. (eds) (1996) *Atlas of Alteration*. Geological Association of Canada, Special Publication, 6, 119 pp.

Thoreson, R.F., Jones, M.E., Breit, F.J., Doyle, K.M.A. and Clarke, L.J. (2000) The geology and gold mineralization of the Twin Creek gold deposits, Humboldt County, Nevada. In *Geology and Gold Deposits of the Getchell Region, Part II*. Guidebook Series, Society of Economic Geologists, 332, 175–87.

Tiratsoo, E.N. (1984) *Oilfields of the World*. Scientific Press Beaconsfield, 392 pp.

Tissot, B.P. and Welte, D.H. (1984) *Petroleum Formation and Occurrence*. Springer, 538 pp.

Tissot, B.P., Durand, B., Espitalie, J. and Combaz, A. (1974) Influence of nature and diagenesis of organic matter in formation of petroleum. *American Association of Petroleum Geologists Bulletin*, 58, 499–506.

Titley, S.R. (1993) Relationship of stratabound ores with tectonic cycles of the Phanerozoic and Proterozoic. *Precambrian Research*, 61, 295–322.

Torsvik, T.H. and 7 others (1996) Continental break-up and collision in the Neoproterozoic and Palaeozoic: a tale of Baltica and Laurentia. *Earth-Science Reviews*, 40, 229–58.

Tredoux, M., Lindsay, N.M., Davies, G. and McDonald, I. (1995) The fractionation of platinum group elements in magmatic systems, with the suggestion of a novel causal mechanism. *South African Journal of Geology*, 98, 157–67.

Troly, G., Esterle, M., Pelletier, B.G. and Reibell, W. (1979) Nickel deposits in New Caledonia; some factors influencing their formation. In D.J.I. Evans, R.S. Shoemaker and H. Veltman (eds), *International Laterite Symposium*. American Institute of Mining Metallurgy and Petroleum Engineering Society, pp. 85–117.

Trudinger, P.A. (1976) Microbiological processes in relation to ore genesis. In K.H. Wolf, *Handbook of Stratabound and Stratiform Ore Deposits, Volume 2*. Elsevier, pp. 135–190.

Tsoar, H. and Pye, K. (1987) Dust transport and the question of desert loess formation. *Sedimentology*, 34, 139–53.

Turner, J.S. (1980) A fluid-dynamical model of differentiation and layering in magma chambers. *Nature*, 285, 213–15.

Ulmer, G.C. (1969) Experimental investigation on chromite spinels. *Monograph in Economic Geology*, 4, 114–31.

Ulrich, T., Gunther, D. and Heinrich, C. (2001) The evolution of a porphyry Cu-Au deposit based on LA-ICP-MS analysis of fluid inclusions: Bajo de Alumbrera, Argentina. *Economic Geology*, 96, 1743–74.

Unrug, R. (1988) Mineralization controls and source of metals in the Lufilian Fold belt, Shaba (Zaire), Zambia and Angola. *Economic Geology*, 83, 1247–58.

Unrug, R. (1997) Rodinia to Gondwana: the geodynamic map of Gondwana supercontinent assembley. *GSA Today*, 7(1), 1–6.

Van Houten, F.B. and Authur, M.A. (1989) Temporal patterns among Phanerozoic oolitic ironstones and oceanic anoxia. In T.P. Young and W.E.G. Taylor (eds), *Phanerozoic Ironstones*. Geological Society London, Special Publication, 46, 33–49.

Van Niekerk, A., Vogel, K.R., Slingerland, R.L. and Bridge, J.S. (1992) Routing of heterogeneous sediments over movable bed: model development. *Journal of Hydraulic Engineering*, 118, 246–62.

Van Wyk, J.P. and Pienaar, L.F. (1986) Diamondiferous gravels of the lower Orange River, Namaqualand. In C.R. Anhaeusser and S. Maske (eds), *Mineral Deposits of Southern Africa, Volume 2*. Geological Society of South Africa, pp. 2309–22.

Veevers, J.J. (1989) Middle-late Triassic (230±5 Ma) singularity in the stratigraphic and magmatic history of the Pangean heat anomaly. *Geology*, 17, 784–7.

Veizer, J., Laznicka, P. and Jansen, S.L. (1989) Mineralization through geologic time: recyc. ̄ perspective. *American Journal of Science*, 289, 484–524.

Viljoen, M.J. and Scoon, R.N. (1985) The distribution and main geologic features of discordant bodies of iron-rich ultramafic pegmatite in the Bushveld Complex. *Economic Geology*, 80, 1109–28.

Viljoen, M.J. and Viljoen, R.P. (1969) The geology and geochemistry of the lower ultramafic unit of the Onverwacht Group and a proposed new class of igneous rock. Geological Society of South Africa, Special Publication, pp. 255–85.

Vogel, K.R., Van Niekerk, A., Slingerland, R.L. and Bridge, J.S. (1992) Routing of heterogeneous sediments over movable bed: model verification. *Journal of Hydraulic Engineering*, 118, 263–79.

Von Grünewaldt, G., Hatton, C.J., Merkle, R.K.W. and Gain, S. (1986) Platinum group element–chromititie associations in the Bushveld Complex. *Economic Geology*, 81, 1067–79.

Wager, L.R. and Brown, M. (1968) *Layered Igneous Rocks*. Oliver & Boyd, 588 pp.

Wager, L.R., Vincent, E.A. and Smales, A.A. (1957) Sulphides in the Skaergaard Intrusion, east Greenland. *Economic Geology*, 52, 855–99.

Ward, C.R. (1984) *Coal Geology and Coal Technology*. Blackwell Science, 345 pp.

Watterson, J.R. (1991) Preliminary evidence for the involvement of budding bactèria in the origin of Alaskan placer gold. *Geology*, 20, 315–18.

Webster, J.D. and Holloway, J.R. (1990) Partitioning of F and Cl between magmatic hydrothermal fluids and highly evolved granitic magmas. Geological Society of America, Special Paper, 246, 21–34.

Webster, J.G. (1986) The solubility of gold and silver in the system Au-Ag-S-O₂-H₂O at 25 °C and 1 atmosphere. *Geochimica et Cosmochimica Acta*, 50, 1837–45.

Wedepohl, K.H. (1969) *Handbook of Geochemistry, Volume 2*. Springer-Verlag, loose leaf.

Wendorff, M. (2001) Grey RAT orebodies with Cu-Co in the Katangan copperbelt of the DRC; genetic implications of tectonstratigraphy. In A. Piestrzynka and 34 others (eds), *Mineral Deposits at the Beginning of the 21st Century*. Society for the Geology of Applied Mineral Deposits, Proceedings Biennial SGA Meeting, 6, 251–4.

White, D.E. (1963) The Salton Sea geothermal brine, an ore-transporting fluid. *Mining Engineering*, 15, 60.

Whitney, J.A. (1975) Vapor generation in a quartz monzonite magma: a synthetic model with application to porphyry copper deposits. *Economic Geology*, 70, 346–58.

Whitney, J. (1989) Origin and evolution of silicic magmas. *Reviews in Economic Geology*, 4, 183–201.

Widler, A.M. and Seward, T.M. (2002) The adsorption of gold(I) hydrosulphide complexes by iron sulphide surfaces. *Geochimica et Cosmochimica Acta*, 66, 383–402.

Williams, P.A. (1990) *Oxide Zone Geochemistry*. Ellis Horwood, 286 pp.

Willis-Richards, J. and Jackson, N.J. (1989) Evolution of the Cornubiari Ore Field, southwest England: part I. Batholith modeling distribution. *Economic Geology*, 84, 1078–100.

Wilson, A.F. (1984) Origin of quartz-free gold nuggets and supergene gold found in laterites and soils: a review and some new observations. *Australian Journal of Earth Sciences*, 31, 303–16.

Wilson, R.C.L. (1983) *Residual Deposits: Surface Related Weathering Processes and Materials*. The Geological Society of London and Blackwell Scientific Publications, 258 pp.

Windley, B.F. (1995) *The Evolving Continents*. Wiley, 526 pp.

Wingate, M.T.D. (1998) A palaeomagnetic test of the Kaapvaal–Pilbara (Vaalbara) connection at 2.78 Ga. *South African Journal of Geology*, 101, 257–74.

Witt, W.K. (1991) Regional metamorphic controls on alteration associated with gold mineralization in the Eastern Goldfields province, Western Australia: implications for the timing and origin of Archean lode-gold deposits. *Geology*, 19, 982–5.

Wolf, K.H. (1976–86) *Handbook of Strata-bound and Stratiform Ore Deposits, Volumes 1–14*. Elsevier.

Wood, B.J. and Blundy, J.D. (2002) The effect of H_2O on crystal–melt partitioning of trace elements. *Geochimica et Cosmochimica Acta*, 66, 3647–56.

Wood, B.J. and Fraser, D.G. (1976) *Elementary Thermodynamics for Geologists*. Oxford University Press, 303 pp.

Wood, B.J., Pawley, A. and Frost, D.R. (1996) Water and carbon in the Earth's mantle. *Philosophical Transactions*, 354, 1495–511.

Wood, S.A. (1990a) The interaction of dissolved platinum with fulvic acid and simple organic acid analogues in aqueous solutions. *Canadian Mineralogist*, 28, 665–73.

Wood, S.A. (1990b) The solubility of Pt and Pd in NaOH solutions and derivation of stability constraints for Pt and Pd hydroxide complexes. In *V.M. Goldschmidt Conference: Program and Abstracts*. Geochemical Society, p. 92.

Wood, S.A. (1996) The role of humic substances in the transport and fixation of metals of economic interest (Au, Pt, Pd, U, V). In T.H. Giordano (ed.), *Organics and Ore Deposits*. Elsevier, Ore Geology Reviews, 11, 1–31.

Wood, S.A. (1998) Calculation of activity–activity and log fO_2–pH diagrams. *Reviews in Economic Geology*, 10, 81–96.

Wood, S.A., Mountain B.W. and Pan, P. (1992) The aqueous geochemistry of Pt, Pa and Au: recent experimental constraints and a re-evaluation of theoretical predictions. *Canadian Mineralogist*, 30, 955–82.

Wood, S.A. and Samson, I.M. (1998) Solubility of ore minerals and complexation of ore metals in hydrothermal solutions. *Reviews in Economic Geology*, 10, 33–80.

Wood, S.A. and Vlassopoulos, D. (1990) The dispersion of Pt, Pd and Au in surficial media about two PGE-Cu-Ni prospects in Quebec. *Canadian Mineralogist*, 28, 649–63.

Wood, S.A. and Vlassopoulos, D. (1996) The dispersion of Pt, Pd and Au in surficial media about two PGE-Cu-Ni prospects in Quebec. In S.-J. Barnes and J.M. Duke (eds), *Advances in the Study of Platinum-group Elements*. Mineralogical Association of Canada, Canadian Mineralogist, 28, 649–63.

Worsley, T.R., Nance, D. and Moody, J.B. (1984) Global tectonics and eustacy for the past 2 billion years. *Marine Geology*, 58, 373–400.

Yang, K. and Seccombe, P.K. (1994) Contrasting hydrothermal behavior of platinum group elements of Ir and Pd sub-groups as exemplified by platinum group minerals in Great Serpentine Belt, eastern Australia. *Transactions of the Institute of Mining Metallurgy*, 104, B39–B44.

Young, T.P. (1993) Sedimentary iron ores. In R.A.D. Pattrick and D.A. Polya (eds), *Mineralization in the British Isles*. Chapman & Hall, pp. 446–87.

Young, T.P. and Taylor, G.W.E. (1989) *Phanerozoic Ironstones*. Geological Society London, Special Publication 46, 247 pp.

Zaccerini, F., Garuti, G. and Cawthorn, R.G. (2002) Platinum group minerals in chromitite xenoliths from the Onverwacht and Tweefontein ultramafic pipes, eastern Bushveld Complex, South Africa. *Canadian Mineralogist*, 40, 481–97.

Index